12/11/39

ECONOMIC AND SOCIAL GEOGRAPHY

THE HUNTINGTON GEOGRAPHY SERIES

MODERN BUSINESS GEOGRAPHY

By ELLSWORTH HUNTINGTON and the late SUMNER W. CUSHING, formerly of Salem Normal School. World Book Company, Yonkers-on-Hudson, New York.

A textbook for grade seven, eight, or nine, in either a junior high school or a grammar and high school organization. Geography is presented in its relation to production, transportation, manufacturing, and consumption. The book is provided with a large number of exercises and problems.

ECONOMIC AND SOCIAL GEOGRAPHY

By ELLSWORTH HUNTINGTON, FRANK E. WILLIAMS, University of Pennsylvania, and SAMUEL VAN VALKENBURG, Clark University. 630 pages, 6 × 9, profusely illustrated with specially drawn maps. Coth. John Wiley & Sons, Inc., New York.

A textbook for colleges, normal schools, and schools of business. Climate, relief, and soil are described, as well as vegetation, occupation, products, social conditions, and the distribution of population and cities. Useful plants, animals, and minerals are discussed, and industry and commerce are treated. Well-balanced examples, drawn from all over the world, are presented for solution.

BUSINESS GEOGRAPHY

By ELLSWORTH HUNTINGTON and FRANK E. WILLIAMS, Professor of Geography and Industry, University of Pennsylvania. With the coöperation of ROBERT M. BROWN and Miss LENOX E. CHASE. Second Edition, Rewritten. 616 pages, 6×9, 155 figures. Cloth. John Wiley & Sons, Inc., New York.

A textbook for schools of commerce, commercial departments in colleges, and the upper high school grades. This book presents the kind of geography that the business man needs. Thought-provoking problems are presented for solution.

PRINCIPLES OF HUMAN GEOGRAPHY

By ELLSWORTH HUNTINGTON and the late SUMNER W. CUSHING. Third Edition, Revised. 430 pages, 6×9, 118 figures. Cloth. John Wiley & Sons, Inc., New York.

A textbook for normal schools and colleges where an advanced treatment of the general principles of geography is desired.

ECONOMIC AND SOCIAL GEOGRAPHY

BY

ELLSWORTH HUNTINGTON
Yale University

FRANK E. WILLIAMS
University of Pennsylvania

SAMUEL VAN **VALKENBURG**
Clark University

NEW YORK
JOHN WILEY & SONS, INC.
LONDON: CHAPMAN & HALL, LIMITED
1933

PRINTED IN U. S. A.

PRESS OF
BRAUNWORTH & CO., INC.
BOOK MANUFACTURERS
BROOKLYN, NEW YORK

PREFACE

A CONTINUOUS thread of geographic reasoning runs through the whole of this book. It begins with a section on the major factors of geographic environment and the principles which govern their relation to plants, animals, and man. Climate naturally comes first because it is the most widespread, pervasive, and variable of the factors. Relief, however, is fully treated in relation not only to transportation but also to vegetation and human responses. Soils are treated equally fully; recent discoveries and personal observations in many lands have made it possible to set forth the principles which govern their world-wide distribution and influence with a logical completeness which has surprised the authors themselves.

Climate, relief, and soil are the main determinants of the geographic regions into which the earth's surface is naturally divided. Therefore the discussion of their influence in Part I prepares the way for the second section of the book. In Part II the earth's surface is divided into fifteen natural regions based primarily on man's use of the land. The descriptions of these regions in Part II provide a brief but comprehensive account of the earth as a whole, including not only climate, soil, and relief, but also vegetation, occupations, products, social conditions, and the distribution of population and cities. In order to concentrate the attention of the students on the geographic qualities of each region as a dist nct unit the main products are merely mentioned in Part II, and their full discussion is postponed till later. Thus we come logically to Part III, which is devoted to the world's great products. Here all useful plants, animals, and minerals of any importance are discussed in respect to the geographic conditions governing both their production and use. This portion of the book has purposely been made encyclopedic, but it differs from similar sections of most books in containing abundant discussions of general principles and world relationships. Since most products have to pass through a manufacturing process of some kind, and a great many are bought and sold, Part IV is devoted to industry and commerce. Here the outstanding feature is the separation of industries into great types based not only on raw materials, but also on the complexity of the industries and the extent to which they produce goods or perform services for the local community as opposed to the outside world in general. In this section of the book, even more than in Part III, the vital differences between the various natural regions and the close relation between economic and social geography are strongly emphasized.

In the use of this book at least three methods are possible. First, the book may be used as a whole, thus providing a well rounded, full course in Economic Geography with enough Social Geography to give a clear idea of how these two phases of Human Geography are related. Second, by omitting the sections that are printed in smaller type a briefer course is possible. It covers the same ground as the other, but omits many detailed examples and minor products, or industries. Third, Parts I and II, with the omission perhaps of Chapter XI on Economic, Political, and Social Factors in Land Utilization, and the inclusion of Chapter XXIII on the Distribution of Four Great Types of Industry together with the introductory sections of the chapters on Minerals (XXI) and Fuels (XXII), provide a well balanced course in the main phases of Human Geography. In fact, Parts I and II consist largely of material which is needed as an introduction to any study of general geography, or of any phase of the subject where man is the dominant interest.

In addition to the general features thus far mentioned this book has the following special characteristics:

1. It goes further than most books in recognizing the fact that much of the importance of Economic Geography lies in its intimate relation to Social Geography.

2. It treats climate in a new way by means of climographs, a device which has proved very acceptable and illuminating to students wherever it has been intelligently tried.

3. It accepts the well established biological principle of climatic and other optima and applies this principle not only to plants and animals and to man's health and energy, but to manufacturing, commerce, and social progress as well.

4. It includes cyclonic storms and variability of rainfall among the climatic factors on which the natural regions are based, thus emphasizing the contrasts between the temperate regions of North America and Eurasia.

5. An historical approach to the problem of the distribution of manufacturing joins with the principle of optima to give a new and illuminating conception of the relative parts played by climate, mineral resources, racial character, and cultural development in guiding the distribution of industry.

6. The concept of the age and quality of soils is applied in a new way to the explanation of many phenomena in tropical countries.

7. The treatment of products is so' complete that the book is in this respect a work of reference.

8. Illustrations of all sorts of phenomena are drawn in great numbers from the world as a whole as well as from North America. Hence an uncommonly large number of place names are used in such a way as to stimulate the student to look them up. thus giving him a wide familiarity with the map of the world.

9. In this book, as in its predecessor, *Business Geography*, pictures have been omitted (except in one case), and the space thus saved has been devoted to maps. Most of the maps are new, being the work of the authors, or of Miss Rebecca M. Taliaferro. Much gratitude is due Miss Taliaferro not only for her work on the maps but likewise for many valuable suggestions as to the text. It will be noted that most of the world maps use a new arrangement of the continents which eliminates the space usually wasted on the oceans. In order to facilitate comparisons of latitude, Professor Paule Goode's semi-homolosine equal-area projection with straight parallels has been used, with his kind permission, but the two Americas have been moved bodily eastward and Australia westward so as to give the maximum land areas with the minimum use of space on the page. The two other features of the maps are the use of the isopleth method in order to show the intensity of various phenomena, such as yield per acre, and the use of dots indicating percentages in order to show the amount of various phenomena, such as the manufacture of iron goods. Both kinds of maps are constructed in such a way as to be read with unusual ease.

Every class in Economic and Social Geography should have access to at least a few reference books, and should be made to use them constantly. It is especially desirable to give the students problems to solve and maps to make based on the abundant data in the statistical publications mentioned below under II and III. The authors recommend the following publications:

I. Atlases.

A commercial atlas. Those published by G. P. Putnam and Rand McNally are excellent.

A good general atlas. Those of Bartholomew, Johnson, The Times, Andree, Kiepert, and others are all excellent.

Geography of the World's Agriculture, V. C. Finch and O. E. Baker. Government Printing Office, Washington, D. C., 1917.

A small atlas purchased by each student. Those of J. P. Goode

(Rand McNally Co.) and the Oxford University Press are recommended. The latter, entitled *Oxford Economic Atlas,* is especially well fitted for use with this book and is frequently referred to.

Graphic Summary of American Agriculture Based Largely on the Census, O. E. Baker, U. S. Printing Office, Washington, 1931.

II. Statistical yearbooks to be renewed at least every two or three years.

The World Almanac and Book of Facts. The World, New York, yearly.

Statistical Yearbook of the League of Nations. League of Nations, Geneva, yearly. World Peace Foundation, Boston, Mass. This is the best of all publications for general statistics.

Commerce Yearbook. 2 vols. United States, and Foreign Countries. Department of Commerce, Washington, D. C., yearly. Indispensable.

Yearbook of Agriculture. Department of Agriculture, Washington, D. C., yearly.

Statistical Abstract of the United States. Government Printing Office, Washington, D. C., yearly.

III. Statistical and other books to be renewed at intervals longer than two years.

The Statesman's Yearbook. Macmillan & Co., London, yearly.

International Yearbook of Agricultural Statistics. International Institute of Agriculture, Rome, Italy, yearly.

The Economic Forces of the World. Dresdner Bank, Berlin. First issued in 1927, again in 1928 and in 1930.

The Salesman's Handbook, Curtis Publishing Co., Philadelphia.

Abstract of U. S. Census. Director of Census, Government Printing Office, Washington, D. C.

Yearbooks of as many foreign countries as possible.

IV. Periodicals.

Economic Geography. Clark University, Worcester, Mass.

Geographical Review. American Geographical Society, New York.

Journal of Geography. A. J. Nystrom Co., Chicago, Ill.

V. Other Reference Books.

A. General Reference Books.

Some good encylopedia (Britannica, International).

International Geography. Ed. by H. R. Mill. D. Appleton & Co., New York, 1900.

The New World, Isaiah Bowman. World Book Co., Yonkers-on-Hudson, N. Y., 1928.

B. Economic and Commercial Geographies.

Handbook of Commercial Geography, George G. Chisholm. Longmans, Green & Co., London, 1925.

An Introduction to Economic Geography, Wellington D. Jones and Derwent S. Whittlesey. University of Chicago Press, Chicago, Ill., 1925.

Industrial and Commercial Geography, J. Russell Smith. Henry Holt & Co., New York, 1925.

Economic Geography, R. H. Whitbeck and V. C. Finch. McGraw-Hill Book Co., New York, 1930.

Economic Geography, John McFarlane. Pitman & Sons, Bath, 1930.

Business Geography, Ellsworth Huntington and Frank E. Williams. John Wiley & Sons, New York, 1926.

C. General Geography and Its Principles.

College Geography, Earl C. Case and Daniel R. Bergsmark. John Wiley & Sons, New York, 1932.

An Introduction to Sociology. Ed. by Davis, Barnes, *et al.* D. C. Heath & Co., Boston. Revised 1931. (Social Aspects of Geography.)

Principles of Human Geography, Ellsworth Huntington and Sumner W. Cushing. John Wiley & Sons, New York, 1924.

The Character of Races, Ellsworth Huntington. Charles Scribner's Sons, New York, 1924.

Environmental Basis of Social Geography, C. C. Huntington and Fred A. Carlson. Prentice-Hall, New York, 1930.

College Geography, Roderick Peattie. Ginn & Co., Boston, 1932.

Environmental Basis of Society, F. Thomas. Century Publishing Co., New York, 1925.

The Geographic Factor, R. H. Whitbeck and O. J. Thomas. Century Co., New York, 1932.

Human Adaptation of the Earth, P. W. Bryan. H. Holt & Co., New York, 1933.

D. Climate.

Civilization and Climate, Ellsworth Huntington. Yale University Press, New Haven, Conn., 1924.

The Climate of the Continents, G. W. Kendrew. Oxford University Press, American Branch, New York, 1921.

Climatology, A. Austin Miller. Methuen & Co., London, 1931.

Climate Considered Especially in Relation to Man, R. DeC. Ward. G. P. Putnam's Sons, New York, 1918.

Climates of the United States, R. DeC. Ward. Ginn & Co., Boston, 1925.

E. Regions.

Source Book for the Economic Geography of North America, Charles C. Colby. University of Chicago Press, Chicago, Ill., 1921.

Geography of North America, George J. Miller and Almon E. Parkins. John Wiley & Sons, New York, 1928.

North America. J. R. Smith. Harcourt, Brace & Co., New York, 1925.

North America, L. Rodwell Jones and P. W. Bryan. Lincoln MacVeagh, the Dial Press, New York, 1924.

Human Geography of the South, Rupert B. Vance, University of North Carolina Press, Chapel Hill, 1932.

South America, Clarence F. Jones. Henry Holt & Co., New York, 1930.

Economic Geography of South America, R. H. Whitbeck. McGraw-Hill Book Co., New York, 1931.

Industrial and Commercial South America, Annie S. Peck. Thomas Y. Crowell, New York, 1927.

Economic Geography of Europe, W. Blanchard and S. S. Visher. McGraw-Hill Book Co., New York, 1931.

Asia, Laurence Dudley Stamp. E. P. Dutton & Co., New York, 1929.

Japan's Economic Position, John E. Orchard. McGraw-Hill Book Co., New York, 1930.

West of the Pacific, Ellsworth Huntington. Charles Scribner's Sons, New York, 1925.

Australia, G. Taylor. Oxford University Press, New York, 1928.

Vegetation and Soils of Africa, C. F. Marbut and H. L. Schantz. National Research Council and American Geographical Society, 1923.

Oxford Survey of the British Empire, edited by A. J. Herbertson and O. J. R. Howarth, 6 vols., 1914.

CONTENTS

ECONOMIC AND SOCIAL GEOGRAPHY

PART I

MAJOR GEOGRAPHIC FACTORS AND PRINCIPLES

CHAPTER I

THE MEANING OF ECONOMIC GEOGRAPHY

A Problem in Economic Geography: Rubber Production.—Geography, like every other science, may be thought of as a series of problems. In solving the problems of the part of this science known as economic geography we need to distinguish between several sets of facts, each of which may work differently. The two most basic sets are, first, the purely physical, or, in a broad sense, the physiographic aspects of geography, and, second, the facts of economics. Other factors of a political, racial, and social nature also play a part and introduce all sorts of complications. Let us illustrate the matter by means of a specific problem, namely, the geographical relationships of rubber. We will consider primary production first, and then manufacturing and the social effect of the rubber industry.

The Physiographic Factors. 1. *Climate.*—The word physiographic is often used merely for facts connected with the lands and their rocks, soils, and relief, but in a broader sense it means all parts of man's environment which are without life. Among these, climate has a wider effect than any other in determining where rubber shall be grown. Although rubber can be made from seventy or more varieties of plants, the genus *Hevea* has thus far proved the most useful. Hevea grows only where the climate is uniformly warm and wet. It prefers an average temperature close to 80° at all seasons and a rainfall of about 100 inches a year with no long periods of drought. It does not thrive where the average temperature falls below 70° for even a single month. It is greatly injured, too, if the rainfall drops below 2 or 3 inches per month for more than a month or two. A typical climate of this kind in com-

parison with that of Chicago is illustrated in A2.* Such climates are
found only at low altitudes in the moister part of the lands near the

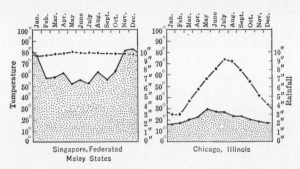

A—A Climate Suitable for Rubber Contrasted with That of Chicago.

(Shaded Areas Show Rainfall in Inches.   Lines —.— Show Temperature in F.)

equator. Nevertheless there are several million square miles of land
where the climate permits the growth of rubber, as appears in B2.

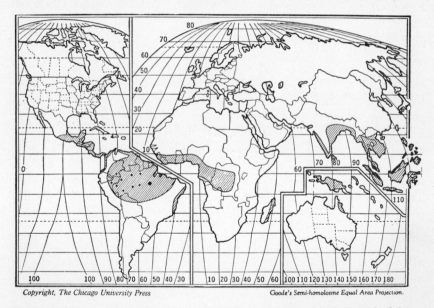

Goode's Semi-homolosine Equal Area Projection.

B—World Map of Areas Climatically Suitable for Rubber (shaded), and of Areas
where Rubber is Actually Produced (black)

* Throughout this book the illustrations are referred to by means of the numbers
of the pages on which they are found.   The letter A before a numeral means the
first illustration on the page in question.   B means the second illustration, etc.

2, 3. *Relief and Soil.*—Much of this great area where the climate permits rubber to thrive is rendered unfavorable for plantations by the relief of the land. One of the most important results of relief is its effect on the soil. In warm, wet tropical regions, such as those best adapted to rubber, the soil on moderate slopes is usually better than elsewhere. On such slopes the soil is very gradually washed away. Nevertheless, being held in place by the roots of the abundant vegetation, the soil disappears no faster than it is renewed by the decay of the underlying rock which thus forms fresh soil at the bottom of the old. Thus the rubber trees are able to grow in mature soil that is neither so young that its plant food is not yet easily soluble, nor so old that the plant food has mostly been leached away by the rain. Where such mature soils are derived from dark volcanic material, such as is common in Java, they are best of all. On the other hand, the hevea trees do not grow well in the new and immature soils of water-logged floodplains such as those in much of the Amazon Valley and along the coast of New Guinea. There the soil consists mainly of fresh material recently washed from the steep slopes of mountains. After it reaches the floodplains it is soaked with water so much of the time that it has little chance to decay and become oxidized by contact with the air. Thus even when it becomes old in years it may still be so immature that its potash, phosphates, and other valuable plant foods are not yet easily soluble. The tropical soils that have remained in the same position for very long periods on flat areas at higher levels than the floodplains are also very poor in many cases. Often they are red in color, a fact which frequently indicates that the warmth and wetness of the climate have caused them to decay rapidly and completely. In such "old" soils most of the plant food has been leached away by the frequent rains and only a poor skeleton of a soil is left, so to speak. Thus the relief of the land acting through the quality of the soil greatly reduces the areas that are favorable to the most rapid growth of rubber trees.

The relief also influences the location of rubber plantations in several other ways. Slopes surpass flat areas as sites for rubber plantations for at least four reasons. First, such slopes are well drained so that they are free from the danger of being water-logged during the frequent periods when heavy tropical showers pour down their water every afternoon for month after month. Second, wherever such slopes face toward the prevailing winds, they generally receive rain more regularly at all seasons than do flat areas, or slopes which face the other way. The prevailing winds in rubber areas are the steady trades, or in some cases the monsoons. Where such winds are obliged to move upward over a slope they are likely to give up some rain even in the seasons which are otherwise dry.   Thus on such slopes there is often rain at all seasons, which is very good for the hevea trees.

A third advantage of gentle slopes is that transportation is much easier on them than on steeper slopes or even on many of the flatter tropical plains where floods and swamps often cause much difficulty. In the fourth place, a gently sloping region is usually more healthful than a flat one.   This is especially important when white men have to live in low latitudes, as they do on rubber plantations.   But it is also important for the natives because they work far better when they are free from malaria and dysentery.   Both diseases are likely to be worse in flat places where standing water harbors both the anopheles mosquito and the bacteria which cause dysentery.

4. *Location in Respect to Land and Sea.*—The areas devoted to rubber are mainly near the sea.   Since white men generally have to live in the tropics in order to supervise the rubber plantations, it is essential that they take special care of their health.   At the low altitudes where the climate is good for rubber, breezy locations near the sea are in general the most healthful.   Then, too, the white people generally want to be near the sea in order to keep in touch with the rest of the world as much as possible.   More important than this is the fact that rubber is never used in large quantities in the countries where it is raised.   Therefore it must be shipped across the sea.   Rubber has now become so cheap that it is fairly heavy in proportion to its value.   So if it is carried far by land the cost of transportation eats up the profit. But transportation by water is cheap.   Hence a location near a navigable waterway and within easy reach of a good seaport is especially valuable.   Examples of such ports are found in Singapore, which serves the hilly peninsulas and islands of Malaysia and the East Indies, and in Pará, which serves the slopes that lie up the Amazon and its branches beyond the limits of the flat floodplain.

5. *Location in Respect to Main Trade Routes.*—Singapore today ships about two-thirds of all the world's rubber.   This is partly because the city lies on the way from Europe not only to Japan, the most active country in Asia, but to about five hundred million other people in Indo-China, the East Indies, Australia, and China.   Among the regions where the climate, soil, and relief are right for rubber there is no other place where ships pass at such frequent intervals.   In actual mileage the eastern slopes of the Andes and the northwestern slopes of the highlands of Brazil are by no means so far from the United States and western Europe as are the Malay Peninsula and Sumatra.   But no oecan ships come within hundreds of miles of these South American regions.   Even

at Pará, some 500 to 2,000 miles from the best rubber country, the number of regular liners is very small. The number would not be great even if all the ships that go from North America and Europe to Brazil, Uruguay, and Argentina stopped at the mouth of the Amazon. These ships carry the trade of only about fifty million South Americans, in contrast with the trade of more than ten times as many Asiatics which passes through Singapore to and from Europe. But most of the liners from North America and Europe to South America do not stop at Pará. That city, unlike Singapore, lies off the main line of travel. It offers so little business that few ships are tempted to go there. Hence, in order to reach Pará promptly, Americans sometimes go to Europe, or even to Rio de Janeiro, and then back to the mouth of the Amazon. On the equatorial coasts of Africa, where there is also good rubber land, a similar infrequency of regular sailings is the rule. The reasons are the same as at Pará except that the active people with whom trade is carried on in the southern tip of Africa are even less numerous than the similar people in temperate South America. The interior portions of Africa that are fit for rubber are even more inaccessible than those of South America, as the falls and rapids of the Congo prevent that river from being a good waterway.

The location of the Malay region fosters the development of rubber plantations in still another way. The frequent visits of ships to Singapore mean that many people, especially Englishmen, are familiar with the place. We are all in danger of overestimating the advantages of places that we know and of underestimating those of unfamiliar places. Thus many people who are unwilling to have anything to do with South America or Africa invest their money in the Singapore region or even go there to live.

The Economic Factors. 1. *Demand.*—Economic conditions reinforce the physiographic conditions in still further reducing the area where rubber is profitably grown on plantations. The two sets of factors together reduce the area to a few black dots in B2, and even these have to be exaggerated to show plainly. The first of the economic factors is the demand for rubber. Tires, overshoes, clothing, insulation, and erasers are the chief products for which rubber is required. The amount that can be thus used is strictly limited. If too much land is planted with rubber, the price goes down, and it does not pay to produce a crop. That is what happened a few years ago when the price dropped from $1.05 a pound to only about 10 cents. Until some new use for rubber, such as for pavements in streets, increases the demand, economic conditions will hold the rubber areas to small size no matter how much land is physiographically available.

2. *Labor.*—Another powerful economic factor in determining the geographic distribution of rubber plantations is need of willing, patient, faithful, and inexpensive workers. The degree to which people have these qualities depends on race, training, climate, and health. In tropical South America the Indians are extremely poor workers. Moreover, there are so few of them that it is not easy to gather enough at any one place. The people of African descent in equatorial America and also the Africans in the part of their own continent that is fit for rubber are somewhat better, but still very inefficient, and not very numerous. On the other hand, the people of the Malay Peninsula and of parts of the East Indies like Java are numerous, and vie with those of continental India and Ceylon as the best of tropical workers. They are slow, to be sure, and we often think of them as lazy. Nevertheless, generations of labor, especially in the rice fields, have gradually eliminated the families where the men were unwilling or unable to work hard enough to supply food for their children as well as themselves. Then, too, Chinese immigrants who excel the tropical people in steadiness and intelligence are numerous in the Malay region. Thus the conditions of human efficiency provide strong reasons for locating rubber plantations in southeastern Asia and the East Indies rather than in tropical Africa, or in South America where the rubber tree was first found.

3. *Demand for Food versus Other Products.*—The need of using the good land for rice is another economic factor which influences the distribution of rubber plantations. In Java, for example, large areas of gently sloping land around the base of the many volcanoes are physiographically almost ideal for rubber. Yet they carry no plantations. The rubber raisers are found on the steeper, rainier, and more remote slopes of the south side of the island. The reason for this is economic. Although the Javanese farmers are among the best of tropical workers, they are very slow, as is natural in such a warm and monotonous climate. Moreover, since Java is the most densely populated country in the world, the farms are extremely small. They average only 3 acres in size, and many families get a living from only an acre or two. It is impossible for such people to raise much of a surplus over and above what they eat. Hence the island does not raise enough food to supply the needs of the small part of the population which is not at work on the farms. The two largest cities, Batavia in the west and Surabaya in the east, have a combined population of only 750,000. That is very few for an island with 40,000,000 people, or as many as the whole of France. Yet even these cities have to get food from outside. If good rice land were taken for rubber plantations, the necessity of depending on imported food would be still greater. Moreover, some of the farmers

would be thrown out of work, for an acre of rubber needs much less work than an acre of rice. Such economic conditions have caused the Dutch who govern Java to forbid the use of good rice land for rubber. Even if this were not so, the high price of the good land would drive the rubber planters into the rougher and more remote regions.

Political Factors.—The familiarity of Europeans with the route via Singapore is both a cause and a result of political conditions which have greatly influenced the distribution of rubber plantations. The main political condition is that the parts of the East Indies and of southeastern Asia which are best for rubber physiographically and in their labor supply are colonial possessions of Great Britain and Holland. This fact has weighed heavily in leading British subjects to establish rubber plantations near Singapore. So has the fact that until the World War the British had more money than any other people to invest in foreign enterprises. The Dutch, likewise, have long been familiar with the East Indies. Being also thrifty and having colonies there, they, too, have started many rubber plantations, especially in Sumatra. Turning to South America, we find that Henry Ford is right in thinking that climatically and in many other ways the regions along the Tapajos River in Brazil are almost as well fitted for rubber as is the Malay region. But his new rubber plantations are in a country which even in our day is subject to frequent revolutions. That fact alone would be enough to explain why such lands have not previously been developed, even if they were more accessible and had a better labor supply.

The Relation between Rubber Plantations and Manufacturing.— The requirements of manufacturing have had little effect on the location of rubber plantations. The process of hardening the sap into a form that can easily be transported is very simple. After the sap has been collected from the little cups into which it flows from the cut bark, it is smoked to prepare it for transportation. This simple kind of manufacturing requires very little equipment; wood for fuel is always abundant in any climate that is fit for rubber trees; and the number of skilled men needed to oversee the work is small. The later processes of manufacturing rubber are practically never carried on near the plantations. This is in harmony with the general fact that manufacturing of a highly skilled type is never found on a large scale in genuinely tropical countries. Moreover, such countries are relatively small consumers of highly manufactured goods. The Dutch East Indies, for example, have only one automobile or other kind of motor car for over 700 people whereas the United States has one for every five or less.

The greatest factor in determining where rubber is finally manufactured is human skill. A second factor is the extent to which the manu-

factured product will be used.   The people who possess skill in manufacturing are essentially the same as those who can afford to use the
manufactured products.   Hence the manufacturing of rubber into tires
and other finished products is almost wholly confined to western Europe,
the United States, and other English-speaking parts of the world.   We
shall see later that this distribution follows very definite geographic
laws.   For the present it is enough to point out that human efficiency
is the main factor in determining where rubber is manufactured as well
as where it is raised.   But the degree of efficiency required for the two
things is very different.

**The Relation of Social Conditions to the Economic Geography of
Rubber.**   1. *Growth of the Use of Rubber.*—Since the discovery of
America, rubber has passed from a position of negligible importance to
one where it has much to do with great social changes.   Columbus found
the Indian children of northern South America bouncing rubber balls,
as generations of our children have bounced them.   In later times,
rubber erasers have helped school children, authors, draftsmen, and
artists, and thus aided in the growth of modern civilization.   About the
middle of the last century, rubber overshoes and then rubber raincoats
were among the early aids in the wonderful reduction of the death rate
which has marked our times.   These uses of rubber awakened enough
interest so that about 1880 a few attempts were made to establish
plantations in the Malay region.   Then bicyles and carriages began
to be fitted with rubber tires, and about 1900 the automobile became
important.   During the next ten years the demand for rubber increased
far faster than the supply, and the plantation price of crude rubber
soared to a dollar a pound in 1910 (A9).   This led to two pronounced
social changes.   It precipitated a terrible crisis in the rubber regions of
Latin America, especially on the Amazon and its tributaries.   It also
led to the very rapid expansion of plantations in the Malay region of
Asia and thus greatly altered the conditions of life in that region.

2. *Social Results of the Search for Wild Rubber.*—Until 1910, practically all the world's rubber was gathered by Indians from wild rubber
trees in the Amazon Basin and other parts of tropical America.   This
gave the Indians a little ready money.   It also supported some Portu-
guese-American traders who established little stores and rubber warehouses in high, dry locations along the banks of the slow equatorial
rivers.   In tropical forests the trees of one kind do not grow in groves
like our maples, pines, oaks, and birches; each kind is widely scattered,
with one tree here and another there among dozens of other kinds.
Hence in order to find rubber trees the Indians had to wander widely.
Often they climbed some high tree, located whatever rubber trees might

happen to be in sight, and then hunted for them. So long as the Indians worked only when they felt like it, their work was not arduous. The warm, moist, monotonous climate, however, made them feel listless, and they were often ill with malaria, hookworm disease, festering sores, and other tropical ailments. Moreover, nothing in their past mode of life

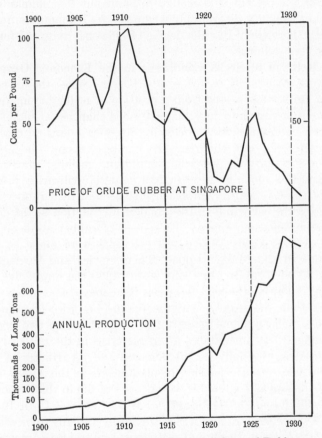

A—Fluctuations in the Production and Price of Rubber.

had ever obliged the Indians to work steadily. The ones who succeeded best in getting a living and in bringing up families of children had not been those who could work steadily, but those who were most clever in finding game, nuts, and seeds, or in driving away enemies. So both the inheritance and training of the Indians made them mentally and physically unfit for steady work day after day. A few hours of rubber gathering each day at occasional intervals harmonized with this temperament very well, but under such a system no one family brought in much rubber.

When the price of rubber went up so fast a new aspect of life presented itself to the Indians. The big rubber dealers in the cities of the United States and Europe urged their South American agents to send more rubber. The agents urged the traders, and the traders urged the Indians. The opportunities to make money induced traders of a rough and cruel type to migrate into the rubber region. This migration consisted of only a few thousand people at most, but like practically all migrations it was selective. In other words, the people who came were not the average kind in the places where they lived. In this particular case they were bolder, more energetic, and more unscrupulous than the average, and at the same time less under restraint than at home. Their one purpose was to get as much rubber as possible. Their way of accomplishing this was to force the Indians to work hard all the time. Since the Indians were few in number—the inhabitants of such an environment invariably are—the rubber buyer often kidnapped the poor savages, or held their wives and children as prisoners and starved them when the men failed to bring in rubber. When the Indians worked slowly and spasmodically, as befits their environment and culture, the traders beat and tortured them. Even when this did not happen, the poor creatures were compelled to bear heavy loads, make toilsome journeys, and work in the heat and moisture and among pestilential insects until they were exhausted or close to death's door with fever.

All this helped to make it harder and harder to procure rubber. The Indians in their ignorance cut the bark too deeply and too completely, thus killing many of the trees. So year by year they had to go farther into the forest, and the rubber supply diminished in spite of every effort. Then suddenly the many plantations which had been set out in Malaysia soon after 1900 became old enough to be tapped. The rubber supply increased enormously, and the price dropped until it reached 13 cents a pound in 1922 (A9). Many of the Brazilian rubber traders gave up in disgust and went away. The Indians were allowed to work more nearly in their old intermittent way. Thus the social problem of the Brazilian rubber industry has become less acute, although it still exists. It illustrates the nature of social geography. It shows how an economic demand in one part of the world may lead to selective migration, new phases of industry, new ways of living, new problems of social conduct, and new types of social selection, so that some kinds of people die out while others survive. In the case of rubber, all these conditions were concentrated in one highly specialized type of geographic environment, because only on the higher and drier banks of the rivers of the lowlands of equatorial South America could the rubber traders establish their stations. The geographic environment did not cause the demand for rubber, nor did it oblige the rubber traders to gather the Indians into settlements and oppress them. But it did determine that these things could happen only under certain definite conditions of climate, relief, soil, and location in respect to land and water.

Social Geography of Rubber Plantations.—The opening of rubber plantations has introduced a new social order in certain areas that are fit for rubber. The rubber planters see that it is to their advantage to have healthy, orderly, contented workers who stay on the plantations through choice rather than force. So the plantations usually supply houses for the native workers as well as for the foreign supervisors. The native houses no longer stand in the midst of the wild, fever-breeding jungle, but in well kept clearings where mosquitoes have little chance to breed. The streams are confined in smooth channels so that there are no back waters and stagnant pools for mosquito larvae; the swamps are drained, and often the drains are oiled to kill the larvae. Moreover, if people become ill with malaria or other infectious diseases they are promptly placed in hospitals. There they are isolated not only from other people, but also from wandering mosquitoes which might spread the infection.

Then, too, the workers on rubber plantations learn new lessons as to working steadily and regularly throughout the year. For good or ill they also learn a great deal as to the European, American, or Chinese modes of life. The net result is that people who formerly were classed as barbarous now conform outwardly to many of the rules of western civilization. Where life was formerly cheap and war was the rule, there are today safety and peace.

An American official in Brazil gives a rosy description of the social changes on the Ford rubber plantation at Boa Vista on the Tapajós River. In traveling from Pará for 600 miles up the Amazon and then another 150 up the Tapajós one sees for a week almost nothing except forest and an occasional group of thatched huts almost hidden in the jungle. Then as one rounds a bend of the river neat rows of American bungalows appear with a big water tank and the towering smoke stack of a power house.

The laborers who live in these houses are a mixed race, with much Indian and Portuguese blood and some Negro. Formerly they were almost like slaves, working for generation after generation for the "patron" on whose property they were born. They lived in roughly thatched huts of sticks. Their work consisted of tapping wild rubber trees, clearing land for the kind of temporary cultivation which was formerly the rule, or cutting wood for passing steamers. This last was almost the only source of real cash as distinguished from credit at the store of the "patron." Carrying ten sticks which weighed a hundred pounds, the laborer would cross the teetering gang-plank between the river bank and the steamer's deck for hour after hour. By working practically all day and all night he earned one and a half milreis, or about 18 cents in our money.   But often for a week at a time he did almost nothing except lie in a hammock.   His wife meanwhile cooked bananas, fish, and manioc meal over a smoky outdoor fire, or if these were not available she went out with the children to hunt for wild food in the forest.

Today this same man works day after day at a wage several times as great as before.   His comfortable frame house may have running water and electric lights. It is well screened from mosquitoes, unless he tears out the screens because they are in the way.   He has leather shoes, and if he is one of the wise minority he wears these regularly and thus largely escapes the hookworm disease which formerly did much to make him lazy and inefficient.   If any of the family get the hookworm, as is likely to happen to the barefooted children, the man has money enough to fill a physician's prescription which soon eradicates it.   He also has money enough to let his wife buy a variety of good food and even ready-made dresses at the store.   His children get a good elementary education, provided he insists on their going to school regularly.

Some of the natives really profit by the new social order, although many tend to fall back into their old shiftless ways.   Here, as in so many other cases, we find a process of selective migration.   Those who like the white man's way of life cluster around the plantations, and some are improved thereby.   Others learn the bad things of civilization without much of the good.   Still others prefer to remain away from the white man and keep on with their old ways.   Nevertheless, there can be no doubt that when plantations are established by Europeans or Americans there is an enormous change in the way of life of the workers. Of course, the entire number of such workers all over the world amounts to only a few score of thousands.   But plantations of other sorts employ much larger numbers.   Moreover, the people who do not work on the plantations, or who work on plantations that are badly managed, do at least get some idea of ways of working and living quite different from those to which they are accustomed.   Thus the plantations are centers from which the virus of change works outward.

Social Effect of Rubber in the Most Progressive Regions.—The use of rubber has probably had much more effect on the most advanced nations than on the people within the tropics.   This is mainly because without rubber the development of the automobile would have been enormously more difficult, costly, and slow than has actually been the case.   In the absence of pneumatic tires the vibration of the early automobiles as they were driven over the rough roads of that day would have made the new vehicle most uncomfortable and correspondingly unpopular.   The jolting would also have made it very much harder to develop a type of car in which the nuts would stay in place, the electrical connections would be firm, the gasoline lines would continue to function, and the whole machine would hang together instead of being promptly shaken to pieces.   Thus we may feel quite certain that if there had been no such thing as rubber, or a suitable substitute, there would probably have been no such tremendous concentration of brains, energy, and capital upon the work of improving the automobile.   Consequently, automobiles would today be comparatively crude, uncomfortable, unreliable, and expensive, and hence rare.

If the development of the automobile had been thus delayed by the absence of rubber, the social consequences due to this new machine would be correspondingly small.   Few people who were born in the present century can appreciate the enormous change which has been wrought by motor vehicles.   A superb system of roads has become a necessity; the number of men needed on farms has been enormously diminished; the isolation of the farms has been largely destroyed; the supremacy of the railroads has been threatened; crimes of all sorts have been made almost inconceivably easier.   People twenty miles from a city can easily come in for an evening engagement.   A map of the suburbs of almost any American city shows quite a different pattern from a similar map thirty years ago.   Then the suburban houses clustered around railroad stations or along street car lines.   Today each good road leading out from the city is more or less lined with houses, even though there is no means of getting to the city by train or trolley line.   Many suburbs of the pleasanter type are now growing up with no means of communication except motor vehicles.   All over the country, small schools are being consolidated into large schools because it is so easy to carry children five or ten miles in buses.   People choose their friends in a new way, also.   Formerly the mere difficulties of travel caused most people to associate mainly with friends who lived within walking distance.   Today we think nothing of driving five miles to play bridge or tennis.   It is easier than walking half a mile.   Hundreds of other social conditions have undergone equally great changes by reason of the automobile.   Thus the United States, where the automobile is by far the most widely used, has changed much faster than have countries like Bulgaria.   Moreover, the changes due to the automobile affect practically all our activities.   Hence the total change has been enormously greater in this country than in the regions where rubber is raised.   Of course, rubber tires are only one of the factors which led to the change, but without rubber or some effective substitute, the change would have been far slower and less revolutionary.

The Future of Rubber Production.—Rubber illustrates the way in which man's activities not only modify the natural environment but also alter the location where all sorts of products can be most profitable. The change from the wild rubber production of the Amazon and Congo basins to the well organized rubber estates in southeastern Asia may not be final. The regular rows of hevea trees, the motor roads leading to the centralized rubber plants, the comfortable or even luxurious houses of the managers, and the hygienic labor quarters now found on the estates may possibly be largely replaced by jungle almost like that which prevailed there previously. A change in this direction is taking place on the rolling lowlands of East Sumatra. In these densely forested regions the agricultural people are almost nomadic, depending on the "milpa" type of agriculture. Small groups of them wander from place to place. Each year they clear a bit of forest, burn the brush, and raise a crop of mountain rice—the kind that does not need irrigation. After the harvest they move to some other suitable spot, perhaps one that they have occupied previously. They have learned that a single crop uses up most of the available plant food or else fills the soil with harmful bacteria. After the World War the Dutch government gave the natives rubber seeds to be planted with the rice. When the forest came up on the abandoned rice fields it was a rubber jungle different from the former equatorial forest. These numerous rubber jungles remained practically unnoticed so long as the price of rubber was low. In 1925–26, however, the price soared as a result of the English attempt to curtail production through the so-called Stevenson Scheme. Then these wild rubber trees were ready to produce, and a steadily increasing native supply of rubber was put on the Singapore market. The weakness of the plantation system of raising rubber then became evident. Rubber does not have to be watched and cultivated like sugar, tea, and coffee, nor does quality mean much. Rubber is rubber. Thus when production was curtailed in British territory and the price went up, these extensive new rubber jungles were at once drawn upon, even though the production of the Dutch estates also increased. Many trees were killed by over-tapping, but for every one that died a hundred others were ready to be tapped. In those years with the price of rubber above fifty cents a pound, Sumatra went rubber mad. Everyone who had a chance went into the jungle to get rubber. The primitive native who had never seen money suddenly found himself rich. Nevertheless, most of the profits were probably made by the Chinese merchants whose flat-bottomed boats went far up the rivers to buy the raw rubber and carry it to Singapore. Money was spent recklessly, and a regular *nouveau riche* atmosphere prevailed. This native rubber production, along with the increased production of the Dutch estates, caused the Stevenson Scheme to break down. The very low price of rubber since then has stopped further increase of native rubber production. Nevertheless one-fifth of the world's production still comes from Sumatra, and the vast rubber jungle is waiting only for better times. Then it will put a great stream of rubber on the market. Thus rubber production, which was once taken away from the forest and concentrated in carefully organized estates, may some day again become more or less of a forest industry.

The Plan of This Book.—This discussion of rubber illustrates many of the topics and principles which will be treated in this book. The first thing that we saw in respect to rubber is that the areas where rubber can profitably be raised are strictly limited, and that within the limits some areas are far better than others. Climate is the most important factor both in setting limits and in making certain areas favorable, but relief, soil, and transportation also act in the same way and are often very potent. Moreover, economic, social, and political factors such as the character of the labor supply, the demand for a product, and the degree to which a region is familiar have a similar effect in causing certain places to be chosen in preference to others. The whole matter may be summed up in three questions: (1) Where is it *possible* for any given product to be produced, or for any given activity to be carried on? (2) Where do people *choose* to produce these products or carry on these activities? (3) Why do they choose these places rather than others? The physical environment never *compels* people to do anything. It merely says that some things, such as getting water power out of frozen rivers, are impossible or at least impracticable, while other things are unprofitable, and man may choose whether to do one, or all, or none of them. He may use a certain piece of land for cotton, corn, a factory, or an aviation field. Our task as geographers is to see what the opportunities are in different parts of the world and how and why man has chosen one or another of them.

In this book we shall devote the first part to getting a clear idea of the principles which govern the relation between the geographic background and human activities. Since climate is the most widespread and pervasive environmental condition we shall discuss first the way in which it imposes limits on all sorts of products and activities, and then the way in which it supplies highly favorable or optimum conditions for these same products and activities in certain definite areas. We shall see that plants, animals, and man all respond to the same climatic laws, and that in many ways the best conditions for crops, domestic animals, human activity, and civilization are all essentially the same. But the relief of the lands, acting especially through transportation, and the soil, acting through crops, also have a powerful effect upon almost every kind of human activity, so that each of these also receives a chapter. Then, too, the effect of the purely physical factors of our environment is greatly altered by economic factors such as the relation between the demand, supply, and price of a given product. It is also altered by social factors such as customs inherited from the past, and by political factors such as the degree of safety and encouragement given by governments.

When we have considered all these various factors we shall be ready for a general survey of the world as a whole. For this purpose we shall divide the earth's surface into a number of natural regions whose main characteristics depend on climate, but which are also influenced by soil and relief. Our next task will be to discuss the relation of the world's vegetation and chief products to this geographic background. In doing this we shall study the cereals, other food crops, industrial crops, and various kinds of animals, including fish. We shall discover distinct laws as to how the various crops and animals are distributed in different types of geographic environment. Then we shall investigate forests, metals, fuels, and water power, thus gaining a clear idea of where and how mankind obtains not only food, but raw materials as well.

This brings us to the final section of the book devoted to the two great occupations of manufacturing and commerce. In studying these we shall find that not only the amount but also the kind of manufacturing in different parts of the world vary enormously. The manufacturing in some regions is little more than the work whereby people keep themselves going. They mend their tools, prepare their own food, and perhaps weave a little homespun cloth, but make practically nothing for sale or to send away. Other regions carry on a kind of manufacturing which prepares raw products so that they can easily be preserved or transported. Such regions often send out a great volume of material, but they are not highly developed as manufacturing regions. A third type of region, very limited in extent, makes goods of all sorts to be distributed widely. We shall see just where these various types of regions are found and why they are found there. Then to finish our work we shall look into the problem of how goods of all kinds are sent from one part of the world to another. We shall discover that the world's trade is concentrated along a few main lines. Curiously enough, these lines are most important where they connect places which carry on the same kind of active manufacturing, rather than places with very different kinds of products. In all these chapters we must constantly bear in mind that geographic environment merely offers opportunities to man. Man's own will determines which of the various opportunities he will accept, and how far he will go in using them.

EXERCISES

1. On the basis of this chapter prepare an outline showing a method of treating the economic and social geography of a region. Use at least four grades of headings, namely major divisions of the subject, main types of factors, individual factors, and detailed effect of factors.

2. Make a second similar outline in which you begin with the final result, namely, the rubber used in tires, erasers, etc., and work backward to the geographic factors which determine the location of the original supply of rubber.

3. Select some familiar product with which you are especially familiar, for example, apples, cotton cloth, copper, or furniture, and make an outline for it like the one in Exercise 1.

4. Use the outline of Exercise 3 as the basis for a brief account of the economic and social geography of the product which you have chosen.

5. Enumerate several localities where people from more progressive areas have refrained from investing their capital and developing industries because of unfavorable political and social conditions. In what ways, if any, are these unfavorable conditions related to the geographic environment?

6. A company organized in some advanced country develops an oil concession in a backward country. During the course of twenty or thirty years fair wages are paid; sanitary homes are built; and general prosperity ensues. Then the oil gives out and the company gradually reduces its business and withdraws. Outline the social effects not only of the growth of the concession but of its decline. State also the effects that will probably remain after the withdrawal. Look up the Mexican oil industry since 1900 and see what it indicates along this line.

CHAPTER II

GEOGRAPHIC LIMITS AND THE UTILIZATION OF LAND

The Laws of Limits and Optima.—Many of the chief problems in economic geography are questions of limits and optima. In the preceding chapter, for example, we sought to discover first what conditions limit the areas where rubber can be grown profitably, and, second, what combination of circumstances within these limits supplies the best or optimum conditions for rubber plantations. The law of limits may be expressed very simply: Almost any environmental condition becomes fatal if it is either too intense or too weak. An animal or plant may be killed by too much or too little heat. It may be drowned if rain is too abundant, or it may die of thirst if rain is too scarce. Overeating and undereating both lead to poor health and may cause death. If a plant needs an acid soil, it will not grow where the acidity falls below a certain limit. But if the soil becomes too acid, the opposite kind of limit is imposed. Or again, suppose that an animal like the mountain goat can protect itself from wolves and other carnivorous animals only in regions that are rugged. Level land will then interpose a limit so that there will be no goats. But an extreme in the other direction, such as a succession of precipices, may also impose a limit so that there will be no goats above the precipices.

The law of optima is equally simple: Between the upper and lower limits of every environmental condition there is a certain degree of intensity which is most favorable to any given organism or activity. Thus every plant and animal thrives best under certain moderate conditions of food, temperature, and water supply. The plant that likes acid soil will thrive best where there is a certain moderate degree of acidity. The mountain goat can best maintain itself where the land is rough but not too rough. Between the optimum and the limit of any condition there is, of course, every gradation. In the present chapter we shall discuss limits, leaving optima for the following chapters on climate, soil, and relief.

The Many Kinds of Climatic Limits. 1. *Temperature.*—A mere list of the conditions which impose geographical limits upon all sorts of plants and animals as well as upon man and his activities would occupy

18

many pages.   Among these limits those pertaining to climate are especially important.   Chief among the limiting factors of climate comes
temperature.   Low temperature and the consequent ice and snow
prevent people from making a living in six million square miles of Antarctica and Greenland.   Temperatures not quite so low limit the growth
of trees so that far northern regions are covered with mossy tundras
instead of forests.   Another temperature limit forbids agriculture north
of the July isotherm of 55°.   Hence there is scarcely one inhabitant per
square mile in about three million square miles of Canada and Alaska
and three and a half million of northern Asia and Europe.   As one

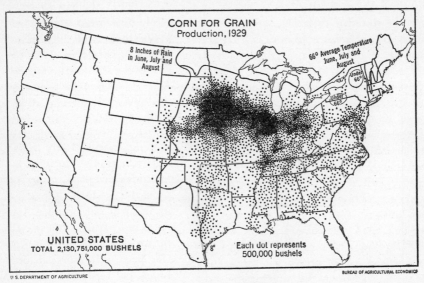

A—Corn in the United States.

travels from high latitudes toward the equator, first one temperature
limit and then another is passed.   A19 is a dot map in which each dot
represents 500,000 bushels of corn.   The line marked 66° summer temperature marks the northern limit of this crop.   Similar isotherms or
lines of uniform temperature mark the limits of still other crops.   Cotton cannot be profitably grown north of southern Virginia and southern
Missouri.   Oranges will not thrive north of Florida on the frosty eastern
side of North America, while on the milder western side they reach their
northern limit in some of the warmest valleys of north central California.   The date palm, the bamboo, and a host of other plants have similar limits.   In ascending a high mountain many such limits are crossed;
one leaves first the cultivated land, next the forest, then the grassland,

and finally comes to the limits even of lichens. A20 shows how many limits are found within a distance of only seven hundred miles in Finland.

The limits of animals are like those of plants. The lion is never found much beyond the tropics. Unless the parrot froze to death, it would perish for lack of food if obliged to remain in snowy latitudes. Even the polar bear cannot live in the interior of Greenland because the low temperature makes it impossible to procure food.

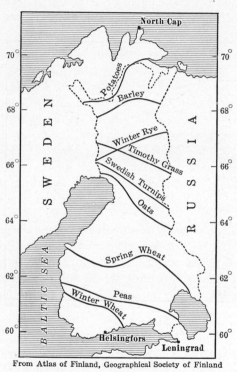

From Atlas of Finland, Geographical Society of Finland

A—Limits of Successful Cultivation in Finland.

The warm limit of plants and animals, although often less clearly defined than the cold limit, is no less real. The sugar maple, for instance, is rarely found south of latitude 40° and even there does not give a good supply of sap. Although potatoes are raised even at the equator, they are not worth raising and will not permanently reproduce themselves in very low latitudes except on high, cool uplands. Many kinds of apples will not produce flowers and fruit unless the flower buds are exposed to the frost. If one-half of a blueberry bush is kept warm in winter and the other half is exposed to low temperatures, only the exposed half will bear fruit. Thus many plants are limited to regions where there is some frost.

Among animals the yak and musk-ox afford good examples of limits set by high temperature. Being creatures of the snow, with long hair and heavy fur, they quickly succumb if brought to warm regions. The yak fails to reproduce itself even when brought down to Kashmir where it is still a mile above sea-level. It is adapted to the Himalayan and Tibetan climate at altitudes of 10,000 feet or more. Horses, sheep, and ordinary cattle have rather vague warm limits. They can live even in equatorial lowlands, but unless the stock is renewed from cooler regions they deteriorate rapidly and the finer types soon die out. Even at Hongkong, near the tropic of Cancer, a good herd of dairy cattle can be maintained only by taking care of the cows almost as if they were hospital patients, and by bringing in new animals at frequent intervals. When the temperature rises in the spring the milk supply promptly diminishes. Such cases bring up the important fact that there are different limits for different functions. The individual can often survive under conditions which do not permit of reproduction. Thus the limits of individual existence are much wider than those for the existence of the species.

2. *The Limiting Effect of Humidity.*—Moisture as well as temperature sets limits to plants and animals. The dry limit is illustrated in the map of corn, A19. On the west the growth of corn without irrigation is practically limited by the isohyet (line of equal rainfall) of 8 inches during the summer. Every plant has a dry limit, as is obvious from the fact that all types of vegetation disappear in the very driest deserts. In the same way there is a wet limit. Cotton, for instance, is raised only in small quantities in Florida. It will grow there, but because of the abundant rain the quality of the fiber is injured. Thus it is limited by humidity in an indirect fashion through competition with other crops. With still more abundant rainfall no cotton would grow at all. If the rainfall is too abundant all crops are ruined, so that very wet regions such as the lower slopes of the west side of the Coast Range in Washington have little agriculture. The effect of moisture displays itself not only in rainfall but also in the condition of the ground. The cranberry, for example, is limited to areas where the ground is usually saturated. Most kinds of trees, on the other hand, will not grow in such places.

3. *Winds as Limiters of Growth.*—Another set of climatic limits is imposed by the movement of the air. For example, in Seistan in eastern Persia, the northerly "Wind of a Hundred and Twenty Days" blows with hurricane force most of the time during the four warmer months. Its violence prevents the growth of trees except in the lee of walls or in sheltered valleys around the edges of the plain. On the west coast of Tierra del Fuego a similar result is produced by the fierce west winds of the "Roaring Forties," as those stormy latitudes are called. The bare, grassy quality of many exposed seacoasts and islands is also due to the fact that they lie beyond the limits of tree growth as set by the winds. Even in the interior it is often impossible for flying insects to live in certain places because of the wind. This is of great importance in those portions of the tropics where the almost steady trade winds keep certain exposed areas free from mosquitoes and tsetse flies. That renders them free from malaria, yellow fever, and sleeping sickness and from allied diseases which make it impossible for most domestic animals to live where the tsetse fly is present. Thus for both man and beast these areas are among the most healthful parts of the tropics. This is one reason why the American government buildings near Panama

City are on Balboa *Heights*, and the big government hotel at Colón at the northern or Atlantic end of the Canal stands directly on the seashore.

In actual practice, the lower limit of atmospheric movement is never reached, for there is no place where the air is motionless. If the air should become absolutely quiet, the exhalations from plants and animals, and from man and his works, would soon contaminate it so that life would be impossible. An approach to such conditions is found in a few sheltered and undrained valleys where volcanic gases temporarily accumulate, and in the streets and tunnels of great cities where the fumes from factories, automobiles, and other sources poison the air.

4. *How Sunlight Sets Limits.*—Some animals, such as those which live in caves or in the depths of the sea, require no sunlight. The same is true of certain parasitic plants and other low forms. For these organisms there is no lower limit of sunlight, but in other cases the lower limit is very clear. For example, in the depths of the forest the ground is often almost bare of small plants simply because of the shading due to the thick trees. Too much sunlight also sets a limit. Many bacteria die promptly if exposed to the full rays of the sun, and so do many shade-loving plants, like the maidenhair fern. For still other plants like the cactus the upper limit of sunshine is never reached.

An interesting phase of this matter is found in the fact that many plants will not produce seeds unless the day is of a certain definite length. For example, a certain type of tobacco produces flowers only when the duration of daylight is reduced to 8 or 9 hours. Chrysanthemums can be made to blossom ahead of the normal time if the plants are darkened for a few hours each day, thus artifically changing the duration of the light. Many fruit trees form flower buds only when the daylight is short in the autumn. Cold weather soon checks their growth, but the buds are ready to blossom as soon as warm weather comes in the spring. Radishes and certain other vegetables will not produce seeds unless the daylight lasts at least 13 or 14 hours. If taken to equatorial regions where the day is only 12 hours long they may produce good roots and leaves, but will never produce seeds unless the period of light is artificially lengthened. Thus the length of the day sets both upper and lower limits to the spread of many species of plants.

Other Kinds of Natural Limits. 1. *The Soil.*—Plants and animals are limited to certain geographical areas by soil and the relief of the land. In many regions, trees give place to grasses where the soil changes from clay or silt to sand. In Cuba the agricultural authorities report that certain poisonous plants are strictly limited to one particular kind of soil produced from a rare igneous type of rock. Many nature lovers know that wild flowers like the arbutus grow only in soils that are somewhat acid, whereas other flowers will not grow in such soils. Where the vegetation changes by reason of the soil the animal life also changes. Certain butterflies are found only where a particular type of soil favors the growth of plants which they like. On certain types of soil the European corn borer, which is a great pest of our corn crop, is said to be found in only small quantities although abundant on other soils not far away.

2. *Limits Set by the Relief of the Land.*—The relief of the land sets limits in several different ways. Where the slopes are too steep the soil

cannot accumlate to any great depth. Thus the growth of trees is often prevented. If exposed to the sun such slopes may become so hot and dry that they simulate deserts. In Connecticut a few slopes of this kind give the cactus a chance to grow far beyond its ordinary limits, but absolutely forbid the encroachment of most of the plants that live close by. On the other hand, many plains are so flat that they are poorly drained and swampy. This condition leads to terrible floods and famines in parts of China and thus sets limits to the development of transportation, manufacturing, and other important phases of civilization. In large sections of northern and western Russia numerous swamps due to the undrained relief set limits to agriculture, and cause considerable areas to be unpopulated. During the World War, General von Hindenburg first sprang into fame because his knowledge of these swamps enabled him to defeat the Russians.

3. *Limits Set by Other Organisms.*—One organism often sets limits upon another. In Africa, the tsetse fly is limited to certain definite types of low, brushy forest near permanent bodies of water. Since the tsetse may carry germs that are deadly both for man and domestic animals it prevents people from living or even traveling in certain areas, and excludes horses and cattle from far larger areas. The weeds in a garden often impose limits on the more delicate flowers. In such cases the limits of the flowers in their wild state are set by some particular combination of temperature, humidity, soil, and perhaps relief which enables the plants to hold their own against all others. Where so many agencies are at work imposing limits on all sides it is very difficult, as well as important, to discover just what factors are the actual cause of limitation.

The Prairies as an Example of Limits.—A good example of the way in which several factors combine to impose limits is found in the prairies. Before the arrival of the white man the prairies of the central United States reached the eastern limits shown in A24. Although the boundary between grassland and deciduous forest was usually sharply defined, there was a wide belt where patches of forest along the streams and lowlands were interspersed with patches of treeless grassy prairie on the *interfluves*, or higher areas between the valleys, as appears in A24. Many theories have been advanced to explain this limitation of the forest. The vast herds of buffaloes which once grazed here are said to have eaten the seedling trees and thus prevented the forests from expanding westward. Grass fires set by the Indians are said to have killed the trees on the edges of the forest and thus to have pushed the limits of the grassland farther and farther east. Again we are somewhat illogically told that the soil has much to do with the matter, for where forests prevail the soil is light brown and relatively poor, while in the grasslands it is black or at least very dark and rich. And finally we are told that the forests prevail only where the climate is sufficiently moist at all seasons.

All four of these factors have undoubtedly played a part. In order to understand them clearly we must realize that climate comes first and that the others are largely the consequences of climate. Evidently the climate cannot be appreciably influenced by either the soil, the fires, or the buffaloes, but each of these is greatly influ-

A—The Boundaries of the Prairies. The most lightly ruled areas are prairies.

enced by climate. Accordingly, we inquire whether the climates within the forest and the prairie, respectively, differ in any such way as to explain why trees grow in one section and not in the other. B24 gives the basis for such a comparison. Akron, Ohio, represents the forest area, and Des Moines, Iowa, the prairies. These places have been chosen because they are as nearly alike as any two places lying well within the limits of the grassland on the one hand and the forest on the other. Both lie in regions of gentle relief. They are in practically the same latitude and so have similar conditions of sunlight and seasons. They have the same average temperature for the year as a whole. The total annual rainfall is not quite so uniform, being 37 inches at Akron and 32 at Des Moines. This last difference, however, does not necessarily mean that Ohio excels Iowa as a

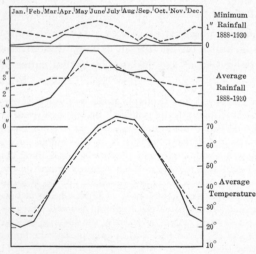

B—Climatic Conditions which Limit the Prairies.
———— Des Moines, Iowa. – – – Akron, Ohio.

place for trees. It all depends on when the rain comes.

In B24 the lower curves indicate that central Iowa is about 6° colder than northern Ohio in winter and about 3° warmer in summer. This means that the Iowa climate is more *continental* than that of Ohio. Thus, in dry winters, when there is only a scanty cover of snow, the ground in Iowa becomes deeply frozen. This injures trees because they need some water from the ground even in winter, but cannot get it if the soil around the roots is frozen. In dry summers, on the other hand, the greater heat of Iowa may cause the ground to be parched, and this, too, is bad for trees, especially when they are young. The value of additional moisture is evident in the fact that trees do grow naturally in the prairie region along water courses and in other moist spots.

Another important difference between the two climates pertains to the rainfall, as appears in the middle part of B24. Here the continental character of the Iowa climate is again evident, for the figures for precipitation fall far below those of Ohio in winter, but rise higher in May and June. The low winter precipitation is bad for trees because the cover of snow in Iowa is often deficient, and the spring rains do not come early enough to enable young trees to begin their growth as soon as is desirable. This hurts trees but does little harm to grasses. Still more important is the upper part of B24. The lines there show the amount of rain (or melted snow) received in each place during the driest January, the driest February, and so forth, from 1888 to 1930. During each of the twelve months except October, the droughts in Iowa have been worse than in Ohio. Thus in a third factor, this high variability from season to season, Iowa shows a condition which is strongly characteristic of continental climates. Such climates present a marked contrast to the *marine* type, which prevails more and more fully as a place comes within the influence of the sea or of other large bodies of water like the Great Lakes. Although Akron is far from having a marine climate, its tendency in that direction is important in relation to the limits of forests. The difference between the droughts of Iowa and Ohio is especially noticeable in May, June, and July. This is just the time when trees grow fastest and are most likely to be injured by dryness. The mildness of the droughts at this season in Ohio helps to explain why forests prevail there while the severer droughts farther west cause prairies in Iowa. Much of the time, trees can grow as well in Iowa as in Ohio, but in Iowa the occasional droughts in spring and early summer either kill off the seedlings and young trees, or weaken them. In the latter case the little trees are smothered by the grasses which shoot up very rapidly as soon as the rains fall after a drought.

The other three factors which are sometimes said to determine the western limit of forests in the United States all depend upon the climate. Because the climate is favorable to grasslands in Iowa, the buffalo formerly wandered there in huge numbers. On the border where trees and grasses are evenly matched, the buffaloes helped the grasses. When grass is grazed or trodden into the mud by the feet of animals, new shoots spring up, but when the same thing happens to seedling trees they die. The prairie fires which the Indians kindled in the dry grass were like the buffaloes in being much more destructive to young trees than to grass. Moreover, the droughts mentioned in the preceding paragraph not only gave an advantage to the grass, but also caused fires to be more common and more destructive to seedling trees on the edges of the prairie than farther east in Ohio. Thus both buffaloes and fires doubtless pushed the forest limits eastward.

The forests and the grasses are themselves largely responsible for the difference in the soils of the two regions. The part of a plant which most enriches the soil is the root. That is the only part which remains almost completely within the soil. Leaf mould forms an excellent soil for many purposes, but when leaves decay the greater part of their material is lost as gases in the air, or is carried away by running water. With roots the case is different. Trees have large roots which spread widely and live for scores or hundreds of years. Thus they do not contribute any great amount of humus to the soil. Grasses, on the contrary, fill the soil with a great mass of closely bunched roots which in many cases die every year, and in all cases are short-lived compared with trees. Thus year by year the grasses add to the soil a great amount of humus which gives it a dark color and makes it very rich in nitrogenous products. These, together with potash and phosphorus, are the greatest chemical essentials in a good soil. From all this we see that the climate sets the main limits, but other factors shift these limits considerably. Our whole study of economic and social geography will be greatly helped if we firmly realize that the relief of the land, the quality of the soil, rocks, and minerals, the interplay of one kind of plant or animal upon another, and finally the striking changes wrought by man all unite in painting an infinite variety of details upon a background which depends primarily on climate.

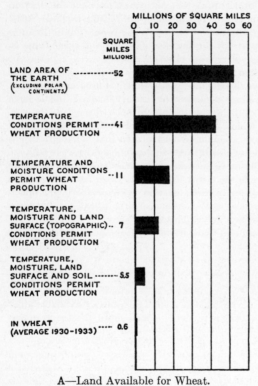

A—Land Available for Wheat.

Wheat as an Example of Crop Limitation.—The variety of conditions which set limits upon a crop is well illustrated by wheat. This crop is more widely spread than any other except grass. It occupies more than one-tenth of all the improved land in the entire world. Yet the areas where wheat can grow are very strictly limited by temperature, rainfall, soil, and relief, as well as by economic factors, which will be discussed in another chapter. According to Dr. O. E. Baker, of the United States Department of Agriculture, wheat will not grow where the average temperature for the three summer months is below 57° or 58°. Therefore, none can grow in the following areas: 5,000,000 square miles in Antarctica; 800,000 in Greenland; 3,400,000 in Canada and Alaska; 4,500,000 in northern Eurasia; 125,000 in the lowlands of southern South America; and about 3,000,000 in various highlands, such as those of Tibet, the Andes, the Rocky Mountains, and the Tien Shan, Altai, and other ranges of Asia. The hot limit for wheat is not reached on any part of the earth's surface. This crop will grow after a fashion even along the upper Nile where the temperature rises above 100° day after day before the crop is harvested.

The limits set by moisture are clear-cut on both sides. At any temperatures where wheat can grow, and especially at high temperatures, a limit to the growth of the crop is set by either too much or too little rain. Near the coldward limit Dr. Baker puts the dry limit for commercial production at 10 inches of rain per year and the wet limit at 40. In a region of intermediate temperature, like the central and southern United States, it does not pay to raise wheat without irrigation unless the average rainfall is as much as 15 inches per year, nor is there any assurance of a harvestable crop if the rainfall rises above 50 or 52 inches. In still warmer tropical regions the dry limit is 20 inches and the wet limit about 70. Among the 41,000,000 square miles or less of the earth's surface which are warm enough for wheat about 17,000,000 are too dry and another 13,000,000 too wet. This reduces the available area to only 11,000,000 square miles, as appears in A26. Compare the distribution of wheat (A28) and the distribution of temperature (A30, A31) and rainfall (A32). Such a comparison hammers home the idea of the three kinds of climatic limits— cold, dryness, humidity—which prevent the growth of wheat. It also helps to build up a picture of the distribution of types of climate.

Among the non-climatic but nevertheless physiographic limits of the growth of wheat, the slope of the land is probably the most important. If land has a slope of more than about 15° the washing away of the soil and the difficulty of using large machines make it of little value for a crop which has to be harvested in the way employed for small grains like wheat. So much of the earth's surface is hilly that on this account Dr. Baker deducts 4,000,000 miles from the area that is climatically fit for wheat. Large parts of the remaining 7,000,000 square miles have soils that are too sandy, gravelly, or peaty to be fit for wheat, while those in cool climates are often too clayey. Such soils form about a fifth of the earth's surface in the parts where the climate and relief are fit for wheat. This leaves only 5,500,000 square miles, or approximately a tenth of the earth's surface, where wheat can be raised with any success.

The following table shows where this tenth is located, together with data as to how much of it is actually used for wheat.

	Area available for wheat, square miles	Area actually used for wheat, square miles	Percentage of available area actually in use
United States.................	1,000,000	95,000	9.5
Canada......................	400,000	40,000	10.0
South America................	500,000	30,000	6.0
European Russia..............	800,000	110,000*	13.8
Rest of Europe...............	700,000	110,000	15.7
Siberia......................	500,000	45,000*	9.0
China.......................	400,000	38,000	9.5
India.......................	400,000	50,000	12.5
Rest of Asia.................	200,000	20,000	10.0
North Africa.................	125,000	16,000	12.8
Central African highlands.......	250,000		
South Africa.................	125,000	1,500	1.2
Australia and New Zealand......	150,000	24,000	16.0

*Estimate based on published totals for entire U.S.S.R.

The Limits of Crops in General.—The limits of crops in general are not much more widely extended than those of wheat. Oats, barley, rye, and a few hardy vegetables like turnips and cabbages can be raised a little beyond the cold limit of wheat. Their absolute limits, however, are set by temperatures only two or three degrees lower than the limit for wheat. The area thus added to the world's cultivated land over and above that available for wheat is not only small, but of relatively little value because the crops there are so uncertain. Even grass does not repay cultivation beyond the limits of these cereals and vegetables. It will grow, to be sure, but in a state of nature it is largely replaced by lichens and mosses which form the overwhelming bulk of the small vegetation in vast areas of Canada, Alaska, and the northern parts of Europe and Asia. Since the warm limit of many other crops as

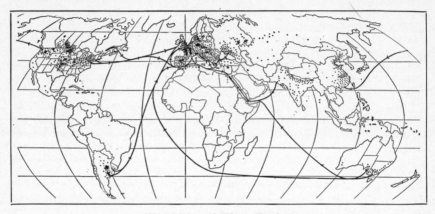

A—World Map of Wheat Production.

well as of wheat is reached only where high humidity complicates the matter, we may defer its discussion till we have considered the dry limit.

Barley, millet, and a few other hardy crops can grow a little beyond the dry limits of wheat, but the areas thus added to the cultivated lands of the earth are relatively small and of poor quality. Grass does indeed grow in large areas beyond the dry limits of wheat, but its growth in any particular year is so doubtful that it is never cultivated as a crop, except under irrigation. Turning next to the humid limits of crops, we find that in the cooler parts of the earth the available areas beyond the wheat limits are likewise of little importance. In a few places, like parts of Norway, the abundance of rain prevents wheat from ripening, yet permits the growth of oats. Such cases are rare. Only when we come to warm regions do we find many useful crops which have climatic limits much beyond those of wheat. In tropical regions where both the temperature and the humidity are high such crops as rice, rubber, bananas, manioc, coconuts, and many others grow excellently under conditions too humid for wheat.

Unfortunately, the nature of the soil where this warm, humid type of climate is found imposes still another kind of limit. Vast areas that are climatically fit for these tropical crops are almost useless because of the leached soils. Such is the case, for example, in large portions of the Amazon Valley and along the coasts of New Guinea. In other parts of the world, however, the limits set by the soil cause the area adapted to cultivation to be appreciably larger than that which is fit for wheat.

Such hardy crops as barley, for example, will grow in soils that exclude wheat. As a rule, to be sure, a soil which is too poor for wheat is of little use for other crops. Nevertheless, such soils undoubtedly add an appreciable amount to the earth's cultivable area. Another small addition is made by utilizing slopes of more than 15°. They are not good for the small grains which require plowed land and must be cut rather than plucked by hand at harvest time, but do very well for crops that grow on trees or bushes. Such crops are almost invariably reaped by hand. Moreover, when once trees have been started they grow for years without requiring that the land be plowed or dug up.

The amount of land that is added to the cultivable area, when allowance is made for crops whose limits lie beyond those of wheat, cannot be accurately estimated. We may roughly put it at 1,500,000 square miles, making a total cultivable area of about 7,000,000 square miles. But bear in mind that a large part of this area lies close to limits of one kind or another. It is so cold that frost spoils the crops at frequent intervals, or else so hot that the crop is always very small. Or again it is so dry that crop failures occur with heartrending frequency, or so wet that the crops rot in the ground. Elsewhere the soil is just barely good enough; it becomes rapidly exhausted, and will yield even moderate crops only in response to abundant fertilizers and an inordinate amount of work in plowing and cultivating. Where none of these conditions obtain, the slopes may be so steep that the soil is badly washed away. In many such places the land would soon be wholly lost without constant labor in building terraces or carrying out other devices such as contour plowing (see page 189) and the building of walls at the heads of gullies. Even where the soil on such slopes is saved, it is often so coarse and stony that much labor is needed to raise even a small crop.

From this study of limits we reach the final conclusion that unfavorable conditions of temperature, rainfall, soil, and relief limit the earth's cultivable area to only about 7,000,000 out of 57,500,000 square miles of land. As a matter of fact, the poor quality of the land near one or another of the various limits reduces the area actually under cultivation to only half this figure. In other words, the limits imposed by nature press upon man so strongly that thus far he has been able to make good use of only one out of every 16 or 17 square miles of the lands that form the earth's seven continents and thousands of islands.

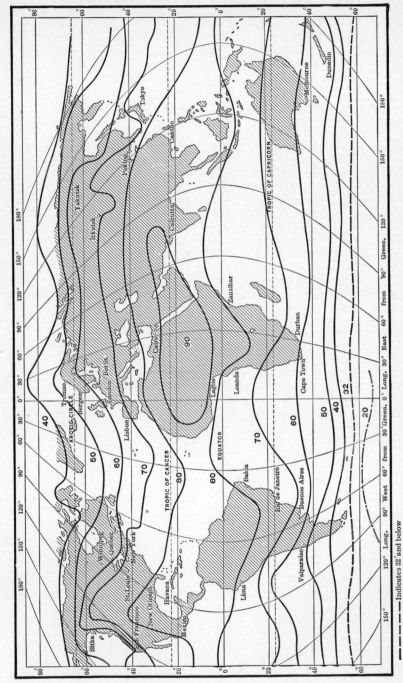

A—World Map of Mean Temperature in July. Note that the isotherms show the temperature which would prevail at sea level.

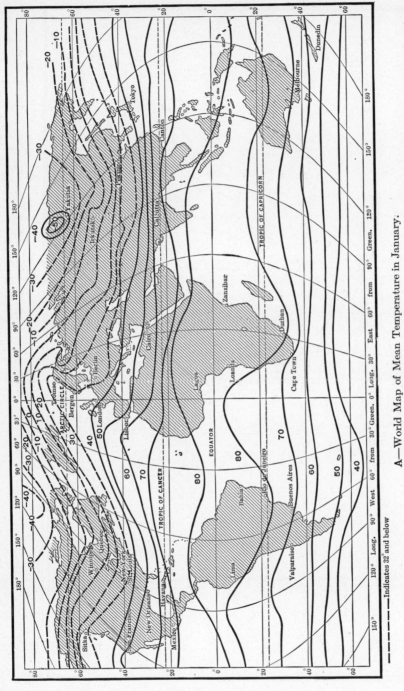

A—World Map of Mean Temperature in January.

Note that here, as in A30, the actual temperatures in the more elevated parts of the continents are lower than appears from these sea-level isotherms.

------- Indicates 32 and below

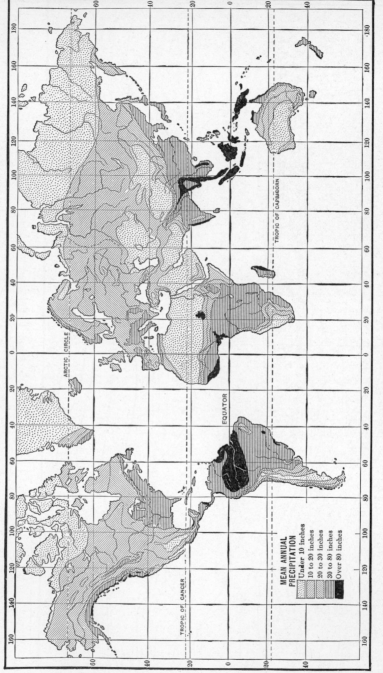

A—World Map of Annual Precipitation.

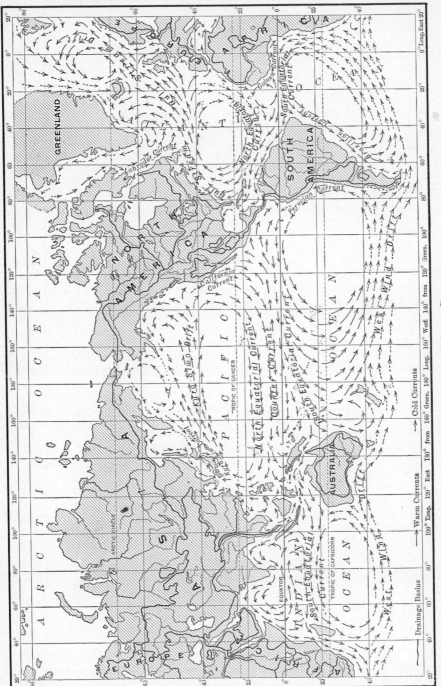

A—World Map of Ocean Currents.

EXERCISES

1. Make a list of three vegetable products, three animals, three human occupations, and two other kinds of human activity. State the main conditions which limit the geographical distribution of each.

2. On an outline map of the world insert the approximate limits of rice (A339), horses (A410), and barley (A342). State whether these limits are due to temperature, rainfall, or some other condition. A30, A31, and A32 in this book, and especially Plates 18, 32, 36, 40, and 47 in the *Oxford Economic Atlas* will help you.

3. Explain the probable reasons why grass lands similar to the prairies extend over a large part of the southern half of the Soviet Republic (U. S. S. R., or Union of Socialist Soviet Republics). In what other regions would you expect to find similar grass lands? Why? Use the index of this book or of your atlas to find maps of seasonal rainfall which help to explain the matter. Why are maps showing the rainfall in summer and winter separately especially helpful?

4. Estimates of the corn crop in Argentina one year showed a decline of 25 per cent from the preceding year. This was due in part to drought but largely to locusts. What similar injury by insects can you describe? What insects hinder agriculture or gardening in the vicinity of your home? What results spring from this, and what is being done to combat such pests?

5. Make a brief outline of the economic and social effects of the limitation of certain forms of production by (a) coyotes in our western states, and (b) rabbits in our western states and Australia. Describe measures used to remove these limitations.

6. Use A20 as the basis for a description of the contrast between the farming of northern and southern Finland.

7. Some communities in the United States are spending much money to prevent the spread of the "potato wart disease." Why is this necessary? What other diseases seriously affect the distribution of crops? Why is this question appropriate in this chapter?

8. In Chapter I it was pointed out that the areas devoted to rubber are limited by law in Java. Cite instances where other crops have been restricted in acreage by edicts of man. Look up opium.

9. Give reasons for thinking that climate, relief, and soil limit potatoes, tobacco, and coniferous trees either more or less than wheat. Use the index of this book and of your atlas in order to find maps of these products, or of vegetation and forests. Use the facts and principles that you can recall from your earlier study of geography,

CHAPTER III

A SKETCH OF THE EARTH'S CLIMATE

Purpose of Chapter.—We have already seen that among the factors of geographic environment climate is much the most important. It excludes practically three-fourths of the earth's surface from cultivation; it dominates the vegetation and crops in the remaining quarter. Thus it has a preponderating influence upon animals, as well as plants, and causes man's main occupation—agriculture—to vary enormously from place to place. Then, too, climate has a great deal to do with other forms of primary production, especially lumbering and fishing, and to some extent, mining. It helps or hinders transportation. It is one of the main determinants of the quality of the soil. In addition to all this it has a great effect upon the health and activity of both men and animals. Such being the case, a clear conception of the fundamental principles of climate is essential to the study of economic geography. In the end we ought to gain the capacity to form a moderately correct estimate of the climate of a place by merely looking at the map. This may seem a large order, but it is by no means difficult, provided we center upon the main facts and ignore minor local variations.

An Example of Climatic Reasoning.—The climate of any given place, as we shall see, depends on the location of the place in respect to (1) latitude, (2) land and sea, (3) the main belts of winds, (4) ocean currents, and (5) mountains and other features of relief. Let us suppose that we are planning a journey that will take us to Lower California, that is, to the southern peninsula belonging to Mexico. Of course we want to know how warm it will be, what season will be most pleasant, when the rainy season will come. In the encyclopedia we read that the northern part of the peninsula is much like southern California. Its climate is similar, with mild temperatures the year round on the Pacificward slope, and with light rains confined almost entirely to the winter season. The central region is the most arid, being a pronounced desert. The Gulf coast, being sheltered from the marine influence, is hot and dry, habitable only in a few widely separated valleys where water exists in sufficient quantities for irrigation.

This is excellent, but it is not as much as we might know for our-

35

selves without any reference book if we really understood the principles which will be set forth in this chapter. If we had such an understanding we should know from the latitude that Lower California must everywhere have warm winters, and that the summers must be extremely hot except where they are moderated by nearness to the open sea or by altitude. The position of the peninsula in respect to the rest of North America and the Pacific Ocean would join with the latitude and the main belts of winds to tell us that the center must surely be a very dry desert, and that the north must get a little rain from cyclonic storms in winter, whereas the south probably gets a little more in summer from the northward migration of the equatorial belt in the wake of the sun. The ocean currents would tell us that on the west coast the summer heat is moderated by sea breezes from an ocean cooled by a current from the north and by the upwelling of water from the depths, but that the east coast gets its winds from a narrow and warm body of water which supplies little of either coolness or moisture. And finally the mountains down the backbone of the peninsula would tell us that more rain falls there than on the lowlands, so that there must be some streams which might be used for irrigation.

At this stage of our study we cannot reason out all this, but the ability to do so should be our objective. If this is kept in mind while reading this chapter, the student will acquire an ability to visualize the world's climate, vegetation, and modes of life which will be of incalculable value. Later chapters on the earth's natural regions will provide further practice. Every student should end this course with a good working knowledge of how to reason out the general march of the seasons as to rainfall and temperature in almost any major part of the world.

Factors That Produce Climate. 1. *Solar Energy.*—The primary cause of climate is the unequal heating of the earth's surface. This inequality results from the varying height of the sun above the horizon and from the varying length of the day. These two variations cause the climates of high and low latitudes to differ greatly, even though all parts of the earth get almost the same number of hours of sunshine in the course of a year. The temperature decreases from low latitudes to high latitudes for three reasons: (1) In high latitudes the sun's rays fall with such a slant that a given amount of sunshine is spread over many times as large an area as at the equator. (2) This slanting light has to pass through much more air than does light that falls vertically. This extra air absorbs the heat before the rays reach the earth. Even at the equator, more than half of the sun's energy is absorbed by the air. At sunset, anywhere, the sunlight scarcely feels warm because the air has taken out practically all its energy. (3) The long winter nights of high latitudes allow the earth's surface to become very cold so that ice and snow accumulate for many months. It takes a great deal of heat to melt these and warm the earth again.

If the earth's surface were smooth and composed of the same materials everywhere, these conditions of sunshine would lead to a perfectly regular change from the highest temperatures at the equator to the lowest at the poles. We should also have absolutely regular solar zones of climate with parallels of latitude as their borders. Such zones do indeed exist from the standpoint of the length of the day and the height of the sun. Thus the *Torrid Zone*, between the *Tropic of Cancer* on the north and the *Tropic of Capricorn* on the south, embraces all the area which comes under the vertical rays of the sun at some time each year. The two *Temperate Zones* extending from the tropics to the polar (Arctic and Antarctic) circles never see the sun vertically overhead, but neither does the sun ever fail to rise above the horizon. The two *Polar* or *Frigid Zones* beyond the polar circles have from one day (24 hours) to six months each year during which the sun fails to rise above the horizon. The distribution of climate, however, has no such regularity. It is greatly interrupted by continents, mountain ranges, ocean currents, and cyclonic storms. All of these alter the direction, force, temperature, and humidity of the winds. Thus they cause the climate of most parts of the world to be quite different from what it would be if influenced only by the sun. As a result, the changes of climate from east to west often rival those from north to south, as happens in California, Peru, and even Europe.

2. *Movement of the Air.*—Even if the earth's surface were everywhere perfectly uniform there would still be winds and other movements of the air. This is because air moves whenever its temperature is disturbed. Hence the sun's heat gives the air a perfectly definite set of movements. Where the sun's rays fall almost vertically, as at 1 in A38, the air becomes heated, and hence expands. This raises the upper parts so that at 2 the upper surface of the air, if there were any such thing, stands too high compared with the corresponding air on the two sides. Hence it flows away (3) like water from a higher pond to a lower one. This diminishes the amount of air at 2, thus producing low atmospheric pressure at 1; at the same time it increases the amount of air at 4, thus giving high atmospheric pressure at 5. The high pressure at 5 pushes the air out on both sides, causing the air at 6 to settle slowly downward, and at the same time producing two sets of winds which blow in opposite directions (7a and 7b). One set pushes its way under the lighter air at 1, where we started, and thus causes the over-

lying air at 8 to move slowly upward. Thus the expansion of the air by heat at 1 starts a circulation which ends by causing the air at that place to rise. This cools the air so that at 9 it forms clouds and gives up rain.

Applying this to the actual conditions on the earth's surface, we find that in a belt about 20° wide where the sun's rays fall most nearly vertically the main movement of the air is slowly upward, and the winds on the earth's surface are light and variable. Since rising air

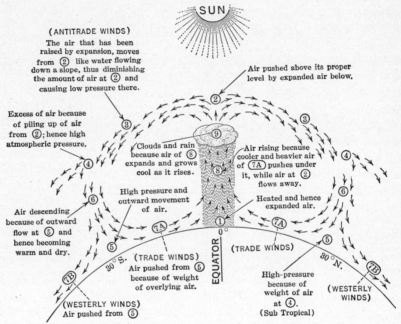

A—Ideal Diagram Illustrating Atmospheric Circulation and the Origin of Climatic Zones.

becomes cool, its vapor is condensed, and therefore falls as rain. On each side of this rainy belt we have a trade wind belt perhaps 20° wide. There the main atmospheric movement at low levels is horizontal and equatorward, from the northeast in the northern hemisphere and the southeast in the southern. Since these regular winds, unless forced to rise over mountains, have no tendency to become cool, the trade wind belts are generally dry. At high levels, however, the air from the equator moves poleward in what are called the anti-trades (3 in A38). Part of this air comes down in about latitude 30°, forming a poleward extension of the trade-wind dry belt. Here, too, just as in the equatorial region, we have calms, the so-called subtropical belt or Horse Latitudes. Still farther from the equator two belts of more or less westerly winds occupy middle latitudes up to about 60°. These winds, especially on their poleward margin, are much interrupted by the variable winds of cyclonic storms, thus increasing the rainfall and giving a second wet belt in addition to the equatorial one. Finally, in high latitudes we find pronounced dry easterly winds. Thus on a globe unaffected by the distribution of land and sea we should have five regular belts of atmospheric movement—equatorial calms, easterly trade winds, Horse Latitudes or subtropical calms, westerlies, and polar easterlies.

These five belts shift their position by some 20° to 40° from season to season with the changing position of the sun. Hence we have intermediate zones which belong to one belt or another according to the latitude at which the noonday sun happens to be in the zenith. Thus the deserts due to the combined action of the trade winds and Horse Latitudes are bordered by zones which are under this desert control only part of the year, but at other seasons they get rain because they are then parts of either the equatorial or the cyclonic belt.

The various winds which have been mentioned above carry the sun's heat this way and that. They diminish the contrast between the equator and high latitudes, but they produce contrasts between places lying in the same latitude. If there were absolutely no movement of the air the Lofoten Islands off the coast of Norway would have the same temperature as northeastern Siberia. But now the islands are often green with grass when the thermometer falls to forty below zero in Siberia.

3. *Distribution of Land and Sea.*—The way in which the distribution of land and sea alters climate can be well observed on a warm sunny summer day at the seashore. On a small scale it repeats the conditions already described as to the heating of the equatorial belt (A38). The air above the land is heated rapidly, and hence expands. It is easier for this expanding air to find a place by spreading upward than by spreading sidewise. Hence in the upper part some of it spills over, so to speak, thus lessening the weight of its own column and increasing that of a neighboring column of cooler, less expanded air. When we see the quivering air rising in especially hot spots it means that air from neighboring cooler, heavier columns is being pushed under the hot air and making it rise. Meanwhile the sea remains relatively cool, for water becomes warm much more slowly than land. After a while the upper part of the expanded hot air over the land flows out over the unexpanded cool air above the ocean. This makes the ocean air so heavy that it begins to push landward in the form of a fresh sea breeze. At night

just the contrary takes place. The land cools off so rapidly that it becomes cooler than the sea, and a land breeze replaces the sea breeze of the day.

Continents and oceans show the same tendency on a vastly larger scale. In summer the heating of the continents, especially in fairly high latitudes where the days are long, causes winds from the ocean to blow inward for many months. Such winds contain much moisture. They cause rain when forced to rise either by the indraft of heavier, cooler air into areas of low atmospheric pressure or because they have to cross mountains. This rainfall generally decreases towards the interior of the continent. It becomes especially scanty on the leeward side of mountain ranges, although heavy rain may fall on the windward side. In winter the opposite conditions prevail. The cold continent with its high atmospheric pressure sends cold, dry continental winds toward the relatively warm oceans. Precipitation is therefore scanty except under special conditions such as the prevalence of cyclonic storms, or the presence of mountains which cause the winds to rise. Such large-scale land and sea breezes are called "monsoons." They are best developed in the largest continent. Accordingly, in Asia not only is the *continental* type of climate far more exaggerated than in the sample which we saw in Iowa, but the monsoon system dominates the climate, especially in the south and east.

4. *Ocean Currents.*—When winds blow constantly or even prevailingly in one direction they cause ocean currents (A33). They do this by moving the surface water in the direction of the wind. Where these currents run poleward from the equator they are relatively warmer than the neighboring land, as in the Gulf Stream. As a result they not only warm the coastal waters but cause the onshore winds to be warm also and to contain more moisture than would otherwise be the case. Such warm winds are easily cooled on reaching land, and may give much rain, as in Japan. If currents run in the opposite direction, from the polar regions toward the equator, as is true in latitudes below 40° along the west coast of both North and South America, the coastal climate is correspondingly cool and dry. This is especially likely to happen if the currents move away from the coast, as in southern California, Peru, and Spanish Morocco. There the cold water, which is everywhere found in the deeper parts of the ocean, wells up to the surface to take the place of the surface water which moves away with the current. Winds blowing over such water are generally cooler than the land, and therefore can take up more moisture as soon as they are warmed by the land. This tends to cause aridity.

5. *Cyclonic Storms.*—In the two belts where westerly winds prevail,

between 40° and 60° north or south of the equator, cyclonic storms constitute an important climatic factor. They are local areas of low atmospheric pressure which move more or less in the direction of the dominating westerly winds, as shown by the heavy arrows in A43. Their characteristics are illustrated in A43 and B43, which bring out the general features shown by the regular Weather Bureau map of A42. Their great climatic and human importance, as we shall see more fully later, lies in the fact that they suck in the air from all directions, and cause it to rise in their centers, which are marked "low" in these maps. Thus they not only cause a great variety of winds as shown by the small arrows of A42 and A43, together with changes of temperatures as shown in B43, but bring rain at all seasons. Regions under the control of cyclonic storms have a most unstable climate from day to day, as may be judged by imagining what happens as the waves of temperature shown in B43 sweep eastward in latitude 40°, let us say. Yet such regions have a correspondingly pronounced stability of rainfall from season to season. They largely escape the danger of droughts arising from continentality and from a leeward location, for the direction of the wind changes so frequently that the chances of obtaining precipitation from one source or another are greatly increased.

Climatic Zones. 1. *Equatorial Low-pressure Belt.*—Let us now start at the equator and expand what has already been said as to the zones of climate as they actually exist upon the earth's surface. In the rest of this chapter refer constantly to A44, which in a simplified and diagrammatic way sums up the facts as to climate and vegetation of the world as a whole. Theoretically, the warmest part of the earth should be where the sun is in the zenith at noon so that its rays fall perpendicularly. This happens at the equator on the *equinoxes*, September 22 and March 21. On these dates, and then only, day and night are of equal length all over the world. The place where the sun's rays are vertical moves northward until June 21, when the sun is the zenith $23\frac{1}{2}°$ N. of the equator, that is, on the Tropic of Cancer. During the summer and fall the vertical position of the sun moves southward until on December 22 it is $23\frac{1}{2}°$ S. of the equator, on the Tropic of Capricorn. Heat, as we have already seen, causes the air to expand, so that its upper surface, if it had one, would rise. This rising of the upper surface forms what we may almost call an excessively broad, flat hill of air high above the earth's surface. This may be compared with the little swelling that one sees in a pool of water above the spot where a submerged pipe discharges into the pool. This "air hill," or ridge, extends around the world near the equator. From it the air flows away on both sides. The poleward-blowing winds thus formed high up in the air are called anti-trades (A38). Since they remove air from the top of the equatorial ridge, the actual amount of air beneath the ridge is less than in corresponding areas on either side. Hence the ridge is an area of low atmospheric pressure (see 2 and 3 in A38). Away from the ridge the addition of outflowing air creates high atmospheric pressure which reaches its maximum in two subtropical belts 30° or 35° from the equator. In these belts the weight of the overlying air causes the lower air to flow outward in both directions. The part which flows equatorward forms the steady trade winds. These enter the heated area of

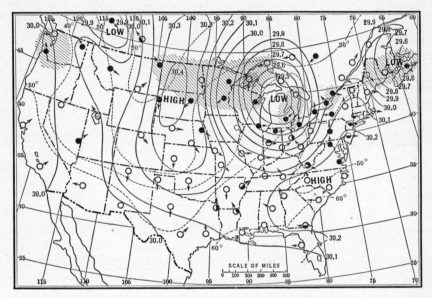

A—A Cyclonic Storm as Mapped by the United States Weather Bureau at 8 A.M., October 29, 1932. Black in circles indicates clouds; shading shows rain during last 24 hours.

equatorial low pressure and there push their way under the expanded air and lift it up. From all this we gather that the belt of low pressure on or near the equator is one of the primary elements in the earth's climate. Because the air rises there, the surface winds are so weak and irregular that we have *equatorial calms* (A44). The strength of the sun's rays varies so little from season to season that the temperature remains almost constant as appears from a comparison of A30 and A31.

Rising air tends to cool off and cause rain. Air always contains a certain amount of moisture owing to evaporation from water surfaces and vegetation. The ability of the air to contain moisture increases with rise in temperature. Hence when air grows warm it also becomes

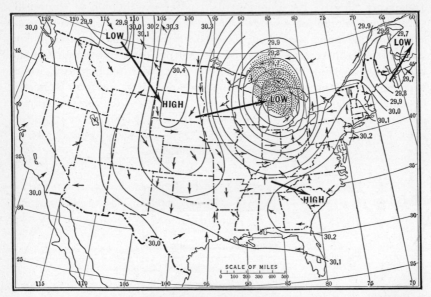

A—Pressure, Winds and Areas Where Rain was Falling in the Cyclonic Storm of A42 at 8 A.M., October 29, 1932.

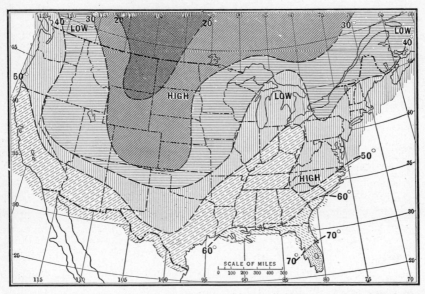

B—Distribution of Temperature at 8 A.M., Showing Relation to Areas of High and Low Atmospheric Pressure in Storm of A42.

relatively drier. In other words, its *relative humidity* diminishes, although the *absolute humidity* or actual amount of moisture remains the same. When air cools off, its ability to contain moisture diminishes. When the relative humidity becomes 100 per cent and the air holds all the moisture that is possible at that particular temperature, a little cooling causes the moisture to condense and fall in the form of rain.

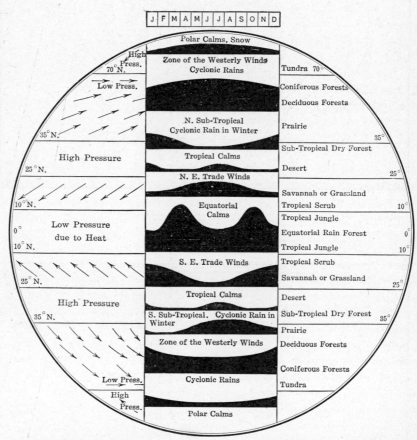

A—Diagrammatic Plan of Pressure, Winds, Rainfall, and Vegetation.

This explains the heavy precipitation in the equatorial zone. The mornings are usually bright and windless, but moist air is gradually rising as the earth's surface becomes warmer. In due time the air rises so far that it becomes cool enough to condense the moisture. So clouds gather, and in the afternoon *convection* of this sort causes heavy showers. By sunset the air is again clear. In this type of climate the temperature averages about 80° the whole year round. Where it is most perfectly developed the heavy rains have maxima not far from October and April, that is, soon after the noonday sun has reached the zenith (A44). The minima come in July and January, just after the time when the sun is farthest from the zenith. In many equatorial regions, however, the form and relief of the lands cause the two rainy seasons to merge into one. Day after day this equatorial type of weather is the same; no cyclonic storms interfere, as in middle latitudes, and the climate is very monotonous.

2. *The Wet and Dry Trade-Wind Belt.*—Ten or fifteen degrees from the equator the contrast between the seasons increases (A30 and A31). During the summer, when the sun is highest, the conditions are of the equatorial type with heavy convectional showers (A38). In winter, when the equatorial low-pressure area moves to the other side of the equator, the trade-wind belt dominates the weather. North of the equator the trade winds blow from the northeast because of deflection towards the right as a result of the earth's rotation. South of the equator they blow from the southeast, being deflected toward the left. In both hemispheres, however, they blow equatorward, and thus go from cooler to warmer regions. Accordingly, their capacity to hold moisture increases, and they are dry winds except where forced to rise because of the relief of the land. From this it appears that the equatorial rainy belt of calm is bordered on each side by a trade-wind belt, or *wet and dry low-latitude* belt of *summer rain* and *winter drought*. The contrast between the two seasons is often extreme, as appears in A44.

The poleward border of this wet and dry low-latitude belt is the great region for *tropical hurricanes*. They are most frequent about 20° from the equator and during the late summer and early fall. They resemble the cyclonic storms of higher latitudes, but are much more violent and do tremendous damage. Parts of Puerto Rico and other West Indian Islands have sometimes been almost ruined by them. Usually they do not cover so large an area as ordinary cyclonic storms, and no one area is likely to suffer from them often (A46).

3. *The Subtropical Desert and Monsoon Belt.*—The farther one goes from the equator the shorter is the rainy season of the equatorial type. Finally it dies out and deserts begin to prevail. These low-latitude deserts generally lie from 15° to 35° from the equator. When the relief is unfavorable to rainfall, however, they may approach much closer to the equator, as in Peru and Somaliland, while in the great continental interiors they reach latitudes of 45° or 50°. They include the hottest parts of the world, being sometimes much hotter than the equator. This is because there are few clouds to interfere with the sunshine, and

little heat is used in evaporating water. The most widespread cause of these deserts is that here the anti-trade winds carrying the overflow of air from the equatorial "air hill" cause high atmospheric pressure. Therefore the lower air is pushed outward along the earth's surface. Consequently the upper air slowly descends to take the place of the air that moves out. Thus in the areas of highest pressure we have the Horse Latitudes with their light, unsteady winds. The air that here

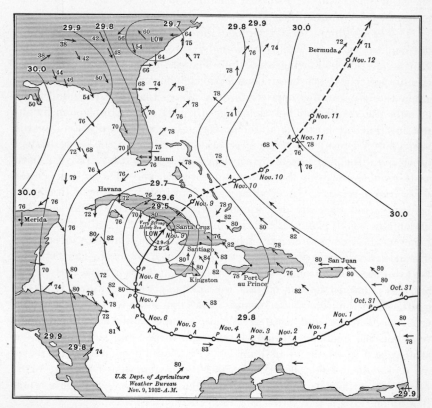

A—Pressure, Winds, Temperature, and Path of a Typical West Indies Hurricane.

comes down from aloft is dry because it lost most of its moisture when it first rose. It grows warmer as it descends, and so sucks up moisture instead of giving it out. Hence this is a belt of deserts. Toward the equator the steady trade winds blowing from the high pressure of the Horse Latitudes to the equatorial low pressure extend the desert belt to latitudes where the equatorial summer rains break the dryness. As trade winds have an easterly factor—northeast in the northern hemisphere and southeast in the southern—the eastern sides of the continents have a great advantage. The trade winds reach them from the sea, and hence are comparatively cool and well supplied with moisture, instead of being very hot and dry. Accordingly, the east side has a good chance to get some rain wherever the air is obliged to rise over mountains or highlands. Hence the subtropical and trade-wind belt of deserts is almost always broken on the east side, although continuous on the west, as we saw in Lower California. A knowledge of this fact is a great help in visualizing the climate of the world as a whole.

The break in the desert belt on the east side is especially evident in Asia. Because of its vast size, Asia is a monsoon continent, and inblowing and outblowing monsoons replace the trade winds. Even in the far south the Malay Peninsula is influenced by monsoons. The climate there does not entirely lose its rainy equatorial character, but in some places the outblowing winds of winter cause a pronounced dry season. Farther north the different parts of the continent have a great variety of climate in the same latitude. Arabia is almost entirely a desert. India has a desert area in the northwest, but most of it, as well as the whole of Indo-China, forms a monsoon region with rainy summers and dry winters. The highest temperatures here appear just before the rainy season. Jaipur in northern India averages 93° for day and night together in June, but drops to 86° in July after the rains "break." China, too, is a monsoon country. The type of rainfall prevailing in these monsoon regions is not shown in A44, but it is like the "NE Trade Wind" type except that the summer rainfall is far greater and the winter may be rainless. Other regions like Japan and the southeastern United States, which lie in these same latitudes on the east side of a continent, also get their maximum rain in summer from monsoon-like winds, but likewise get rain at all seasons from cyclonic storms.

4. *The Belt of Westerly Winds and Cyclonic Storms.*—From the high-pressure area of the Horse Latitudes the atmospheric pressure tends to decline until a low-pressure belt is reached approximately 60° from the equator. In the southern hemisphere this low-pressure area is continuous, but in the north the continents break it into two parts, the Aleutian low over the Pacific which disappears in summer, and the permanent Icelandic low over the Atlantic. The prevailing winds blow from the subtropical high toward this low belt. Since the earth's rotation deflects the moving air toward the right in the northern hemisphere and the left in the southern, this causes westerly winds in latitudes 40° to 60°. Thus we have the belt of westerlies which includes most of the world's most progressive countries. On the west side of the conti-

nents these westerly winds cause heavy rain and a marine climate with slight differences between summer and winter, as in Vancouver Island, southern Alaska, Ireland, and Norway. Their effect in these respects is intensified by the warm Japanese Current and Gulf Stream.

The outstanding climatic factor in this belt is the cyclonic storms. We shall soon see more as to the advantages which they bring to the United States and Europe in the form of climatic variability from day to day and rain at all seasons. In the interior of the continents the regular succession of westerly winds and cyclonic storms is often broken up, especially in winter when steady, cold, still weather becomes dominant. This occurs to some extent in North America, but far more in Asia. There the monsoon control continues as far north as Manchuria, and most of the east coast has decidedly warm, rainy summers, and cool or cold winters with frosts as far south as Canton. In Siberia this continental climate displays its greatest extremes. The winters are very dry, with temperatures averaging as low as −60°, but the scarcity of winds makes this endurable. The summers are fairly rainy and rather warm with temperatures averaging as high as 65° during July, even in latitude 60°. The interior basins of Asia, as well as of North America, are so far inland, or so surrounded by mountains, that they contain continental deserts, cold in winter and warm in summer.

5. *The Mediterranean Transition Belt.*—The shifting of the zenithal position of the sun and the corresponding shifting of the climatic belts brings a section in latitudes 35–40° under the control of the westerlies in winter and of the Horse Latitudes and trade winds in summer ("Subtropical" in A44). This type of climate with mild but rainy winters and hot, dry summers is called after its classical example, the Mediterranean Climate. It is found along the west coasts of the continents. Only along the Mediterranean does it extend far inland. There it goes so far east as to give a Mediterranean touch even to Persia and Mesopotamia.

6. *High Latitude Belts.*—In high latitudes, relatively high pressure prevails because of low temperature, especially in Greenland and Antarctica. Therefore, the winds tend to blow away from the poles toward the low-pressure belt on the northern edge of the westerlies. Because of the deflective action of the earth's rotation this gives more or less easterly winds. So westerly winds and cyclonic storms both disappear for the most part. Quiet, clear weather prevails as a rule on the ice caps, or over the frozen Arctic Ocean, while violent outblowing winds sweep over the edges of such areas.

Summary of Climate.—The elements on which to base an understanding of the more common types of climate are now before us. So far as temperature is concerned there are only a few main points to remember. First, the temperature near the equator is practically the same at all seasons. At sea-level it never departs far from 80° all the year round; for every three or four hundred feet of altitude it diminishes about 1° F. Second, in latitudes lower than 30° the winters rarely have much frost except at high levels; the summers generally have a temperature of about 80° at sea-level on east coasts, but this rises much higher in continental interiors, and falls as low as 70° on west coasts where water wells up from the depths of the open ocean. Third, in the interiors of the continents the temperature varies much more than on the coasts, being relatively high in summer, and showing an even greater departure in the other direction in winter. This variation reaches a maximum about 60° from the equator, where the length of the summer days allows the land to warm up a great deal, and the long winter nights allow it to become extremely cold. Fourth, as one goes away from the equator the west sides of the continents become cool much more slowly than the east sides. In high latitudes, regions warm enough to be pleasantly habitable are found on the west side 10–15° nearer the pole than on the east side.

The points to be remembered as to rainfall are almost equally simple. There are four main sources of rain. One is the equatorial girdle, 10–15° wide, which shifts back and forth after the vertical sun, with a lag of a month or two. With only minor exceptions all regions within 25° of the equator have their heaviest rain within one to three months after the time when the sun rides highest in the heavens. If this one fact is borne in mind it will help greatly in giving a true idea of climate. It explains why the shading for summer rain prevails so widely in A50. Along the equator, to be sure, this type of shading gives place to the kind indicating rain at all seasons. This, however, merely means that there the *two* seasons when the sun is vertical almost merge into one another so that there is no long dry season.

The second source of rain is the trade winds, including the reversed trade winds known as monsoons. Wherever fairly high land in latitudes lower than 25 or even 30° is exposed to the trade winds there is a fair abundance of rain at other seasons as well as in summer. This is the case in the heavily shaded areas of A50 along the east side of the Central American Highlands, the Andes, the Brazilian Plateau, South Africa, Madagascar, Australia, Indo-China, southern India, and a few minor places.

A third source of rain is the indraft toward the interior of the continents in summer by reason of the rapid heating of the lands. The monsoons are part of this. In A50, vast areas in the non-tropical parts of all the continents are shaded to indicate summer rain on this account. Parts of these areas, to be sure, have some winter rain, but even in Iowa we saw that the amount is much less than in summer.

The fourth source of rain is cyclonic storms together with the prevailing westerly winds. These account for the heavily shaded areas of A50 in western Canada, the eastern United States and Canada, western Europe, northern Japan, southern Chile, southern Australia, and New Zealand. The United States is fortunate because the storms go far south in the eastern part and thus join with the continental indraft in giving abundant rain at all seasons in much lower altitudes than is common elsewhere.

In addition to the areas of summer rain and rain at all seasons, A50 shows unshaded areas which never have much rain, and barred areas

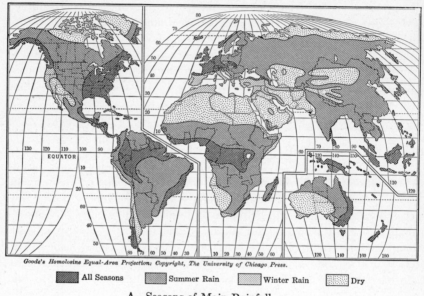

Goode's Homolosine Equal-Area Projection: Copyright, The University of Chicago Press.

All Seasons   Summer Rain   Winter Rain   Dry

A—Seasons of Main Rainfall.

having winter rain. In the latter the rain comes mainly from cyclonic storms and westerly winds. It is limited to the winter, however, because only at that season do the cyclonic storms swing far enough south. The contrast between the rains at all seasons in our southern states and the absence of summer rain in the corresponding latitudes of Europe on the one hand and of winter rain in the corresponding latitudes of Asia on the other is highly important, and greatly to our advantage.

EXERCISES

1. Without looking again at the book draw the following: (a) A diagram illustrating how solar heat produces movements of the air; (b) a circle within which are illustrated the earth's main belts of wind, rain, and vegetation. Correct your drawings from the book.

2. Investigate the relative importance ascribed to climate in this book, in your atlas, in some elementary geography, and in any three of the books listed under B, C, or C on pages ix and x (omit the books written by the authors of this book). In doing this make a table showing for each book: (a) the number of climatic maps; (b) the number of climatic diagrams; (c) the number of pages devoted to climate; (d) the number of times the index refers to climate, rainfall, temperature, frost, wind, seasons, growing season, droughts, natural regions, and other climatic conditions. Sum up your conclusions as to the part played by climate in geographic textbooks.

3. Without looking it up, state your own ideas as to the following conditions in at least six of the regions named below, then verify your results as far as possible from A30, A31; A32, and A50, or better, from the *Oxford American Atlas* or some similar book: (a) average temperature in July and January; (b) approximate rainfall (light, heavy, etc.); (c) seasons of rainfall and drought; (d) abundance and season of cyclonic storms.

West coast of America at latitudes 60° N., 29° N., 0°, 30° S., 45° S.
West coast of Europe and Africa at latitudes 50° N., 20° N., 15° S.
Southern Kamchatka; Shanghai; Java; center of Persia; Rome; Stalingrad (formerly Tsaritsyn); Montreal; Memphis, Tenn.; Puerto Rico; Edmonton; El Paso.

4. On A30 and A32, on pages 4, 6, and 9 in the *Oxford Economic Atlas*, or on temperature maps elsewhere, pick out at least four places where you see evidence of the effect of ocean currents (A33). Explain how the effect arises.

5. Use A42, A43, and B43 to explain what happens when a cyclonic storm occurs. Describe the movement of the storm (A43), the rainfall at any given time (A43) and during the preceding 24 hours (A42), the cloudiness (A42), the winds (A42), and the temperature (A43). Illustrate the matter by drawing two east and west cross sections across the United States in about latitude 40° to show the ups and downs of temperature and barometric pressure in relation to the center of a storm.

6. Why are regions with cyclonic storms relatively free from drought?

7. Describe the following features of the tropical hurricane of A46: (a) the distribution of temperature (perhaps you can make your own isopleth map of this); (b) the barometric pressure; (c) the winds; (d) the path and rate of movement of the center of the hurricane. When allowance is made for the different scales of A46 and A42, in which of the two storms thus represented should you expect the winds to be stronger? Look up this hurricane in old papers or magazines and see what it did.

8. A certain city receives 60 per cent of its precipitation of 14 inches during a cool but not cold period in June, July, and August. In December, January, and February, when there are many sunshiny, warm and often hot days, only 0.3 inch of rain falls. Locate the area in which this city is found. Do you get more help in this from A30, A31, A32, or A50?

9. A recent popular but unscientific book on geography says that, on March 21, the position of the earth in relation to the sun is such that the light of the sun illuminates exactly one half of the surface of our planet. Is there any significance in this statement? Why?

CHAPTER IV

CLIMATIC OPTIMA OF CROPS AS ILLUSTRATED BY CORN

The Place of Climatic Optima in Economic Geography.—The foundation of economic geography is production. The kind of production which occupies by far the largest proportion of people is agriculture. Even in an industrial country like the United States about 30 per cent of all our people are either directly dependent upon farming or are engaged in supplying the immediate needs of the farmers and their families. In the world as a whole no less than 60 per cent of all the people get their living by agriculture. Including the merchants, officials, and others who care for the immediate needs of the farmers, two-thirds of the world's two billion inhabitants are intimately dependent on agriculture. The most important of all factors in determining the nature and success of agriculture is climate. The most important features of climate are the limits which it sets and the degree to which it approaches the optimum for any particular crop or animal. In order to gain a clear comprehension of climatic optima, we shall study corn and wheat in considerable detail. This will help us to grasp the basic principle that every species of plant and animal, including man, has a certain optimum climate in which it thrives better than under any other condition. A realization of the significance of this biological law will greatly simplify our study of other crops and of economic geography in general.

The Place of Corn in Economic Geography.—Although corn is only one of about a hundred crops for which statistics are given by the United States Department of Agriculture, it is in many ways the most important. In the world as a whole the only crop that occupies a larger area is wheat. In the United States no other single product derived from either plants or animals is so valuable as corn, and only grass occupies a greater area. Even the wood cut in the forests of the whole country is less than one-half as valuable. If milk, meat, and hides are all combined, the cattle products do indeed reach a larger total value than corn alone, but the difference is not great. The position of corn in the United States is evident in the following table, which shows the approximate average annual value of all farm products which average over $100,000,000 per year when prices are reasonably high (1924 to 1928).

Cattle (Milk, $1,920,000,000; young animals, meat, leather, etc., $930,000,000)	$2,850,000,000
Corn	2,240,000,000
Cotton (Lint or fiber, $1,375,000,000; seed, $210,000,000)	1,585,000,000
Hogs	1,500,000,000
Hay	1,280,000,000
Poultry (Eggs, $700,000,000; chickens, etc., $430,000,000)	1,130,000,000
Wheat	1,040,000,000
Fresh Vegetables (Truck crops, $315,000,000; farm gardens $290,000,000)	605,000,000
Oats	595,000,000
Potatoes	400,000,000
Sheep (Meat, etc., $175,000,000; wool, $95,000,000)	270,000,000
Tobacco	255,000,000
Apples	200,000,000
Barley	155,000,000
Oranges	110,000,000
All other farm products (not including forestry products)	1,220,000,000
Grand Total	$15,435,000,000
Net Total, deducting animal feed, etc., so that it may not be reckoned twice, and including $315,000,000 of forestry products derived from farms each year	$11,725,000,000

If there were no corn the farmers of the United States would have to look elsewhere for one-fifth of their total income. This is evident from a comparison between the value of the corn crop and the net income of the farmers as given at the end of the table. Moreover, if there were no corn the three animals which stand near the top of this list would probably be produced in much smaller quantities than at present. Hence, meat, eggs, and milk would form a smaller proportion of our diet. Cattle, hogs, and poultry all consume great quantities of corn in the form of grain for fattening, and dairy cattle consume quantities of silage. Such feed is very cheap when one considers how rapidly it produces meat, eggs, and milk.

Fully five-sixths of the corn raised in this country is kept on the farm mainly for cattle, hogs, and hens (A54). Only about one-fifteenth is consumed by human beings. Even this, however, is one-fifth as much as all the wheat in the United States. Hence the amount of corn eaten by people is quite large, especially in the South. Corn pone, corn meal mush, corn syrup, and corn cereals for breakfast are favorite dishes. In the southeastern sections of Europe and Asia, where considerable corn is also raised, it is used chiefly as human food, and only a little is fed to animals. Still farther south, in many tropical regions like Mexico, Peru, and Rhodesia, corn forms the most important article of diet. This widespread use for both people and animals makes corn a good product with which to begin our detailed study of the economic geography of production. Its clear-cut relation to climate, soils, relief, transportation, density of population, and other factors which are mainly economic and social increases its value as an illustration of geographic principles.

The Geographic Distribution of Corn in the United States.—Many features of the economic geography of corn in the United States are summed up in A19, A57, and B57. These three are also valuable as samples of different types of maps. B59 is a dot map of a standard type which can scarcely be excelled for many purposes. Each dot stands for 500,000 bushels of corn. One of the chief features of the map is the concentration of dots in the so-called Corn Belt from Ohio west-

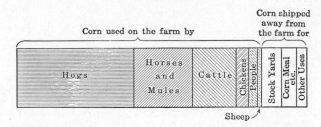

A—Use of the Corn Raised on the Farms of the United States.

ward through Indiana, Illinois, northern Missouri, and Iowa to eastern Nebraska and parts of South Dakota and Kansas (A55). Other important features are as follows: (1) the scarcity of corn in most parts of the Middle Atlantic and New England States; (2) the complete disappearance of corn only a few hundred miles north of areas where it is most abundant, the limit being the line where the temperature averages 66° during June, July, and August; (3) the scattered and unimportant occurrence of the crop west of the Corn Belt; (4) the moderate abundance of corn in the South from the Atlantic Ocean to central Texas but not in the peninsula of Florida.

The Use of Isopleth Maps and the Yield of Corn per Acre.—A57 and B57 illustrate the fact that the yield of corn per acre varies greatly from place to place, being generally high in the Corn Belt and low in the South. Two maps are here used for the same purpose in order that two methods of map-making may be compared. Both employ the same types of shading. The darkest shade indicates a production of over 40 bushels per acre; the next lighter shade means 30 to 40 bushels, then 20 to 30, and below 20. In A57, however, each state is shaded *as a*

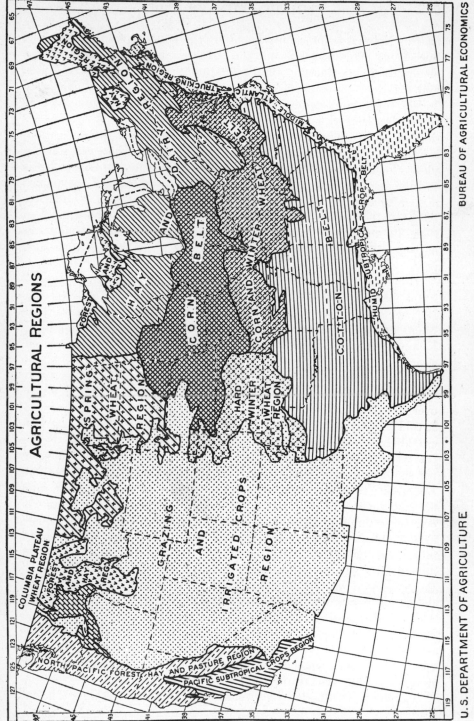

AGRICULTURAL REGIONS

U.S. DEPARTMENT OF AGRICULTURE

BUREAU OF AGRICULTURAL ECONOMICS

A—Agricultural Regions of the United States.

55

whole. Nebraska, for example, carries the shade indicating 20 to 30 bushels per acre and Oklahoma the shade for under 20 bushels. This creates the impression that similar conditions prevail all over each state, and that there are sudden changes in production at state boundaries. In B57 this is corrected by the use of *isopleths*, or lines of equal productivity. An isopleth is a line drawn only through points where the condition with which we are dealing has a given degree of intensity. The isopleth of 40, for example, passes through points where the average yield of corn per acre over a long period is 40 bushels. Of course, it has to be generalized into a smooth curve or else its many bendings would make a small map too hard to study. On one side of the isopleth of 40 the heaviest shading indicates that the average yield of corn is more than 40 bushels per acre; on the other side a lighter shading indicates less than 40. Similar isopleths indicate yields of 30, 20, and 15 bushels per acre.

Now examine the isopleths to see how they bring out the true quality of the distribution of the corn crop. Notice how the 40 isopleth in B57 swings smoothly across Pennsylvania and New York to southern Maine instead of following the state boundaries and thus jutting up to Lake Erie, then south to New York City, out around Long Island, and clear to the north of Maine as happens to the corresponding shading in A57. Long Island and the southern part of New York State are really like the neighboring parts of Connecticut and New Jersey and raise over 40 bushels of corn per acre. Northern Maine, on the contrary, is so cold that no corn is raised there for grain. The same is true of northern Michigan, Wisconsin, and Minnesota. No one would ever guess this from A57, but it is very clear in B57. A production of 30 bushels per acre swings westward through these states into South Dakota and Nebraska. Slightly north of the 30 isopleth we reach the isotherm of 66° in summer, and thus come to the northern limit of the production of corn for grain, although some is raised for fodder and silage. Therefore in B57 all the isopleths down to the one labeled "O" have to be crowded into a narrow space in the middle of these states. This shows that although the yield of corn averages 37 bushels in southern Wisconsin, the coolness of the summers causes the yield to drop off very rapidly toward the north. But just at the edge of the Corn Belt there is a strip where a good crop can be raised in warm years, although in other years the frosts may ruin it. It pays the farmer to take a chance, however, because the stalks are good cattle feed even if there is no grain. Of course, the average yield of corn for good years and bad in such a region drops off rapidly toward the north.

Farther west, A57 loses all resemblance to B57. Knowing that the

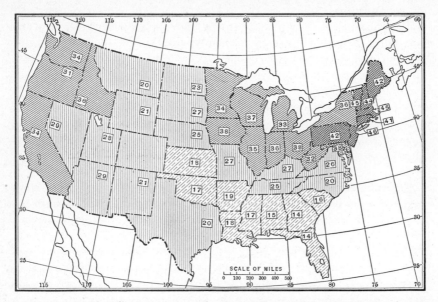

A—Average Yield of Corn per Acre in the United States, 1910–1929, Shaded According to State Lines.

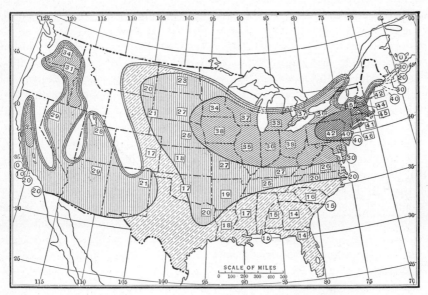

B—Average Yield of Corn per Acre in the United States, 1910–1929, shown by Isopleths.

66° isotherm in summer is the coldward limit of corn we insert this isotherm and thus exclude large tracts from the area where there is any possibility of raising this crop. Then we take this isotherm as our zero isopleth and draw the other isopleths accordingly. Thus we see that an isopleth map presents a far truer picture than does a map shaded according to arbitrary political boundaries. Such maps are not difficult to make, provided one practices a little and uses his powers of reasoning. Every student of economic geography ought to learn to make them. They can be profitably used to illustrate an astonishing number of phases of geography. The making of them is an ideal way of fixing both facts and principles in one's mind.

Turning once more to B57 we see that in the northeastern United States the production of corn per acre is extremely high. Westward the yield diminishes slowly as far as eastern Nebraska. Then, because of a decrease of rainfall, it diminishes until the average for Colorado is only 17 bushels. Still farther west, irrigation raises the yield almost to the level of the Corn Belt, but the amount of production is negligible, as appears in A19. Aside from irrigated tracts the western limit of corn in the United States, as we saw in the last chapter, is the isohyet, or rainfall isopleth of 8 inches during the three summer months. Southward from the highly productive Corn Belt the yield falls gradually until it is lowest in the most southern states.

Where Corn Grows in Other Countries.—In the rest of the world the raising of corn is subject to the same limits as in the United States, as appears in the dot map of A59. All of Canada, except the very southern part of Ontario and the St. Lawrence Valley as far as Montreal, lies beyond the northern limit. So does most of Europe, except the south and southeast from Portugal through southern France and Hungary to southern Russia and Bulgaria. Most of Asia is either too cold, as in the north, too dry, as in the west and center especially in summer, or else too warm and moist, so that the whole mainland raises scarcely 5 per cent as much as the United States. Even where the summer rainfall is abundant, as in China, it is often difficult to raise corn without irrigation, because the spring is too dry. In warm, tropical regions the combined effects of heat and moisture usually limit corn to restricted areas in the highlands. This handicap and the great desert combine to cause Africa to raise less than half as much as South America, although much more than the whole continent of Asia. Egypt, however, raises a good deal under irrigation, and so do the parts of South Africa where summer rains prevail. Even in South America, where corn probably originated, Argentina is the only country with a really large yield, although in Brazil and all the Andean countries corn forms one of the main kinds of food. Thus although corn is a widely spread crop, its climatic requirements are so strict that it is limited to a much smaller area than wheat.

The yield per acre in foreign countries is far less than in the United States. Nevertheless, a few places like the most southerly part of the Canadian province of Ontario and the warmest valleys of Switzerland south of the Alps rival New England. Certain irrigated areas like Egypt and a very insignificant area in New Zealand also stand at the Corn Belt level or higher. Otherwise, even the best regions, such as Hungary and Japan, raise only about 25 bushels per acre. Aside from the irrigated oasis of Egypt these best regions are like the Corn Belt in lying close to the coldward limit of corn.

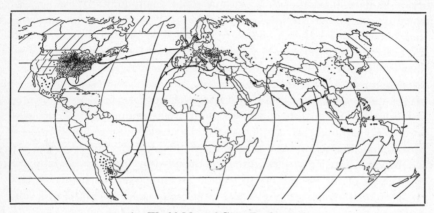

A—World Map of Corn Production.

A Method of Studying Climate.—Our aim in this chapter and the next is to study corn and wheat not only as two of the world's greatest crops, but also as illustrations of climatic optima. Consciously or unconsciously, man is constantly trying to locate himself and his works as near the climatic optimum as possible. We are well aware of this when we visit summer resorts, or go to California, Florida, or the Riviera in the winter. We are not so conscious of it when we crowd by the million into the vicinity of cities like Boston, New York, Philadelphia, Chicago, Milwaukee, Seattle, San Francisco, Los Angeles, and others, or into the districts centering in London, Amsterdam, Paris, and Berlin. Yet all these cities are located in climates which approach the optimum in many respects. They owe much of their growth to this fact. Indeed, the world's great cities to a large extent are located in good climates, or at least in the best climates of their respective countries. This is especially true of the great modern manufacturing cities. The greatest universities, the most highly developed factories, and the strongest political organizations are still more likely to be located as near as possible to the optimum climate. This happens without conscious planning on our part. The reason is merely that in such locations people are especially active and energetic, as we shall see more fully later.

Our aim now is to build up a picture of what the optimum climate really is. We shall use the data of weather bureaus and departments of agriculture in order to decide what kind of climate is the optimum for corn and winter wheat which grow in intermediate climatic positions. Then we shall investigate the optimum for insects, birds, and domestic animals, remembering always that the optimum for animals depends partly on the direct effect of the climate upon the health of the animals and partly on its indirect effect through the food supply. Having ascertained the optimum for the most valuable crops and animals, as well as for their insect enemies, we shall be able to decide what kind of climate is most favorable for agriculture in general. Then we shall investigate the optimum climate for man's own health and activity. After determining the optima for crops, domestic animals, and man we shall be able to define the kind of climate which comes nearest to providing the optimum for all three types of living organisms. This is not so difficult as might be supposed, for the three types of optima come fairly close together. This general optimum, when once determined, will be very convenient as a yardstick by which to measure the climates of all parts of the world. With such a yardstick we can quickly detect the peculiarities of the various climatic regions of the earth, and thus easily see the value of each such region for human occupation.

The Climograph as a Tool in Economic Geography.—In studying climatic optima and the climates of different regions we shall make much use of a device called a climograph.* One form of this is shown in A61. The vertical scale on the left shows the temperature, and the horizontal scale at the top the monthly rainfall. The words in the corners indicate the character of the climate at the extremes. In many ways a climograph is like a map in which hot regions lie at the top and cold regions at the bottom, as they do on maps of the southern hemisphere. In the same way, rainless regions lie on the extreme left, and very rainy regions on the right. This is like maps of any of the great land masses in lati-

---

* This word is sometimes spelled "climatograph," but the shorter form seems better. Griffith Taylor has been one of the first and most effective users of climographs. He uses wet-bulb temperatures and relative humidity instead of dry-bulb temperatures and rainfall, but his method of connecting the positions of the different months by lines is like the one here used. A climograph of the kind here used is also called a hythergraph.

tudes 20 to 40°. In North America, for instance, the dry regions
of Lower California, northwestern Mexico, and the southwestern
United States lie on the left of our maps, and the humid regions of
the Mexican and Texan coasts and the South Atlantic States on the
right. Since Europe, Africa, and Asia really form one great land mass
we have the same thing there, with the Sahara and Arabian Deserts

on the left and the well
watered lands of southern
China and Japan on the
right. The resemblance of
our climographs to South
Africa and especially Australia is still greater; not
only does the upper part of
the map of Australia rep-
resent very hot and the
southern part comparatively
cool regions, but the left
side is a desert while the
right side is everywhere well
watered.

One way of using the
climograph is illustrated in
A61, where the climate of St.
Louis is represented by what
we may call a *local* climograph.
In January the temperature
there averages 31° and the
rainfall 2.3 inches. Therefore
we put a cross at the point of
our climograph representing
this combination of temperature and rainfall, and label it

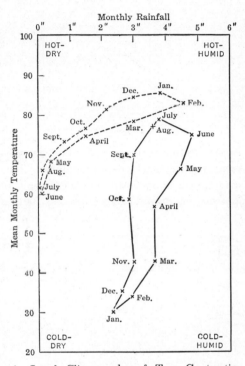

A—Local Climographs of Two Contrasting
Places.
Rivadavia, Northern Argentina ————————
Saint Louis, Missouri ————————

"Jan." The February conditions—temperature 34.5° and rainfall 2.8
inches—are similarly represented by another cross slightly higher up
and to the right, and a line is drawn between the two crosses. In the
same way each month is located at its proper point and connected with
the preceding and following months, thus making an irregular, many-
sided polygon. It may be asked why we use such a local climograph
when it is possible to represent the same thing more simply as in A62.
The answer is that both types of diagrams are needed. A62 is the
best way of representing the march of temperature and rainfall from

season to season. A61 is especially good in four other respects: (1) It enables us to grasp the relation between temperature and rainfall at a single glance. When one becomes used to climographs it is far

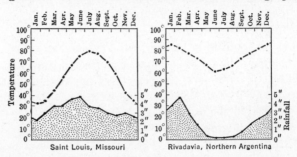

A—Ordinary Temperature and Rainfall Diagram of Two Contrasting Places.
(Shaded Areas show Rainfall in Inches. Lines _____ show Temperature in F.)

easier to get an idea of the general characteristics of a climate from them than from a diagram like A62. (2) When the local climograph is used there is no danger of getting confused as to the seasons on opposite sides of the equator. Similar conditions of tem-

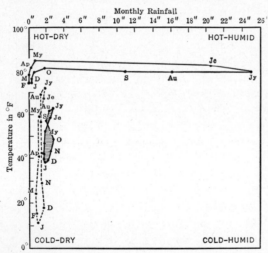

B—A Climograph for Comparing the Climate of London with That of Bombay and Saratov.
London—the Solid Line with Shading; Bombay—the Solid Line; Saratov—the Dash Line.

perature are shown in the same part of the graph no matter in what months they occur. Both of these advantages are evident when the dotted line of A61 representing the climate of one of the several Argentine places called Rivadavia—the one in the far northwest close to the Tropic of Capricorn—is compared with the solid line representing St. Louis. One sees at once that (a) Rivadavia has no cold weather; (b) its cooler season is dry; (c) its summer is very hot and also rainy; (d) the range of temperature from winter to summer is far less than at St. Louis; and (e) the corresponding range of rainfall is greater than at St. Louis. (3) The climograph also affords an admirable way of comparing any given climate with some standard such as an ideal or optimum climate. In B62, for example, the shaded area represents the climate of London—one of the best climates in the world. It is easy to see that the climate of Bombay, the solid line, is far too hot and wet, and that of Saratov in southeastern Russia is too dry as well as far too cold in winter. (4) The climograph is a great help in making comparisons between climate and some third condition such as the yield of crops per acre, the density of population, or the activity of manufacturing. For this last purpose we use another form of climograph as described in the next paragraph.

An Isopleth Climograph of the Yield of Corn per Acre.—C64 is an example of this other form of climograph. It shows how many bushels of corn are raised per acre under different conditions of weather in twenty-four states from New York westward and southward. These states were selected because they raise large crops of corn without irrigation. The scale on the left of C64 shows the average temperature of the months of June, July, and August during which corn makes most of its growth. The scale at the top shows the average rainfall per month during the same period. The lines which separate the different kinds of shading are isopleths exactly like those already described in B57. The only difference is that in C64 we do not put the isopleths on an ordinary map. Instead we put them on a chart in which, as we have already said, a position toward the top means hot weather, toward the left dry weather, toward the bottom cold weather, and toward the right rainy weather. During the sixteen years on which this climograph is based, a summer temperature of 72° and an average rainfall of $3\frac{1}{2}$ inches per month occurred together in one state or another a number of times. In those particular years the average yield of corn in those states was 35 bushels. Therefore we write "35" on our climograph in the place where it appears in C64. In various other years and states the temperature averaged 68° and the rainfall 5 inches. Under such conditions, also, the yield of corn averaged 35 bushels. The same was true when the temperature averaged 70° and the rainfall either 3 inches or nearly 6. Thus on our climograph we can insert a yield of 35 bushels at enough points to enable us to draw the 35 isopleth in much the same way that we drew it on the map B57.

Whenever the data are sufficiently abundant we find that the isopleths on a climograph of this kind are surprisingly regular, like those in B57. There the heaviest shading means that when the weather in various states has the qualities indicated by that part of the climograph the yield of corn averages more than 35 bushels per acre. Under no other conditions is the average yield so high. Therefore summer weather with an average temperature of 68 to 72° during June, July, and August, and with an average rainfall of 3 to 6 inches, is the optimum for corn. Of course, a farm with good soil or good cultivation and optimum weather may average 45 bushels, whereas another with poor

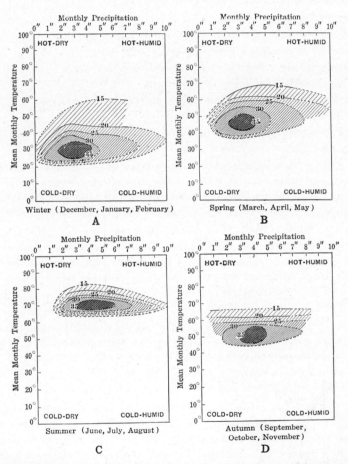

A–D—Isopleth Climographs Showing Relation of Temperature and Rainfall to Yield of Corn per Acre in Bushels. Based on 24 States, 1914–1929.

soil or poor cultivation and the same weather may produce only 25. But we are talking about averages for many different years and many different states. If, however, the temperature runs above 72°, or the rainfall above 6 inches, or if the temperature drops below 68° or the rainfall below 3 inches, the average yield of corn falls below 35 bushels. Knowing the yields under all sorts of weather, we are able to draw other

isopleths. Thus in C64 the second degree of shading between the isopleths of 35 and 30 bushels indicates kinds of weather which are good,
but not so favorable as the heavily shaded optimum. With greater
and greater departures from the optimum the yield drops off as appears
in the lighter shades of C64 until we find no corn at all in places having
summer weather like that shown in large parts of the unshaded sections
of that climograph. To sum the whole thing up, an isopleth map like
B57 shows where corn finds its optimum conditions when soil, cultivation, and all other factors as well as climate are taken into account.
An isopleth climograph like C64, on the other hand, shows the optimum weather for corn when everything else is left out of account.
Both the map and the climograph also show how the yield declines as
the environmental conditions become more and more unlike the optimum.

The Optimum Weather for Corn at Other Seasons Besides Summer.—In
A64, B64, and D64 we see what happens to the corn crop when various kinds of
weather prevail at other seasons as well as in summer. These climographs are made
exactly like C64 except that A64 uses the weather during the preceding winter from
December to February, B64 uses the weather during the spring (March to April),
and D64 during the autumn (September to November). A64 shows that the yield
of corn averages 35 bushels when the temperature of the preceding winter ranges
from 25° to 35° with a rainfall of 1½ to 4 inches. It is impossible to tell how much
this cool winter weather has to do with the yield of corn. It may merely be the kind
which commonly accompanies the best sort of summer. The facts stated later as to the
extraordinary yields of corn at an altitude of 2,000 feet or more in North Carolina
suggest that a winter temperature averaging as high as 38° or 40° is the optimum.
We are certain, however, that except under irrigation such high yields are never
obtained unless the winters are cool enough for frost. The cool winter appears to
help the corn directly by killing insects and bacteria, by keeping down the weeds
which would grow if the air were warmer, and by allowing the ground to freeze or
to be covered with snow so that it has less chance to be leached and eroded or to
become unduly dry in the spring.

The weather during the spring has a direct effect upon the corn crop. In many
states most of the corn has already been planted by the end of May. Even where
the seed is planted at the latest reasonable time, namely the first half of June, the
temperature and moisture depend largely on the weather of the preceding weeks in
May. No seed will germinate properly if the soil is too cool, too warm, too wet, or
too dry, but corn is especially particular about this. Coolness and dryness prevent
germination; heat and dampness cause the seed to rot in the ground. Even if the
seeds sprout in unfavorable weather the seedlings are generally weak. It is easy
then to see why B64 shows that in the spring the best weather for corn, as appears
from the heavily shaded area, is an average temperature of 42° to 50° with a rainfall
of 2 to 4 inches. This means that by May the average temperature has risen to
about 60°. As for the autumn, D64 shows that corn thrives best when the temperature averages 46° to 56°, or a trifle higher than the optimum for spring. A good but
not extreme rainfall seems to be of special importance in the autumn. Among the
four climographs for corn this is the only one where the average yield per acre rises

above 40 bushels. This occurs only when the autumn temperature averages close to
50° with 3 or 4 inches of rain per month. It suggests that only when the growing
season is prolonged by such weather does the corn have the best chance to fill out
the ears, make the kernels plump and solid, and thus produce the heaviest harvest.
In this connection it is interesting to note that the North Carolina Department of
Agriculture reports that in that state, where the average weather of the state as a
whole is by no means the optimum, yields of 230 or more bushels per acre have been
obtained. This is amazing when we note that in Connecticut, where the average
yield of the state as a whole is best, the maximum is only 140 bushels. But the
extraordinary crops of North Carolina appear to have been raised in the cool
uplands where the weather is much like that of Connecticut. Experts in corn culture,
such as Donald F. Jones, say that such extraordinary yields must be due to special
conditions of soil plus summers that happen to be free from any extreme heat,
and especially to a long growing season in the fall.

The Value of Good Weather at all Seasons.—Although summer is
the most important season for corn, good weather at other seasons seems
to be highly important. The rare instances when the optimum weather
for corn prevails during a whole year before harvest time are especially
noteworthy. During the sixteen years used in preparing our climographs this happened three times in New York, twice in New Jersey,
Pennsylvania, Ohio, and southern Michigan, and once in West Virginia
—twelve times in all. The effect was admirable, as appears from the
following table showing how the yield of corn in these six states has
varied according to the length of the period which had optimum weather
during the year leading up to each harvest.

Number of seasons (winter, spring, etc.), with optimum weather	Average yield of corn in bushels
0 or 1	33.7
2	35.8
3	37.3
All 4	40.9

Evidently the yield increases in direct proportion to the duration of
the optimum weather. Moreover, the failure of any season to have the
optimum weather seems to do harm no matter in what season the failure
occurs. In fact, in the northern United States where rain falls at all
seasons it seems to be as important to have favorable weather at one
season as at another, as appears in the following table based on the same
six states as the preceding table.

Yield of corn per acre at the end of years in which optimum
weather had been experienced in

Winter...... 38.4 bushels		Summer..... 37.4 bushels
Spring...... 37.0		Autumn..... 38.0

One would naturally expect that the weather in summer or spring would be of more importance than in autumn or winter in producing good crops. Such is undoubtedly the case when all sorts of climate are considered. If the summers have an average temperature below 66° or if the growing season is rainless and without irrigation there will be no corn crop at all, no matter how favorable the other seasons may be. In the regions on which our table is based, however, all the seasons are moderately favorable practically every year. Hence, good weather at other seasons may lead to a good crop even if the summer weather is only fair. This fact, together with a study of crops in many other parts of the world, leads to a very important conclusion which is not usually appreciated. The conclusion is that the yield of corn, and of many other crops, depends on the weather of the *whole year*. For example, if all seasons except summer were decidedly unfavorable to corn, the yield might be only 10 bushels per acre. If two seasons were favorable the yield might be 20 bushels; with three favorable seasons, 30 bushels; and with four, 40. In other words, in order to understand the effect of any given region upon the crops we must know the character of the weather not only while the crop is growing and ripening, but also while its seeds are dormant and while the soil, the insects that help or injure the plants, and the weeds that compete with them are getting ready to do their part in making or marring the crop. If we understand all this, we shall be able to explain why Belgium and eastern Pennsylvania, for example, are such extremely good agricultural regions, while China, contrary to the usual supposition and in spite of extraordinarily good cultivation, falls far behind them in the yield per acre of almost every kind of crop. The weather at all seasons in Belgium and Pennsylvania is generally favorable for a large number of the best crops. In China, on the contrary, especially in North China, the very dry and cold winters are never favorable, and the springs are often too dry and the summers too warm and wet.

In the following pages this principle is illustrated more fully in respect to corn. Bear in mind that although the growing season is the most important period, unfavorable weather at any other season cuts down the yield of the crops.

Types of Climate in Relation to the Corn Crop. 1. *Practice in the Use of Climographs.*—The climographs of A68 illustrate the relation of corn to twelve types of climate. They accomplish five purposes. (1) They afford practice in the use of climographs. (2) They show how clearly this type of diagram brings out the differences between one climate and another. (3) They familiarize us with certain important types of climate which we shall study more systematically later. (4) They verify the reliability of our climographs of corn by showing that conclusions based on the United States hold good in other continents. (5) They illustrate the following great principles which apply to plants, animals, and man, and which lie at the very foundations of geography: (*a*) every living creature thrives best in a certain optimum climate; (*b*) the optimum depends on the weather not only of the growing season but also of other seasons; and (*c*) the optimum for any crop shows a tendency to occur close to the coldward limit of that crop.

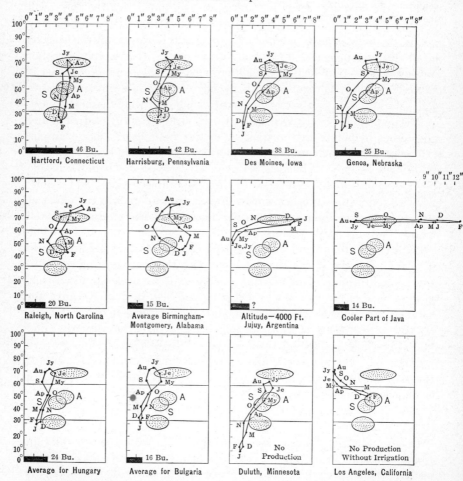

A—Local Climographs Showing the Relation of Various Climates to the Optimum for Corn. Black bars indicate 20-year average yields per acre.

In A68 the shaded areas are the same in each of the twelve climographs. The shaded oval at the top shows the summer optimum of temperature and rainfall for corn. It is the same as the area bounded by the isopleth of 35 bushels in C64. The lower shaded area shows the similar optimum for winter. The optima for spring on the left and autumn on the right are indicated by the letters *S* and *A*. The irregular lines with the initial letters of the months are local climographs.

They are placed with the isopleth climographs in order to show to what degree various climates approach the optimum. In interpreting them, bear in mind that months lying above the optima are too warm for the best results; those lying below, too cold; those on the left, too dry; and those on the right, too rainy or snowy. Remember also that the isopleth diagrams are based on the average conditions for three months in a great number of places, whereas the local climographs indicate the conditions in individual months at only one place. In an optimum climate the *average* weather for each season must fall within the proper shaded area, but one month such as July or January may fall outside this without doing any appreciable harm. In the autumn and spring the ideal average is almost always the result of one month which is cooler than the optimum, one month that is warmer, and one that falls midway between the others and has almost the optimum temperature. Remember, too, that except on the coldward side the *limits* of corn or almost any other crop are far from the optimum. Hence, fairly good crops can be raised even when no season has weather which falls within the optimum shaded areas of the climographs.

The bars at the bottom of A68 indicate the average number of bushels of corn per acre in the states and small countries whose corn-producing sections are represented by the climographs. The states have been chosen to represent different degrees of productivity per acre.

2. *The Optimum Corn Region.*—The first four climographs of A68, beginning at the left above, show what happens to both climate and corn as one goes inland from the east coast to the interior in the part of the world where corn thrives best. Hartford in Connecticut and Harrisburg in Pennsylvania represent the east coast region which extends from the southern parts of Maine, New Hampshire, and Vermont through southern New England and southern New York to New Jersey and eastern Pennsylvania. Aside from New Zealand, southern Switzerland, and southern Ontario, this is the only part of the world where the average yield of corn for all sorts of farms has stood above 40 bushels per acre for 20 years or more. Connecticut stands at the very head with a yield of 46 bushels. Examination of its climograph (Hartford) shows that the climate is almost ideal for corn. This is evident from the fact that the average temperature and rainfall for both summer and winter fall within the respective shaded areas of A68. The climograph for Harrisburg is almost as good, although the fact that Harrisburg lies 1½° farther south than Hartford and also farther inland gives it a higher summer temperature. Hence, the kind of hot, dry days which are especially harmful to growing corn are a little more common there than in Hartford. Perhaps this is why the average yield per acre in Pennsylvania is 42 bushels instead of 46 as in Connecticut and 44 in Massachusetts.

3. *Corn in the Regions Where Climate, Soil, Relief, and Economic Factors Make It Most Profitable.*—The climographs for Des Moines in central Iowa, and Genoa near the center of the corn-raising part of Nebraska, illustrate the kinds of changes which occur as one goes from the eastern coast to the interior of a continent in middle latitudes. Hartford, Des Moines, and Genoa are all in the same latitude. Moreover, Hartford is forty miles from the coast. Yet the following differences stand out by reason of the fact that Hartford is influenced by the sea, while the other places lie far in the interior: (1) The interior is hotter than the coastal region in summer. The average difference during June, July, and August is only about 2°, but that is enough to allow the interior to have many more of the dry, scorching days which are one of the chief reasons why the yield of corn per acre is less than in the eastern states. (2) In winter there is a greater difference, about 7°, but at this season the

interior is colder than the coast instead of warmer. Because of this the period without frost in the autumn is shortened in Iowa and Nebraska, thus cutting down the yield of corn. (3) The interior has a marked summer maximum and winter minimum of rainfall, as appears from the way in which the slope of the local climographs from the right above to the left below becomes more and more pronounced as one goes from Hartford to Harrisburg and then to Des Moines and Genoa. Hartford has 12.7 inches of rain in June, July, and August, and the rain and melted snow of the three winter months amount to 10.3 inches. Des Moines, on the other hand, has 12.9 inches of rain in May, June, and July, but only 3.6 inches in December, January, and February. Because of this winter minimum both the autumn and winter in Iowa and Nebraska are a little too dry to provide the optimum conditions for corn. Even the spring is just barely included within the optimum as indicated by the isopleth of 35 bushels.

(4) Variability is a fourth important quality of a continental climate. The great contrasts between summer and winter which have just been mentioned are one evidence of this. Another is the fact that both the rainfall and the temperature of any given month vary more from year to year in the far interior than farther east near the sea. Suppose, for example, that we take the average rainfall of the five driest Januaries during the period for which records are available, and express it as a percentage of the normal rainfall for that month. Then do the same for February, March, and the rest of the months. The average of these twelve percentages, as given in the table below, is 28 for Hartford and 20 for Des Moines. This shows that taking the year as a whole the droughts in the interior are more severe than near the coast. In the same way the rainfall of the five rainiest Januaries, Februaries, and so on throughout the year amounted to 200 per cent of the average rainfall for the same months at Hartford, and to 226 per cent at Des Moines. Thus the interior is subject to greater extremes of moisture as well as of drought. In Europe the contrast between the steadiness of the maritime rainfall on the west and the variability of the continental rainfall in the interior is stronger than in the United States. This is evident from the European part of the table below. We shall see later that the steadiness of the climate around the North Sea, as illustrated by Utrecht in Holland, is a great help to agriculture and also in other ways. The variability of the rainfall in the interior, on the contrary, as illustrated by Odessa on the Black Sea, is a tremendous handicap.

	Rainfall of the five driest Januaries, Februaries, etc., as percentage of average	Rainfall of the five rainiest Januaries, Februaries, etc., as percentage of average
Hartford (1879–1930)...........	28	200
Des Moines (1879–1930)..........	20	226
Utrecht, Holland (1876–1920)..	30	194
Belgrade, Yugoslavia (1888–1924)..	26	208
Odessa, Russia (1881–1915)..	15	248

The relative steadiness of the rainfall in North America saves our Corn Belt from the very great continental extremes which affect southeastern Russia and Central Asia. For this reason, Iowa comes near to having the optimum climate for corn in spite of its location in the far interior. Such a climate, together with the wonderful dark soil, gives that state an average yield of 38 bushels of corn per acre. Eastern

Nebraska is much the same, although a little drier as appears in A68. Westward, however, the continental character of the climate increases rapidly. Hence, Nebraska as a whole has an average yield of only 25 bushels, although here, too, the soil is wonderfully good. Part of the difference between Nebraska and Connecticut is due to greater use of fertilizer and more intensive cultivation in the East than in the interior, but still more is due to the climate.

The Contrast between the Optimum Climate for Corn and the Climate Where That Crop Originated.—The second row of climographs in A68 shows how both corn and climate change as one goes to lower latitudes and to regions warmer than those of greatest productivity. In North Carolina the yield of corn averages 20 bushels. This happens in spite of the fact that the fields are well fertilized. In that state, according to the United States Department of Agriculture, the fertilizer and manure given to the average acre of corn are worth six times as much as in Nebraska where the yield per acre averages 25 bushels—two and one-half times as much as in Iowa (38 bushels) and two-thirds as much as in Pennsylvania (42 bushels). A68 shows that in North Carolina the rainfall is about right, as is the case in most of the eastern half of the United States, but temperatures higher than those farther north are a disadvantage to corn much of the year. This does not contradict what was said above as to the marvelous yields obtained in North Carolina. That appears to have been near Asheville, which is so high that the July temperature averages 72° instead of 76° to 80° as in most parts of the state. So far as can be ascertained, this maximum in North Carolina apparently occurred under conditions almost identical with those of Connecticut except that the winters are a little warmer and the growing season in autumn longer. In Alabama the yield of corn drops to only 15 bushels per acre, even though the value of the fertilizer and manure applied to the fields is greater than in Iowa. Part of the trouble lies in the fact that there is less selection of seed and less care in cultivation than farther north. Other disadvantages are that here, as in most warm regions, the soil is comparatively poor, and insect pests and parasites are active. All these conditions, as we shall see later, are to a considerable degree indirect effects of climate, but the climate also has a direct effect on the corn. The heavy rainfall and high temperature cause a strong departure from the optimum.

The next two climographs in A68 take us to the southern hemisphere and to climates which closely approach that in which corn probably originated. In order to find the most favorable temperatures in these low latitudes it is necessary to go up into the mountains or plateaus. At Jujuy, in northwestern Argentina, we are at an altitude of about 4,000 feet and are just south of the Tropic of Capricorn. Evidently the planting season there must be October, but that month is much too warm for the best germination of the seed. Therefore, the corn is at a disadvantage, even if part of it is helped out by irrigation. The next two months are ideal in both temperature and rainfall, but January and February are too rainy. Hence, the corn does not fill out its ears properly and the kernels do not harden well. Moreover, insects and bacteria have a much better chance to do damage than in regions where cool weather soon checks their activity. The corn crop, like every other, is helped not only by the optimum weather for its own growth, but by weather that is as far as possible from the optimum for its enemies.

The middle line of climographs in A68 ends with Java, only a few degrees from the equator. Note how the local climograph is compressed into a long, narrow horizontal strip because the rainfall varies greatly, but the temperature scarcely at all. At the right elevations in Java one can find temperatures that are ideal for the sprouting of corn, for its growth, and for its ripening, but no one place has all these conditions. Nevertheless, at elevations of 3,000 to 6,000 feet where the best Javanese corn is grown, the climate for several months is ideal for the growth of corn after it is once started. It is also very delightful for human beings, except that the uniform temperature is monotonous. Most of the Javanese corn, however, is grown at low altitudes on the neighboring island of Madura, where the soil is not nearly so good as the dark volcanic soil of Java. There the climatic conditions depart so far from the optimum that the average yield per acre falls to scarcely more than 12 bushels, the average for all Java being 14. Poor cultivation and poor soil have much to do with this, but in such a climate even the best cultivation would not give yields like those of Iowa, Connecticut, or the mountains of North Carolina.

Why Europe is Not a Great Corn Continent.—In Europe, corn is an important crop only in the southeast, especially in Hungary, Rumania, Yugoslavia, and Bulgaria. These corn regions show a strong climatic resemblance to those of the United States, but with some interesting differences. Hungary, with 24 bushels, has the largest yield per acre of any European country except Switzerland. Taken as a whole, its climate also shows the nearest approach to the optimum for corn. The temperature, as appears in the lower line of A68, is almost identical with that of Connecticut, but all seasons are a little too dry for the best results. Hence, a yield of 24 bushels per acre is about what one would expect. This fact brings out the great value of cyclonic storms. Both the United States and Europe have such storms, but they are more numerous and bring more rain in the interior of the United States than in that of Europe. Hungary is nearer the sea than is Iowa, but because it has fewer and weaker cyclonic storms it gets less rain, especially in summer. Moreover, it is shut off from the Mediterranean Sea by the Alps so that there is no free inward sweep of moisture like that which brings moisture from the Gulf of Mexico to Iowa. These facts in themselves, even if all other conditions were similar, would make its crop smaller and less regular and its farmers poorer than those of Iowa. Bulgaria is not quite so favored as Hungary. Even its best portion, represented by Philippopolis in A68, is a little drier than Hungary, and the danger from drought is greater. Most of the corn-raising part of the country is both warmer and drier than Philippopolis, so that Bulgaria's yield of 16 bushels per acre as the average for all sorts of farms and all sorts of farmers is about as much as could be expected. Here, as in every other case, it is surprising to see how closely the yield per acre harmonizes with the climate. Europe is not a corn continent. If the United States had no areas where the climate approaches the optimum for corn any more closely than does that of the main corn areas in Europe, our total yield would probably be only about 570,000,000 bushels instead of 2,750,000,000. In other words, our climate is so different from that of Europe that we raise more than 2,000,000,000 bushels of corn in climates which have no exact counterpart in Europe. Most of this is raised in an area of about 600,000 square miles from Ohio westward to northeastern Colorado and southeastern South Dakota—an area which is popularly supposed to be almost like Europe in climate. Of course, the climates are similar. There is just enough difference, however, so that even with their intensive methods of cultivation the Europeans cannot rival the yields per acre in the best parts of the United States. This shows how extremely sensitive corn is to climate, and the same is true of almost every other crop.

Where Corn Cannot be Grown.—The last two climographs of A68 illustrate two types of climate which lie beyond the limits where corn can be cultivated except by special methods such as hothouses or irrigation. The climograph for Duluth shows a typical mid-continental climate with rainfall enough for corn, but too cool. No corn can mature in places where the summer temperatures average appreciably below 66°. The Los Angeles climograph illustrates a typical climate of the Mediterranean type with rainy winters and very dry summers. The summer temperature is admirable for corn, but in other respects the climate is too warm and dry unless irrigation is practiced.

EXERCISES

1. Make a local climograph illustrating the temperature and rainfall of your own home. In what respects does it differ from the climograph of the ideal region for corn?

2. Tables of monthly temperature and rainfall are given in Kendrew's *Climate of the Continents*, Miller's *Climate*, and various other books. Select at least two stations in each continent, making sure that half of all your stations are on the seacoast and half in the interior, and that they are well scattered between 60° N. and 50° S. Make a climograph for each, and decide which of the climographs in A68 it most resembles. Explain how the climate of each station differs from that of the ideal region for corn.

3. Make climographs of two or three places in latitude 30° in each of the six continents, letting one place in each continent be on the east coast, one on the west, and one in the interior if possible. Arrange your climographs in order according to the size of the continental area lying farther west and farther from the equator. What does this arrangement show as to the effect of continents versus oceans on seasonal range of temperature and on the amount and season of rainfall? Which of your climographs indicate conditions favorable for corn?

4. Write out a statement of at least three important principles which are set forth in this chapter.

5. On the basis of the 5-year yields of oats or barley, as given by states in the *Yearbook of Agriculture*, make two maps like A57 and B57, but do not attempt to show the limits of the crop. Compare your maps with the corn maps and explain their features. Keep your maps for future reference.

CHAPTER V

WHEAT AND THE RELATION OF TEMPERATURE TO AGRICULTURE

The World-wide Distribution of Wheat.—We saw in a previous chapter that climate, soil, and relief limit wheat to about one-tenth of the lands of the earth, but that it is cultivated on only one-tenth of this tenth. Nevertheless, aside from grass no other crop is so widely cultivated, nor does any other single crop, unless it be rice, provide so large a share of the food of mankind. Wheat provides about 30 per cent of the calories or heat units in the diet of the United States, and still more in that of western and southern Europe. This wide use is due to several causes: (1) Long experience has proved that cereals are the best kind of staple food by reason of their nutritive value, ease of cultivation, yield per acre, keeping qualities, small bulk in proportion to the amount of food, and adaptability to a great diversity of climates and soils. (2) Among the cereals wheat is one of the best balanced so far as its proportions of proteins and carbohydrates are concerned. Only oats excel it in this respect, but on an average they are twice as bulky and do not keep so well. (3) Wheat is also the most appetizing of the cereals as a steady diet. Hence, the majority of mankind choose it rather than rice, corn, rye, barley, or millet, provided they are economically free to do so. (4) Wheat is rivaled by few crops except barley in its ability to grow in a great variety of climates. This is partly because it can be raised both as a winter crop sown in the fall and reaped the following spring or summer, or as a spring crop sown in the spring and reaped the following autumn. (5) Wheat is so hard, firm, and free from oil that it keeps better than any other cereal, and can stand long transportation.

The wide distribution of wheat resulting from these causes is illustrated in A75, where the following areas of especially heavy production can be distinguished:

1. A spring wheat area in the northern United States and Canada from Minnesota and Manitoba westward.
2. A winter wheat area in the central United States.

3. A mixed area in Oregon and southern Washington.
4. A winter wheat area covering much of western Europe from Great Britain and France eastward and southeastward to the northern shore of the Black Sea.
5. A spring wheat region merging with the preceding region in southern Russia. It occupies all but a narrow strip close to the Black Sea and extends far into Siberia.
6. A Mediterranean winter wheat region extending from Morocco, Algeria, and Tunis through the Nile Valley, and the Near East, and around to Greece, Italy, and Spain.
7. A winter wheat region in northern India.
8. A winter wheat region in northern China merging into No. 9.
9. A spring wheat region in Manchuria.
10. A winter wheat region in southeastern Australia with a little in the southwest.
11. A winter wheat region in east central Argentina.

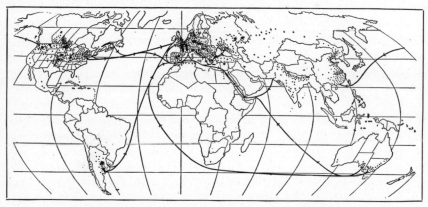

A—World Map of Wheat. Each dot represents 5,000,000 bushels.

Contrasted Qualities of Wheat Regions.—These regions obviously differ greatly in climate, soil, and methods of cultivation, but most of them enjoy nearly the same kind of gentle relief. The climate ranges from the Maritime Cyclonic Type of the North Sea region—cool, moist, and rainy at all seasons (Brussels in A76)—to the extreme Continental Type of Siberia (Irkutsk in A76) with its excessively cold, dry winters and moderately warm, rainy summers. It also includes the Mediterranean Type (Algiers in A76) with rainy winters which are often free from frost, and long, hot, rainless summers. But notice that even in three such diverse types of climate, the temperature and rainfall are approximately the same at the seasons when wheat makes its chief growth—March and April in Algiers and June and July in the two other regions. The soils in which wheat is grown range from rather poor sandy types in Flanders, where the yield per acre is enormous, to the richest of black loams in the Dakotas and the Black Earth Region of Russia, where the yield per acre is small. The methods of cultivation also differ exceedingly. In some sections, such as Turkey, most of the wheat is still cut in the primitive, back-breaking way by bending over with a sickle. It is carried to the threshing floor on the backs of donkeys, and is threshed by driving cattle or donkeys around and around

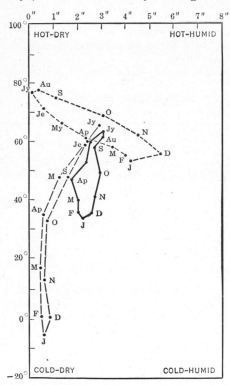

to trample out the grain on a floor of dried mud. In Europe, much of the wheat is cut with horse-drawn reaping machines which lay the cut stalks in piles ready to be bound into sheaves. A surprising amount, however, is still cut by hand with cradles, that is, scythes to which are attached wooden fingers for gathering the stalks into piles that can easily be picked up and tied into sheaves with bands which may be made of straw. Only a small fraction of the European wheat is cut with motor-drawn reapers or with self-binders, although the Russians are trying hard to introduce them. The cheapest and most efficient of all methods of harvesting crops, the combine, has hitherto been almost limited to the dry parts of new countries like the United States, Canada, and Australia. There alone do we find the necessary capital,

A—Three Widely Different Wheat Climates
Brussels—the Solid Line
Irkutsk—the Long Dash Line
Algiers—the Short Dash Line.

together with sufficiently large level fields and a climate in which the wheat can be left standing until all the heads are ripe enough for threshing. In such places a combine run by a gasoline engine can cut off the heads of wheat, thresh the grain, and put 500 bushels into sacks with the same amount of human labor that is needed to cut, stack, thresh, and bag one bushel where a sickle is used.

Almost the only important respect in which the world's great wheat regions are alike is their gentle relief. Wheat and other small grains need level fields more than do almost any other crops. The work of reaping as well as plowing cannot easily be done on slopes, and the use of large machines is out of the question unless the slopes are very gentle. Yet in China, Syria, and elsewhere wheat is still raised on slopes or on little terraces laboriously laid out on the mountain sides.

Although soils, relief, and methods of cultivation are highly important in respect to wheat as well as other crops, they will not be discussed further in this chapter because here we are concentrating upon climate. Our problem is to determine the principles which have guided mankind in devoting so much land to wheat in climates like those of the eleven

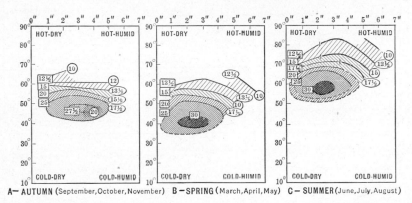

A— AUTUMN (September, October, November)   B —SPRING (March, April, May)   C— SUMMER (June, July, August)

Yield of Winter Wheat in Bushels per Acre for 18 Countries of Europe (1901–1920) and for 21 States of the United States (1914–1929) under Various Conditions of Temperature and Rainfall. The numbers in squares indicate the yields for Europe; the numbers in circles indicate the yields for the United States.

regions named above rather than in other regions. The first step is to discover what climate is best for wheat. In doing this we shall follow the method already employed for corn. Then, in a later chapter, we shall be ready to inquire how economic, social, and political considerations cause the regions actually devoted to both wheat and corn to be very different from what they would be if only the climate had to be considered. Since winter wheat is raised almost exclusively in seven of the eleven regions named above, we shall devote our attention to that rather than to spring wheat. As a matter of fact, about three-fourths of the world's wheat supply is the winter variety.

The Climatic Optimum of Wheat.—A77, B77, and C77 are climographs like those for corn. They show the climatic conditions of autumn, spring, and summer under which wheat produces various yields per

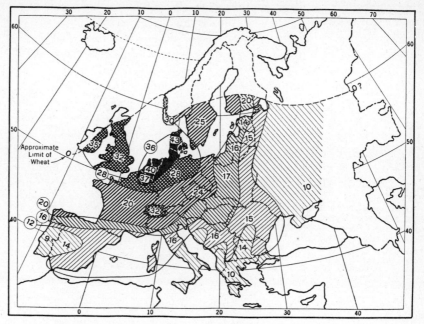

A—Average Annual European Yield of Wheat per Acre, in Bushels, 1910–1929.

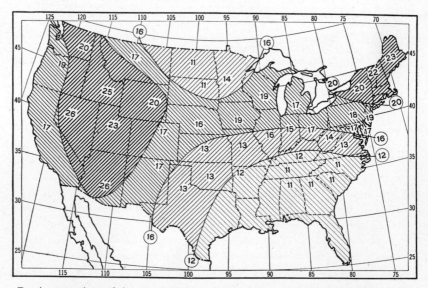

B—Average Annual American Yield of Wheat per Acre, in Bushels, 1910–1929.

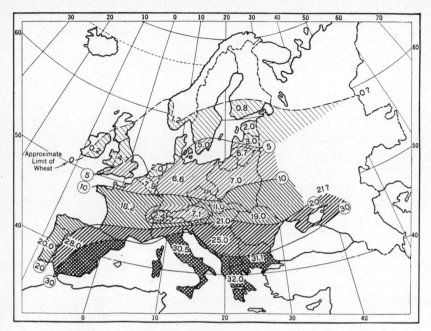

A—Percentage of Harvested Land Devoted to Wheat in Europe.

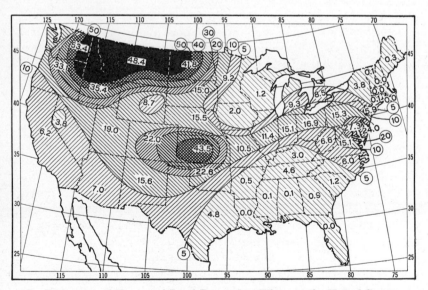

B—Percentage of Harvested Land Devoted to Wheat in the United States.

acre. The heavily shaded areas show that the optimum climate for
wheat has the following characteristics:

Autumn: Temperature 46–50°, Rainfall $2\frac{1}{2}$–4 inches per month.
Spring: Temperature 38–43°, Rainfall $1\frac{1}{2}$–3 inches per month.
Summer: Temperature 57–61°, Rainfall $1\frac{1}{2}$–3 inches per month.

These climographs are based on the 21 states of the United States where
winter wheat is raised in appreciable quantities without irrigation, and
on 18 similar countries in Europe. When the climographs of wheat for
autumn, spring, and summer are made separately for the United States
and Europe the two sets are essentially alike in shape and in their indications as to the optimum. In our wheat regions, to be sure, there is
no section with cool, moist summers like those around the North Sea,
and in Europe there is no section with such hot and humid summers as
we have in states like Missouri, Tennessee, and Arkansas. Nevertheless, the climate in large sections of North America and Europe is sufficiently alike so that the climographs of the two continents overlap a
great deal, and can be put together as is done in A77, B77, and C77. In
putting them together, however, we find a curious difference. Under
climatic conditions where the yield is only 10 to 15 bushels per acre, a
given combination of temperature and rainfall is accompanied by almost
the same yield in both Europe and the United States. Where the climate
in autumn, spring, and summer, however, is such as to favor a yield of
more than about 15 bushels, the yield in Europe is always larger than
in the United States. This is evident from a comparison of the numbers
in squares (Europe) on the three climographs with those in circles
(United States). This same fact is illustrated in A78 and B78, where
isopleths show that a large area around the North Sea has a higher yield
of wheat per acre than has any part of the United States. From that
region the yield drops off in every direction. Moreover, in the United
States the highest yield per acre without irrigation is found in the northeast, with a decline in all directions. Curiously enough A79 and B79
show that a large percentage of the land is used for wheat in parts of
both continents where the yield per acre is low, whereas only a small
percentage is generally used where it is high.

Why Europe Achieves Large Yields of Wheat Per Acre.—In attempt-
ing to explain why Europe thus goes ahead of the United States in its
yield of wheat we meet one of the most vital questions of economic geography. Is the higher European yield due to purely human factors such
as intensive cultivation, abundant fertilization, careful selection of seed
and the use of only the best land, or to geographic factors among which
climate and soil are by far the most important? We can answer at once
that the difference is not due to better seed in Europe, for the two

regions constantly interchange seed, and the United States has been quite as active as Europe in developing new and better varieties. Neither is it due to soil. C. F. Marbut, of the United States Bureau of Soils, points out very forcibly that in northwestern Europe where the yield of wheat per acre is largest the soil is by no means so rich as that of many parts of the United States where the yield is much lower (Plate II). Moreover, in neither continent are the largest yields obtained in the best soil. The superb Black Earth of Russia, for example, produces only about 10 bushels per acre, and the similar soil of Kansas only 13 compared with 39 and 23 respectively in the far poorer soils of Belgium and Maine.

We can also say positively that the high yields of wheat in Europe are not due to the selection of the best land. The best land is always allotted to crops like vegetables which bring a high return per acre. In countries like France, southern Germany, northern Italy, Austria, Belgium, Denmark, and southeastern England the rest of the land is devoted to crops which form part of a general rotation. Each main type of crop is raised on each piece of land in turn. Moreover, in most parts of the continent of Europe all the available land is most assiduously cultivated even when it is so poor that American farmers would not think it worth using. But Europe is very crowded, and the farmers have so little land that they are eager to cultivate every possible acre. Hence there is scarcely more selection of the best land for wheat in Europe than there is in the United States.

This limits us either to cultivation, including fertilization, or to climate as the reason why the yields of wheat are so much larger in Europe than in the United States. There can be no doubt that cultivation and fertilization are important elements in the problem. Because of their small fields and their large number of cattle per square mile the people of most parts of Europe cultivate their land much more intensively than do the farmers of America. The beneficial effects of abundant fertilizers, and especially of barnyard manure, can scarcely be overemphasized. Nevertheless, neither cultivation nor fertilization can produce a great effect unless the climate is also favorable. If the soil is too dry, fertilizers are generally of little use because they are not dissolved and thus made available to the plants. If the rains are too frequent and violent, whatever plant food has been dissolved is likely to be carried away before the plants can get it. What the crops most need is steady but not excessive moisture. They need this not only in summer, but at other seasons as well, so that the fertilizers will be broken down and spread through the soil, thus putting the plant foods into such a form that the plants can steadily feed upon them.

This explains why the steadiness of the rainfall at all seasons around the North Sea and in the northeastern United States is so valuable. This steadiness means not only about the same amount of rain at all seasons, but also relatively slight variations from year to year, and few long spells of either very dry weather or excessive rain. Southeastern Russia, and still more, China, illustrate the opposite extreme. J. L. Buck in his intensive study of Chinese farms has found, as we have seen, that in spite of very intensive cultivation and abundant fertilization, the yield per acre in China is far below that of northwestern Europe, and even below ours. The trouble lies in the frequent droughts at some seasons in China and the excessive rains and heat at others. Both conditions prevent the cultivation and fertilization from producing their full effect.

In solving the problem of how far the large yield of crops in western Europe is due to cultivation and how far to climate, we must consider the case of corn as well as that of wheat. If cultivation and fertilization were the main causes of the large yields of wheat in Europe, similar conditions ought also to cause the European yields of corn to surpass those of the United States, but we have seen that this is far from the case. In view of all this we seem forced to conclude that although cultivation and fertilization make an enormous difference among the various farms in any given region, they account for only part of the great differences between one region and another.

The Value of Cool but Not Cold Winters.—This brings us again to the effect of climate upon the yield of wheat per acre. In discussing the climographs of wheat on page 77, we omitted the winter. The reason is that the winter climographs for Europe and the United States (A83) are so different that it is not easy to combine them.

The most significant difference is that our largest crops per acre are raised in seasons and states where the temperature of December, January, and February averages between 20 and 30°, whereas in Europe much larger yields are obtained in seasons and regions with an average temperature of 32 to 38°. Let us see what such a difference signifies to the plant itself. With an average winter temperature below 30° the American wheat that is sown in the fall cannot grow appreciably for three months, even in the areas where the climate at other seasons is such as to give the greatest yield per acre. Meanwhile the wheat in the best European areas is enjoying temperatures which average above freezing so that for weeks at a time it is able to grow a little. The size of the wheat crop is greatly influenced by the number of stalks which spring from each root. To quote a report of the United States Department of Agriculture, "Wheat branches (or tillers) only at the ground, and produces no more heads than stalks. . . . It only sends out these branches early in its growth or during cool weather, and when the growth is comparatively slow."

So important is this branching of the wheat that in Mesopotamia and other parts of western Asia, where the winters are mild and the springs warm and dry, the people allow their cattle and sheep to graze on the growing wheat during the coolest weather in order to cause it to send up more shoots from each root. Thus we see why the Department of Agriculture goes on to say that in the chief wheat-growing parts of the United States "a cool, prolonged and rather wet spring is . . . best for the ultimate yield of the crop. . . . A warm, rather dry, rapidly growing, and early spring (such as is common in the main wheat regions of the United States and still more in Russia and Asia) . . . diminishes the yield; there are then fewer stalks, and the heads are fewer. . . . The ideal climate for wheat is one with a long and rather wet winter, with

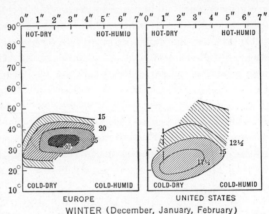

WINTER (December, January, February)

A—Yield of Winter Wheat in Bushels per Acre for 18 Countries of Europe (1901–1920) and for 21 States of the United States (1914–1929) under Various Conditions of Temperature and Rainfall.

little or no frost, prolonged into a cool and rather wet spring, which gradually fades into a warmer summer, the weather growing gradually drier as it grows warmer."

In the part of Europe around the North Sea almost exactly these conditions prevail for several months during the winter and early spring. This suggests that the high yields of wheat per acre in northwestern Europe are due in part to the direct effect of the cool, damp maritime winters as opposed to the cold, dry, continental quality of our winters. Thus near the shores of the North Sea the climate does everything possible to make it worth while for the farmers to fertilize their wheat and cultivate it carefully. Therefore they get a yield four times as great as that of Russia, and two or three times as great as that of our main wheat areas.

How the Contrast between Corn and Wheat Illustrates the Importance of Climate.—Corn and wheat present an interesting and significant contrast. Corn, which is a native of America, gives the highest yields in parts of the continent which have a continental climate even though they may lie near enough to the Atlantic coast to be somewhat modified by the ocean. This continental, cyclonic type of climate with fairly warm summers and cold winters, but with plenty of rain at all seasons, has no exact counterpart in Europe. In harmony with this we have seen that, in spite of intensive cultivation, no appreciable section of Europe has a yield of corn that rises to any such level as in the United States. Wheat, on the other hand, which is an Old World product, gives its highest yields in regions having a type of oceanic climate with cool, but not cold, winters, and with distinctly cool summers. The United States has no counterpart of such a climate except on the Pacific coast in the far northwest, and there around Seattle we find exceptionally high yields of wheat. For example, in 1915 in a soil which is of only moderate quality, a fifteen-acre field in Island County, Washington, produced the greatest yield of wheat ever recorded in the United States, 117 bushels per acre. The temperature there, more nearly than in other parts of the United States, agrees with that of the optimum for wheat in Europe, as appears in the following table:

	Island County	European Optimum for Wheat
Autumn..............	51°	46–50°
Winter..............	40°	32–38°
Spring..............	52°	40–44°
Summer..............	59°	58–61°

The only important difference is that the spring is warmer near Puget Sound than in the North Sea region.

A similar case in respect to corn is found in the Alpine Valleys on the south side of Switzerland, near the famous lakes of Lugano, Maggiore, and Como. There the yield of corn for many years has averaged 40 bushels per acre, the highest in Europe. The temperature of this Swiss corn area is almost ideal at all seasons, the summers being like those of Connecticut and the North Carolina mountains, and the winters midway between those of the other two regions. The only trouble is that the rainfall at some places like Lugano is too abundant except in winter, but in many places that are more protected by the mountains it is considerably less. On the whole, then, these Swiss valleys appear to depart from the optimum for corn just enough so that a yield of 40 bushels per acre is about what we should expect. Thus in Europe, as in North Carolina, an exceptional region where the climate, and especially the temperature, approach very closely to the optimum for corn has a yield of corn almost like that of the best parts of America. On the other hand, in America an equally exceptional place with a climate like the European optimum for wheat has also a European yield of wheat.

Turn, now, to northern China, where the soil is cultivated and fertilized more carefully than almost anywhere else on earth, but where the climate departs widely from the optimum for either corn or wheat. The yield per acre is correspondingly far from the yields obtained where the climatic optimum prevails. According to Buck's carefully prepared tables it drops to 13 bushels for wheat and only 11 for corn, even in years when there is neither drought or flood. If cultivation were the dominant factor in crop yields, the production not only of corn and wheat, but also of many other crops, ought not to fall so low in China. In all these cases, however, and also in hundreds of others, the average yields of crops per acre all over the world, when good farms and poor are taken indiscriminately, fall closely in line with what would be expected on the basis of climate. This does not mean in the least that intensive cultivation and fertilization do not produce remarkable results, but merely that they pay best and are most likely to be practiced where the climate is best for the crops. Hence the average yield on all farms, good and bad, varies from region to region in close harmony with the degree to which the climate approaches the optimum for the particular crop in question.

Best Crops Near Coldward Limits.—The great majority of crops are at their best near their coldward margins. Connecticut with its maximum yield of field corn lies only about 250 miles south of the extreme northern limit of this crop near Montreal. Southern Maine and southern Wisconsin, still nearer the northern limit, are almost unrivaled for the excellence of their sweet corn. Southward from these places the corn becomes poorer and poorer. Yet it is a staple crop and often the one of most importance for 3,000 miles to the equator. The way in which the yield of winter wheat increases from the equator northward is illustrated in A86. There the yield per acre in countries at various latitudes is seen to increase regularly with distance from the equator. It reaches a maximum in Denmark, only about 200 miles south of the northern limit of wheat. Even in Sweden at the northern limit the yield drops off only a little from that of Denmark. Rice behaves in the same way, as appears in B86. There the bars show the average yield for all regions in strips five degrees wide beginning with latitudes 0–5°, 5–10°, and so on. The yield increases more or less steadily to latitude 35°, and even in the cool regions north of this it is still twice as high as in most of the regions near the equator where rice is the dominant crop. Of course, the yield in any given latitude fluctuates according to rainfall, soil, and method of cultivation, as well as temperature, but all these other conditions together cause only a little irregularity in B86. Similar conditions prevail in respect to the other cereals. The yield per acre of oats is 10 or 15 bushels per acre in latitude 30°, but rises to 40 or 50 bushels in latitudes 45° to 60°. The maximum of 60 comes in Belgium in latitude 52°. Barley ranges from 10 bushels in Portugal and similar latitudes to 50 or more in Belgium.

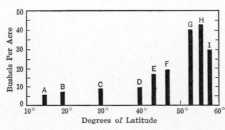

A—Yield of Wheat per Acre in Different Latitudes.

A. Eritrea 5.0.
B. Mexico 6.8
C. Basutoland 8.2.
D. Portugal 8.7.
E. Italy 16.4.
F. Austria 18.6.
G. Netherlands 40.0.
H. Denmark 42.6.
I. Sweden 30.0.

Vegetables and fruits also do best close to their cooler limit. Omitting the irrigated areas, the yield of potatoes in the United States is largest and the quality best along the northern border. Idaho is famous for its enormous potatoes, often 6 or 8 inches long, with smooth, well rounded surfaces. Northern Maine, and likewise New York, Wisconsin, Minnesota, Michigan, and North Dakota, supply seed potatoes for thousands of farmers farther south. Yet A87 shows that except near northern Maine every province in Canada raises more potatoes per acre than does the part of the United States just south of it. Maine holds its high position because Aroostook County has a soil as well as a climate remarkably well adapted to potatoes. The Canadian provinces, however, have no special advantages of soil, nor is there any reason to think that the methods of cultivation there are any better than in the United States. Hence the high yields seem to arise directly or indirectly from climate.

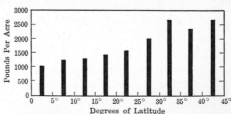

B—Yield of Rice per Acre in Different Latitudes.

That this is so is suggested also by the fact that the yield of sweet potatoes in the United States increases with considerable regularity from south to north. It is highest in New Jersey, Maryland, and Delaware, provided we disregard a few high yields due to irrigation in places like Arizona. Again, the cool northern states of Maine, Vermont, Idaho, and Wyoming produce exceptionally high yields of beans per acre.

Virginia, North Carolina, and Tennessee, which are near the northern limit of peanut production, are also the largest producers of that crop per acre. The excellence of the northern apples of Nova Scotia, Maine, New York, and Washington, as well as of those grown on cool mountains farther south in places like Virginia, is well known. The best oranges are raised in places like Florida, California, Spain, and Palestine. The lemons of northern Italy and Florida are unsurpassed. All these regions are within a few hundred miles of the coldward limits of citrus fruits. Such fruits are grown in warmer regions extending across an enormous

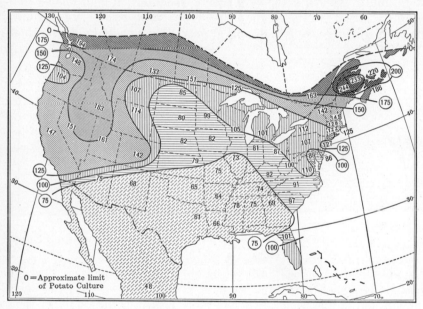

A—Average Yield of Potatoes per Acre, in Bushels, in the United States, 1910–1929.

belt including all the latitudes nearer the equator, but they are small, greenish, and sour compared with the great, luscious, yellow globes raised in some of the warmer valleys at the very northern limit of orange culture in northern California. Many industrial crops and plantation products also grow best near their coldward limit. A88 shows that the yield of cotton per acre in the United States increases regularly toward the north and except for the irrigated areas of the Southwest is highest in southern Missouri. The same is true of tobacco. The yield in Massachusetts, Connecticut, New York, Pennsylvania, Wisconsin, and Minnesota averages above 1,000 pounds per acre, whereas farther south it drops to an average of less than 500 in Louisiana. In tropical countries the best tea and coffee are raised on plateaus so high and cool that the plantations sometimes suffer from frost.

Of course, these various cereals, root crops, fruits, fibers, and stimulants all diminish in both quality and quantity when the temperature is too low. The point to be noted, however, is that these crops, as well as scores of others, follow the same general law. They can be raised in large areas which are too warm to give the best results. As their coldward limit is approached they improve in quality and in yield per acre until the optimum climate is reached. The optimum is close to the coldward limit. Beyond it the crop generally declines in both quality and quantity, just as to the south. The decline, however, is very rapid, so that the crop may entirely disappear only a few hundred miles north of

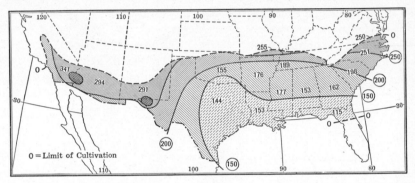

A—Average Yield of Cotton per Acre, in Pounds, in the United States, 1910–1929.

the optimum. All this, it should be noted, is different from what we find in the majority of wild plants. With them, as a rule, the finest growth and largest yield are found more nearly in the center of their range. The size and vigor of birch trees, oaks, pines, or wild grasses, so the foresters say, decline no more rapidly toward the poles than toward the equator.

Causes of Excellence of Products Near Their Colder Margin.— Although the geographic principle of abundant production and high quality near the coldward margin has very wide application, it has been recognized so recently that it is not fully understood. Undoubtedly the good cultivation given to the crops by the energetic people of the colder regions is a factor. By means of proper cultivation, the yield of tobacco as far south as Florida, for example, is raised almost to the northern level. Good cultivation, however, does not explain such phenomena as the much higher yield of potatoes in Canada than in states like Pennsylvania, Ohio, and Missouri. Nor does it explain why China, with its extraordinarily intensive cultivation, raises only one-half to one-third as much wheat per acre as do Denmark, Belgium, Great Britain, and the other North Sea countries, less than half as much corn per acre as the United States, far less cotton per acre than Egypt, and less rice than Japan. Only in sweet potatoes, a crop for which China seems to be especially well adapted, does that country get a yield per acre far in excess of that of the United States. Another alleged cause of the high production near the northern margin is that only the best land is there given to crops. This is true in some cases, but in the Scandinavian and North Sea countries, and likewise in Ireland, Canada, and our northern states, practically all crops show high yields per acre. Chile and especially New Zealand also excel the other countries in the southern hemisphere in the same way. Since this applies to practically all kinds of crops it must include those grown on all kinds of soil.

A third and more important reason for large and excellent crops near the coldward margins is that there the process of selection has gone much farther than elsewhere. These are the regions where the farmers long ago began to choose their seed very carefully. Now they are the places where agricultural experiment stations are most numerous and active, and where the farmers are most eager to get seed of new and improved varieties. A new kind of sweet corn, for example, ripens a week earlier than any hitherto known. A new kind of cotton is said to do well with a growing season a month shorter than is required for the old kind. A new, hard, red spring wheat that grows very rapidly was produced some decades ago by crossing old varieties and selecting the best strains year after year. This advanced the limits of wheat cultivation several hundred miles northward in Canada. Even at Winnipeg the first settlers more than a century ago were almost in despair over raising wheat because their crops so often failed to mature. Similar improvement and development of varieties that mature quickly have taken place with almost every crop. Such new varieties push the limit of the crop into colder regions. Moreover, they are almost invariably selected for their quality and productiveness as well as for their early ripening. Thus man himself is one of the greatest reasons for the excellence of the crops near their coldward limits.

Still another reason must not be overlooked, although it is not yet fully understood. Many experiments have shown that plants grow best under variable temperatures. For every crop there is a certain optimum temperature for germination of the seed, for the growth of leaves and stalks, for the production of flower buds, and for the ripening of the seeds or fruits. All these optima may be the same, but outside of equatorial regions they are generally different, the optima for flowering and fruiting being usually higher than for germination and vegetative growth, although the witch-hazel flowers in winter. But no matter what the optimum may be, the plant generally grows better if the temperature varies instead of staying always at the optimum. For example, Longwood Gardens in southeastern Pennsylvania, north of Wilmington, Delaware, contain one of the world's most superb greenhouses. The greenhouse is famous for the size, deep color, and general beauty of its flowers, and for the excellence of its grapes and melons. Visitors there in cold weather are surprised to find how cool the greenhouses are at night, or even by day when the sky is cloudy. Azaleas, amaryllis, and dozens of other flowers are blossoming superbly in a temperature of only 50°. Even the banana room may be only 60°. But on sunny days the temperatures may run from 70° to 80°, or even 90°. Long experience has shown that the majority of plants grow best when the temperature varies a good deal from night to day and also from day to day. Each plant wants an optimum appropriate to its own needs and to its stage of development. But if the optimum is 70°, the temperature ought usually to vary up and down from perhaps 60° to 75°, giving an *average* of 70° but introducing plenty of variability. Near the coldward margins of their growth crops generally experience much more variability of temperature than in warmer regions. In addition to this, the coldward margins are far less likely to suffer from drought or from excessively hot days which are among the worst elements in lessening the yield of crops like corn. In far northern regions the long duration of sunlight is another reason for the marvelous growth of vegetables. This accounts in part for the yields of 400 to 800 bushels of potatoes per acre which A. D. Albright describes north of latitude 60° in the Mackenzie region of Canada. Thus the direct effects of climate combine with man's activity in making the coldward margins the best regions for agriculture.

Still another highly important factor in the production of the best crops near the coldward margins is the comparative freedom of these regions from insects and other pests. The boll-weevil that does so much harm to cotton is killed by prolonged frost. Wheat and other grains are much more likely to suffer from rust and smut in hot, humid weather than in cool weather even if the humidity is equally great. The chinch bug, locusts, and many other insect pests thrive in warm weather. They often find their coldward limit at higher temperatures than do the crops on which they feed. Many crops are comparatively free from insect pests and blights along their coldward margin. Thus when we sum up the whole thing we see that in the main the geographical location of the best quality and largest yield of a crop depends partly on its own climatic optimum, partly on the climatic optima of its enemies, and partly upon what man does in the way of selecting, improving, and cultivating it.

EXERCISES

1. In A75, A337, A59, and A19 compare the location of the main wheat areas listed on pp. 74–5 with the main corn areas, noting in each case the latitudes where the crops are most abundant. Where corn and wheat are both raised in the same continent, how do their latitudes compare? Why does wheat have areas of very abundant production in so much wider a range of latitude than corn?

2. Compare the latitudes in which wheat is raised most abundantly in the various continents. Explain whatever differences you find.

3. Briefly point out how temperature, coupled with winter precipitation, determines whether an area shall grow winter wheat or spring wheat. If the yield of winter wheat is greater than that of spring wheat, what temptations and dangers confront the farmers in the belt which separates the winter and spring wheat areas?

4. Suppose that a lowland area in the northern United States has the same average temperature as a highland area in tropical South America. In which area would wheat be in greater danger of being injured by freezing? Why? In which would it give the greater yield under similar conditions of soil and cultivation? Why?

5. Pick out the three or four paragraphs in this chapter which most nearly sum up the gist of the whole chapter.

6. Which illustrations in this chapter seem to you most significant? Why?

7. Compare the maps which you made in Exercise 5 of Chapter IV with A–B86, A87, and A88. What geographic principle do you thus test? With what result?

CHAPTER VI

CLIMATIC OPTIMA OF ANIMALS AND MAN

Universality of Optima.—The principle of climatic optima, as we have already seen, applies to all sorts of living beings. For every species of animal, as well as of plant, some special combination of temperature, humidity, variability, sunshine, air movement, and other climatic conditions forms an optimum which is more favorable than any other combination. This optimum generally varies according to the age of the individual, and according to whether we deal with growth, reproduction, or some other function. A92 shows that various types of living creatures have the same sort of relation to temperature. The plants of the lowest curve grow fastest when the highest temperature of the day is about 85°. The next curve shows the rate of cell division among paramoecia, which are among the lowest forms of animals. In raising this one-celled creature for thousands of generations, L. L. Woodruff found that at temperatures below 40° F. its cells refuse to divide into new individuals. As the temperature rises, the rate of fission increases, reaching a maximum between 80 and 85°. At still higher temperatures it drops off rapidly, until death finally ensues. Obviously these creatures behave like the average plant. A similar example among somewhat higher animals is seen in the middle curve of

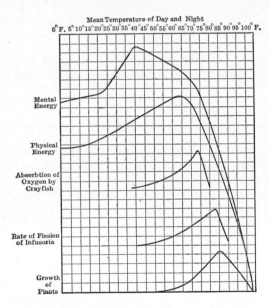

Mean Temperature of Day and Night

0° F. 5° 10° 15° 20° 25° 30° 35° 40° 45° 50° 55° 60° 65° 70° 75° 80° 85° 90° 95° 100° F.

Mental Energy

Physical Energy

Absorbtion of Oxygen by Crayfish

Rate of Fission of Infusoria

Growth of Plants

A—Optimum Temperatures for Various Vital Processes.

92

A92. This indicates that the activity of the lobster-like crayfish, as indicated by its use of oxygen, is greatest when the temperature is near 75°.

The Climatic Optima of Insects.—In the realm of economic geography many kinds of insects are of almost incalculable importance. Plagues of locusts in countries as far apart as Kansas, India, Argentina, and Australia may eat up the crops for thousands of square miles and impoverish hundreds of thousands of farmers. Locusts that probably were hatched on the west coast of Africa have been known to migrate as far as England. Others have been found at sea 1,200 miles from land. A swarm which crossed the Red Sea in 1889 was estimated to be 2,000 square miles in extent. The authors of this book have seen thousands of acres of young wheat eaten up completely by swarms of hopping locusts in the oases of Transcaspia (Turkmenistan). As long as their crops were good the Turkoman farmers there were satisfied with the Russian government. The ravages of the locusts, by destroying the food supply, aroused serious political discontent. As soon as the insects had done their work the unreasonable farmers began to think the government very bad, and to plot rebellion. In our own country the insects that harm fruit do an enormous amount of damage. Fruit farmers often spray their orchards four to ten times each season in order to kill insects and other pests. The boll-weevil diminishes the value of our cotton crop by hundreds of millions of dollars. Millions upon millions of human beings are rendered inefficient by malaria, which is carried by mosquitoes. Such conditions make it clear that insects are of the utmost importance in all sorts of human problems.

The vigor, abundance, and geographical distribution of insects depend upon climate and weather more than upon anything else. If the weather for two successive years happens to be favorable both to an insect and to its main supply of food, the insect may become so numerous and widely spread as to be a serious threat to man. V. E. Shelford's studies of the chinch bug illustrate the matter. The chinch bug is an extremely destructive little black and white insect about a sixth of an inch long. If often damages the crops of the central United States to the extent of millions or even hundreds of millions of dollars in a single year. It lays its eggs behind the leaves of young wheat or other grains, or in the ground near by. After the eggs hatch, the bright-red young at once begin to suck the sap of the plants. They grow rapidly, shedding their skins five times, and moving from plant to plant. Often they move along the ground in vast numbers from wheat fields where the plants are becoming hard to corn fields where the leaves are still soft and juicy.

The chinch bug thrives best in warm weather with little rain. Yet it must have moist air in order to do well. This is illustrated in A94, which is like earlier climographs except that the horizontal scale shows the relative humidity of the air instead of the rainfall. The relative humidity is the amount of invisible atmospheric water, or vapor, expressed as a percentage of the total amount of water that the air is capable of holding at any particular temperature. The fact that A94 is heavily shaded on the right at about 85° F. means that if the air at that temperature has a relative humidity of over 80 per cent the bugs will hatch and pass through all five of the so-called nymphal, or skin-shedding, stages in about 30 days. Hence they will increase very rapidly, for there will be several generations in a season. If, however, there should be much rain, the creatures are washed away and drowned. Thus an abundance of atmospheric moisture affects them quite differently from an abundance of rain. If the temperature is either higher or lower than about 85°, the bugs grow less rapidly, and it takes a longer time for them to become adult and ready to lay eggs. This is indicated by the fact that in A94 the shading becomes lighter both upward and downward from the optimum. If the air is dry the development of the bug is also hindered, as appears from the fact that A94 becomes more lightly shaded toward the left. If the temperature rises above 120°, or falls below about 60°, the bugs will not grow at all, no matter how great the atmospheric humidity. In dry weather they will not grow at temperatures below 70°, as appears from the position of the line marked "no growth" in the lower left hand part of A94. Thus in regions having cool summers, such as those in most parts of Canada, the chinch bug ceases to be a danger. The fact that many other harmful insects also find their optimum in warm, moist air, and do not thrive where it is cool or dry, has a great deal to do

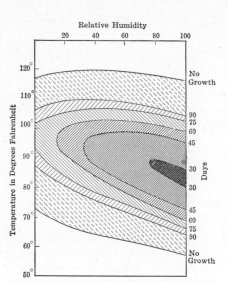

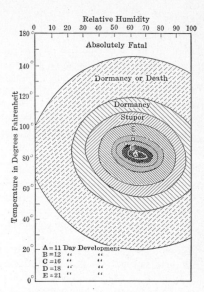

A—Climograph of the Development of the Chinch Bug from the Egg to Maturity. (After V. E. Shelford)

B—Climograph of the Development of the Cotton Boll Weevil. (After W. D. Pierce)

with causing crops to be at their best near their coldward limits. The boll-weevil, which does so much harm to cotton, illustrates this same point. Its climograph (B94), constructed by W. D. Pierce, was one of the first to be made. It is like that of the chinch bug in its essential features. This helps to explain why the largest yields of cotton are found near the northern limit of cultivation.

The Stimulating Effect of Variations in Temperature.—The *variability* of the temperature is often as important as the average temperature, the atmospheric humidity, or the rainfall. When Shelford kept his chinch bugs in uniform temperatures they died, even though the temperature was near the optimum. When he gave them plenty of variation of temperature, like that which occurs normally out-of-doors from day to night, and also from one day to another, they flourished. B. P. Uvarov has collected reports from many investigators which show that in most cases, although not necessarily in all, variations of temperature increase the rate of growth and improve the vigor of insects that live in the open air. He also finds that as a rule variations *above* the optimum are not so helpful as those *below* the optimum. Excessive variations in either direction are indeed harmful, but very high temperatures are more likely to be fatal, whereas those equally far below the optimum frequently serve merely to make the insects dormant, as happens in winter. Thus variability seems to belong with temperature, atmospheric humidity, and rainfall as one of the four great climatic conditions which determine how fast insects shall grow and how abundant and destructive they shall be.

For some insects, light may be a fifth climatic condition of similar importance. Bees, ants, and many other insects are active only by day, and diminish their activity very greatly when the sun is clouded. Other insects are active only at night, but some of these, such as certain moths, are far more active on moonlight nights than on others. Nevertheless, variations in the amount of light from one year to another do not appear to make any great difference in the harm done by the insects, and hence need not concern us further.

Climatic Optima of Birds. 1. *Conditions Controlling Egg Production.*—The vigor of birds as well as of insects is greatly influenced by weather and climate. This becomes apparent when we try to solve the problem presented by A96. Why do hens produce such different numbers of eggs in different parts of the United States? They produce more in the Northwest and Northeast than anywhere else. In North Dakota and the South they produce very few, but in Florida their production rises high above that in the neighboring states. All sorts of factors enter into the problem, including climate, markets, transportation, supplies of feed, character of the population, breeds of poultry, and methods of care. Each of these deserves careful geographic treatment, but in this chapter we shall merely attempt to discover whether any features of A96 are connected with climate.

2. *Egg-Laying Contests at Storrs.*—Let us see whether the egg production of the hens in the famous egg-laying contests of the Agricultural Experiment Station at Storrs, Connecticut, shows any distinct relation to the weather. Young hens are brought there from all over the country and even from Canada and England. A hundred pens are kept for a full year, and under the direction of W. F. Kirkpatrick a record is kept of the eggs laid by each hen. The discussion that follows is based on 100 hens each year for 18 years, half being White Leghorns and the rest Rhode Island Reds with a few of other breeds in the earlier years. The hens which were used all began to lay within three days of the beginning of the contest on November first and continued in the contest until the end. Many of these hens are among the best layers in the world; a few actually lay more than 300 eggs per year in contrast with 100 for the ordinary hen.

A97 shows how many eggs the average White Leghorn hen laid per month at different seasons in earlier and later periods. The noteworthy features here are (1) the maximum in May or June, (2) a great decline in September and October due to moulting, (3) a very low level in winter in earlier years but only a moderately low level in later years after the hens had been improved and when their pens were lighted in winter so that the length of time during which they could feed was increased.

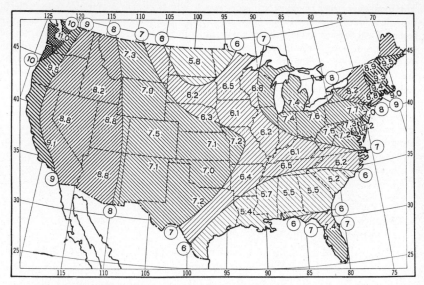

A—Dozens of Eggs per Chicken per Year in 1929. The word "chicken" as used by the U. S. Census means in this case any fowl of the chicken species over three months of age.

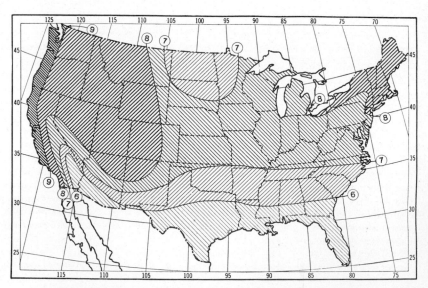

B—Dozens of Eggs to be Expected per Hen per Year on the Basis of Temperature Alone.

The most surprising thing in A97 is that the improvement in the hens has come in the winter with practically none in the summer and fall. Yet in spite of this the seasonal rhythm persists. Making allowance for the gradual improvement in the egg-laying powers of the hens and for the moulting period, we find that hens have a climograph (B97) similar to that of corn, chinch bugs, and many other forms of life. Taking the year as a whole, the hens that are not moulting lay the most eggs when the temperature averages 40 to 45° with a rainfall of 1 to 3 inches. This optimum represents the biological fact that hens inherit a physical constitution such that they tend to lay eggs when the temperature in the spring is that in which the young chicks will have the best chance to live. The importance of this rise of temperature in bringing on egg-laying is evident from the fact that when hens are taken to the

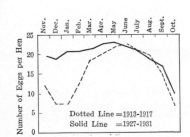

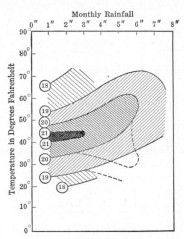

A—Average Number of Eggs per Month of 30 Days for Each White Leghorn Hen in the Storrs Contest Based on 50 Hens per Year.

B—Climograph of Eggs per Month of 30 Days for Each Hen in the Storrs Contest. (Dotted line = result of artificial light during winter months.)

southern hemisphere they immediately give up the seasonal rhythm of their old home and lay the most eggs in the southern spring corresponding to our autumn.

It is easy to interpret B97. The fact that the isopleths swing upward and to the right shows that, if the rainfall as well as the temperature goes above the optimum, these hens at Storrs keep on laying almost the maximum number of eggs until a temperature of about 60° and a rainfall of about 6 inches are reached. At higher temperatures the number of eggs falls off rapidly, especially if the weather is dry. The rainfall itself, however, probably has little to do with the matter, the humidity and dustiness of the air being, presumably, the important factors. Just what happens at high temperatures and with abundant rain at medium temperatures we do not yet know.

At low temperatures, the egg production falls off decidedly. This seems to be especially true in rainy weather, probably because the days then are cloudy and dark, as well as short, so that the hens do not have time to eat as much as is necessary if many eggs are to be produced. Just how much the egg production would naturally fall off in cold, rainy weather we do not know, for here an artificial factor plays a part. This factor is the lighting of the pens for an hour or two in the evening. This artificial prolongation of the day gives the hens more time to eat. It thus raises the egg production all through the winter, and is especially effective during rainy months at the beginning of the winter when the temperature averages 30° to 40°. The dotted isopleths in B97 illustrate this.

3. *Comparison of Actual Egg-laying with Expectation on Basis of Temperature.*— Having seen that a climograph for egg-laying has essentially the same qualities as one for insects, let us apply our conclusions from the Storrs egg-laying contests to the problem of the distribution of egg-laying in the United States as shown in A000. Inasmuch as we do not yet know just what effect is produced by rainfall and atmospheric humidity, especially under extreme conditions, let us simply draw a map (B96) showing how many eggs per hen would be expected on the basis of monthly temperatures alone. We assume that the effect of high temperature will become worse and worse, for it is quite certain that if the temperature should average 120°, let us say, for night and day together, the hens would all die, and long before that they would cease laying. Thus B96 shows how many eggs would be expected per hen on the basis of temperature, without regard to any other climate feature, or to food, care, markets, or anything else. The similarity between A96 and B96 is obvious. Both show high areas in the Northeast and along the Pacific Coast, and low areas in North Dakota and the Southeast. This suggests that the main pattern of the geographic distribution of egg-laying is set by the weather. If we could make proper allowance for rainfall, humidity, and variability, the resemblance of the two maps might be still greater. But other factors must not be overlooked. Both in the Northeast and on the Pacific Coast the high proportion of urban population and the concentration of great wealth cause the development of many fancy poultry farms, and this leads to the wide use of unusually good fowls and to extra good care on ordinary farms. In Florida the people who have come from the North during recent decades have brought fowls of this same kind. They give them good care, not only because they know the methods used on the fancy farms but because the high cost of both feed and good hens here tends to make people careful. In the Southwest, especially in Arizona, similar conditions prevail, and irrigation introduces favorable conditions not only for crops but also for poultry. Hence in A96 both Florida and Arizona rank higher than would be expected from B96.

4. *Climatic Control of Egg-laying.*—Putting together all the information thus far available, it seems that climate is the basic factor in determining how the production of eggs per hen shall vary from one part of the country to another, but other factors like migration and markets are also of high importance. The climate works in this way: A narrow strip close to the Pacific Coast is peculiarly free from either cold winters or hot summers. Moreover, the air there generally contains a fair percentage of vapor, even when there is no rain. That is where the hens lay best. In the Puget Sound region of Washington there are more summer rain and more variability from day to day than farther south. These conditions probably combine with the favorable temperature to give Washington a climate which perhaps approaches the ideal for hens more closely than does that of any other part of the country. Probably this is the main reason why A96 shows a yearly production of 11 dozen

eggs per hen in Washington, or one-sixth more than in any other part of the country and twice as many as in the Southeast. On the northeastern coast the conditions are not quite so good because the extremes of both heat and cold are greater. Nevertheless, within 50 or 60 miles of the New England Coast, where most of the poultry farms of that region are located, the winters are distinctly warmer and the summers cooler than farther inland, while the degree of atmospheric humidity is also greater. When we add to this a decidedly higher and more favorable degree of variability than on the Pacific Coast we see that the climate probably approaches the optimum for egg-laying, even though it does not quite rival that of the West Coast. In the South, on the other hand, high temperatures and great extremes of humidity in the east and dryness in the west reduce the vigor of the hens, although this handicap can be partially overcome by proper care. In the Dakotas a combination of hot summers and very cold winters has a similar depressing effect. Thus our final conclusion is that the climatic optimum of hens is as pronounced as that of corn. It is one of the main factors in determining how profitable it is to raise hens in various parts of the country.

Climatic Optima of Domestic Animals. 1. *Best Season for Milk.*—The best measures of the usefulness of dairy cattle are the amount and richness of their milk. Judged by this standard, cows have an optimum much like that of hens and wheat, and not very different from that of corn. Let us study the production of milk per cow per day at three Walker-Gordon farms in New Jersey and Massachusetts. These farms are run almost like factories. At the largest of them, near Princeton, N. J., about 1,300 cows are milked three times each day by means of a rotolactor, or revolving platform, on which fifty cows are milked at once by machines. In this way it is possible not only to have the milk absolutely clean and sterile, but to milk the cows three times a day. This costs no more than milking twice a day in the ordinary way and gives 15 per cent more milk. Incidentally, this illustrates the highly significant tendency of modern agriculture toward mass production, the use of machinery, and an organization like that of a factory. The cows milked by the rotolactor receive uniform care and uniform food at all seasons. They never go out to pasture and are fed essentially the same kind of green fodder or ensilage all the year round. Moreover, the number of calves born at various seasons throughout the year is practically constant. Therefore, whatever seasonal differences are found in the yield of milk must be due mainly to changes in the weather.

The upper part of A100 shows how the yield of milk varied from season to season during seventeen years. The most milk was produced in February, but from January to June the amount did not change much. Then it declined rapidly to a minimum in September. Afterwards it rose again steadily until January. In other words, as long as the temperature remained below 60° the milk production remained high; when the temperature rose above this point, production declined and continued low until the temperature once more fell below 60°, but when the temperature continued to average below 60° it rapidly rose once more. This same seasonal change is found year after year whenever other conditions such as feed and the number of calves that are born each month remain the same throughout the year. It is illustrated in another way in the lower curve of A100. This is based on John A. Gowan's records of a great number of cows during fifteen years. It shows the amount of milk given in eight months by cows whose calves were born at different seasons. When the calves were born in winter the cows gave much more milk than when they were born in summer.

Note that in A100 a large part of the vertical scale is omitted because it would take too much space to insert the entire height of the scale from zero upward. In A100, the omission is indicated by wavy lines, but in many diagrams this is not done. The student should pay attention to this point in every such diagram in order not to get an exaggerated idea of the meaning of the ups and downs in curves.

2. A Climograph of Milk Production.

2. A Climograph of Milk Production.—B100 is a climograph based on the Walker-Gordon cows. The climograph shows the variations in

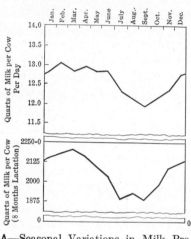

A—Seasonal Variations in Milk Production.

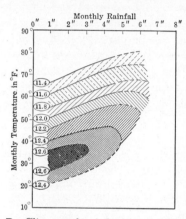

B—Climograph of Quarts of Milk per Day from Each Cow at the Walker-Gordon Farms, 1812–1924 and 1928–1931.

the yield of milk under different conditions of temperature and rainfall, but the effect of the rain must be mainly through the humidity of the air. The cows give the most milk when the temperature averages about 30° to 35° and the rainfall from 1 to 3 inches. This is almost identical with the January conditions in Denmark, which is the world's most remarkable dairy country. At higher temperatures the yield of milk steadily declines. At the same time the degree of rainfall which is best increases up to about 5 inches when the temperature averages 75° or more. Thus the cows behave much like the hens of B97, except that their optimum temperature is lower and artificial light does not enter into the matter. The lowest production is found at high temperatures not only when the air is very dry but also when it is very moist. In addition to this, W. P. Hays, F. A. Davidson, and other investigators have found that the amount of butter fat in cows' milk is low at high temperatures and increases as the temperature falls. The milk appears to be not only most abundant but richest in fat at temperatures a little above freezing, and then declines again in both respects at lower temperatures.

It is well known that ordinary cattle produce not only the most but the best milk in regions with cool, moist, fairly rainy summers, and with winters that are cool enough to have frost but not to freeze up very hard. It is not so generally recognized that such a climate not only is good for the grass which is normally the main food of cattle, as well as for silage, but also is the optimum for the cattle. Doubtless this adaptation to climate was acquired during the long process by which the world's best breeds of cattle were originally developed in the North Sea region, but it is doubtful whether such good breeds could be developed in any other climate.

3. *Distribution of Milk Production and its Climatic Relationships in the United States.*—A102 and B102 are two maps showing the actual production of milk per dairy cow in various parts of the United States and the production that would be expected on the basis of temperature alone. They correspond to A96 and B96 for eggs. We find in both sets of maps the same sort of general agreement between climate and production, together with decided differences due to conditions other than temperature. The resemblances are as follows: (1) high yields in a northeastern section from Iowa to the Atlantic Coast; (2) high yields in a large western section; (3) decidedly greater yield along the coast of California than a short distance inland; (4) a low yield in the Southeast. The greatest differences are seen in the dry Southwest, and near the cities of the Pacific and northeastern coasts where the actual production of both milk and eggs is higher than would be expected on a purely climatic basis. We may safely conclude that the general resemblance between A102 and B102 means that with cattle, as with corn, wheat, chinch bugs, boll-weevils, and hens, the general pattern of the geographical distribution of productivity is set by the climate. There is reason to believe that fuller data as to the effect of humidity and variability might partly explain the high production of milk on the two coasts, but other factors enter into the matter, just as with hens. The proximity of the large cities causes the development of fancy farms where highly bred animals give enormous yields of milk. For example, the Walker-Gordon cows used in A102 have now reached an average of nearly 14 quarts per day, whereas the average dairy cow in the United States gives only half as much. From such farms many high grade animals are sold to smaller farms, thus raising the general average. In the

Southwest the yield of milk per dairy cow is high in A102 not merely because California has many fine farms like those in the East, but also

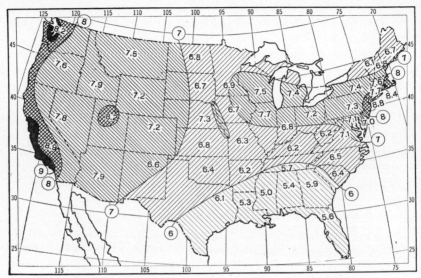

A—Milk per Day per Cow on Dairy Farms in the United States.

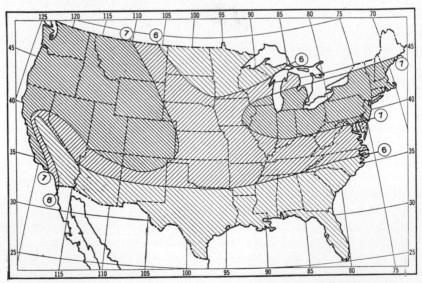

B—Milk per Day per Cow to be Expected on the Basis of Temperature.

because the presence of irrigated tracts farther inland favors such a yield in two ways. First, the irrigated areas raise alfalfa, which is highly nourishing in its fresh state and also retains its vitamin content when dried, especially if it dries quickly as is possible in these warm, sunny regions. Second, the number of dairy cows is very small in proportion to the whole number of cattle. Outside the oases, most of the cattle are of the beef type, and even when milked are not counted in the statistics on which A102 is based. Thus those statistics apply only to the exceptional herds and not to practically all herds such as are counted in the East and South. Thus with cows, as with hens, the general pattern of productivity is set by climate, but other factors modify it. Moreover, the optimum for cattle is not very different from that of corn, wheat, and chickens, but it is decidedly different from that of chinch bugs and boll-weevils.

Relation of the Seasons to Human Health. 1. *The United States.* — For man, just as for plants and animals, certain definite conditions of temperature, humidity, and variability form a distinct climatic optimum. This optimum varies according to people's age, race, previous habitat, and degree of civilization. It also appears to be different for physical and mental activity. For general statistical purposes the death rate is the best means of measuring the variations in health from place to place, or from one time to another.

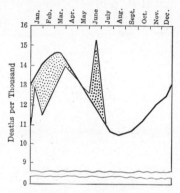

A Seasonal Variations in the Death Rate in the United States.

——— Average Death Rate
▨ June, 1925
▨ January to March, 1932

Where the death rate is high the number of people who suffer from serious illnesses is also sure to be high. A great many investigations have likewise shown that, in the long run, if deaths are numerous, minor ailments such as colds, headaches, stomach troubles, and the like are also numerous. Thus people as a whole do not feel very energetic or hopeful, and commerce and industry suffer accordingly.

The heavy line in A103 shows how the death rate varies from season to season in the large cities of the United States. Year after year the number of deaths is high and the general level of health low in winter. This happens even when there are no special epidemics. Our health and activity are diminished not only by the low temperature itself, but by the unduly warm, dry, and unchanging air in our houses. These conditions seem to render the human body especially susceptible to disease. A strong reason for thinking that the weather is the cause of this seasonal variation in health is seen when the weather is unusual.

The light line which begins in January and extends to March in A103 shows what happened in the winter of 1932. At that time the temperature of most parts of the United States was much higher than usual. The death rate remained correspondingly low, so that the winter as a whole was the most healthful ever known in the United States. The number of deaths in the whole United States is estimated as having been about 275,000 less than it would have been if the temperature had fallen to the normal level. The light line of A103 in June shows what happened in 1925 during a short but very hot spell which affected a large part of the United States. It broke many records, and was accompanied by great discomfort, inefficiency, illness, and death. Among both children and adults many persons were so weakened that they succumbed to

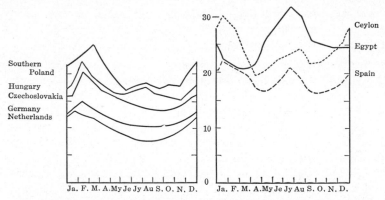

A—Seasonal Variations in the Death Rate in Countries with Diverse Climates.

disorders which might otherwise have been avoided. The death rate shot up so far that the number of deaths for the entire country appears to have been about 110,000 greater than would have been expected with normal temperatures. Similar evidence of the effect of low or high temperatures can be found on a smaller scale in the records of every year.

2. *Other Countries.*—The death rate in other countries is controlled by seasonal changes in the weather just as closely as in the United States, as appears in A104. There the left hand diagram shows how the death rate varies from season to season in five countries halfway from north to south in Europe. Each of them has a maximum at some time from January to March, and a minimum in the late summer or fall. When read from below upward, the five countries are arranged in the order of their position in respect to the Atlantic Ocean. Thus the curves show that as one goes to more and more continental regions, even though the latitude remains nearly constant, the following changes occur: (1) the

death rate as a whole increases; (2) the contrast between the best and the worst seasons increases; (3) the summers, being warmer in the interior than on the coast, begin to show a minor maximum of deaths, as appears in Hungary and Poland. We shall see later that these contrasts in health from the oceanic west to the continental interior are very significant and agree exactly with the climate. The conditions shown on the right of A104 are equally significant. In Spain the total death rate is about the same as in Poland, but since the winters are milder and the summers hotter the two maxima are nearly equal. Japan, which is not shown in A104, has a mortality curve almost identical with that of Spain except that the maxima come a month or two later. A104 shows death rates in Egypt and Ceylon still higher than those of Poland, Spain, and Japan. In Egypt the excessively hot, dry summers cause that season to have far higher death rates than the winters which are only pleasantly cool. In Ceylon the temperature is so nearly constant that it makes very little difference in the death rate. The two maxima of deaths come at the two dry seasons. All over the world the health and spirits of the people swing back and forth with the weather.

3. *Epidemics.*—The effect of the weather upon epidemics appears to be about the same as upon other types of disease. For example, during the great influenza epidemic of 1918 the death rate varied from city to city in fairly close harmony with the temperature before the onset of the disease and at its crisis. If the weather was cool and invigorating, but not cold, the ravages of the disease were reduced. The death rates during the first ten weeks of the main epidemic in the thirty-six cities of over 100,000 inhabitants for which data are available were as follows:

	Mean temperature for 30 days before outbreak of epidemic and for 10 days at Crisis	Death rate per thousand from influenza and pneumonia
6 coolest cities	54°	2.6
6 next coolest cities	57½°	3.0
6 next coolest cities	61°	3.5
6 next coolest cities	63°	4.2
6 next coolest cities	65°	5.0
6 warmest cities	70°	5.2

No other known factor, not even the sanitary and medical conditions of the various cities, shows any such close relationship to the death rate.

This does not mean that the weather caused the epidemic; there is no evidence of that. It merely increased or diminished its severity.

Effect of the Seasons on Energy and Work.—A106 gives another example of the effect of the weather not only on health but upon energy in general. The lower curves show the death rate in Connecticut (*C*) and in Pennsylvania (*D*) for four years among persons more than two years of age. The curves are inverted, so that good health is indicated by high parts and poor health by depressions. The two upper curves show the average hourly earnings of piece workers in three Connecticut factories (*A*) and in a huge Pittsburgh factory (*B*) during the same period. Notice how nearly the four curves vary in harmony. In Janu-

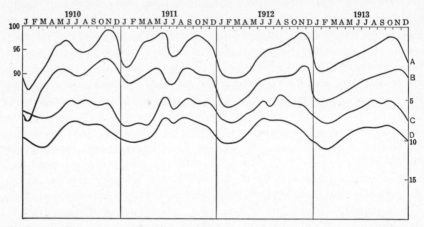

A—Seasonal Variations in Health and Efficiency. Amount of piece work in factories of Connecticut (A) and Pittsburgh (B). Death rates (inverted) in Connecticut (C) and Pennsylvania (D).

ary of the first year, people's energy fell off very badly, as appears in curves *A* and *B*. At the same time many became ill so that during the next two months the death rate was very high, as indicated by the low level of curves *C* and *D*. During the following spring both health and energy improved rapidly and reached a high point in May and June. When the summer heat came on, it was great enough to diminish the energy of the factory workers materially so that curves *A* and *B* show a sag. Ill health also increased somewhat, so that curves *C* and *D* become flat and sag a little, but not seriously. If children under two years were included, the health of this and of other summers would appear worse than in A106.

Follow the curves through the four years. Without exception they are low each winter. Of course, the worst health lags behind the lowest level of work. An illness may be contracted at the time when the rate of work is lowest, but it may take weeks before it ends in death. In the second summer, which was extremely hot and trying, especially in New England, all the curves of A106 show a dip, but in the third summer and especially the fourth, when the hot spells were short and well separated, the heat had almost no effect. In the late autumn the curves for health drop sooner than those for energy. This perhaps means that the approach of cold weather at first stimulates people who are in good health, while those who are feeble feel at once an ill effect from the low temperature. In winter, however, a drop in energy is regularly followed by a long period of poor health.

The four curves fluctuate so closely together that they seem to be subject to the same influences. The four factories were engaged in different kinds of work; there were no strikes, labor troubles, or shutdowns to cause fluctuations in any of them; and the cities of Connecticut are 400 miles from Pittsburgh. There were no epidemics of any importance to cause the curves of health to go up and down together, and the agreement would be equally great if all contagious diseases were omitted. The only factor which seems competent to explain the curves and which varies in approximately, though not exactly, the same way in both places is the seasons and the general character of the weather. Records of deaths and factory work in more southerly states including the Carolinas, Georgia, and Florida show that the winter in the South is less harmful than in the North, and that the long, hot summers have a correspondingly bad effect upon both health and energy. Tens of millions of deaths in all countries where reliable records are available, and much evidence as to rates of work, suggest that seasonal rhythms of health and efficiency corresponding to those of the weather are universal. They prevail on a mild scale even in tropical countries. In India and Mexico, for example, the wet season brings a decline in the death rate and an increase in physical activity.

Many other conditions, such as the growth of children, the mental activity of students, and the occurrence of mental diseases, show pronounced seasonal fluctuations which appear to depend mainly on the weather. These human rhythms are closely similar to those of animals and plants. That they are due to climatic causes and not to some innate quality of the organisms is generally inferred from the fact that they vary with the weather, not only from one year to another, but from place to place. In the southern hemisphere, for example, the physiological conditions of July are the same as those during January in corresponding climatic regions of the northern hemisphere. People, like hens, change their seasonal physiological rhythms when they change their climate. This has been observed again and again, and is equally true of plants, animals, and men.

A Human Climograph.—Let us now use data such as those just discussed in order to construct a climograph like those which we have already seen for corn, wheat, chinch bugs, egg production, and cattle. A108 and A109 are two different forms of the same climograph based on several million deaths during 16 years in 28 cities of Italy and France. In A108 the numbers show the deaths during months when any particular combination of temperature and humidity prevailed. The death rates are expressed as percentages of the normal rates for the various individual cities. Thus when the temperature averaged about 56° and the relative humidity about 65 to 70 per cent, the deaths in a number of cities averaged 2.5 per cent below the normals for those same cities. A108 affords a good illustration of how isopleths are used in making this kind of climograph. Notice how the innermost isopleth, which indicates a death rate 10 per cent below the average, curves around between the numbers that are above — 10.0 and those that are below. In the same way the 0 isopleth, the heaviest line, always has on one side minus numbers and on the other side plus numbers. It passes through all the combinations of temperature and relative humidity at which the death rate is exactly the average.

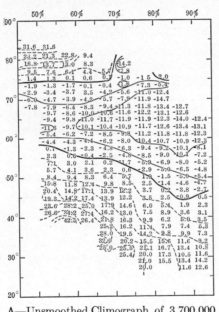

A—Unsmoothed Climograph of 3,700,000 Deaths in France and Italy, 1899–1913.

The most favorable area in A108 surrounds the number — 14.0 near the top of the second column from the right. This means that among the 50,000,000 people represented by the 3,700,000 deaths used in making this climograph the conditions of health were best during months when the temperature for day and night together averaged 64° F., while the relative humidity was from 85 to 90 per cent. With a higher humidity the death rate was less favorable, as appears from the fact that just to the right of — 14.0 we find — 12.4. Lower humidities were also less favorable. To the left of — 14.0 the numbers steadily increase until

—9.4 is found at a relative humidity of 50 to 55 per cent. This means that even at the optimum temperature very dry weather is not so favorable to health as is humid weather. Above the optimum, however, high relative humidity ceases to be favorable and soon becomes extremely harmful. In France and Italy great heat and great humidity do not happen to go together, but abundant evidence elsewhere shows that under such conditions the death rate rises enormously.

Contrary to what is often supposed, the death rate in hot weather rises nearly as much when the air is extremely dry as when it is extremely humid. This appears from the fact that in the upper left hand corner of A108 we have figures rising as high as 31.6 per cent, or nearly one-third above the average death rate. At a temperature of 80°, an average relative humidity of 60 per cent for night and day together appears to be better than either a greater or less degree of humidity. At low temperatures also we find a high death rate associated with dryness. The worst percentage in A108 is 42.5 at a temperature of 10° and a relative humidity of 55 to 60 per cent. Beginning with this figure, notice how the percentages decline toward the right. When the highest degree of

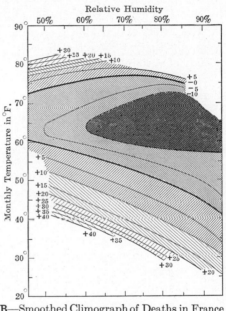

B—Smoothed Climograph of Deaths in France and Italy.

atmospheric humidity is reached they have fallen to 3.5, or only a little above the average. Hence we conclude that, although low temperature is always somewhat injurious to health, it does far less harm if the air is humid than if it is dry.

Climographs for many other regions such as Sweden, Japan, and various sections of the United States all show the same features as A108. Even for Negroes in the cities of the United States the optimum temperature seems to be only about 4° higher than the 64° which appears as the optimum in A108. In Java, where the people live near the equator but at various altitudes, an average temperature of about 70° appears to be the optimum. Even among white people, the optimum may vary several degrees on either side of 64°, by reason of special conditions of wind or some other complicating factor.

A109 is the same as A108 except that the irregularities have been smoothed and the areas between the different isopleths have been shaded. Judging from it and from many other climographs the optimum climate for the physical health of the white race has an average temperature of 60° to 68° and a relative humidity of 70 to 90 per cent, but very little harm is done if these limits are extended to 58° and 72° and to 60 and 100 per cent. This optimum is of the same type as that which we found within the isopleths of 35 bushels for corn, 20 bushels for wheat, 30 days for chinch bugs, 21 eggs for hens, and 12.6 quarts for cows.

The Effect of Variability on Man.—The facts illustrated in the climographs that we have just been studying need to be supplemented by a study of variability. A committee appointed by the National Research Council of the United States has compared the daily deaths in New York City with the interdiurnal changes of temperature, that is, with the change from the average temperature of one day to that of the next. These interdiurnal changes are the kind which our cyclonic storms keep bringing as the weather grows cloudy, rainy, and then fair with the passage of each storm. Within the tropics and in other regions where cyclonic storms are rare such changes are also rare, except as they arise from alternating days of cloud and sun. Wherever they occur, however, they appear to exert a pronounced stimulating effect, especially if they introduce differences of temperature between one day and the next. Turning back to New York, we find that, if the interdiurnal changes of temperature are very great, the deaths become moderately numerous. If the changes are very slight, on the contrary, the deaths become still more numerous. The best condition is found when the interdiurnal changes are moderate but frequent, averaging 3° or 4° in summer and 4° to 6° in winter. At all seasons and temperatures a moderate but not extreme degree of variability is better than very great variability or than monotony. The effect of variability seems to be as great as that of relative humidity, and almost as great as that of mean temperature.

Relation of Climate to Mental Activity.—Mental as well as physical activity enters into the problem of the best climate for man. We have seen that the optimum weather for the hatching of chinch bugs is not the same as for the later stages of their growth. We know also that for children ten or twelve years old the optimum temperature is lower than for their grandparents or for newborn babies. In the same way the optimum temperature for mental activity appears to be lower than for physical activity and health. This is illustrated in A92, where the upper curve shows the daily marks of students at West Point and

Annapolis in relation to the temperature. In those institutions the instructors are in many courses obliged to give each student a mark every day or every other day. On an average, the best marks in both institutions are obtained when the outdoor temperature averages about 40°. A111 illustrates the same thing in another way. The curves labeled *F* and *G* show how the marks at Annapolis go up in the early spring and again in November. Curve *E* shows that the same thing happens at

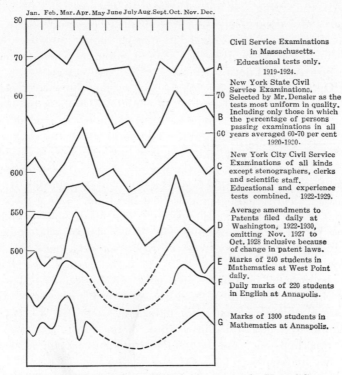

Civil Service Examinations in Massachusetts. Educational tests only. 1919-1924.

New York State Civil Service Examinations. Selected by Mr. Densler as the tests most uniform in quality. Including only those in which the percentage of persons passing examinations in all years averaged 60-70 per cent 1920-1930.

New York City Civil Service Examinations of all kinds except stenographers, clerks and scientific staff. Educational and experience tests combined.   1922-1929.

Average amendments to Patents filed daily at Washington, 1922-1930, omitting Nov. 1927 to Oct. 1928 inclusive because of change in patent laws.

Marks of 240 students in Mathematics at West Point daily.

Daily marks of 220 students in English at Annapolis.

Marks of 1300 students in Mathematics at Annapolis.

A—Seasonal Variations in Mental Activity in the United States.

West Point except that the peaks when the highest marks are obtained are shoved a little farther from the winter. This is what would be expected if the weather has much to do with mental activity, for Annapolis is farther south and warmer than West Point. Curve *D* shows the results obtained by J. Rossman in a study of applications for amendments to patents. When people who have applied for patents get new ideas before their patents have been granted, they are in great haste to apply for changes in the wording and drawings of their original applications. Curves *A*, *B*, and *C* represent the percentage of persons passing civil service examinations in Massachusetts, New York State, and New

York City. Not all examinations can be used in such a study, because
the different kinds vary greatly in difficulty and in the degree of severity
with which they are marked. Nevertheless, when we use the ones that
are most fully standardized and that are least influenced by temporary
exigencies we find in all three cases a strong tendency toward success
in the spring and again in the late autumn. In all these cases there
appears to be some climatic factor which spurs people's minds to special
activity in the spring and fall. Experimental studies and the personal
experiences of a great many people point in the same direction. Since
so many lines of evidence agree, it appears highly probable that for
people who live as we do there is a mental optimum when the outdoor
temperature averages not far from 40°.

The Optimum Climate for Man.—We are now prepared to sum up
our conclusions as to the best kind of climate for human progress and
economic activity. So far as data are yet available, the ideal climate for
people who live as we do appears to be one in which the summers, for
as long a period as possible, approach closely to the most favorable conditions for physical health, and the winters in similar fashion approach
the conditions that are most favorable to mental activity. If such is
the case, the ideal climate averages about 60° to 68° during the summer
and about 36° to 44° during the winter. The spring and autumn must
of course lie between these limits. In such a climate the temperature
of the average summer day may rise to 75° or even higher, but more
often does not rise much above 70°. The nights never have a temperature much above 65°, and more often of 60°, 55° or even 50°. Thus work
and exercise are a pleasure so far as temperature is concerned, and the
nights are always cool enough for refreshing sleep. In winter, on the
other hand, the temperature in the heat of the day ranges from about
45° up to perhaps 55°, and at night it drops low enough so that mild
frosts occur frequently.

Temperatures such as have just been described do not produce an
ideal climate unless the humidity and variability are also favorable.
In the optimum climate the air at all seasons is fairly humid. This does
not mean fog or any kind of visible moisture, but merely the sort of clear
but nevertheless moist air which one enjoys at the seaside when the
wind is blowing gently onshore. If the relative humidity averages about
80 per cent, which seems to be not far from the best figure, it is likely to
fall to about 60 per cent during the warmest part of the day, and at
night to rise toward 100 per cent so that dew is formed.

The Value of Cyclonic Storms.—The third element of an ideal climate is constant but not excessive variation. One type of variation is
that which occurs from day to night. Very little investigation has yet

been made to determine exactly how important this is, but human reactions in this respect are probably not different from those of plants and animals. We have already seen that fluctuations of temperature from day to night are essential to the growth of many if not all plants and of many insects. Moreover, we all know that one of the most important factors in making hot weather tolerable is cool nights. So far as the geographical distribution of good and bad climates is concerned, changes of weather from one day to another seem to be even

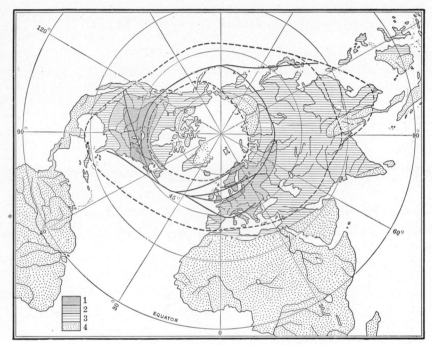

A—World Map of Distribution of Cyclonic Storms.
1. Many.   2. Fair Number.   3. Few.   4. Practically None.

more important than the contrasts between day and night. This is because such changes, as we have already said, arise largely from cyclonic storms or cyclones of the kind which commonly bring rain to most parts of the United States (see page 41). These are very unevenly distributed over the earth's surface, being very abundant in the United States, abundant in northwestern Europe and fairly abundant even in northern Italy and Austria, but diminishing in number eastward (A113). In Asia they are scarce except in Japan. In all the rest of the world they are almost unknown except for a belt in the far southern ocean. The storms also vary in position and intensity from summer to winter, as appears in A114 and A115. In June, when the sun is highest, but not when the temperature is highest, the storms are least frequent and on an average follow the most northerly courses. In December, when the sun is lowest, but before the temperature is lowest, they are most numerous and swing farthest south. At all seasons these low-pressure areas a thousand miles or so in diameter sweep across the United States in curved paths from west to east. They are likely to be heralded by a rise of temperature, and bring variable winds, moist air, clouds, rain, and changes of temperature, at all seasons. One reason for their value is that their inward-blowing winds (A42 and A43) bring

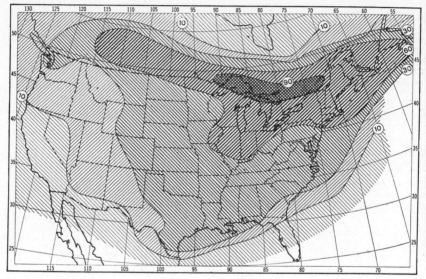

A—Frequency of Cyclonic Storm Centers in December from 1883 to 1912, after
C. J. Kullmer.

moisture from all directions from distances as great as one or two thousand miles. Another is that, since the winds blow in different directions during the passage of a cyclone, variations of temperature are bound to occur. Winds from the north, or from the interior, usually present strong contrasts to those from the south or from the sea.

In most parts of the United States the anticyclones, or areas of high pressure which move forward between the cyclones, signal their approach by westerly winds, a drop of temperature, and a clearing of the air. That is how our cold waves arrive in winter. In western Europe, on the contrary, because the westerly winds blow from the sea, this transition phase between a cyclone and an anticyclone is likely to be rainy.

Cold waves of the winter in western and central Europe come when easterly or northeasterly winds blow outward from the high-pressure anticyclone of the far interior, bringing the low temperature of that region. In both continents, however, the establishment of anticyclonic conditions of high atmospheric pressure generally brings a few days of sunny weather during which the air is likely to grow colder in winter and warmer in summer. Thus the frequent passage of cyclones and anticyclones introduces constant variations not only in temperature but also in atmospheric moisture, cloudiness, rainfall, and sunshine. In this way both agriculture and human health are greatly benefited.

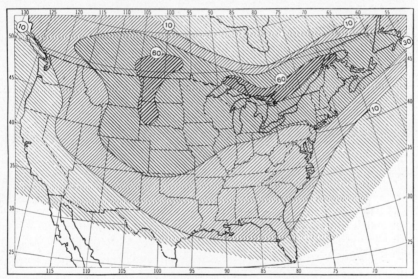

A—Frequency of Cyclonic Storm Centers in June from 1883 to 1912, after C. J. Kullmer.

Moist air and rain are provided at all seasons even though the prevailing or most common winds may blow from the land; stimulating changes in temperature and in other climatic elements are also constantly introduced. Thus cyclonic storms rank with the zonal distribution of temperature and the distribution of land and sea as a factor in determining the degree to which a climate approaches the ideal for human health and activity. These three factors combine to produce the vast diversity which arises from the geographical distribution of all sorts of climates. The optimum, at least for people of our race and culture, is a marine, cyclonic climate in middle latitudes.

A Standard Climograph as a Measuring Rod of Climate.—We are now in a position to construct a standard climograph (A116) based on plants, animals, and man. By means of this we shall be readily able to test the qualities of all sorts of climates. In A116 the upper heavily shaded oval shows the climatic conditions under which man enjoys the best physical health, provided there are sufficient atmospheric humidity and variability. It therefore represents the conditions which man needs during the summer in order to insure his best physical development. If such conditions prevail during the entire year, however, it is impossible for people to receive the tremendous stimulus to thrift and activity which comes from the necessity of providing for a cool season. Moreover, the degree of change of temperature is bound to be slight so long

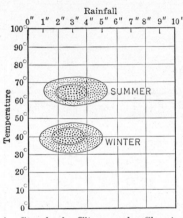

A—Standard Climograph Showing Kind of Climate Best for All Purposes.

as the storm tracks follow their present paths. Under such conditions no season provides so great a mental stimulus as is desirable. When winter conditions such as those represented in the lower heavy oval in A116 are added to the summer conditions of the upper oval, the climate also provides the maximum mental stimulus, provided there are enough cyclonic storms. Thus the highest human development may be expected where the warmer months lie within the upper heavy oval and the winter months within the lower heavy oval. The lightly shaded areas outside the heavily shaded ovals represent conditions which are moderately favorable for man and highly favorable for one or another of the most valuable non-tropical crops such as corn, cotton, and oranges, the optima of which are found at higher temperatures than those of man. If the most extreme months lie within the lightly shaded areas, the effect on man is still good, and the effect on certain kinds of crops is admirable. By placing a local climograph of a given place upon this ideal, or standard climograph, we can estimate the character of the climate at a glance.

EXERCISES

1. What evidence can you cite from your own observation and experience as to the optimum temperature for human beings?

2. What similar evidence can you cite as the optimum for plants? for animals?

3. You have been offered a position in a foreign land, which promises to be more or less permanent. What phases of climate and related condition would you investigate before making a decision to accept?

4. A certain city on the west coast of tropical South America includes a considerable number of North American, English, and other foreign families. The city is not excessively hot, but the women, though they do not suffer from the temperature, are not vigorous. The men, many of whom are called to

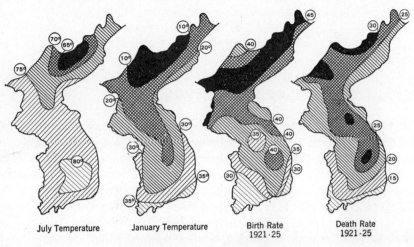

| July Temperature | January Temperature | Birth Rate 1921-25 | Death Rate 1921-25 |

A—Four Maps of Chosen (Korea).

various parts of the country in relation to their business, seem to have plenty of energy. How do you account for the difference?

5. Do any two of the four maps of Chosen (A–D117) resemble one another enough so that they suggest a causal relation? If so, look up the relief of Chosen, and then find maps or other illustrations in this book or in your atlas which help to explain the resemblance. Discuss the probable economic effects as well as the causes of this peculiar distribution of health.

CHAPTER VII

CLIMATE, HEALTH, AND THE DISTRIBUTION
OF HUMAN PROGRESS

A Map of Climatic Energy.—A comparison of many kinds of maps shows that climate is directly or indirectly the main determinant of the geographical distribution of economic activity and civilization. This happens partly through its effect on crops and animals, but primarily through its effect on man's health, energy, and mental alertness. The chief evidence of this is that maps of what we may call climatic energy are practically identical with maps of health, crop yields, transportation, income, wages, education, and a host of other economic and social conditions. Maps of relief, soils, mineral resources, and bodies of water show no such similarity to either health or economic and social conditions. Locally, to be sure, they show striking relationships to these other factors, but not when all parts of the world are taken into account. Maps of rainfall, mean temperature, and even storminess, when taken by themselves, also fail to show any such close similarity to those of health and of economic and social conditions. Only when these three elements of climate are combined so as to show their joint effect do we find the similarity which this chapter will make evident. Maps of race, religion, inventiveness, and various other social conditions do indeed display considerable similarity to the maps of health, transportation, education, and so forth, but the similarity is not so great as is displayed by the maps of climatic energy. Moreover, these *human* conditions cannot by any possibility be the cause of the peculiar distribution of the *physical* conditions whose distribution is shown by the maps of climatic energy. Yet the resemblance between the climatic and human maps is so close and far-reaching that it can scarcely be accidental. Therefore the only logical conclusion is that the main geographical pattern is set by climate. The other factors mentioned in this paragraph either owe their geographical distribution largely to the past and present effect of climate, as in the case of crops and racial character, or else are modifiers which alter but do not conceal the climatic pattern, as in the case of soil and minerals.

A119 is a world map of climatic energy. It shows the combined physical and mental activity which might be expected if people's activity depended on climate alone, and if the response of their bodies and minds to temperature, humidity, and storminess were the same as that of the people discussed in the last chapter. In making the map it is assumed that vigor of body and mind are equally essential, and that people have the power to protect themselves from cold and exposure. From the data described in the last chapter we know what proportion of people die, how fast the average factory hand works, and how well the mind usually functions under various combinations of temperature,

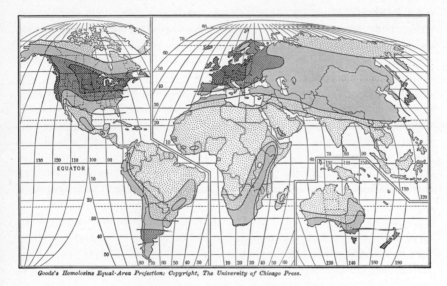

Goode's Homolosine Equal-Area Projection: Copyright, The University of Chicago Press.

A—The Distribution of Climatic Energy.

humidity, and storminess. We know this, to be sure, only for certain groups of people, mainly in the United States and Europe, but even if we make allowance for a slightly higher optimum temperature in warm countries this does not alter our map essentially. Our method, then, is simply to take the monthly averages for the weather all over the world, and from them calculate how energetic and alert people would be if their activity depended solely on climate.

In the darkest areas of A119 we should expect very great activity because the climate is especially favorable both to physical and mental well-being. In the next type of shading the degree of energy to be expected is high, although not equal to that of the darkest areas. Then come types of shading indicating medium and low energy, while the lightest shading indicates very low energy.

Two large dark areas stand out conspicuously in A119, one centering around the North Sea in western Europe, and one about halfway from north to south in North America. Two minor dark areas occur on the Pacific coast of North America and in Tasmania and New Zealand. The next type of shading, indicating good climates, is found around the darkest types and in South America, Australia, and Japan. The South American data are imperfect, and the good area ought perhaps to be located somewhat differently. No area, even of the darkest shading, has an absolutely ideal climate. Where the temperature is close to the ideal, as on the shores of the North Sea or on the Pacific Coast near Puget Sound, the degree of variability is not quite great enough. Where cyclonic storms occur with sufficient frequency and vigor, as in the northeastern quarter of the United States, the extremes of both heat and cold are too great. Nevertheless, northwestern and central Europe, the northern United States with an adjacent strip of Canada, the Pacific Coast of the United States, and New Zealand with the southeastern part of Australia stand out as the parts of the world where the climate is most nearly perfect for the health and activity of people in the present stage of civilization. Japan, central Argentina, part of Chile, and a tiny bit of the southern tip of Cape Colony in South Africa also stand fairly high. Japan is too hot and humid in summer, but it is the only part of Asia with many cyclonic storms, and that helps a great deal. The parts of Argentina, Chile, and Cape Colony having the best temperatures and rainfall do not have enough variability because they lie in latitudes lower than those where cyclonic storms are frequent. Moreover, both Chile and Cape Colony suffer from dry, monotonous summers. Only in winter do they have even the edges of cyclonic storms, but both are benefited by nearness to great oceans from which come healthful winds.

The parts of the world with unfavorable climates are far larger than those with good climates. All regions that are steadily warm throughout the year and all that have long periods of extreme cold stand low in A119. This is partly because cyclonic storms are unknown or rare in such regions, especially in the warm parts. Moreover, even when the occasional cyclonic storms known as hurricanes come to warm regions they do not bring much change of temperature. In the cold northern regions of Asia and North America, on the contrary, the few cyclonic storms often bring changes of temperature so severe that they do much harm. Perhaps the most surprising feature of A119 is the way in which the climate deteriorates as one goes inland from the North

Sea across Europe to Siberia and Central Asia. In North America a similar deterioration is hinted at, but it is mild compared with Asia. The trouble in Asia is that the size of the Eurasian continent causes the far interior to have an extremely continental climate, thus producing three handicaps, namely, great extremes of temperature, long and severe periods of dryness, and a scarcity of cyclonic storms. The high atmospheric pressure which prevails over Eurasia in winter almost prevents cyclonic storms from sweeping across the continent and thus bringing the benefits which they give to Nebraska or Alberta. Even when storms do penetrate to the far interior, especially in the spring and fall, they are likely to be of the blizzard type with terrible winds and bitter cold. In summer the conditions are much better. Even then, however, the low atmospheric pressure which characterizes the continent keeps the storms out of Asia. Cyclonic storms are themselves areas of low pressure, but they tend to skirt the main continental or oceanic areas of permanent low pressure rather than to pass through their midst. In this respect they resemble thunder storms, which are small areas of low pressure that often skirt the borders of the cyclonic storms themselves.

A Comparison of the World-wide Distribution of Climate and Health. —The geographical distribution of health, as indicated by the death rate, is almost the same as that of climatic energy. For all the areas that have the two darker shades in the map of climatic energy (A119) we have fairly exact data as to deaths. Thus we are able to prepare B123 for Europe and B122 for the United States. These are remarkably like A123 and A122 showing climatic energy. For the rest of the world the data are not yet sufficient to enable us to draw a reliable map of mortality. Nevertheless, we have data from several Caribbean countries, the Philippines, the Dutch East Indies, and other countries like India, Egypt, and Palestine that are under the control of more northern countries. These show that lowland tropical regions and hot deserts generally have death rates more than twice as high as those of the regions that are climatically most favored. In tropical highlands, however, and in places like Hawaii that are fully under oceanic influence, the death rate falls much lower. The mortality rates that are usually published are often misleading because they take no account of the fact that some countries have enormously high birth rates, and therefore their population contains a great many infants among whom the death rate is very high, whereas other regions that are no more healthful have a high percentage of people in the prime of life, so that their death rates appear low. Bearing these conditions in mind, we find that so far as data are yet available a map of death rates in the world as a whole would be almost identical with the map of climatic energy (A119). We may generalize this by saying that all areas of high climatic energy

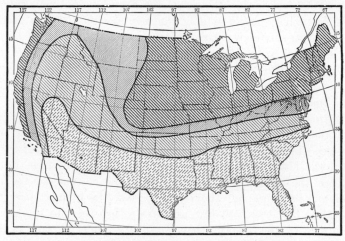

A—Climatic Energy in the United States.

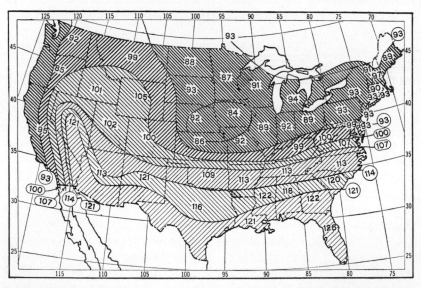

B—Distribution of Health in the United States According to Life Insurance Statistics at Different Periods from 1900 to 1930. 100 indicates the number of deaths expected according to the ordinary mortality tables on which the insurance rates are based.

have low death rates unless some special circumstance like industrialism or urbanization introduces a disturbing factor. It is doubtless this

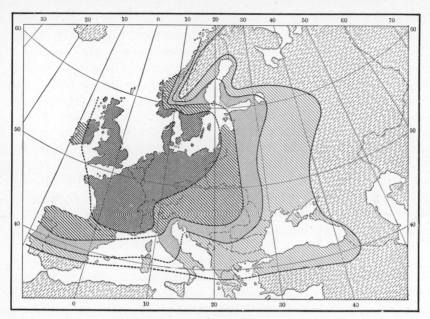

A—Climatic Energy in Europe.

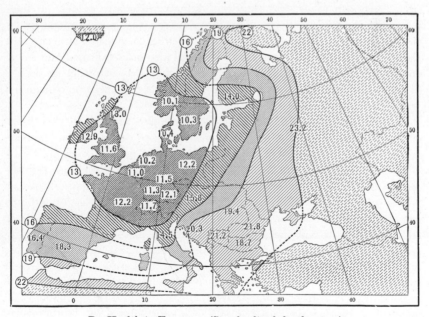

B—Health in Europe.   (Standardized death rates.)

factor which gives the northeastern states in B122 a slightly higher death rate than the agricultural region centering in Iowa and Nebraska. Denmark, New Zealand, Holland, and western Oregon and Washington are among the other especially healthful parts of the world. On the other hand, all regions of low climatic energy have high death rates unless some disturbing factor like the recent immigration of especially vigorous people causes improvement, as in northern Australia. Among the countries in good but intermediate positions climatically, Argentina and Uruguay rank well in health. The sparsity of population, the comparative prosperity, and the fact that there is little manufacturing all help in this respect. Japan does not stand nearly so well, although it is ahead of its neighbors on the mainland and farther south. The extreme density of population and the great poverty of the masses of the people keep the death rate comparatively high. This is doubtless still more true of China, although no statistics are available.

Direct Relation of Climate to Tropical Inefficiency.—No one questions the connection between climate and efficiency. The only question is how far does this efficiency depend upon climate directly and how far indirectly through race, diet, parasitic diseases, hygiene, sanitation, and social and political customs. We shall omit race except to say that there is a widespread belief that tropical races are inherently different from European races, and that this difference is more evident in temperament than in intellect. This may be true, but purely racial qualities are so easily confused with qualities due to climate and customs that there is as yet no certainty. We shall also omit political and social conditions because they show the same general distribution as do the other factors that will be discussed. Moreover, they will be considered when we study the separate climatic regions.

If the inefficiency of tropical people is due mainly to the direct effects of climate, the main remedy may perhaps be to control the temperature and humidity of houses and to move people often from one climate to another. Cool houses would insure comfortable and refreshing sleep, and would provide stimulating changes of temperature as people go in and out. Frequent movements from lowlands to highlands would accomplish the same purpose. On the other hand, if the indirect effects of climate are the most important, the best line of attack presumably lies in improving people's diet, eradicating specific diseases, and introducing good sanitation and hygiene. As a matter of fact, both sides of the picture seem to be true, and it is hard to say which is more important. The case is like that of crops or domestic animals. The yield of a crop is certainly influenced enormously by temperature, atmospheric humidity, and rainfall. Yet the yield is also influenced enormously by soil, insect pests, parasitic diseases, and the skill and thoroughness with which cultivation is conducted.

Confining ourselves for the present to the direct effects of climate, we saw in the last chapter that repeated measurements of the work done at different times by people in good health show strong variations according to the weather. Experiments such as those of the New York State Ventilation Commission also show that, even when people's ability to work remains unimpaired, their *desire* to work falls off greatly when they are hot. Numerous experiments such as those of E. S. Sund-

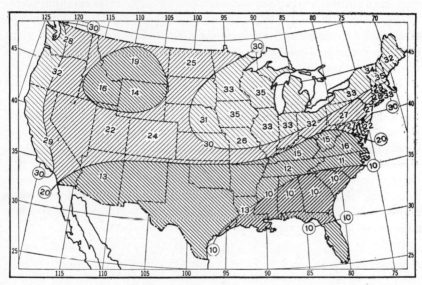

A—Annual Deaths per 100,000 People in the United States from Certain Glandular Diseases. (Diabetes, Pernicious Anemia, Exophthalmic Goiter, and Addison's Disease.)   Data from C. A. Mills.

stroem indicate that among healthy people living permanently in the tropics the composition of the blood and the general functioning of the physiological system differ slightly but systematically from those of people in cooler climates. In general, the processes of metabolism whereby food is changed into heat and other forms of energy are not so active among tropical people as in more stimulating climates.

Still further evidence as to the direct effect of climate is found in the work of C. A. Mills. He has shown that the deaths from diabetes, ophthalmic goitre, certain forms of heart disease, and other degenerative ailments have a geographical distribution the reverse of that of the majority of diseases. Where A125, showing the death rate from these diseases, is dark, B122, showing the deaths from all causes, is light. These diseases arise largely from over-exertion of the organs which they affect. What seems to happen is that in an extremely stimulating climate like that of the northeastern quarter of the United States the body is so stimulated that people not only work hard but also have a high resistance to the great majority of diseases. This stimulation, however, may overtax organs like the heart, kidneys, and glands that are concerned with metabolism. Thus these parts of the body are overworked and break down. From a great body of evidence like this it seems clear that in tropical countries the vital activities of the body are diminished. For white people, as A. Balfour points out, this almost certainly means that their susceptibility to disease increases, while their power to work declines. Tropical natives are probably less susceptible to tropical disease than are white men, but they seem to become tired more quickly than do people who live in more stimulating climates. Thus their actual power of achievement is presumably diminished by the direct effect of the climate. Their desire to work is diminished vastly more. Their power of mental concentration also appears to be diminished in the same way. Some individuals, to be sure, may not feel this, but we are talking about the average. No matter what races we deal with, we can scarcely expect the same degree of activity and progress among tropical people as among people in more favorable climates. This same reasoning applies with diminished force to other relatively unfavorable climates such as are found in China, Central Asia, and the far north.

Diet as a Cause of Tropical Inefficiency.—The direct effects of unfavorable climates are greatly increased by indirect effects such as diet. Although the most progressive people bring food from long distances, the food of the vast majority of mankind depends almost entirely on local supplies. This means, of course, that it depends upon the crops and animals that thrive best in each climate. In a general way, the more stimulating the climate, the more favorable is its type of diet. Thus in tropical countries the natives live largely on bananas, yams, millet, cassava, peanuts, rice, and sometimes corn. Contrary to what is often supposed, the amount of fruit consumed by an ordinary tropical native, aside from bananas, is usually small. Fresh vegetables are almost unknown, and meat is very scarce. Thus the diet is far too starchy and bulky, and is deficient not only in proteins but also in vitamins. In a word, the ordinary tropical native is generally badly nourished throughout his whole life. This is both a cause and a result of inefficiency. If the natives were more alert and active they would provide themselves with a better diet. Perhaps they will do this some day, but they are always likely to be handicapped by the fact that their inefficiency keeps them poor, their poverty makes it difficult to bring the better kinds of food from a distance, and their climate prevents dairy cattle, hens, and a large number of the best vegetables from thriving.

In other unstimulating climates we also find relatively poor kinds of diet. In northern China, wheat, barley, or some kind of millet, together with both green and dry beans and some sweet potatoes, form the main diet most of the time. Other fresh vegetables and fruits, according to Buck, occupy only one half of one per cent of the land. Meat is used only occasionally. In the deserts, the Arabs and others rely far too largely on milk and dates, or else on millet and dates in the oases. In our own southern states, pork and corn meal, "hog and hominy," form much too large a proportion of the diet among great numbers of farmers, especially the Negroes. In countries with the Mediterranean Type of climate the variety of foods is greater than in the other types thus far mentioned, for wheat, olive oil, grapes, and other fruits, as well as milk and meat, are abundant. Nevertheless, an astonishing number of people in Spain, Italy, Greece, Turkey, and similar countries live much of the year on wheat bread with one other dish, which may be olive oil, sour milk, wine, or grapes, according to the country and season. All these kinds of diet are so limited that they are far from ideal. Only in the cyclonic areas where the climate is most

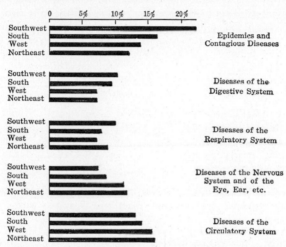

A—Percentage of Deaths Due to Certain Types of Diseases in Different Parts of the United States.

energizing do we find the rank and file of the people using a really wide variety of foods, including not only wheat, corn, milk, eggs, and meat, but a profusion of fruits, green vegetables, and root crops like potatoes.

Disease and Hygiene in Unfavorable versus Favorable Climates.—The great majority of diseases display a strong geographic variation in frequency and virulence. Diseases of the respiratory organs, aside from tuberculosis, are much more frequent in winter than in summer, and in dry months than in moist. Diseases of the digestive organs show the opposite condition, being prevalent chiefly in summer. The geographical distribution of these diseases accords with the seasonal distribution (A127). In the dry and warm Southwest, epidemic and contagious diseases, among which tuberculosis is the most important, account for a larger percentage of the deaths than in the cooler Pacific Coast and Northeast. Diseases of the digestive organs shown a similar distribution, and so do those of the respiratory system, except that the far northern states are almost as bad as the Southwest. On the other hand, diseases of the nervous and circulatory systems vary in the opposite way, their percentages being lowest in the less stimulating dry and warm climates and highest in the stimulating climates where the general death rate is lowest. This agrees with what we have just seen as to the high percentage of deaths from heart diseases, kidney troubles, and many kinds of degenerative diseases in the more stimulating climates even though the death rates there are low. On the other hand, in tropical and oriental countries, the death rates from the epidemic and contagious diseases and from those of the digestive organs often rise to very high levels. Moreover, such countries suffer terribly from diseases like malaria, the more malignant types of dysentery, filariasis, hookworm disease, yaws, and various others which are almost unknown in the better climates.

Insurance statistics agree with A127 in showing that, in spite of the common opinion to the contrary, respiratory diseases which afflict the nose, lungs, and throat are especially characteristic of dry climates. This includes tuberculosis, even though physicians often send sufferers to dry climates. In such regions the insurance companies take special pains not to insure anyone who shows the least sign of tubercular susceptibility. Yet in spite of this dry regions have an especially high death rate from this disease. The outdoor life there is undoubtedly a great blessing, but the harm done by dust is probably far greater than is commonly realized. This is illustrated by the following figures showing the relative number of deaths from tuberculosis per hundred thousand among special classes of adult Englishmen:

Farmers..................................... 57
All Englishmen.............................. 100
Granite workers............................ 127
Limestone workers.......................... 129
Slate quarry workers....................... 220
Sandstone workers.......................... 415

The dust which quarrymen breathe seems to explain why they have so many more deaths than the farmers. This seems to illustrate the reason why dry regions and deserts have especially high death rates. Cairo in Egypt has one of the highest death rates in the whole world. Madrid in Spain, Johannesburg in South Africa, Allahabad in India, and Mexico City also have peculiarly high death rates. Chile, Spain, and Palestine are countries where the death rates are exceptionally high in proportion to the temperature. All of these have long dry seasons so that the air is repeatedly filled with dust during many months of the year. In places like Cairo, the dust often consists of particles of quartz from the desert. This is the kind of dust which gives the workers in sandstone quarries an especially high deathrate.

The harm done to human health and efficiency by malaria, dysentery, filariasis, hookworm disease, yaws, and the constant sores resulting from insect bites and minor infections can scarcely be exaggerated. Malaria is especially potent in reducing man's economic value and also his own comfort and happiness not only in tropical regions but in many others likewise. It prevails only where conditions favor mosquitoes of the genus *Anopheles* and certain bacteria which they carry. The most dangerous mosquitoes and bacteria are confined to low latitudes. Mild forms live in Mediterranean and other subtropical countries, and practically none farther north. Only a few species of *Anopheles* can live in running water. In tropical climates, vast numbers breed in stagnant pools and in the damp hollows among the trees or grass. In middle latitudes, malaria is especially abundant in regions with the subtropical type of climate where the rain falls chiefly in winter and the summer is dry. In such a climate, after the dry season, stagnant pools usually abound along the water courses, and many other pools result from irrigation.

The harm done by malaria becomes especially clear when we examine the results of the elimination of the disease. In many tropical regions the conditions are like those at Baoe-Baoe in the island of Celebes. Until 1922, when sanitary reforms were instituted, practically every European there was frequently incapacitated by malaria. In the Dutch military encampment the brigades were often "only able to march by combining two brigades into one." Out of an average of 350 people in the civil infirmary and the prison, 20 died each month. The draining of swamps and the building of proper sewers, gutters, privies, and the like promptly reduced the amount of malaria to one-fourth of its former level. Previous to this work, all the native children who were examined had enlarged spleens, and practically all the adults were anemic and inefficient as the result of repeated malarial infections, especially in childhood. Afterward, only 13 per cent of the children had enlarged spleens, and even the older people worked with new cheerfulness and vigor. Sibolga in Sumatra was made practically free from malaria by keeping cattle between the mosquito-infested area and the city, the cattle attracting the mosquitoes. Panama is a widely known example of tropical sanitary improvement. Sanitary work there has reduced the death rate by one-half in the cities of Panama and Colón. It has made it possible for white people to live in the carefully protected Canal Zone with little fear of the ordinary tropical diseases. But the effect of such work must not be exaggerated. The death rate in the two cities at the ends of the Panama Canal is still twice as high as that of the North Sea countries and the northern United States. Americans still find the climate there both enervating and trying. Large numbers of them are still invalided home every year.

Non-tropical countries which have long dry seasons and much warm weather also suffer terribly from malaria. This is true no matter whether the rain comes in winter, as in Spain, Italy, Greece, and Turkey, or in summer, as in China, southern Brazil, and northern Argentina. Up to almost the end of the last century, from a quarter to a half, or even three-fourths, of the inhabitants in many parts of these countries were infected with the disease or at least had it during childhood. Malaria is preeminently a disease which saps people's energy for a long time. It keeps recurring at intervals of months or years, even without a new infection. It has a special tendency to cause people to be mentally as well as physically inert. In tropical countries it is still worse, for there it often takes more virulent forms and is fatal in a short time. In the present century great progress has been made in eliminating malaria from the chief tropical seaports and in the areas where Europeans and Americans carry on plantations. Nevertheless, by far the greater portions of both tropical and oriental countries still suffer terribly. Theodore Roosevelt and the Prince of Wales are examples of white men who have suffered from malaria as the result of brief sojourns in tropical countries.

Another disease of a similar baneful character is caused by the hookworm. This also is confined largely to fairly warm countries. The worm lives in the mud, and enters the body by attaching itself to the skin and boring its way into the blood vessels. Naturally it has a chance to touch the human skin chiefly in places where people go barefooted. The extent to which such diseases reduce human productivity is astonishing. In Egypt, more than half the laboring population is infected with hookworm, in the Malay states 60 per cent, in British Honduras 70 per cent, in Sumatra and Java 90 per cent in some regions, and so on for almost all tropical countries (A130).

The Rockefeller Sanitary Commission estimates that well over half of the world's two billion people live in areas where hookworm disease is prevalent. Half the people within the tropics probably suffer from the disease at all times, and many others have it at some time during their lives. It stunts the growth of children, retards their mental development, and makes adults anemic and incompetent. Many people believe that it is the chief cause of the relative backwardness and lack of economic development among the mountain whites of our southern Appalachians. The improvement that follows its eradication is almost incredible. In Costa Rica, 66 laborers before being treated for hookworm normally cultivated 563 acres of coffee monthly. After treatment they cultivated 750 acres. In India the amount of work increased 20 per cent on one estate and 50 per cent on another, and on both was of better quality than before the laborers were treated; reports from British Guiana indicate that the efficiency of the laborers employed by one company increased

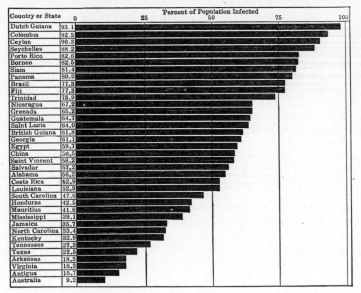

A—Distribution of Hookworm Infection.

from 25 to 50 per cent after measures to eradicate the hookworm were put into operation.

But note that all this occurs only when energetic people from the cyclonic types of climate go to the poorer climates. The efforts to overcome disease relax as soon as the influence of these people is removed. Taking the tropical and other unfavorable climates as a whole, the improvement in health during the last two generations has been far less than in the cyclonic climates. There is reason to think that not for many generations, if ever, will the health and energy of tropical regions equal those of the better parts of the world. As things now stand, it is far harder to combat disease in poor climates than in good, and the vigor for doing this is also less. Thus disease merely joins with diet in emphasizing the contrasts in human efficiency arising from climate. Social and political conditions act in the same way. They suffer from exactly the same inertia as do the efforts at better hygiene. This is illustrated in what follows as to education.

The Distribution of Agricultural Income.—In order to get further light on the relative geographic distribution of climate and other conditions let us make a more detailed study of the United States and Europe. These two regions are chosen because they are the only large and diverse areas for which really good statistics are available. The United States is particularly good because its people, government, and social system, as well as its statistics, are comparatively uniform in all parts. The great drawback for our present purpose is that it has been settled so recently that the density of population, the size and productivity of farms, the methods of running schools, and many other economic and social conditions have not yet become fully adapted to the environment. In Europe, on the other hand, there is more diversity of race, government, and customs, but there has been relatively little recent immigration and the people are well adjusted to their environment. Such conditions, together with good statistics and strong contrasts in climatic energy, make Europe the best of all regions for our comparisons.

A132 and B132 show the average income per man on the farm in the United States and Europe. This is easily ascertained in the United States because the census gives tables showing the total values of all crops and animal products sold from normal farms or consumed by the people on such farms. When the cost of feed and fertilizer is deducted from the totals of this kind, we have the real farm income for each state. Dividing this by the number of men who work on the farms, including owners, tenants, managers, and laborers, we obtain approximately the average annual income per man on the farm. It might also be desirable to deduct what is spent for tools. In the United States as a whole in 1929 this amounted to 8.6 per cent of the total farm income, provided automobiles and tractors are included. Such expenses are heaviest in the North and especially the West, and are slight in the South.

For Europe a somewhat different method must be employed. Official records for practically all European countries and for some in other continents give the total production, or at least the acreage, of every crop of any importance. The United States census gives the average value of each crop per pound, ton, bushel, or acre, as the case may be. Hence it is possible to calculate the total value which all the crops in other countries would have if prices were everywhere the same as in the United States. Of course we must leave out the value of the crops fed to animals, since they either are mere fuel for work animals, or produce an income only by adding to the value of the animal products. In order to get the value of the animal products we omit the horses, mules, asses, and oxen, since these animals provide little income except through the

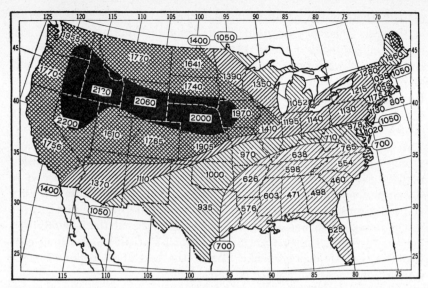

A—Annual Farm Income per Mán on the Farm in the United States Expressed in Dollars, 1929.

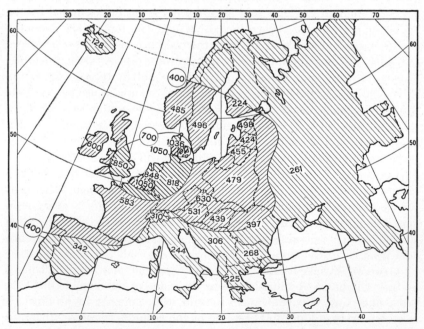

B—Estimated Annual Farm Income per Man on the Farm in Europe Expressed in Dollars, 1929.

crops. Oxen, by the way, are still used in great numbers in many parts of Europe. Then we ascertain the value of the milk, meat, wool, and eggs produced in the United States in a single year. From this we calculate the average value produced by a single cow, hen, sheep, or hog. Applying these values to Europe, with some but not enough allowance for differences in the quality of the cattle in different countries, we obtain an estimate of the average value of the animal products per man on the farm and add this to the value of crops. Thus we get B132. This can be directly compared with A132 for the United States, and also with the other maps of Europe, but the incomes here shown in the poorer parts of Europe are systematically too high, because it is impossible to make proper allowance for the relatively poor quality of many crops and animals in the south and east.

The significant fact about the whole matter is that in Europe the map of agricultural income, like that of health, agrees almost exactly with the map of climatic energy (A123). In the United States there is a similar agreement which is modified considerably by non-climatic factors. The relatively low position of the Southeast, for example, is accentuated by the presence of colored people. In southern New England the farm incomes are reduced by the fact that many people who live on farms earn part of their living by working in the towns. On the other hand, in the West the incomes are large because of the fine soil in certain areas and also because the whole region from Texas and Minnesota westward is so new that it is not densely populated, the farms are large, and machinery is used on a large scale. Moreover, the people there have the kind of energy which is characteristic of pioneers. In Europe the figures for Switzerland, Finland, and to a less extent Germany, Sweden and Norway do not represent the full productivity of the farmers. This is because the income from crops and animals is considerably supplemented by toymaking, woodcarving, and work in the factory towns during the winter in Germany and Switzerland, by lumbering in Sweden and especially in Finland, and by lumbering and especially fishing in Norway. In view of the abundance of such complicating factors, however, the most surprising fact about A132 and B132 is that they agree so closely with the corresponding maps of climatic energy, health, and education.

General Prosperity and Mobility.—The next maps to engage our attention illustrate both the prosperity and the mobility of people in different regions. A134 shows the number of persons per motor vehicle in the world as a whole. Its general resemblance to the map of climatic energy and education is evident. The great prosperity of the United States, however, causes the heaviest shading to spread over the whole country. Two noteworthy facts in this respect are that in the United States, Canada, and Australia, which alone have less than 10 persons per motor vehicle, the passenger car is overwhelmingly predominant, and farmers and other people who live outside the large cities have a larger ratio of cars of all kinds than do the city people. Thus, Nebraska has 9 passenger cars for every truck or bus. New York City has only one motor vehicle for every 9.2 people, but the rest of the state has one for every 3.7. In Europe, on the other hand, the percentage of trucks and buses is much higher than here. Italy, for instance, has only $2\frac{1}{2}$ passenger cars for every truck or bus. Motor cycles, too, are very

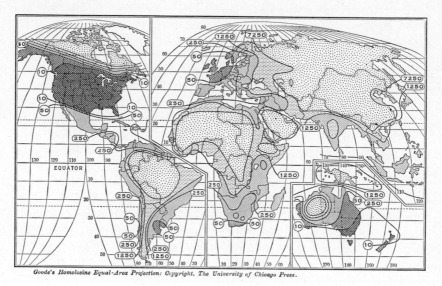

Goode's Homolosine Equal-Area Projection: Copyright, The University of Chicago Press.

A—Persons per Automobile.

numerous in Europe. Germany has only one other motor vehicle for each motor cycle, whereas, the United States has about 250. Europe cannot afford to own private cars. Moreover, the motor vehicles of all kinds are owned almost exclusively in the towns and cities. In more backward regions, like Peru, private passenger cars become so scarce that outside of the big cities there is often only one for every 10 trucks and buses. The percentage of passenger cars among all the motor vehicles is a good measure of the degree of prosperity.

The map of persons per motor vehicle in the United States (A135) reflects the features of the climatic map (A122), but also shows the effect of relief, of cities, and of migration. The relative scarcity of cars in New York City, Philadelphia, and Pittsburgh raises the number of persons per car much higher in the states of New York and Pennsylvania than in Ohio or even Connecticut. The Appalachian Mountains, along most of their length, constitute an area of relatively few cars. The presence of colored people lowers the number of cars in the Southeast, thus raising the number of people per car three or four times as high as in California. Recent migration, however, makes the figure for Florida as high as for Illinois, and human energy, natural resources, and big farms make the North Central and Pacific States rank very high.

Distribution of Education.—The way in which the direct and indirect effects of climate combine to cause civilization to have a distribu-

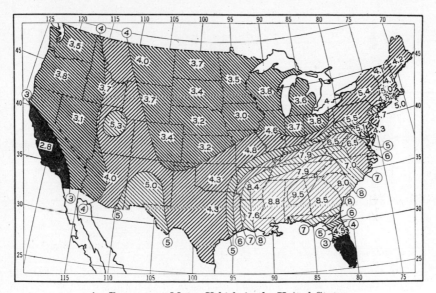

A—Persons per Motor Vehicle in the United States.

tion like that of climatic energy is well illustrated in A136. This shows the extent to which the children and young people are studying in schools, colleges, and other educational institutions. Its isopleths are based on a comprehensive study of all available statistics of education. In only a few places like China and Arabia has it been necessary to resort to estimates. The figures on which the isopleths are based represent the total number of students of all ages in both public and private educational institutions in each country, province, or state. In order that the various regions may be easily compared, the number of students is expressed as a percentage of the total number of children aged five to fourteen years. Such percentages, which might better be called index numbers, give no exact information as to the quality of the education in the different parts of the world. We know, however, that as a general rule the schools are well run, the teachers well trained, the pupils regular in attendance, and the seasons of instruction fairly long and regular in the regions where a large percentage of the children and young people are in school.

The United States is far in the lead with index numbers above 100 everywhere except along the Gulf of Mexico. A conspicuous strip with numbers above 120 runs directly across the northern United States and includes the part of the Canadian province of Ontario which forms

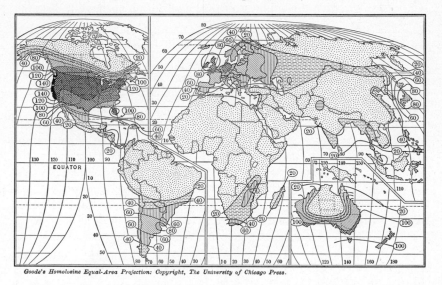

Goode's Homolosine Equal-Area Projection: Copyright, The University of Chicago Press.

A—Education. Persons of all ages in ordinary educational institutions per hundred children, aged 5–14 years. The data for Russia are unreliable because of rapid changes and methods of classification quite different from those elsewhere. The data for China, Persia, Arabia, etc., are merely estimates.

the most southern portion of Canada. On the west coast this strip expands just as does the favorable climatic area in A122. The only other parts of the world where a level of 100 or even 90 is reached are the countries east and west of the North Sea, Switzerland, and the southern and eastern parts of Australia, together with New Zealand. Aside from a few little islands run by England or the United States the only other regions where the percentages approach 80 are the three Scandinavian countries, Japan, and central Argentina. Part of Russia may belong in this group, but Russian educational statistics are based on such different methods from those of other countries that it is very difficult to interpret them. With the possible exception of parts of

Russia, the regions with the two heavier types of shading in the map of climatic energy (A119) are the only ones where the great majority of the children go to school. Where the climate deteriorates, as in Central Asia, the Australian desert, the Amazon basin, much of Africa, and the tropical regions elsewhere, education is sadly neglected.

The effect of non-climatic as well as climatic factors can be seen in A136. The wealth of the United States, arising from its great resources and relatively sparse population, has much to do with the country's high rank in respect to the number of children in school. The recent migration of competent, well-to-do people from other regions largely explains why California, Texas, and Florida stand high compared with their neighbors. The presence of American or British administrators explains why Hawaii, the Philippines, the Bahamas, and Trinidad also rank far above what would otherwise be expected. Nevertheless the general aspect of the educational map agrees in a remarkable way with that of the map of climatic energy.

Distribution of Professional People and General Culture.—Another way of testing the progress of a country is by means of the percentage of its men engaged in the liberal professions. A138 and B138 show that in both the United States and Europe the percentage of doctors, lawyers, clergymen, teachers, engineers, artists, and so forth among the men varies in almost the same way as does education. Recent migration, to be sure, shows its effect in raising the level of Florida and the southwestern United States, and the presence of the Negroes depresses the southeast. The presence of great cities is also apparent in the high levels along the North Atlantic and California coasts, but such conditions do not destroy or even conceal the basic climatic pattern. In Europe, too, the same basic pattern is very clear, although the fondness of the Greeks and Bulgarians for calling themselves lawyers, physicians, and teachers, even when they do not practice those professions, produces a high spot in the southeast.

Another evidence of the close relation between climate and general progress is seen in A139. There some statistics culled from the Australian official records by A. N. Price show the way in which drunkenness, suicide, and illegitimate births decline in number from the tropical Northern Territory through states of better and better climate until the best social conditions are reached in cool cyclonic Tasmania.

The General Problem of Climatic Energy and Human Progress.—We now have before us three maps of the world and four each of Europe and the United States. Each map shows its own individual characteristics due to such factors as migration, relief, density of population, and the location of cities. The significant fact, however, is that even in

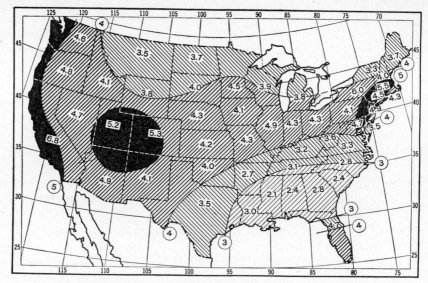

A—Percentage of Occupied Men in the Liberal Professions in the United States.

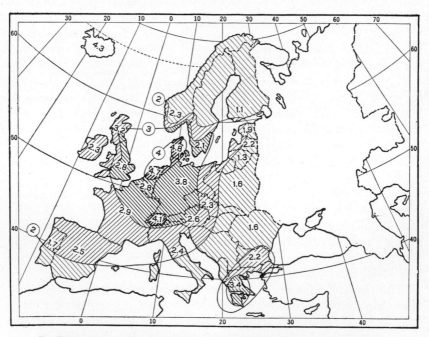

B—Percentage of Occupied Men in the Liberal Professions in Europe.

America, where the other factors are especially powerful, the non-climatic maps all strongly reflect the main features of the climatic map, while those of the world are all highly similar, and the various European maps are so much alike as to be almost interchangeable. Moreover, our maps of the yield of crops per acre and of the productivity of domestic animals follow nearly the same pattern. We shall later see that this pattern is also followed by manufacturing, railroads, and various other conditions of civilization.

There is only one reasonable way in which this widespread similarity can be explained. It cannot possibly start from the distribution of human activities and work back to climate. It must start with climate. The climate influences human health and both physical and mental activity. These in turn lead to the kind of activity which makes a man cultivate a fairly large area, and improve his crops and animals, thereby not only increasing their productivity but making their optima agree more and more closely with his own. His activity and energy also lead him to adopt high standards of living which manifest themselves not only in large agricultural production, but also in the use of automobiles, the spread of education, and the maintenance of a large body of professional people who make no material contributions to society, but serve it as

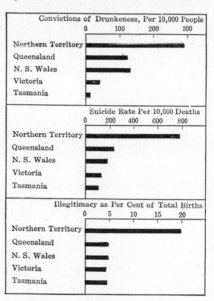

A—Social Conditions in Diverse Climatic Regions of Australia. After A. N. Price.

teachers, scientists, clergymen, authors, lawyers, doctors, engineers, artists, actors, and so on. Of course the engineers help to increase the wealth of the farmers by building machinery, planning bridges, and laying out roads; the scientists make people richer and more healthy by new inventions and discoveries; the physicians improve health not only by their work as healers but likewise by devising methods of hygiene and diet, and so it goes. Practically every element of civilization reacts thus on other elements and in general helps them. For this reason many people think that education is the main cause of the higher level of civilization and progress in some countries than in others.

That education helps to raise the level is certainly true. But the main point of this chapter and of those that precede it is that the fundamental condition which determines the *parts* of the earth's surface where progress is rapid or slow is climate. This is because man is first of all an animal. As an animal he is like plants, insects, birds, and beasts in having distinct climatic optima which vary somewhat according to age and function. Thus, aside from the distribution of land and sea, the primary fact in the whole science of geography is that the general pattern of the distribution of man's qualities and activities is set by climate. Climate, however, does not set the final details of the pattern. Some of the very large details are set by migration, as we have repeatedly seen. Other factors such as the soil, metals, fuels, water power, good harbors, easily traversed valleys, and even the accidental location of industries also introduce a great many important local details. Migrations on a sufficiently large scale, such as an interchange of the populations of Europe and Africa, would revolutionize the maps that we are studying. On the other hand if the white man and his civilization should spread all over the world and have time to become fully adjusted to the environment, it is almost certain that, although the general level of civilization and progress would be greatly raised in continents like Africa, the general pattern would still be the same as now. The only great change would be that the *contrasts* between the highest and the lowest would be much diminished. In other words, the white people of the Amazon Basin would then be enormously in advance of the present natives, but they would almost certainly not have the energy to make progress so rapidly as those of Michigan and Holland.

The Development of Man's Climatic Adjustment.—People sometimes question the conclusion stated above because the distribution of civilization has not always been the same as now. In the past, some of the highest civilizations developed in tropical plateaus like Peru; others developed in tropical lowlands like Guatemala and Yucatán; and the greatest of ancient civilizations arose in Egypt and Babylonia only 30° from the equator, and later in Greece, which is now far behind the leaders. The explanation of this lies along two lines. In the first place there is abundant evidence that the world's climate fluctuates considerably from century to century, and that the general conditions two or three thousand years ago were somewhat different from now. One of the most striking evidences of this is the growth of the great sequoia trees of California. The rings of those ancient trees show that for three thousand years the climate of California has swung back and forth from moister to drier conditions in cycles of hundreds of years. Another important line of evidence is the fact that thousands of ruins are located in places which are now too dry to support a tenth of the ancient population, or perhaps none at all. For example, in Peru near Arequipa a certain small valley now provides water enough for the scanty flocks of two shepherds about four months each year. During the other eight months the flocks are driven a mile or so down the valley to a larger spring. Yet in the past the stream at the upper spring was so large that the ancient people built a long canal to carry the water to hundreds of terraced fields which they carefully and with great labor built upon the mountain side. Again, in the most desert part of Arabia, which was never penetrated until 1931, Bertram Thomas found traces of ancient roads leading to an unknown city and proving that once there was far more water. Evidence like this might be multiplied a hundredfold. It indicates not only that there was once more rain than now in many of the drier parts of the world, but also that the storms swept farther south and thus that the stimulating qualities of the climate in lower latitudes were increased. Moreover, the only accurate weather record that has come down from antiquity points to the same conclusion. It was kept by Claudius Ptolemaus in Alexandria in the first century of our era. It shows that in those days the northerly trade winds and absolutely clear weather which now prevail steadily in summer were often interrupted by winds from the south and east due to cyclonic disturbances, and even by thunderstorms. The stimulus to man's health and activity arising from such conditions may have been even more important than the increase in rainfall, especially in countries like Babylonia, Egypt, and Greece. Nevertheless, many good authorities doubt whether such changes of climate have had much to do with changes in the location of the main centers of civilization. The authors of this book believe that climatic changes have been important, but they also believe that another reason for the shifting of the centers of civilization and progress has been far more important.

This other reason is that man's optimum climate, or rather the optimum for human progress, keeps changing as man obtains greater control over nature. When men were naked savages without fire, clothing, or any artificial shelter, they certainly would not have found the climate of Chicago very favorable. Even when they learned to use fire, to clothe themselves with skins, and to make rough tepees, the winter climate of Chicago was far too cold for them. They could not possibly be as comfortable, and probably could not preserve such good health, as could the Indians in Arizona, Florida, or the Mexican plateau. Moreover, they could scarcely develop a type of civilization as high as that of the Pueblo Indians because they had neither iron tools nor beasts of burden. In Arizona, permanent villages and complete dependence upon agriculture were possible because the dry climate, summer rains, and floods from the hills made it easy to raise corn, pumpkins, beans, and other crops without iron tools or plowing. But in a grassy land like Illinois this was impossible except in a few favored spots where the floodplains of rivers provided soil that was not held by a mat of grass or by a great forest.

Many sorts of inventions have made it more and more feasible for man to get a living and be comfortable in cooler and cooler climates. Thus he has moved forward in larger and larger numbers into environments like that of the North Sea region. This has brought him into more and more stimulating climates, and thus has helped to raise the level of civilization. The taming of cattle, horses, and sheep all helped to make man able to live in cooler climates. The discovery of how to use iron was especially important because it made it possible not only to plow grassland and cut down forests, but also to keep the grass from swamping fields that were already cultivated. Such seemingly simple inventions as the fireplace and then the chimney were also a great help in making it possible to preserve good health in cool regions. The invention of spinning and weaving helped to provide clothing as a protection against the cold. Thatched roofs may seem primitive to us, but they were a wonderful invention from the point of view of protecting people against winter rains and melting snow.

Window glass acted in the same way. Along with fireplaces and chimneys it made it possible for people to carry on all sorts of work like carving, tool-making, weaving, reading, and studying in comfort inside their houses even in the coldest weather. Before that, the choice lay between getting both daylight and cold air by opening doors or shutters, or having warmth and semi-darkness with closed doors and shutters. The artificial sources of light in those days were very poor and smoky. Yet the invention of even so simple a thing as a lamp with a wick floating in oil, and still more of a candle, helped to cause the optimum for civilization to move into cooler regions. Even in the last century this "coldward march of civilization," as S. C. Gilfillan calls it, has proceeded steadily. Kerosene lamps, iron stoves, furnaces, electric lights, modern methods of making houses warm and tight have all helped. Thus it becomes clear that each stage of progress from extreme savagery upward has its own particular climatic optimum. Always, so far as we can tell, the most rapid progress has taken place in the climate best adapted to each particular stage of culture, except where migrations or other local circumstances have temporarily upset this rule. Today we seem to have reached almost, if not quite, the northern limit, for we are able to make ourselves comfortable in almost any degree of cold, and we have gone far enough to obtain the maximum stimulus from changes of temperature and the march of the seasons. Perhaps the next step will be back toward warmer regions as we learn more perfectly how to overcome the inertia and weakness that arise from too much heat. Even if that happens, mankind will still apparently follow the great biological law which ordains that his best health, greatest activity, and highest progress shall in general be found where the climate most nearly approaches the optimum for each particular stage of culture.

The Changing Optimum of Crops.—It has already been suggested that the optimum climate for crops and domestic animals changes in much the same way as does the optimum for man. One of the most remarkable results of our study thus far is the close agreement between the climatic optima for crops and domestic animals on the one hand, and for man on the other. The optimum for winter wheat, for example, is almost identical with that for man. The optima for oats and potatoes are very nearly the same. The optimum for corn is a little different from that of the other crops, but it conforms quite closely to the optimum for people of our kind when storminess assumes an especially important position. Again the optimum climate for cotton is such that the largest yield per acre is obtained where the summer temperature is only 72° to 77°.

Among animals we have already seen that the best kinds of hens and cattle both have optima which differ very little from that of the most advanced types of men. This is likewise true presumably among horses, sheep, and hogs, although no exact data are available. It is certainly true, however, that the finest of all draft horses are the Percherons and other huge breeds of Flanders and neighboring regions in Belgium and northern France. Again the fastest race horses are bred in England or the northeastern United States. The average weight of the fleeces is higher among British sheep than among almost any others. So, too, with hogs. The heaviest and most quickly growing animals are found where we also find the best of almost all types of plants and animals. The process of selection which has made them so valuable has probably also altered their optima so that they conform fairly closely with that of man. But the exact data already known as to crops, cattle, and hens are enough without the cases like horses, where the statistical evidence has not yet been studied.

The fact that so many crops and animals have climatic optima much like that of man is doubtless due in part to the fact that under such conditions man gives them the best care. But even if we limit ourselves to a single small region, or even a single farm where man's care is the same from year to year, the yield of the crops and the productivity of the animals vary from year to year according to the degree to which the weather approaches their own optimum. This makes it clear that a climatic optimum is a genuine biological characteristic of each species. Why then are so many of the optima like our own? The answer is that man himself has steadily changed the optimum of the crops and animals that he has found most valuable. For thousands of years, as we have seen, he has been gradually moving into cooler climates. As he moved forward he carried his crops and animals with him. When wheat was planted in a new region cooler than the one that had previously been best for it, part of it died because it did not mature soon enough to escape the autumn frosts, or because the winter was too severe. Thus varieties of wheat adapted to different parts of the world have come into existence. Today there are dozens of such varieties. They are so different in their climatic relationships that certain types of Indian wheat will not mature in England, while English wheat does not do well in the hottest parts of India. The selection of wheat and other crops has taken place not merely accidentally but also of set purpose. This has become more and more true until the process of improving all sorts of crops and animals is now going on with almost incredible speed.

In this process of improving plants and animals the alert people who live in the most stimulating and healthful climates have been by far the most active. Mental activity has been of especial importance in this respect. Thus it has come to pass that the people living on the coldward margins of the habitats of the various crops and animals have been the leaders in choosing new varieties which not only are adapted to cool climates, but which also give large yields per acre. Accordingly the climatic optimum of all sorts of crops and animals tends more and more to become the same as that of the most active people. The more valuable the crop the more likely this is to happen. This explains why the best varieties of wheat, oats, barley, rye, potatoes, corn, apples, grapes, oranges, cotton, tobacco, and various minor crops all have climatic optima only a little different from that of man.   Even for tropical crops this same thing is happening.   Bananas cannot stand frost, to be sure, but within the present century the limits of their cultivation have been greatly extended toward the north.   Today they are raised as far north as the Syrian coast in latitude 33°.   Various other tropical products such as the avocado or alligator pear have likewise started on a march toward cooler regions.   Although sugar cane cannot stand freezing, human energy has carried it into southern Spain and half a dozen of our southern states.   Man helps it to overcome the dangers of frost by protecting the canes in the fall so that they may be cut up and planted in the spring.   If we had not found out how to get sugar from beets, it is not impossible that before now some one would have developed a variety of sugar cane which could resist frost.   Many people think that the history of sugar cane and sugar beets will be repeated in a possible contest between tropical rubber from hevea trees and rubber of the temperate zone made from goldenrod.   Man's power to produce the kinds of crops and animals that he wants in climates close to his own optimum is marvelous.

EXERCISES

1. Use A31, A32, and A234 (or plates 6, 9, and 12 in the *Oxford Economic Atlas*) in order to determine what parts of the earth have a sparse population because of unfavorable climate.   Classify these sparsely populated areas according to whether they are too cold, too hot, too dry, or too wet.

2. From a study of the maps in this chapter and the atlas determine how your home area ranks climatically as a place for man.   What facts of climate are favorable?   What are the climatic disadvantages?

3. From the standpoint of economic geography do you think that the effect of climate on crops or on man is more important?   Why?

4. Use the maps in this chapter and the maps of other conditions in the *Oxford American Atlas* for a study of the distribution of conditions favorable to progress.   Make a table in which for each map you record at least three areas where the conditions are very good and three where they are very poor. Color an outline map of the world in such a way that the darkest color indicates the regions that appear most often as good in your table, while the lighter shadings indicate less frequent appearance as good and the lightest indicates dominantly bad conditions.   Explain the significance of your map.

5. Run through this book, the *Oxford American Atlas*, or Goode's *School Atlas* and make a list of maps which show the distribution of human progress in the United States, Europe, or the world.   Which of them resemble the corresponding maps of climatic energy?   Which are different, and why?   What conclusions do you draw from both the resemblances and differences?

6. Make a map of climatic energy as you think it must be for savages who have not yet learned to use clothing or to make fire except with great difficulty.

7. On the basis of some of the many kinds of data given by states in the United States Census, the *Yearbook of Agriculture*, the *Commerce Yearbook*, or the *Statistical Abstract of the United States*, let the class prepare a series of isopleth maps like A135. Bring all the maps together for discussion. How far are the resemblances due to climate? Bear in mind that the *total amount* of anything cannot be mapped by isopleths, because it depends on the sizes of states and these vary greatly. But *ratios* like the number of sheep per hundred people, the yield of crops per acre, and the number of farms per square mile, or *percentages* such as those of children of school age, the rates of interest on mortgages, persons engaged in various occupations, and tenants on farms, can all be used.

8. What kind of civilization prevails in each of the seven areas of A119 where climatic energy is highest? What do the maps that you studied in the preceding exercise show as to industry, commerce, and agriculture in these regions?

9. How would you describe the state of civilization and the occupations, commerce, industry, and wealth of the people in five areas where A119 shows very low climatic energy?

10. What are the chief arguments both for and against the theory that climatic energy plays an even more important part than race, coal, or iron in determining the present distribution of civilization and progress?

CHAPTER VIII

RELIEF AND TRANSPORTATION AS FACTORS IN ECONOMIC AND SOCIAL GEOGRAPHY

California and the Sierra Nevada. A journey eastward from Monterey across the Coast Range, the San Joaquin Valley, and the Sierra Nevada into the desert shows the effect of relief upon temperature, rainfall, and vegetation, and upon habitability, transportation, and human modes of life. Near the coast, as T. H. Means describes it, low mountains are covered with grass, which turns brown in the summer; trees grow naturally only in the canyons; and the gardens around the towns are irrigated and contain mainly vegetables that can stand cool weather and the oceanic fogs that prevail in summer. Yet the flower gardens contain huge geraniums that live outdoors all winter. Such conditions give a picture of a thoroughly oceanic Mediterranean climate with less than 20 inches of rain, all of which falls in the cooler season. In traveling eastward several ranges of grassy foothills or low mountains must be crossed, for the main valleys run parallel to the coast. The valleys are thickly populated. As soon as one gets a little back from the ocean, fruit trees as well as vegetables begin to be common, for the summer fogs no longer prevail, and there is brilliant sunshine to make sugar in the fruit. After crossing the Salinas Valley and another valley which is the continuation of the one occupied by San Francisco Bay, we climb the main Coast Range dominated by Mount Hamilton and the shining dome of Lick Observatory a little to the north. Our way winds upward over a paved road with heavy cuttings and high fills. Bits of the winding old road and even traces of the steep trail used by the Indians and early white men in crossing Pacheco Pass suggest how hard it is to cross even a low mountain range like this, and how much it must have cost to build the new road.

As we ascend, the rainfall increases and the temperature becomes lower (A147). The vegetation is much the same as lower down, but more abundant. The grass-covered hills are broken by brushy canyons, particularly on northern slopes. Live-oaks in the ravines and valley oaks on the sediment-covered floor, with an occasional bull pine, make up the forest vegetation. Manzanita shrubs, California lilacs, and many other bushes with tough, drought-resistant leaves thrive on the cooler northern slopes, but grass, burr clover, and other weed-like plants furnish the only feed for the cattle which roam the hills. Population is very scanty, being limited almost wholly to cattle ranchers with headquarters in the canyons.

On the east side of the Coast Range a rapid change takes place. Trees and shrubs vanish, grass alone remains, and even this becomes thinner and thinner. The rainfall decreases rapidly from 30 inches at places like the Lick Observatory to less than 8 at the eastern base of the Coast Range where we are fully in the rain shadow. Here, in the great San Joaquin Valley, salt-loving vegetation in the form of grease-wood and salt grass confronts us. Before us stretches a desert plain, hot and rainless in the summer, and with only 6 inches of rain in the cooler season. Although the sea is only 60 miles away, the Coast Range shuts out its influence so much that we have a continental climate with very hot summers such as are

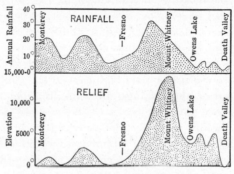

A—Diagram of the Rainfall and Relief Across California.

good for the growing and drying of raisins. In summer an average temperature of over 80° for night and day makes this region 20° warmer than the seacoast, whereas in winter an average temperature of 45° is 5° cooler than on the coast.

On clear days the Sierra Nevada can be seen from the foot of the Coast Range as a great snow-capped wall a hundred miles away. For ages the rivers that are fed by the Sierra's abundant rain and melted snow have been forming huge and very flat alluvial cones which spread out fanwise from the mouths of great canyons. Today the use of these same rivers for irrigation has changed the fans and much of the flatter valley floor from a desert into a garden. The abundant water, warm sun, fertile soil, and gentle relief have led to the development of great areas of vineyards, fruit orchards, and alfalfa fields with grain fields around them. Hence towns and cities have sprung up. Fresno, the center of the raisin industry, is the best known of these, but each of the eight major streams that flow from the Sierra Nevada supports an agricultural community. Even in the spaces between the streams large areas are irrigated from ground waters supplied by the rivers and minor streams and by sub-drainage from the irrigated tracts.

This plain is also favorable for transportation. So in traversing the fifty-mile width of the San Joaquin Valley we cross three main lines of railroad and many paved highways running north and south. Even the airway from northern to southern California follows the valley, as is evident from the line of beacons. Moreover, the San Joaquin River would be navigable and would presumably carry commerce were not its waters taken away and spread over the land in summer.

Continuing eastward from Fresno we reach the foothills of the Sierras. Here we find orange groves, for the warm afternoon sun and the drainage of the cold night air downward from the slopes give rise to a zone almost free from frost. The foothills are well rounded and bare except for grass. As we climb higher, the rainfall once more increases, and brush and oak mantle the slopes. Then at elevations of 2,500 to 8,000 feet great pine forests heavily clothe the rain-drenched mountains. In the upper part of this zone the giant redwoods, the largest and oldest of living things, are found in a few favored spots, most of which are now national parks. Above 8,000 feet, however, the trees decline rapidly in size. Soon only a few scrubby tamarisks survive, and then we find a zone of alpine grass which in turn gives place to bare rock and at last to eternal snow. On this western slope of the mountains the rainfall increases from 10 inches at Fresno to 40 or possibly 60 at a height of five or six thousand feet. Higher up it diminishes once more, for the cooler air at greater elevations cannot carry so much moisture as the warmer air lower down. So here, as on all very high mountains, there is a zone of maximum rain part way up the slope.

Above the lower foothills there are very few people—almost none in winter. The grazing of cattle and sheep, which are driven into the mountains as the snow recedes in the spring, is almost the only industry other than that of lumbering among the magnificent pines. Summer resorts line the streams and climb the slopes wherever roads penetrate into the mountains, but in winter the caretakers around the camps are almost the only residents. Further north, along the so-called Mother Lode, gold seekers once occupied the mountain valleys, but they are gone now. The high Sierra is here so rugged that for a hundred and fifty miles north of Walker Pass, near the point where the main railroad from the east enters the San Joaquin Valley, the mountains are crossed only by the roughest trails. Farther north the Tioga Road, which crosses the summit east of the Yosemite Valley at an altitude of 9,900 feet, is closed by snow except in late summer. The hardy mountaineer, however, may climb far higher with comparative ease in summer, and even reach the highest peak, Mount Whitney.

Eastward from Mount Whitney the view is totally different from that to the west. Westward a forest-covered slope, deeply scored by huge canyons, leads gradually down to the San Joaquin Valley 75 miles away. To the east an almost precipitate drop of 9,000 feet to Owens Valley presents a chaos of rocks tumbling down to a land that is dry, barren, and desert except for thin green stringers along the dwindling streams. Farther east, beyond the place where Owens River used to flow before Los Angeles took it, bare, rocky mountains, scarred by cloudbursts, are piled in ridge after ridge parallel to the Sierra. Beyond the third ridge, but visible on a clear day, lies Death Valley, 278 feet below sea level. From where we stand on Mount Whitney, the highest point in the United States, to the bottom of Death Valley, the lowest place in the country, the distance in an air line is about 90 miles. So rugged is the country, however, that to visit both places on the same day is a great feat. To do it one must travel first on foot, then on horseback, and finally follow a very circuitous route by automobile.

As we get below the limit of perpetual snow on our steep eastward descent from Mount Whitney, we soon see how the rain shadow of these high mountains causes the vegetation to change. After traveling 10 or 15 miles horizontally and descending from an altitude of 14,500 feet on the mountain to 4,000 feet on the floor of Owens Valley, we find a rainfall of only 5 or even 3 inches. Here we are in a real desert where many slopes are utterly bare and there is nothing green except the thin line of alder, willow, and cottonwood beside some diminishing stream. On the valley floor a few salt-loving little bushes and grasses are scattered about, but at the south end of the valley there is not even this amount of vegetation. There lies a barren salt flat, the old bed of Owens Lake, which is flooded now only in wet years when there is a surplus of water which does not go to Los Angeles. Wave-cut strands on the surrounding slopes show that Owens Lake was once a large body of water, but that changes of climate had reduced it greatly even before Los Angeles diverted its waters into the world's greatest aqueduct. Now that Los Angeles has taken its irrigation water, Owens Valley is largely depopulated. Nevertheless, a few little towns still survive to take care of summer tourists and of people who use the smooth valley floor as an easy line of travel north and south.

Farther east the mountain ranges are desperately barren, with only a few piñon pines on their moister slopes, and the valleys are almost empty. The rain-bearing winds from the Pacific Ocean are dry by the time they have crossed the Sierra Nevada, and only the fringes of cyclonic storms drop moisture. Each range to the east catches less and less moisture until in Death Valley the annual average is less than 2 inches, and a whole year may go by with scarcely a drop of rain. Life east of the Sierra is limited to stock raising and mining. Stock can be raised only in a few places where there is enough water for a little irrigation in order to raise feed for the saddle horses and for the cattle when rain is especially scanty. Mining goes in cycles, and even at its best never supported anything except widely scattered little towns. Today most of these are gone because the mines are exhausted. So the desert is dotted with empty ghost towns. Even the borax business, which furnished the earliest and only population for Death Valley, has been abandoned in favor of more cheaply operated deposits in the Mohave Desert. Tourists in search of sunshine and scenery are almost the only people now met in Death Valley, but even they keep away in July when the temperature averages over 100° for night and day together. The relief of the land has been marvelously powerful in making this region so different from the cool Pacific Coast where we started, or from the fruitful vineyards around Fresno, the superb forests in the Sequoia National Park, and the snowy top of Mount Whitney.

The Relief of Peru. 1. *The Alluvial Fan of the Rimac and the Western Coastal Plain.*—In Peru the effect of relief is almost more remarkable than in California. Landing at Callao the traveler crosses a small alluvial plain which has been built by the Rimac River where it leaves a narrow gorge in the Andes. On this plain lies Lima, the beautiful capital, with old narrow streets, historic palaces, and massive churches in the center, and attractive parks and modern quarters farther out. This is one of the world's driest deserts because it lies in the rain shadow of the mighty Andes which shut out the trade winds. Nevertheless, the water of the Rimac supports nearly half a million people in Lima and Callao and the neighboring villages. Fifty-one other streams from the west side of the Peruvian Andes water cotton, sugar cane, and rice as well as bananas, mangoes, and other tropical fruits and vegetables on narrow alluvial strips which they themselves have formed. Each stream, in many cases, leads to the growth of two towns. One is a pleasant place like Lima in the midst of irrigation. The other is a port like Callao. This second town often lies beyond the limits of irrigation and consists merely of little one-story houses made of bamboo slats and sheet iron and set on an utterly dreary sandy waste beside the rolling surf of the Pacific.

2. *The Dry West Slope of the Andes.*—In old days one had to travel from the coastal plains to the great Andean plateau on foot or on horseback up a tremendously steep, winding, stony trail. In the entire 4,000 miles of western South America such trails are still the only way of getting across the western range of the Andes except in seven places. Even in these seven the railroads have no easy task. In the entire length of South America only two railroads completely cross all the ranges of the Andes, one in Bolivia and the other in Chile. In Colombia a railroad starts bravely from Buena Ventura for Bogotá, but after crossing the western range gives way to a motor road. Many unfinished cuttings and tunnels attest the difficulty

of making railways here. Only in the easier relief of the Magdalena Valley does the railroad appear once more.

The Central Railroad of Peru, leading inland from Lima, was built because American and Canadian capitalists wanted the copper of the Andes. At first the railroad runs quite straight up the gentle slope of the excessively dry alluvial fan of the Rimac (A151). There one realizes that the trees and flowers in Lima are possible only because the Rimac brings abundant water from high in the Andes. At the head of the fan the railroad reaches a well watered, sunny winter resort. Lima lies only twelve degrees from the equator. Yet, strange to say, its people come here to escape the chilly fogs that prevail because the Humboldt Current carries antarctic coolness northward along their coast.

Entering the gorge the train twists its way up a grade so steep that the road not only passes through 65 tunnels and crosses 67 bridges, but backs up 16 switchbacks where it is impossible to build curves. Only a few tiny gray bushes and dry, thorny cactus plants break the monotony of the barren gray and reddish surface. Yet the slopes often show old terraces and fields dating from Inca days or earlier. In many cases these are not now cultivated, perhaps because they are no longer moist enough.

3. *Difficulties of Mountain Life.*—The irrigated patches are few, small, and far apart, although every available bit of valley bottom and every tiny pocket where a spring is found has its little patch of green. At altitudes of 5,000 or 6,000 feet the temperature has become cool enough so that corn, alfalfa, potatoes, and fruits like the peach replace

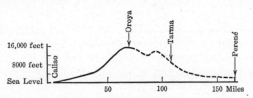

A—Cross-section of the Andes from Callao to Perené along the Railway (Solid Line) and the Motor Road (Dotted Line).

the tropical products lower down. At the railroad stations, roses, carnations, violets, and other flowers like our own, although sold at a mere pittance, give the natives a little ready money. At higher and cooler levels, evaporation is less active, and there is an appreciable rainfall. Hence, although the slopes are still very barren, corn, barley, and potatoes are grown without irrigation. The small size and steep slope of many fields are almost incredible. In some, one must walk carefully to avoid a fall that would send him sliding down hundreds of feet. The waste of time involved in cultivating such fields and in the mere work of getting to them is enormous. Moreover, the crops are very poor because the soil is thin and stony. One wonders how a family can possibly get enough to eat, to say nothing of anything to sell in exchange for clothing, tools, and money for taxes. Life is so difficult that the standard of living would have to be low even if the people were much better workers than they are. Almost the only tool is a big hoe. Clothes are made from the wool of the people's own sheep; and a dress or suit lasts many, many years. These mountain slopes are densely populated in proportion to their resources, but the population is sparse compared with that of the irrigated plains down below or the relatively level plateaus higher up.

4. *Physiological Effect of Altitude.*—Ascending still higher, the railroad reaches a height of 15,680 feet above sea-level only 106 miles from the sea. It takes the train most of the day to climb to this altitude, but that is not long enough to enable people to become accustomed to such great heights. At an altitude of 12,000 feet

the rarity of the air gives most people a severe headache. At 15,000 feet, where each filling of the lungs gives only half as much oxygen as at sea-level, even the natives of the high plateaus cannot be very active. Many lowlanders suffer severely from mountain sickness, or *soroche*, including nausea. Some cannot safely remain, although the majority become used to the altitude after a few days. Because of this, each train on the Central Railroad of Peru carries a doctor, a nurse, and a liberal supply of oxygen.

5. *The Well-Populated Andean Plateau.*—Beyond the pass over the western Andes the railroad descends to Oroya, a smelting center with an evil odor of sulphur at an altitude of 12,000 feet on the narrow Andean Plateau. Going north from here one comes to the great copper mines of Cerro de Pasco. There Americans and Canadians have built little villages for themselves, and neat little houses for the Indians and others who work for them. One mining village lies at such an altitude that little can be grown except grass and a few hardy vegetables. Yet by going 4,800 feet down an inclined cable railway one drops 2,000 feet vertically and in five minutes reaches a little valley with a great variety of vegetables and flowers. South of Oroya, although the mountains are always close at hand on both sides, there is enough level or gently sloping land to support many people. There is rain enough for crops, and the slopes too steep for cultivation, as well as the areas too high and cold for potatoes, are given over to sheep and llamas.

The difference between life here and on the low desert coastal plain is enormous. Except in the towns the plateau people are mainly pure Indians instead of a mixture of Spaniards, mestizos, and a few Negroes. Instead of dressing in cotton garments cut like ours, as do the coastal people, the Indians wear their own peculiar home-made woolen clothes,—short knickerbockers for the men, flaring skirts for the women, and ponchos, or striped woolen blankets with a hole in the center, for all. When the cold wind blows, or the sun is low or hidden, the ponchos are very comfortable. Even the gait of the people on the cold plateau is different from that of the lower altitudes. Men, women, and children jog along at a little trot, especially if they happen to be carrying loads. These rest on their backs but are supported by straps over their foreheads. Although the Indians are dull and slow, like most people within the monotonous tropics, they are much more active than those in the warm, moist lowland plain to the east of them.

6. *The Humid East Slope.*—If the traveler would continue eastward from Oroya he must cross the eastern Andes by automobile on a new mountain road so narrow and winding that it is limited to one-way traffic, in opposite directions on alternate days. As the road winds down the eastern slope it often lies hundreds of feet above an upper tributary of the Amazon. On the sharp curves it is by no means rare for one of the small trucks, which comprise nine-tenths of the motor vehicles, to pitch over the edge and fall scores of feet. Even along this highway much of the freight is still carried by donkeys and llamas. The eastbound freight consists of food, clothing, tools, and other goods for the plantations at the eastern base of the mountains; the westbound, of bananas, alligator pears, sugar, coffee, and rum from those same plantations.

As soon as one descends a little from the pass at a height of 14,000 feet the vegetation shows that the climate is far more humid than on the west slope. First, heavy grass covers the slopes, and then a dripping forest full of tree ferns, huge blueberry bushes, brilliant orchids, and a curious mixture of temperate and tropical vegetation. Then comes a genuine tropical rainforest where great trees are hung with snaky vines, or lianas, like great ropes. Evidently the trade winds from the southeast give plenty of rain even in the drier season when the sun is farthest north. At altitudes below 5,000 feet both climate and soil favor the growth of tropical plantations. These are not numerous as yet, for even with the new automobile road transportation is still extremely expensive. The road ends at a coffee plantation 2,000 feet or more above sea-level. Needless to say, the coffee has to be of very fine quality to warrant the cost of getting it out over the Andes. Even on the railroad the freight rate from Oroya to the coast is very high, but it costs over seven times as much to carry a sack of coffee (500 pounds) up the mountain to Oroya (75 miles) as from that city by rail to the port of Callao (140 miles). Nevertheless it would cost still more to send the coffee eastward across the almost uninhabited forest of the Amazon plain.

The Relief of Switzerland. 1. *Valley Plains.*—The diverse effects of the relief of the earth's surface are brought into especially vivid contrast in Switzerland. There fertile plains, villages, inaccessible cliffs, high snowy mountains, and even glaciers are often parts of a single view. In the glaciated valleys of the Rhine, Rhône, and other rivers a narrow plain is often bounded by almost vertical cliffs over which the side streams fall in beautiful cascades. The plain is green with grass or divided into carefully tilled fields. It is studded with neat, red-roofed villages full of trees and gardens. Smooth roads and railroads run almost straight from village to village. Hotels, buses, and automobiles with foreign number plates show that tourists are plentiful. The plain, even though very small, seems thickly populated, and the people appear prosperous.

2. *Mountain Slopes.*—On the sides of the flat floor of the valley the cliffs in many places are so steep that no one can climb them. Occasionally, however, a road winds back and forth up a steep slope heavily wooded with pine trees, or worms its way up a steep side valley where a stream tumbles constantly over little waterfalls. It is hard to get out of the valley, because ancient glaciers plucked away its sides, changing its cross section from V-shaped to U-shaped.

Above the oversteepened lower portion the slopes become less steep, the forest has been cleared away, and the mountain side is covered with grass. Here and there stands a chalet, or little house of unpainted wood with a carved wooden balcony completely surrounding the second story. People from a lower village move to such summer homes in order to cut the hay and feed their cattle on fresh mountain pastures. The chalets are signs of *transhumance*, or seasonal migration. In many places, even where there are no chalets, the steeply sloping fields are dotted with little buildings in which to store the mountain hay until the villagers have time to take it lower down.

3. *Cool Highlands.*—Above the hay fields there may be more pine forests but they end at the tree-line, or temperature limit of trees.

Grass, however, grows at higher levels, forming the *alps,* or mountain pastures, which give the mountains their name. There the low temperature has long fostered a large production of milk per cow and a high percentage of butter fat, thus favoring the dairy industry and helping to make Swiss cheese famous. Now, however, the alps are more and more used mainly for young cattle, since it is more convenient to keep the milk cattle down below. When snow covers the alps the cattle are taken down to the mountain hay fields, and then to the villages in the valley. On the alps the famous Swiss edelweiss grows amid dozens of other dainty, sweet-scented little flowers. Higher still the slopes and peaks consist of bare rocks or of a *scree* of angular fragments. The heads of the main valleys are filled by slowly moving glaciers with lines of *moraine* at their edges, centers, and lower ends.

4. *North Slopes Versus South.*—Down in the lowlands the contrast between the north and south sides of almost any east and west valley illustrates another curious effect of relief. Lakes Geneva, Luzern, Neuchâtel, and Zürich are among the many which lie in hollows that were gouged out or dammed by ancient glaciers. Where their shores run east and west the hills on the north side are covered with vineyards, gardens, and orchards. Every available spot seems to be cultivated. Villages are numerous, and a much-used motor road skirts each lake. On the south side the slopes are generally steeper than on the north side, but even where they are of similar slope, vineyards and gardens are replaced by hay fields, pastures, and forests. The villages are far apart and small, and the roads that connect them are comparatively poor and unfrequented. In latitudes as high as this the slopes on the north side, *which face the south,* receive the sun's rays at a high angle and hence are well warmed. Slopes facing southwest are particularly good because the afternoon sun makes them so warm at sunset that they remain warm through the night. Thus the north side of a lake or valley not only is good for crops, but also tends to be worn down to a gentler angle because of more rapid weathering. The slopes facing the other way receive the sun's rays at so low an angle that snow stays on them far into the spring, and they are too cold and wet for most crops except grass and forests.

The Upper Rhône Valley.—A more detailed example, from the Swiss canton of Valais, will illustrate still more clearly the economic and social influence of relief. Valais consists mainly of high mountains on the southwest border of Switzerland toward Italy. A glance at the atlas shows the Rhône flowing westward in a large valley into which enter many side valleys from the south where they have their origin among the glacier fields of the high Alps. The Rhône Valley itself shows abundant evidence of glacial erosion. Having been overdeepened and straightened during the Ice Age, it was later floored with alluvial material. It is now a wide, level valley, in which the Rhône meanders between the alluvial fans of its tributaries. Rugged little islands of rock in the midst of the alluvium represent remnants that were hard enough to resist the erosion of the ancient glacier. Steep slopes, sometimes nearly perpendicular, border the valley on both sides. Where rocky terraces provide small areas with gentler slopes the cool south side is forested or covered with grass, while the sunnier north side is used for vineyards and crops. The flat valley bottom, except where it is too flat and hence swampy, is divided into carefully tilled fields. Because this is a region of abundant cyclonic storms the protection afforded by the mountains does not create a desert as in Death Valley, but it makes the climate so warm and dry that even at an elevation of 1,500 feet it is good for apricots and peaches, as well as wheat and even corn. The isolated hills, like the north slopes, are covered with terraced vineyards, and the Valais wine, a product of the warm sun, is one of the best in Switzerland. Straight, smooth roads bordered by poplars connect the many little towns and villages, located where floods cannot reach them. Old ruined castles and the thick, impressive old walls of towns show the historic value of the valley as the main trade route between northern Italy and France. The Simplon Tunnel near the head of the valley is a great factor in Europe's railroad system. The acrid fumes of chemical factories show the importance of water power even at such a distance from the main centers of population.

Hanging Valleys.—The floors of the tributary valleys on the south lie much higher than the floor of the main valley. This is because the main glacier deepened its valley much faster than did the minor glaciers. Hence when the ice melted away the side valleys were left hanging above the main one. In some cases the side streams fall into the main valley in beautiful cascades; in others the postglacial rivers have carved deep gorges and reach the Rhône at its own level. Steep, winding trails, or in the more important cases smooth motor roads, lead up to the wide floors of the hanging valleys two to four thousand feet above the Rhône Valley. But the broad, level river plain of the main valley is missing up here, and the white glacier-fed streams tumble along among boulders and smooth rocks. Except where the slopes are steep and hence covered with pine forest, grass is the dominant vegetation, although around the little villages there are small patches of crop land. These meadows with their brilliantly colored alpine flowers and their borders of dark forest beyond which rise frowning cliffs and eternal snow and ice may lack the economic value of the well prepared lowland fields of clover and alfalfa, but they make up for this in beauty and attractiveness. Hotels provide accommodations for tourists who come to find health in this beautiful environment or to use these valleys as the starting point for high mountain climbing. Even in wintertime the deep snow and the high probability of blue skies and brilliant sun are great attractions, not only to the person who wants to use skis, but likewise to the seeker for health.

A Sample of Transhumance.—In these valleys the influence of relief in causing the human migrations known as transhumance is especially strong. It has been well described by the French geographer, J. Brunhes, in his study of the Val d'Anniviers. The main village here lies in one of the hanging valleys approximately 4,000 feet above the sea. The houses, which cluster around the church, are built of stone and wood with wooden galleries around them and with stones on the roofs to keep the shingles in place. Here the families stay, during the winter period of comparative rest, preparing for the coming season. As soon as they learn that the snow has melted from the Rhône Valley, which happens usually in March, a complete migration takes place, as is indicated by No. 1 in the solid line in A156. Practically every inhabitant, from priests, chiefs of communes, and justices of the peace down to dogs and cats, moves down to some secondary villages which the Anniviers people own in the Rhône Valley. The main village is completely deserted except for a few watchmen. The people stay at this lower, warmer level throughout Lent, working in the vineyards. Then about Easter time they climb back to their main village (2 in A156). By this time the snow there has melted; the cattle can graze on the grasslands, the small fields can be plowed, and potatoes, barley, and hemp can be planted.

As soon as the snow retreats on the mountains higher up, the cattle are driven upward (A in A156), following it from one level to another, as shown in the dotted line of A156. At first a fairly prolonged stay is made at a level of about 5,000 feet, the so-called *mayen*, where another set of temporary villages is occupied. From there the cattle move up the mountains in three more stages (B, C, D), during which time the men who look after them stay in small cabins. Finally, in August the highest level, 9,000 feet, is reached. In September the early autumn snow forces a rapid retreat, broken by another brief stay in the mayen, but in October the main village is reached once more. Meanwhile the rest of the family divides its time. Part is spent in the main village, in order to harvest the rye and wheat sown almost a year before in the previous August, and then to do the fall plowing, sow next year's cereals, harvest the crops sown in the spring, and cut grass for the cattles' winter hay. Part of the time is also spent in the Rhône Valley village to work in the vineyards. In October the vintage brings everyone together in the lower village for a time of recreation and festival. By the end of November all this is over and the families and cattle are once more united in the main village for the winter. Only rarely is transhumance so complicated as this, but in some form it is very common among mountaineers. Even among our own city people a great many now live on old farms among the hills in summer.

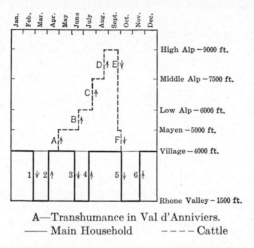

A—Transhumance in Val d'Anniviers.

—— Main Household   – – – – Cattle

Population of Lowlands versus Mountains.

The distribution of Switzerland's four million people represents another important effect of relief. Four-fifths of them inhabit a hilly northern lowland beyond the limits of the Alps. Zürich, Basel, Geneva, Berne and all the other larger cities are located there. There, too, one finds not only the famous Swiss factories for clocks, silks, and other fine goods, but the greater part of the agriculture, the institutions of learning, and the other activities. Almost the only mountain activities which surpass those of the lowland are cattle raising, lumbering, water power development, and the care of tourists. (A171.)

California, Switzerland, and Peru illustrate how relief influences transportation, agriculture, irrigation, temperature, rainfall, soil, mining, and the health, occupations, prosperity, and density of the population. They also show that many of the effects of relief spring from its influence upon climate.

The Effect of Small Differences of Relief.—Even where the relief is gentle it exercises a remarkable control over transportation and the location of various types of population. Around Chicago, for example, a little hilliness due to old moraines causes certain suburbs like Oak Park to be far more desirable than their flatter neighbors. In the same way, southwest of the city, a line of moraines determines the location of almost the only desirable suburbs and of a park that seems almost like New England. A break in this moraine where the Des Plaines River has cut a shallow gap forms an extremely busy artery of travel close to the wild park. The river, the Chicago Drainage Canal, a main highway, and two railroads all crowd into it just as similar facilities crowd into the Mohawk Valley.

A similar condition is seen about 35 miles west of Philadelphia. A158 shows how this appears on the topograhic map of the United States Geological Survey. Beneath it is a cross section from north to south just west of Downington. The smoothly floored central valley— the Chester Valley or Little Valley as it is called to distinguish it from the Great Valley of the Appalachians farther west—owes its origin to a band of limestone which is softer than the adjacent crystalline rocks that form the slopes and uplands. Long ago the whole region stood lower than now and was worn down to an almost flat peneplain. Since the subsequent uplift the forces of erosion have carved out a broad valley on the limestone, but in adjacent harder rocks the streams have as yet merely carved rather narrow valleys between which are almost undissected upland portions of the old peneplain. The maximum range of elevation is only 400 feet, but the effect on man's use of the land has been emphatic.

A159 shows that the Chester Valley has no woods whatever, although shade trees, orchards, and strips of trees along the fences are abundant. The land is mainly used for hay, pasture, and forage, for the progressive farmers have learned that large herds of dairy cattle pay them best. The farms are well cultivated, there is practically no waste land, and the houses are substantial. A158 shows that other human activities as well as farms are crowded into the lowland. Most of the houses and the only large village are there. The valley carries the Lincoln Highway, the Reading Railway, and the main four-track line of the Pennsylvania Railroad. Outside the valley floor the handicaps of relief at once become evident. The soil on the slopes is thin and the farm land is almost limited to the flatter areas away from the streams, as appears in A159. To reach these upland farms the roads have to sidle up the slopes

A—Relief Map and Cross-section of the Chester Valley near Philadelphia.

of the main valley or else follow the windings of the streams. The farmers raise much more corn than do those of the valley bottom, together with wheat, a little oats, and much hay including some alfalfa. But they are poorer than those of the lowland and do not employ such advanced methods. Part of this is due to the poorer quality of the upland soil, especially where the underlying rock is quartzite, but much is due to poor roads, distance from the railway, and other causes connected with the relief.

Effect of Relief upon Transportation and Communication. 1. *Railroads.*—One of the chief reasons why relief is so important is that trans-

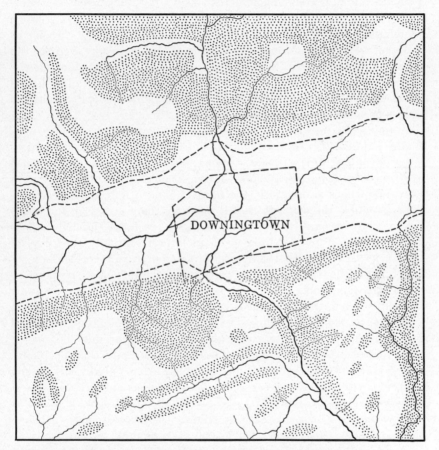

A—Use of the Land near Chester Valley West of Philadelphia. Dotted areas are forested; the rest is cultivated or used for roads, buildings, etc.

portation is generally more difficult in rugged than in level regions. The ease with which a load can be moved along a road or trail varies according to the steepness. A railroad that rises one foot in ten is considered extremely steep. No road or railroad ever rises one foot in every two, for wheeled vehicles are useless on such grades. But trails up which loaded animals are driven are sometimes as steep as this not merely in backward mountainous countries like Turkey, Persia, China, and Colombia, but in the more rugged parts of our own country. As a rule, however, trails wind back and forth to avoid steep grades. With railroads the winding may become so intense that two or three miles of track are used to join two places only a mile apart. The mere length of such a railroad would make it expensive, but the expense is enormously increased because the cost per mile among mountains is much greater than on plains.

Japan is so mountainous that some of its railroads, even in the southwest near the sea, run through a constant series of expensive tunnels. Argentina is so flat that in several places the railroads run absolutely straight for over a hundred miles and need practically no bridges or embankments.

A mountain railroad is expensive not only because of its grades, length, and high cost of construction, but also because it requires many men. A train of thirty freight cars needs as large a crew and as much attention from train dispatchers, station masters, and others as does a train three times as long. If the mountains also reduce its speed one-half and double the distance that it must go, the cost *per car* for wages and so forth becomes twelve times as great as for a similar distance on the level. Moreover, upkeep on mountain railroads is expensive. The tracks as well as the rolling stock wear out rapidly. The tremendous force with which a heavy trains trikes the rails at a curve strains both engine and cars. The constant application of the brakes wears them out. Then, too, the railroads in rugged regions are very likely to be injured by floods, avalanches, snowslides, and falling boulders. All these conditions, as well as the difficulty of seeing around the curves, cause accidents to be more common among mountains than on plains. The train from Guayaquil to Quito in Ecuador runs only by day, partly because on so poorly equipped a road the windings and grades make it dangerous to run at night. It takes two whole days to go 286 miles.

2. *Roads and Motor Traffic.*—Similar conditions create expense, delay, difficulty, and danger when animals or motor vehicles are used for transportation among mountains. In order to reach a place 100 miles away among the mountains one sometimes has to travel two or three hundred miles over roads so rough, steep, and winding that a motor car must run in second gear much of the time. Moreover, in the low atmospheric pressure at high levels an automobile engine is less efficient than at low altitudes. Hence it may easily cost ten times as much to reach a place 100 miles away across the mountains as it would over a smooth, level road in the plains. If a bridge is carried out by a flood it may be months before the mountain road is passable, whereas

in the plain the bridges are rarely carried away, and can usually be temporarily replaced in a few days. In rugged Vermont, in November, 1927, a great flood carried away 900 bridges and put hundreds of miles of road and railroad out of commission. It did damage estimated at $7,000,000 and caused much human hardship.

Although mountains need better, longer, and far more expensive roads than plains, the money available there for road-making is usually much less abundant. As a rule, the people among mountains are not only far fewer but much poorer than in the corresponding plains. Moreover, even if money can be raised for good roads, it may not pay to spend it because the poor mountain people do not provide traffic enough to make it a paying investment. Hence most of the good roads and practically all the railroads among the mountains are not built by the mountaineers themselves, but by outsiders with more money who want to cross the mountains or exploit their resources. We have seen this in Peru and California. It is equally true of the Union Pacific, Great Northern, Canadian Pacific, and other railroads that cross the Rocky Mountains, and of the Swiss railroads which run through the expensive tunnels under the Simplon, St. Gothard, and other Alpine passes. In the Appalachian region the same thing is true of the roads across northern Pennsylvania and through the famous Cumberland Gap where Virginia, Kentucky, and Tennessee all meet.

In spite of all this, there are some ways in which transportation in plains is less favored than in mountains. One of these is the supply of road material and railroad ballast. On the plains of Kansas, Russia, northern India, and China the good stone or gravel needed for this is often not available for hundreds of miles. In Holland, constant watch has to be kept so that certain railroad lines may not sink in the swampy ground, thus causing serious accidents. In Argentina many travelers wear long linen dusters to protect their clothes from the choking dust which is blown up from dirt ballast on the railways. In such regions good roads are so expensive that they can be built only in small numbers and by very prosperous communities like our own. Hence many plains are served by common roads of earth or clay which become slippery, soft, and sticky when wet. There is scarcely a good road in Argentina or Russia outside the main cities. When dirt roads freeze while cut into deep ruts, as is common in Russia and Manchuria, they become extraordinarily rough. Moreover, some plains are so flat that they become vast swamps or almost lakes in wet weather, as happens near the Wei River in China and in the Gran Chaco and Amazon regions of Brazil.

3. *Air Traffic.*—Rugged regions make difficulty even for airplanes.

Level areas large enough for landing fields are hard to find, and forced landings are dangerous because smooth fields are scarce. Higher flying levels must be attained, which is especially difficult for heavily loaded planes. Fog and cloud often hang over mountains. Many bad accidents have happened because aviators ran into hills or mountains in the fog, not knowing that the land rose in front of them. Moreover, the great distances between cities among rugged regions make air routes less profitable than in plains where people are more numerous.

4. *Lines of Communication.*—Communication is hindered by the same conditions which hinder transportation. Telegraph and telephone lines suffer among mountains because they are likely to be broken by

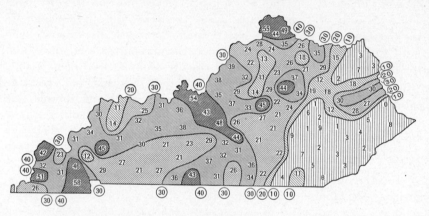

A—Percentage of Farms Having Telephones in Kentucky, 1930.

storms, lightning, snow, floods, and the falling of trees. The chief difficulty, however, does not lie in accidents, but in the fact that, because of the sparsity and poverty of the population, lines of communication are few and poorly served. The post offices are usually widely scattered, and so are the railroad stations. Telegrams are so little used by mountaineers that it scarcely pays to maintain telegraph stations. Telephones are rare because of poverty and also because the population is so scarce that a great length of wire is required for each telephone. The result may be seen in A162, which shows the percentage of the farmers having telephones in different part of Kentucky. In the mountainous eastern section, except where there are coal mines, less than 10 per cent have telephones, whereas in the more level sections such as the Blue Grass regions around Lexington the percentage rises to 30 or 40. The soil has something to do with this, but the relief is the main factor.

EXERCISES

1. Make an enlarged copy of A147. From the description in the first pages of this chapter insert in their proper places brief notes indicating the kind of scenery, vegetation, crops, occupations, etc., which are found at the different levels and on the different slopes.

2. Repeat Exercise 1, using A151 and the Andes in the latitude of Lima.

3. In an encyclopedia or atlas find out what the Northwest Territory was. When this territory was surveyed it was divided into sections a mile square, and square farms containing a quarter of a section were allotted to settlers. When roads were laid out they nearly always followed the section lines. How, where, and why does such a system hamper transportation? Is it better for the regions near rivers or for those far from rivers? Does glaciation make this system more or less desirable? Examine the United States topographic maps of various areas such as northern Illinois, southern Indiana, central Kansas, and southwestern Missouri, and see what effect the relief in each case has had upon this rectangular system of roads.

4. Give at least three reasons why it is more difficult to construct a railway over the Western Range of the Andes than over the Rockies in Colorado.

5. From the relief map of the world (atlas) make a list of mountain systems that trend east-west and those that trend north-south. In what continents does each kind prevail? What regions have mountains near the coast? Try to cite examples showing the effect of each of the main mountain ranges on transportation and trade.

6. Name and locate the large plains of the world. Which are well populated? Which have few people? What conditions other than topography may have retarded the development of the latter?

7. Describe some of your own experiences in which the relief of the earth's surface has played an important part. How does your experience differ from what might be expected on the basis of this chapter? Explain.

8. The Alps are remarkable for their close combination of level land and very rugged relief. Explain how this contrast originated and what results it produces.

9. Find a good relief map of Kentucky and compare it with A162. How far do the two agree? Point out the chief disagreements, and see if you can discover their explanation.

CHAPTER IX

ECONOMIC AND SOCIAL EFFECTS OF RELIEF

Effect of Relief upon Agriculture. 1. *Difficulties of Work and Size of Farms.*—The conditions of relief which make transportation difficult have a similar effect upon agriculture. Relatively speaking, it takes as much extra work, time, and expense for a horse to drag a plow or for a man to carry his tools uphill as for an engine or automobile to climb a steep grade. Moreover, the fields in a rugged region are usually small and widely scattered because of the scarcity of large tracts of arable land. This is one reason why the average man on the farms in hilly Greece cultivates only about three and a half acres of land compared with ten times as much in the United States. Moreover, the Greek farmer's land is usually divided into several parts. Since the fields are often far apart and perhaps far from the village a great amount of time is wasted not only in going back and forth, but in hitching up the horses or oxen in order to do just a little work. Similar conditions prevail in the central upland of Germany, where the average farm consists of only about 10 acres including pasture and woodland, while in the level region of Prussia to the northeast the average is several times as great. A165 shows that among the farms run by their white owners the average number of acres of harvested land per farm varies from less than 15 in the rugged parts of North Carolina to 30 or 40 in the more level sections. B165 indicates corresponding differences in the values of the crops per acre. Thus in large sections of the more rugged parts of the state the average farmer raises only 10 or 12 acres of crops, whereas in many sections of the coastal plain he raises more than 20. Moreover, in the last census year the average farmer got only $25 to $30 worth of crops per acre against at least $40 per acre in the coastal plain. Thus the return per farmer is often three times as much in the plain as in the mountains.

2. *Texture and Depth of the Soil.*—Relief also influences farming through the quality of the soil. On slopes the finer soil is likely to be carried away. In Palestine, Syria, Italy, and Spain, as well as in our own Appalachian region, many slopes that were once covered with soil are now bare and rocky. So long as the native vegetation remained undisturbed its roots held a fairly deep cover of soil in place. As soon

as the land was cleared and cultivated, the rains washed away the
unprotected soil, or at least the finer parts, leaving partly decayed,
unproductive material of coarse texture. The washing away of the soil

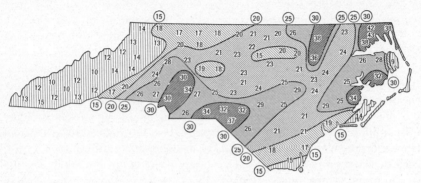

A—Acres of Land Harvested by the Average White Farmer Who Owned a Farm in
North Carolina in 1929. Note the banded arrangement. Rugged relief on the west
and the sands of the Coastal Plain in the southeast cause the harvested area per farm
to be very small. On the other where the soil and topography favor truck farming
in the northeast, tobacco in the north center, and cotton in the south center, the
harvested area per farm is large.

is often prevented by making terraces, which also provide small level
patches. This practice is common in southern China, southern France,
the Rhine country, Bolivia, and other rugged regions, but it involves

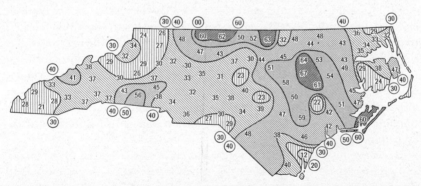

B—Average Value of Crops per Acre of Harvested Land in North Carolina in 1929.
Compare this with A165 in order to see whether the areas with low values per acre
have few or many acres of harvested land per farm.

much labor and greatly increases the difficulty due to the small size of
the fields. Many terraces are too small to permit the use of mowing
machines, reapers, or even plows and scythes. Thus everything com-

bines to make the farmer in rugged regions cultivate only a little land and get a relatively small return per acre. In tropical lands, however, the case is often different. For reasons to be discussed later, the soil on the slopes is often better than anywhere else. This is one of several reasons why rugged regions are relatively favorable in low latitudes.

3. *Kinds of Crops Adapted to Slopes.*—Sloping land handicaps some crops much more than others. Small grains, like wheat, barley, rye, and oats, are handicapped the most. They are the crops for which the largest and most complex machinery is used. Where raised most cheaply they require no handwork for either cultivation or harvesting, but big machines are of little use either on slopes or in small fields. Corn, millet, rice, sugar cane, and hay rank next as crops which need level land in order to be raised profitably. Nevertheless, in at least one way, each of these crops is a little better adapted to hilly land than are the small grains. Corn and the larger millets are harvested by hand instead of with big machines. Rice, as usually raised, is set out and harvested by hand, which makes it well adapted to small fields on hillsides. As raised in the United States, however, it is a small grain, like wheat, for which big machines and level land are needed. Sugar cane is always cut by hand and needs little cultivating after it is once well grown. Moreover, it is often left in the ground for several seasons without replanting, so that plowing is not needed each year. This last is also true of hay, but if the hay crop is to be really good the fields ought to be plowed up and resown every few years. The difficulty of doing this on sloping land is perhaps one reason why the hay fields of Switzerland and the highlands of Bavaria and Austria are so weedy and hence so beautiful with flowers. Potatoes, beans, cabbages, and other vegetables suffer less from being raised on slopes, because hand work such as weeding, thinning, and in many cases harvesting can be done almost as quickly on a slope as on the level. Nevertheless, new inventions are steadily increasing the advantages of level land. Machines are making it easier to plant the seed so that no thinning is necessary, and to cultivate and even harvest the crop with horses or tractors.

4. *Advantages of Tree Crops for Slopes.*—Crops growing on bushes and trees can be raised almost as cheaply on slopes as on level land. Even with such crops, to be sure, the sloping land is handicapped by the extra cost of hauling away the product, bringing fertilizer, and doing whatever cultivating or clearing out of grass and weeds is needed. But if these kinds of work can be done more cheaply by hand than by machines, as is the case in tropical countries, the bush and tree crops cost scarcely more on slopes than on the level. This is one reason why orchards and vineyards are located on slopes more often than on level

land. Another reason is that slopes are better drained and are in less danger from frosts. At night the air cools fastest and hence becomes heaviest where it touches the earth. On a slope such cool, heavy air easily flows downward. As it descends to the hollows its place is taken by warmer air which has not yet been cooled by touching the earth. Nuts are so easy to handle that they can be grown on slopes even more readily than can fruits. J. Russell Smith has written a book to show how profitable it would be to utilize a great deal of sloping land for walnuts, pecans, chestnuts, and other nuts as well as fruits. Such tree crops, along with olives and grapes, are among the main sources of wealth in the Mediterranean region. If the population should increase so that level land is scarce and the prices of farm products rise, it is probable that many more nuts will be raised. If we are going to use the sloping land at all, it seems wise to follow the example of Spain, Portugal, southern France, Italy, and Greece and use it for crops which require no annual plowing and sowing and only a minimum of cultivation.

5. *Relief and Abandoned Farms.*—The preceding paragraphs largely explain the numerous abandoned farms in our northeastern states. In southern New England and New York, as we have seen, favorable temperature and rainfall cause the yield of crops per acre to be large, even though the soil is not so rich as farther west. Nevertheless the farming population has declined for almost a century. Even in Connecticut, which is by no means the most hilly part of New England, the amount of cultivated land is today only about 40 per cent as much as in 1850. Practically all of this decline has been in the more hilly "towns," as the New Englanders call the townships. Dividing the towns into equal halves, we find that the population of the more hilly half declined about 10 per cent from 1830 to 1930, while that of the more level half increased tenfold. The decline of the hill towns is due largely to the abandonment of practically all the farms on the more sloping land. Wherever there are level areas of any considerable size with fairly good soil they are almost invariably cultivated. The farmers there are as prosperous as those of the prairies, providing their farms are of equal size. But whenever the land has much slope or is broken into small fields because of the relief, it no longer pays to cultivate it. The introduction of machinery has caused grain and other crops to be grown so much more cheaply on the level western land that it is not worth while to use the rough lands of the East except for pasture or trees.

6. *Tropical Crops and Plateaus.*—This study of relief helps to explain why practically all the tropical plantation crops except sugar and tobacco are largely grown on slopes. Coffee, bananas, tea, cacao, quinine, spices, rubber, Manila hemp, and sisal all come from trees,

bushes, or other perennial plants which when once set out do not need to be renewed for many years. All of them are also cultivated and harvested by hand. Tropical labor is still so cheap that there is no special incentive to devise ways of doing this work by machinery. Thus these crops suffer little or no disadvantage through being planted on slopes. On the other hand, they gain the very great advantage of having better soil, as will appear in the next chapter. This latter condition, together with other reasons such as better drainage, likewise causes a surprisingly large share of the so-called sustenance crops of low latitudes, that is, crops like rice and corn which sustain life, to be raised on slopes and hence in rugged regions rather than on lands that are more level.

Temperature and rainfall also cause tropical agriculture to seek the more elevated and therefore, as a rule, more rugged regions. Most crops, as we have seen, are at their best near their cooler limit. The best tea and coffee are grown in places which barely escape frost; the same is true of quinine, which comes almost entirely from the mountains of Java, and of corn and rice, the two main sustenance crops of low latitudes. Moreover, at higher elevations such as 2,000 to 5,000 feet, the rainfall is likely to be more abundant and regular than lower down. Since tropical people use almost no machinery and very few animals, they can get the advantages of these conditions by using the more rugged areas and yet not suffer from the disadvantages which cause the rugged lands to be abandoned in cooler and more progressive regions. Thus we see why many of the most densely populated tropical regions are relatively rugged plateaus, as in the Indian peninsula, southern China, southern Brazil, El Salvador, Uganda, and the neighboring part of the Congo Free State known as Ruanda and Urundi.

Contrast this with what happens in the North Atlantic States or England. There an altitude of no more than 2,000 feet usually makes a region not only too rough for machines but also too cool for crops. In England a rise of only 1,500 feet causes the lovely Devonshire lowland with its beautiful trees and hedges to be replaced by the treeless, grassy moors of Dartmoor, so cool, damp, and worthless that they are of little use except for sheep. Wild ponies still roam there at will.

7. *Relief and Domestic Animals.*—The raising of cattle and sheep is one of the main occupations in regions of rugged relief. It is often supposed that this is mainly because such regions are not good for crops. Such is in part the case, but rugged regions have certain positive advantages for animal farming. The coolness and dampness cause an abundant growth of short, soft, and very nutritious grass. This causes the young animals to grow rapidly and the old animals to become fat. The climate also causes the fleeces of the sheep to be thick and

long. Moreover, although this is not yet widely recognized, low temperature causes the milk of the cows to be both abundant and full of butter fat. There are many sheep in the uplands of Scotland, northern England, and Wales. The Swiss, Norwegians, and others who practice transhumance not only save their lowland grass for winter use, but presumably get decidedly more butter and cheese than they would if, with similar food and care, they kept their animals all summer on the lower and more level land. In tropical regions the effect of altitude in improving the quality of domestic animals is probably even greater than in higher latitudes. One of the finest cattle regions in Africa is the high, cool Kenya plateau.

Lumbering and Mining as Mountain Industries.—The relation of these two important industries to relief is discussed so fully in other chapters that it will be dismissed very briefly here. In regions with a climate favorable for agriculture the level lands, as we have seen, are likely to be cleared for that purpose, provided their soil is good. The rugged areas, however, are left in forests. Even if they are cut over and perhaps used for a time as pasture, the tendency for them to revert to forests is strong. In New England and New York many abandoned farms in the more rugged areas are fast growing up to forest. The entire Appalachian area, the Ozarks, the Black Hills, and the mountain ranges from the Rockies to the Pacific are all more or less completely covered with forests. They are the main sources of American lumber aside from the areas of poor soil in the Southeast. This is partly because the mountains in the drier parts of the country cause the climate to be more humid than that of the lowlands, but the greatest of all our lumber regions, the northern section of the Pacific Coast, would presumably have been largely cleared for agriculture had it not been so rugged.

Mining is preeminently a mountain industry mainly because ores are not only more numerous, but also more easily discovered, in mountains than in plains. The fact that mining camps are so often among mountains adds to their social disadvantages by making them relatively inaccessible. Mining communities are likely to be ephemeral because the supplies of ore are speedily exhausted. They are likely to be unattractive because the heaps of rubbish thrown out from the mines are unsightly and the smelters are usually very smoky and ill-smelling. Coal mining camps are more permanent, but they are generally grimy with black dust. Practically all kinds of mining are rough, hard work. They offer few opportunities for workers who stand much above the laboring class. Women with families generally form only a small proportion of the inhabitants in mining towns. These conditions react still further to lower the desirability of such places as places of permanent residence.   Thus, although some mining towns are good places in which to live, the majority do not rank very high.

Why Manufacturing is not a Common Mountain Industry.—A few conditions favor manufacturing in rugged regions, but others of greater importance hamper it.   One of the favorable conditions is water power. Yet water power is of little use without level land to make transportation easy and to furnish sites for towns.   So in the old days, before power was transmitted electrically, few waterfalls and rapids were used for power unless they happened to be in districts of low relief, as in southern New England.   Now the water power of rugged regions is largely transmitted long distances to the lowlands, as in California and Sweden.   Another advantage of mountains for manufacturing is the industrious character of the people, but this is offset by the sparsity of the population which makes labor scarce at any one point.   The poverty as well as the sparsity of the mountain people also mean that the local market for manufactured goods is small.   The presence of ores in rugged regions might be supposed to favor manufacturing, but it rarely has that effect.   The almost universal tendency is to free the metal from the useless parts of the ore and ship it in the form of "pigs" to the main lowland areas of manufacturing.   Or else the ore itself is shipped to the vicinity of coal mines.   Coal has a stronger tendency than metals to localize manufacturing in rugged areas, but, even so, blast furnaces where coal from rugged areas is employed are likely to be located in the broader valley bottoms as in the case of Pittsburgh, or on plains or places of mild relief as at Cleveland.   The tendency of manufacturing to seek the valley bottoms and plains where transportation is easy is very evident in the contrast between the small hilltop villages of New York and New England, which are mainly devoted to agriculture, and the manufacturing towns, big and little, like Nashua, Holyoke, Springfield, Waterbury, and Schenectady which are located in the valleys.   A similar contrast is seen in Normandy, southwestern Germany, and parts of Great Britain like the Pennine Hills and the highlands of Wales and southern Scotland.   The larger manufacturing cities like Boston, Providence, New York, Philadelphia, Sheffield, Lille, and Essen are almost always located outside the highlands, even though depending on them for coal, water power, wool, wood, metals, or other raw materials.

Sparsity, Poverty, and Backwardness of Mountain Populations.— We have already found many reasons why the population of rugged regions is scanty, poor, and backward.   The scarcity of level land, the scattered location of the fields, and the small yield per acre usually cause the agricultural population to be sparse and to have standards of living lower than those of the plains. The difficulties of transportation and the scarcity of broad level sites discourage the growth of manuturing. Sheep and cattle raising employ only a few people who are widely scattered, while mining and lumbering offer more or less temporary occupation in only a limited number of places. Under such conditions, doctors, lawyers, or engineers can rarely make a good living. Able teachers and clergymen cannot easily be held where salaries are bound to be low and the schools and churches poorly equipped. When new mines, power plants, sawmills, hotels, or other enterprises are established the mountaineers rarely have the capital to finance them, and

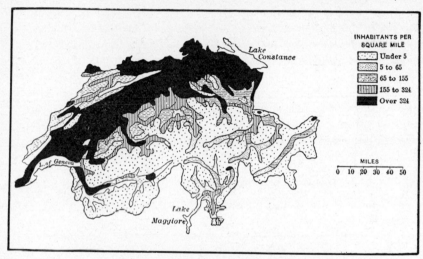

A—Density of Population in Switzerland.

the profits go to the richer people in the lowlands. We have seen how difficult it is for mountain people to provide good transportation facilities. Such facilities are not only financed by lowlanders, but likewise run for their benefit. It is not surprising, then, that the maps of Switzerland (A171), and New York State (A172) show a scanty population in their more rugged parts.

Colorado furnishes an excellent illustration of the relation of relief to distribution of population. The western half, because of its relief, has considerably more rain than the eastern. Other things being equal it would therefore have more people, but B172 shows an opposite condition. In the western half the highly rugged Rocky Mountains reduce the average density of population to less than one per square mile in some counties and to less than five everywhere except in four isolated areas. The most central of these four contains the mines of Leadville.

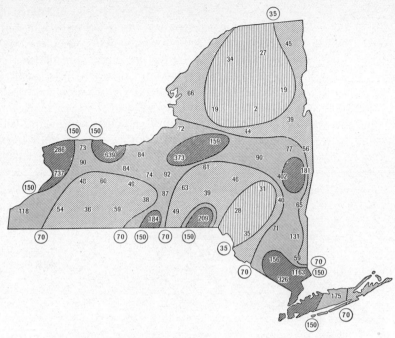

A—Population per Square Mile in New York State, 1930.

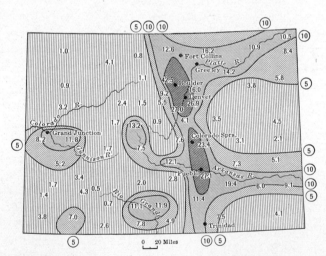

B—Density of Population per Square Mile and Cities of Over 10,000
in Colorado, 1930.

The other three contain the valleys of the Uncompahgre and Gunnison Rivers in the west, the headwaters of the San Juan in the southwest, and the Rio Grande in the south center, in all of which irrigation is possible. So great is the advantage of level land that a six-mile tunnel has been dug under a mountain to bring the abundant water of the Gunnison River out of its narrow valley to the broader and smoother Uncompahgre Valley, where 150,000 acres can be irrigated. Eastern Colorado is different. Along the base of the mountains where streams are available for irrigation we find all seven of the state's cities of over 10,000 inhabitants, aside from Grand Junction. We also find more than 10 persons per square mile all along the Platt and Arkansas Rivers. Even in the driest portions, far from the mountains and the rivers, no county has less than 2.1 persons per square mile, or four times as many as in the most sparsely settled county among the mountains. The relief of the land outbalances the rainfall so fully that the population in the drier, but level eastern half of Colorado numbers about 17 people per square mile, while that of the moister but more rugged western half averages only 4.

How Rugged Relief Favors Health, Energy, and Recreation.—The disadvantages of mountain regions are partly balanced by decided advantages. Mountaineers generally have better health and more energy than lowlanders. They take more exercise, because their houses are farther apart, automobiles are less common, and it is necessary to walk up and down hill instead of on a level. The water and air among mountains are usually more pure and wholesome than in lowlands. Mountain climates are ordinarily more healthful than lowland climates because they are cooler, more humid, and more variable. In summer the coolness is beneficial wherever the temperature of the lowlands averages above 70°. The lower winter temperature does little harm provided its effect is largely offset by clothing, fires, and exercise. The humidity of the higher and more rugged areas is due to the fact that as air rises it grows cooler, but retains its moisture until clouds begin to form. The frequency of cloud caps over mountains is a sign that at slightly lower altitudes the air must have almost the optimum condition of humidity. Only where the temperature is high does the humidity do harm. Variability arises partly from the tendency for clouds to gather over mountains, thus giving alternations of sunshine and shadow as well as of fair weather and showers. It also arises from the fact that the unequal cooling of the slopes causes warm breezes to blow up the mountainside by day or in the morning and cool breezes to blow down by night. In addition to this, the general movement of the winds is greater on mountains than in lowlands, being less impeded. This is a decided nerve stimulant, which may easily become too great. These conditions give to the mountains a climatic stimulus like that of cyclonic storms. No wonder, then, that mountain people are famous for their strength, vigor, and activity. No matter whether one is in Switzerland, Afghanistan, Venezuela, or North Carolina, the mountain people are generally better workers than the people of corresponding position and innate ability in the plains. In tropical regions the effect of altitude is especially valuable. It is the main reason why the most active, progressive, and prosperous people are found on the plateaus, as in southern Brazil, Peru, Ecuador, Venezuela, Uganda, Kenya, Ethiopia, and the higher parts of India, the Philippines, Ceylon, and Madagascar.

The healthfulness of mountains is one reason why they rival the seashore as places for recreation. If a rugged region is attractive enough its disadvantages may be almost entirely overcome. Thus the White Mountains, Adirondacks, and Alps are comparatively prosperous and progressive. Roads, railroads, and other means of transportation and communication are far more abundant and highly developed there than in many regions of gentler topography. Even in the high Alps it is generally easier to travel than in most parts of Russia, for the roads are superb and countless railroads not only wind high among the mountains, but even plunge under them in tunnels.

The Different Effects of Young and Old Mountains.—The effect of mountains varies greatly according to their age. The Rocky Mountains in Colorado are young. Therefore they still retain much of their original height; their slopes are steep and rocky; and the valleys are deep, narrow, and V-shaped with fertile floodplains only in rare instances. Such conditions are admirable from the standpoint of scenery and the discovery of minerals, but very unfavorable to transportation, agriculture, stock raising, lumbering, and manufacturing. They also cause the rainfall to vary greatly not only according to altitude, but also according to the degree to which the slopes are exposed to the sweep of rain-bearing winds. The Alps, Pyrenees, Caucasus, Andes, Himalayas, Kwen Lun, and Tien Shan are among the other young mountains of the world. In all of them the young quality of the mountains encourages health and vigor, but it also encourages sparsity of population, ignorance, backwardness, distrust of strangers, and scarcity of all except a few primitive occupations. Such regions are hard to conquer in war and often hard to govern in peace. Switzerland, in spite of its small size, has maintained its independence and avoided invasion for hundreds of years. Napoleon did indeed cross the Alps, but the terrific march across the high pass of St. Bernard was very costly. In Europe the tiny states of Andorra and Lichtenstein have been able to maintain semi-independence largely because they are highly mountainous and hard to conquer. In Asia, aside from southern Arabia, the hardest of all countries to penetrate are Afghanistan, Tibet, and the northeastern corner of Siberia, all of which are protected by high, young mountains. The people of Nepal and Sikkim on the south slope of the Himalayas are noted for warlike qualities. The Sikhs are employed by the British as policemen and soldiers all over Asia because they are so bold and independent. Their state, like Nepal, has retained almost complete independence because the mountains and the sturdy character of the people make it very difficult even for the British army to conquer them.

In Turkey the eastern regions of Kurdistan and Armenia have always been hard to govern because they contain such high, young mountains. Among the high mountains of Dersim between the two main branches of the upper Euphrates River the Kurds are so cut off from the world that they still retain many customs like those of the old feudal system in Europe. They follow their chiefs on raids, they refuse to pay taxes to the government, and they have their own special form of religion different from that of either the Mohammedans or Christians. Among the Druses of the young Lebanon Mountains and the still younger volcanoes of Jebel Druse near Damascus, similar political, religious, and social characteristics are found. In Africa the rugged young plateau of Ethiopia is the only part which has been able to resist the encroachment of Europe. It still retains not only its independence and its old form of religion and government, but a great many antique customs as well. In northwestern Spain the Basque mountaineers have retained their individual language, habits, and traits of character for thousands of years in spite of all sorts of changes around them. Today they are among the bravest, most independent, and most competent people in Spain, and when they migrate to other countries, such as Chile and Argentina, their energy and capacity for cooperation make them valuable citizens.

As mountains grow older their distinctive characteristics become less marked but do not disappear. The slopes become gentler, the soil deeper, the peaks less lofty, and the valley bottoms wider and more often floored with level plains. In such places the density of the population increases and the people become more like those of the lowlands. Thus in the Appalachian highland the density of the *farming* population in the mountain counties is as great as in the lowland counties. If the village and city population is also included, however, the lowland density is much the greater. In Kentucky the ten counties (A176) where the ruggedness of the mountains causes the largest area of poor farm land have a farm population of 32.7 per square mile, while the ten counties in the Blue Grass lowland where relief and soil combine to make the land most valuable have 31.1. The mountaineers have only 2.6 acres of harvested land for each person on the farms, while the low-landers have 4.4. Moreover, the yield of crops per acre is much lower in the highlands, being valued at $25.60 per acre in 1929 versus $60.10 in the lowlands. Hence the income per capita of the farmers from crops alone according to the last census was only $68 per person in the highlands against four times as much ($263) in the lowlands. This shows that the density of the agricultural population among mature mountains may be as great as in the neighboring lowlands, which almost invariably means that low standards of living prevail among the moun-tains. This helps to explain why the Kentucky mountaineers persisted

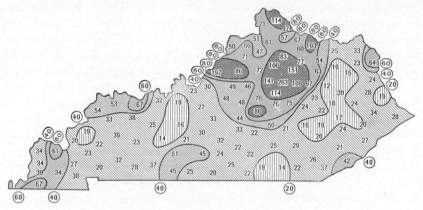

A—Value of Land and Buildings per Acre in Kentucky.

so long in using old-fashioned spinning wheels, archaic plows, home-spun clothes, old forms of speech, and many other primitive customs. Similar conditions are found among the hills of some parts of New York and New England, and in places like the Black Forest of Germany, the rough Cevennes of central France, and the highland of southern China.

The tendency of old habits to perpetuate themselves in spite of modern improvements is accentuated by the outward migration among the better educated and more able young people. The greater the opportunities in the neighboring lowlands the more likely are the young people to be dissatisfied with the poverty and isolation of life in the mountains. Their departure for decade after decade leaves the moun-tain people poorer and poorer in the inherited qualities which make a people progressive. Mature mountainous regions surrounded by more prosperous lowlands suffer from this more than do the more isolated regions of young mountains. There the extreme isolation and primitiveness not only prevent the young people from knowing much about the rest of the world, but also make it hard for them to go out and hard to get along if they do go out. But in regions like the Ozark Mountains the outward migration of the abler young people makes it difficult for the people who remain in the hills to catch up with the rest of the world.

Plains and the Distribution of Population.—The disadvantages and advantages of plains are almost the opposite of those of mountains. The overwhelming advantage of plains is that they favor agriculture and transportation, and hence manufacturing and trade. Where the four most fundamental occupations thus prosper, the conditions are also favorable for the accumulation of wealth, and thus for the development of political power, education, science, art, and the other occupations which are required by a high civilization. Under such conditions the percentage of the population found in towns and cities is sure to be much higher than in the mountainous regions belonging to the same climatic province. The parts of Europe with a population of over 250 per square mile are all either lowlands or uplands of very gentle relief. Mexico City, Denver and Johannesburg almost complete the list of large cities lying high above sea level even on plateaus.

The Relative Advantages of Different Kinds of Plains.—Although people and cities rarely abound except in plains, by no means all plains are densely populated. The greatest reason for this is the climate. Northern Russia, Siberia, Canada, the Sahara, southern Arabia, the Amazon Basin, and Patagonia are examples of this. Even where the climate is good, plains differ greatly according to their origin. Coastal plains like the southeastern parts of the United States and India generally contain belts of sand which are of little use for cultivation. The youngest parts of such plains may contain large shallow hollows which form swamps like the Dismal Swamp of North Carolina and the Everglades of Florida. Elsewhere the soil of such very young plains may not have had time to become sufficiently mature, and is therefore not of high fertility. Again, the coast of a newly uplifted coastal plain is generally smooth and without protected harbors where ships can lie safely. The ocean off such a coast is usually shallow so that ships have to anchor far out. Sand bars are formed with lagoons back of them. The presence of numerous lagoons along our South Atlantic Coast makes it possible for the government gradually to construct an inland waterway which will eventually enable small pleasure craft to sail from New Jersey to Texas without fear of wind or waves.

The alluvial plains and deltas formed by rivers are quite different

from coastal plains. For reasons which we shall see in the next chapter
their soil is usually rich. Their chief disadvantages are swampiness and
the danger of floods. South of Calcutta the delta of the Ganges and
Brahmaputra is almost uninhabited because of its swampiness. Similar
conditions prevail at the mouths of the Indus, and of the combined Tigris
and Euphrates. The Mississippi Delta, as seen perhaps from a banana
boat en route from New Orleans to Guatemala, Honduras, Nicaragua,
and Colombia, looks as if it were half land and half water. Another
trouble in such regions is the shallowness of the sea and the bars which
the rivers are apt to build across their mouths. At the mouth of the
Mekong the bar is built up so rapidly that a channel cannot easily be
kept open, and ships can enter only when the tides, which are here
extreme, rise to their greatest height. Although Saigon is primarily
the port of the Mekong Valley it is located away from the main river
in order to avoid bars and currents off the delta. Marseille is similarly
located in respect to the rapid Rhône which brings a vast amount of
coarse detritus from the Alps. Portland, Oregon, has made itself a
great seaport only by dredging a deep channel through a similar bar
and along the course of the lower Columbia.

The Floods of Alluvial Plains.—The main trouble in alluvial plains
arises from floods. This reaches a maximum in China, where large,
rapid rivers from poorly forested mountains vary greatly in volume
because the winters are dry and the summers very rainy. The Hwang
Ho, Wei, Yangtze, and other rivers have brought from the mountains
so much material that they have built vast and very flat plains of fine
silt. The richness of the soil, together with the warmth and abundant
rain of the summer, enable the plains to support an extremely dense
population which sometimes rises to a thousand or more per square
mile. With such a density of agricultural population, the people are
bound to be poor; but in northern China, floods due to the high relief
of the mountains and the low relief of the plain increase the poverty so
much that, in spite of the industry and economy of its people, this is
one of the poorest regions in the world.

The relation of the floods to the relief of the land may be illustrated
by the Hwang Ho, or Yellow River, with its load of yellow loess from
which it gets its name. When the river leaves the mountains and is
forced to flow slowly in the plain, it cannot carry so much sand and silt
as before. Hence at low water, when the stream moves sluggishly, it
deposits sand bars in its bed and in general builds up the bottom of the
channel. When the next flood comes, the channel is less spacious than
before. The river not only fills it, but even pours over the sides. As soon
as the water gets out of the channel its speed is checked, and part of the

silt which it carries is deposited. Thus the banks of the river, as well as its channel, are gradually built up. Each annual flood increases this tendency. Hence when the Chinese began to cultivate the plains they found the rivers flowing in grooves on the tops of ridges. Near Tsinan on the railway from Nanking to Tientsin it is a strange sight to find one's train rising on a high embankment in order to get to the top of what looks like a long flat ridge, and then at the top to come upon the turbid water of the Hwang Ho many feet above the plain. Finding such rivers running across their plain the Chinese naturally tried to keep them in place by building dykes on top of the banks. This only makes matters worse, for it helps the rivers to raise themselves still higher and makes the floods still worse when the rivers break loose.

Sometimes the rivers merely flood the whole country for miles on either side. Occasionally, they leave their old courses and carry destruction to entirely new areas. This happened in 1852 when the Hwang Ho shifted its mouth about 250 miles from south of the peninsula of Shantung to north of it. The harm done by these shiftings and floods of the Chinese rivers is almost incalculable. In 1931 it brought about fifty million people face to face with starvation. Floods, together with the droughts which often afflict China in the spring, bring famine to some part of that country every year or two. Scarcely a generation passes without famines which kill at least ten million people and often far more. Thus the relief of the alluvial plains combines with the relief of the mountains and the peculiar type of climate to foster almost incredible misery, poverty, and misrule. If the harm done by the habits of the rivers could be overcome it would add billions of dollars to the world's wealth and would benefit all countries.

Other alluvial plains suffer in the same way, but not so severely. In Holland, the Rhine and its branches, as well as many canals, lie higher than the tops of the houses which line the base of the dykes on either side. It costs the country a great deal to keep the low parts safe and dry. The ancient kingdoms in Mesopotamia and Iraq were destroyed partly because floods ruined the irrigation works and the people could no longer support themselves. In New Orleans the only hilly streets run upward to the top of the levee and end beside the river. Along the lower Mississippi the cross section from the river outward consists first of a grassy levee where cattle, horses, and mules are often grazing. At the bottom runs a road on the outer side of which is a line of farm houses set rather close together. Behind them long narrow fields of cotton and corn, or perhaps of sugar cane, stretch back a long distance. They end in a swampy forest, where the land lies too low to be drained. There a stream may flow parallel to the main stream during floods. Since

1900 the United States government has spent hundreds of millions of dollars in building up the levees, strengthening the river banks, and straightening curves. Nevertheless the river frequently breaks loose. In 1927 the worst flood in the Mississippi Valley drove 750,000 people out of their homes, and did damage estimated at $355,000,000. Yet such a flood would hardly be noticed in China.

Plains of Denudation.—Such plains are not so level as coastal or alluvial plains. They are formed where the rocks have slowly been worn down to a *peneplain* or "almost plain" under the influence of rain, wind, sun, and frost. The Piedmont strip which stretches southwestward from Philadelphia to Atlanta between the Atlantic coastal plain and the Appalachian ridges approaches this type, although much of it is hilly. The same is true of large parts of the Siberian Plain and of certain parts of the Dry Plains or High Plains which are not covered by material washed out from the Rocky Mountains to the west of them. Such plains, unlike the other two kinds, are generally well drained. Their chief drawback is that the soil is likely to be so old that it has lost much of its plant food. This is especially true in tropical regions where several plains of this sort have been uplifted into plateaus, as in southeastern Brazil, central and southern Africa, Madagascar, and the peninsula of India. Parts of such plains have been dissected, but even in the dissected parts a good deal of flat land still remains, while in some portions like the Matto Grosso of Brazil there has been so little dissection that the peneplain still dominates the landscape. Even in New England the hilltop villages stand on remnants of an old peneplain, while the level tops of the Blue Ridge and other parts of the Appalachians are also remnants of an ancient peneplain.

The Economic Value of Different Kinds of Seacoasts.—A seacoast with good harbors is a great help to a country, as can be seen at Seattle, San Francisco, New York, London, Hamburg, Naples, Bombay, and Yokohama. Nevertheless, if people are highly progressive they will make their own seaports even on a very unfavorable kind of coast, as at Los Angeles. While one is sailing comfortably out of the safe, busy harbor there, it is extremely interesting to read R. H. Dana's account of the same place a hundred years ago when he wrote *Two Years Before the Mast*. The sailors who came around Cape Horn to get hides in California hated San Pedro, as the harbor is called, because their ships had to lie three miles from shore. The men who carried hides on their heads had to walk over the broad stony beach with bare feet because they had to wade far out into the shallow water in order to put the hides into the boats. The ships had to be ready to slip their anchors and put to sea at any moment when a gale arose. Yet today, thanks

to the petroleum trade, more tonnage of freight is carried out between
the breakwaters at Los Angeles than from any other American harbor
except New York.

Seacoasts may be divided into two main types, uplifted or emergent,
and submerged or drowned. When they are young the two types are
utterly different, as appears in A181. On the emergent coast the coastline lies on what was recently the level floor of the sea; it has few indentations and runs in smooth curves with no deep bays or promontories.
The water is shallow far out from the shore; the only harbors are the
mouths of rivers, and these are likely to be blocked by sand bars through
which channels must be constantly dredged as at Savannah. To make
matters worse, the coast soon becomes fringed with sand bars which

A—A Sinuous Submerged Coast with Fiords in Norway and a Comparatively Smooth
Emergent Coast with Lagoons in India.

may grow into a long series of islands backed by lagoons as on the southeast coasts of India, Brazil and Africa, as well as of our own country.

A young drowned coast, on the other hand, is extremely sinuous;
the ocean penetrates far into the land in deeply branched bays, while
many hills and ridges have been converted into islands (A181). Well
protected harbors abound, and deep water often allows large ships to
come close to the land for long distances as at New York, Liverpool, and
Glasgow. In fact, some drowned bays, like many along the coast of
Norway, are not good for shipping because the water is so deep that it is
hard to anchor. Another trouble is that if the drowned region is rugged
there may be little level land for cities. This is the case along the
Pacific Coast of America where at San Francisco and Valparaiso many

streets are so steep that cable cars have to be used instead of trolley cars. At Seattle it has been necessary to cut away big hills and dump them into the shallower parts of the harbor in order to make level land; at Prince Rupert, the terminus of the Canadian National Railway, many of the streets are too steep for automobiles. At a slightly later stage of development alluvial fans and deltas are formed at the heads of the valleys, while sand bars are formed at the heads of many bays, and bluffs are cut by the waves on the projecting headlands. Such changes sometimes provide room for seaports and may make the harbors of better depth for anchorage.

In general, the coasts of high latitudes have been drowned, whereas those of low altitudes have emerged. The drowning has given us the *fiord* coasts of Norway, Labrador, British Columbia, Chile, and the southern island of New Zealand where ancient glaciers deepened and steepened the valleys which now are drowned. It has also produced many excellent harbors in middle latitudes where a more moderate drowning has taken place and where the relative positions of land and sea have suffered many minor changes in recent geological times. Thus we find an abundance of good harbors and enough level land for cities along the Atlantic Coast from Montreal to Norfolk, and from Oslo, Stockholm, Helsinki, and Riga to Lisbon. The so-called rias coast of northwestern Spain is fringed with the narrow gulfs of deeply drowned valleys which are like fiords except that they have never been glaciated. These good drowned harbors are one of the many conditions which make the two sides of the Atlantic Ocean in middle latitudes such populous, wealthy, and powerful regions. Similar conditions of drowning have produced many good harbors in the corresponding latitudes on our west coast and in Japan and in the parts of China where the seacoast does not consist of great river plains. But in all these regions the mountains generally rise so steeply from the ocean that there is only limited room for seaports and not much good agricultural land farther back.

The coasts in low latitudes, on the contrary, are mainly emergent. One of the great handicaps of Africa, South America, and Australia is the scarcity of good harbors except at a few places like the superb drowned bays of Rio de Janeiro and Sydney. The west coasts of Africa and Australia do not possess a single really good harbor, and on the west coast of South America one must go more than two thousand miles from Guayaquil to southern Chile in order to find a seaport which is deep and at the same time well protected from all sorts of wind and weather.

As seacoasts grow older the emergent and drowned types become more and more alike. The smoothness of the emergent type is destroyed because the streams build out deltas in some places, while the waves and currents cut back into the land in others. The drowned coasts become smoother, because deltas fill the bay heads, bars are formed across the smaller indentations, and the waves cut back the headlands and wear away the islands. In extreme old age the two kinds of coasts become practically alike, just as do plains or soils of all kinds, but examples of this are almost unknown because the shores do not stay long enough at the same level.

EXERCISES

1. What story or book that you have read brings out the effect of relief upon man's prosperity, trade, or character? How does it do this?

2. What instances of the effect of either rugged relief or plains upon people's occupations and mode of life have come within your own observation?

3. What ground, if any, can you find for the statement that if a plain is too flat the effect on man is as bad as though the region were extremely rugged or had a climate as cold as that of northern Alaska?

4. Make a table showing in parallel columns the advantages and disadvantages of (a) large areas of very level land, and (b) large rugged areas.

5. Compare A162 and A176. In what respects are they both indicative of the effect of relief? How is your interpretation of these maps and of the effect of relief helped by knowing where coal is mined in Kentucky and that the Blue Grass Region around Lexington has extremely good limestone soil?

6. Explain why some crops are especially well fitted for rugged regions and others for plains. Give examples to prove your point from your own observations and reading.

7. Explain why rugged relief is far more of a handicap in some parts of the world than in others. Prepare an outline for a theme on this subject.

8. In the community where you live are there abandoned farms? If so, were they abandoned because of steep slopes or for some other reason? Are there any important tree crops in your neighborhood? Could others be developed?

9. From your atlas make a list of six coasts where bays and gulfs are very abundant for a distance of five hundred or a thousand miles, and of six where they are scarce. List the important ports found on each of these coasts. What conclusions do you draw as to the relation between the relief of the coast and man's utilization of the harbors?

CHAPTER X

THE SOIL AND ITS EFFECT ON PRIMARY PRODUCTION

Examples of the Effect of the Soil.—The influence of the soil is readily apparent when adjacent regions with different soils are compared. Southern Wisconsin is a fine dairy region. In June the gentle hills are blanketed with forage crops of sweet-smelling clover, corn, grass, and oats. Big herds of Holsteins and Jerseys chew the cud in rich pasture lots. Comfortable white farm houses are half hidden by shade trees and orchards above which rise big red barns and silos. By the roadside stand little platforms where big milk cans are left to be collected by trucks. At longer intervals one sees and smells neat butter or cheese factories. In the villages big white milk trucks bound for Chicago back up against creameries to be loaded with the milk brought in from the farms. In certain districts, however, the scene suddenly changes. The land is as level as ever, but the big red barns, the silos, cheese factories, and creameries are gone. The houses are mostly of one story instead of two, and many are weatherbeaten or abandoned. Clover, hay, and corn are replaced by straggling crops of potatoes, beets, sweet corn, cabbages, and other vegetables, or else by large areas of barren, windblown sands. The people here are American farmers like their neighbors, but something causes them to farm differently and to be poorer.

In another part of the country, the coastal portion of the Atlantic states from New Jersey southward contains a sparsely cultivated strip given over to pine trees which stand far apart amid thin grass. Only a few miles inland the country is rich with fields of corn, tobacco, vegetables, cotton, or other crops, according to the latitude. Central France presents similar contrasts. For mile after mile a smooth road winds among fields of wheat, barley, oats, and sugar beets. Big two-wheeled carts drawn by white oxen or cows haul the beets to sugar factories in the autumn. The road is frequently interrupted by a village where a crooked street with no sidewalks is paved with stones and runs between the gray stone walls of houses which touch each other like those of a city. Suddenly fields, carts, oxen, and villages disappear, and nothing but a pine forest is seen. In Germany this same sort of contrast is common. In southern England one drives for miles among green fields,

184

hedges, and charming villages with stone churches and neat, well-walled gardens. Then comes a desolate tract of heather and bushy forest. It is the Heath of Aldershot, the site of huge military camps during the Great War, but now almost unused.

These contrasts arise from differences in the soil. In each comparison the poorer region has an infertile soil, sandy in most places but chalky at Aldershot. The infertile soil has somewhat the same effect as mountains, for it generally causes the population to be scanty and poor. Hence the houses are small and widely scattered; the villages are far apart; the roads tend to be poor; and schools, libraries, and other means of culture are neither numerous nor well equipped.

This general principle is sometimes reversed and we then find that the majority of the people on rich soils are inefficient peasants and tenants who raise only a few crops with low yields per acre. Such reversals are too common to be accidental. They may arise because the opportunities for work favor the growth of a large laboring population on good land, as in the Black Belt of Alabama, or because land that is called poor is really good for certain uses which have developed only recently. Thus in northern Florida, the rich, heavy, clay soils are devoted largely to corn, but the yields are small, the farmers are poor, and a large percentage of them are colored. Farther south the poorer sandy soil furnishes much greater wealth, because it happens to be fit for early vegetables and oranges and has attracted many energetic people from farther north. But perhaps it is not fair to call a soil with such possibilities really poor. In Holland there is a similar case. A line of sand dunes separates the ocean from low, clayey fields where thick grass encourages the dairy industry. The junction of sand and clay is an excellent place for bulbs and vegetables. There, at certain seasons, some fields are gay with tulips, hyacinths, lilies, narcissus, and daffodils, while others provide fine vegetables for the industrial regions of neighboring countries.

Java and New Guinea present a contrast which follows the general rule that good soil promotes prosperity. Java is about the size of Iowa and less than one-sixth as large as New Guinea. Yet Java supports about forty million people and New Guinea only a million. In Java almost every bit of land is cultivated except among the highest and steepest mountains. Steep slopes are terraced for rice at low elevations and for corn or other crops higher up. Clumps of trees shade the little thatched villages, which are so close together that you can almost call from one village to another. People are generally in sight. Some are planting rice, some work or play near their huts, and at evening many take their daily baths in the water that irrigates the rice fields. In

New Guinea only small regions are well populated. One travels scores of miles through dense forests without seeing anyone. The scattered inhabitants are usually wild, barbarous, and almost naked. Some are cannibals or head hunters and use tools like those of the Stone Age.

So great a difference arises, of course, from many causes, but the soil has much to do with it. In Java most of the soil is fresh, rich volcanic material. In New Guinea such soils are rare, for much of the soil has largely lost its good qualities through excessive leaching, or else lies so low that it is water-logged. Here as in many other cases the soil takes high rank among the factors which cause *local* differences in economic and social conditions.

The Classification of Soils. 1. *The Nature of Soil-making Rocks.*— There are several ways of classifying soils. In all of them, color is one of the best indications of quality. Dark soils are generally rich; light ones are likely to be poor. One method of classification is based on the rock from which the soils are derived. All soils consist mainly of decayed rock, and each rock makes its own kind of soil. Rocks such as granite which contain much quartz make light-colored, sandy, and relatively infertile soil. Limestone makes a reddish, fine-grained, fertile soil. Chalk although consisting largely of lime does not form so good a soil. The best soils come from dark rocks like basalt. These are usually volcanic in origin or at least have been brought up from the lower parts of the earth in molten form. They contain large amounts of *basic* materials like potash, soda, and lime, in distinction from *acid* materials like quartz. They usually form soils that are dark and fine-grained. As time goes on, however, and soils become old, the differences due to diversity of origin become less and less.

2. *Soil Texture.*—Soils may also be classified according to the sizes of their particles. The size determines how well the soil will hold water, and how easily the plants can get food materials. On the basis of the size of the particles and the consequent texture, soils are commonly divided into gravel, coarse sand, fine sand, silt, and clay.

No ordinary soil consists entirely of particles belonging to any one of these groups. Even a gravel contains sand and silt, while sandy soils contain both silt and clay. On the other hand, most of the so-called clays are more than half fine sand and silt. The best soils, which are often called loams, contain 3 to 15 per cent of clay, considerable silt, and some sand especially of the finer kind. In all soils the true clay is probably the sole source of mineral food for the plants. Even the fine sand and probably the silt consist of unaltered particles of rock in which the minerals are not available for plant food. They serve as a reservoir whose gradual decay supplies new materials for thousands of years.

Their immediate value lies in the fact that they give the soil the right texture or structure. The importance of this can scarcely be overestimated. Louis A. Wolfanger says that "a favorable structure is more important than the presence of potash, phosphorus, or other so-called plant foods, since structure appears to be extremely difficult if not impossible to correct, especially over large areas." Fertilizers can be added to a soil, but heavy, stiff clay or coarse sand cannot be converted into friable loam that holds water and yet is porous and easily cultivated.

The texture of the soil is closely related not only to the availability of plant food, but also to ease of cultivation. *Sandy soils* possess the excellent qualities of being loose, friable, and easily plowed. The roots of plants readily enter them; air permeates them whenever the water drains away, thus aerating the roots. The alternation of water and air in the soil has a direct effect in promoting the breaking down of the silt and sand into clay. It also has an indirect effect of greater importance because it promotes the growth of bacteria or other minute living organisms which convert dead plants or animals into forms fit for plant food. Some of the bacteria take nitrogen out of the air. Sandy soils are also readily warmed by the sun and can easily be improved by fertilizers provided they are kept moist. Hence they are much used for fruit raising, market gardens, nurseries, and especially for raising early vegetables. Most of the southern market gardens are located on sandy soil because it gets warm so quickly. One of their great defects is that their supply of plant food is often very limited because so much of their material is not yet decomposed. A second is that water runs through them quickly and they soon become dry. For these reasons sandy market gardens require a great amount of fertilizer, and many need a network of overhead pipes for irrigation.

At the opposite extreme from coarse sands stand *clays*. They are good in just the points where sands are bad, and bad where sands are good. Because their particles are very minute, whatever plant food they contain is readily available. Their fine texture causes them to hold water even in very dry times. On the other hand, water penetrates them so slowly that an underlying layer of clay often causes the soil above it to become water-logged. Under such conditions aeration is checked and so is the nitrification and other work carried on by bacteria. Moreover, clays are sticky when wet and stiff when dry. Such a structure makes them difficult to cultivate and hard for roots to penetrate. These qualities often cause clayey soils to be used mainly for grassland, although they are well suited to crops like wheat, beans, and corn. They are especially common in tropical regions, in old plains

elsewhere, and in lowlands like the Piedmont district at the eastern
base of the Appalachians and the plain of southwestern Siberia. Lime
helps to prevent clay from sticking or being stiff, and so does *humus*,
which is the material left in the soil after plants have decayed. We
shall soon see that certain climates favor the accumulation of both lime
and humus.

Loams are intermediate between sands and clays and possess many
of the good qualities of both. They do not allow either water or air to
enter them so easily as do sandy soils. Hence, while they are well
aerated, they hold water fairly well without becoming water-logged.
They are also easy to plow and the roots of plants can readily penetrate
them. They contain enough clay so that plant food is abundant, provided the clay is not too old. These qualities make loams the best kind
of soil for general purposes. In the rich agricultural regions from
Pennsylvania to Iowa and in northern France and Belgium most of the
soils are loams.

Soils vary from the top downward because something is added to
the upper layer, while something else is taken away from it. The main
addition is *humus*, resulting from the growth and decay of plants and
to a less extent of animals. The accumulation of humus is one of the
most important of all means not only of enriching soils and especially
of giving them nitrates, but also of giving them a good structure. Its
effect can be seen almost anywhere, for the upper part of the soil is
usually darker than the portion a foot or so lower. Only in exceptionally good soils does the dark part with plenty of humus extend to greater
depths.

The other condition which changes the character of the soil as one
goes downward is the amount of leaching and chemical deposition. As
rainwater passes through the upper soil it leaches out some of the soluble materials and carries them downward. Below a certain level, however, the water begins to deposit some of the material which it has dissolved higher up. The level where this occurs is often marked by a
sharp line where the color changes from the darker tint of the soil to the
lighter shade of the *subsoil*, perhaps from brown to gray, or from almost
black to yellow. The subsoil below a poor top soil may contain abundant
plant food, although lack of aeration commonly renders this unavail-
able. The line between subsoil and soil usually marks the lower limit
of thorough aeration and of other processes which give to the soil the
final qualities that fit it for the growth of plants. Sometimes the subsoil is so impervious that water seeps along its top without sinking and
the soil becomes water-logged. Many grassy tracts in tropical forests
are the result of this condition. Where the subsoil is well developed,

the upper soil is almost always deficient in lime, and thus tends to be impoverished.

3. *Residual Soils.*—All soils may be divided into residual soils, which *reside*, so to speak, where they were first formed, and transported soils which have been carried to other places. A very *young* residual soil is likely to be thin, coarse, and full of angular fragments of rotten rock or sand with very little silt or clay. Hence plant foods are not readily available, the soil is infertile, and water runs through it quickly. Such soils are deficient in humus. This is serious, for humus is by far the most important source of nitrates, which are among the most essential plant foods. The youngest of all soils are found in regions like the interior of Labrador and northern Scandinavia where the ice-sheets scraped off all the old soil, leaving bare rock. During the 30,000 years (more or less) since the ice melted from these regions only a little young soil has accumulated in the hollows.

As a residual soil grows older, it becomes more clayey, until in *old age* there may be many feet of almost pure clay. This is bad not only because clay is hard and tough, but also because in the oldest clays the soluble materials which alone are of use to the plant have been almost completely removed. Somewhere between the sandy young stage and the clayey old stage a residual soil has a more or less loamy character. From the top downward a residual soil of course becomes gradually younger. A gully in such soil may pass through all ages until it reaches young soil above rotten rock.

The Location of Residual Soils.—Residual soils cover the earth's surface mainly in upland regions and on slopes. In the United States residual soils attain great depth in the southeastern states from Pennsylvania and Missouri southward, typically in the Piedmont Plateau. This is an advantage except where erosion sets in as the result of cultivation. Residual soils generally accumulate under a cover of vegetation. This holds them in place until the land is cleared and plowed. Then the rain may cut gullies. Where the soil is 20 or 30 feet deep even the smallest gully may soon become greatly enlarged. It is estimated that $17\frac{1}{2}$ million acres of formerly tilled land have been spoiled by erosion in the United States. Gullying may be prevented by planting bushes at the heads of the gullies, or more often by contour plowing. This means that the furrows are plowed horizontally along the side of a slope like contour lines on a map. The rain collects in the furrows, and sinks without getting a chance to run down the slope and wash gullies. Even in regions where there are no gullies the upper part of any land that slopes even a little is very slowly carried away by rain and wind. Such sheet erosion gradually removes the upper humus-bearing layer in many places where cultivation is carried on, thus permanently impoverishing the soil.

In a region of residual soils the oldest soil is found on the flatter interfluves, or areas between the valleys, while the youngest is found on the steepest slopes. On the flat parts of the interfluves there is almost no erosion, whereas even on a gentle slope the soil gradually creeps downward. The creeping soil accumulates at the base of the slopes. It is also washed into the valleys and lowlands, or carried to the sea, thus becoming part of the transported soil. The relative youthfulness of the residual soil on slopes is very important in tropical agriculture. In regions like Panama, Honduras, Brazil, central Africa, and India, the traveler often finds broad level uplands uncultivated and covered with grass, while the slopes are cultivated and the valley bottoms forested. At first it seems absurd to use the level upland only for pasturage, and laboriously cultivate the slopes and even make terraces on them. The soils of many tropical regions, however, are very old. On the level interfluves they have remained stationary so long that they have lost most of their good qualities. On the slopes they are younger, because their upper layer is slowly but surely washed away by the rain. On slopes of moderate steepness the soil is carried away just fast enough so that what remains has the optimum condition of maturity. At the foot of such a slope the transported soil is often waterlogged. It requires considerable skill to pick out a really good location for a banana patch in Uganda or a coffee plantation in Guatemala.

Transported Soils. 1. *Those Carried by Water.*—Hundreds of millions of people live on transported soils. Such soils are found in glaciated areas, floodplains, deltas, young coastal plains, alluvial slopes at the base of mountains, and the basin deposits and sand dunes of dry regions. Transported soils, unlike residual soils, are generally derived from a variety of sources. Hence they usually have a relatively varied chemical composition and contain material of all ages, which gives them a mature quality. Most of them have also been sorted into different grades of coarseness. Thus their texture varies far more than does that of residual soils. It ranges from the coarsest gravel to the finest clay.

Soils are transported by water, wind, and ice. Those transported by water and wind are usually well sorted; those transported by ice are not sorted. The transportation of soil by *water* begins with the muddy water, little gullies, and deposits of pebbles, sand, and mud that one sees when rainwater runs over the earth. Little by little such transported material is carried into the streams and is finally deposited in floodplains and deltas or carried out to sea. Nearly half the people in

China and India, and a still larger proportion in Iraq, Egypt, northern Italy, Holland, and Louisiana, live on alluvial plains of rivers like the Hwang, Yang, Min, Brahmaputra, Ganges, Indus, Nile, Tigris, Euphrates, Po, Rhine, and Mississippi. The waves and currents of the ocean also transport much soil, and sift it as they go. Thus they form beaches of gravel or sand, while finer sand and silt are washed into sand bars, and clay is deposited as mud on the floor of the oceans. When ocean bottoms are uplifted or drained and form land, they become coastal plains like those of our South Atlantic Coast and southeastern India. The best soils around the Baltic Sea are found in small coastal plains that were deposited when the land stood lower for a while not many thousand years ago.

2. *Soils Deposited by Wind.*—The work of the wind in transporting soil is especially evident on seacoasts and in deserts. The French coast of the Bay of Biscay and the southern and eastern shores of Lake Michigan are bordered by broad lines of high sandy dunes. In France the dunes move inward so rapidly that the French have gone to great expense to fasten them down by planting grass and bushes. Gary, Indiana, is located on white sand blown inland from the lake shore. In the world's great deserts hundreds of thousands of square miles are covered with dunes from one to five hundred feet high. The finer parts of the desert soil are often blown away by strong winds and deposited as yellow dust called *loess*. At a height of over 12,000 feet on the north side of the Kwen Lun Mountains in Central Asia the authors of this book have watched new loess rise as dust from the sandy desert sixty miles away to the north. The dust advanced like a murky cloud and finally fell in a fine yellow powder. Loess is much like loam, but is full of vertical pores, probably because it was laid down in the midst of small grasses. It sticks together so firmly that in North China many people dig caves in it, and live there permanently. Nevertheless, roots penetrate it easily. Such loess soils are very fertile. The bluffs above the Mississippi, Missouri, Danube, and other rivers bear a cap of loess formed in dry times during the glacial period. By far the largest deposits are those of northwestern China. They appear to have been blown from Mongolia and the neighboring desert section of inner Asia.

3. *Soils Transported by Ice.*—Soils of purely glacial origin are not sorted. As an icesheet moves slowly over a region where residual soils have long been developing, it scrapes up everything that is loose and gradually mixes all parts of the old soil together. This gives a soil which is neither young nor old, neither gravel nor clay, but a mixture of everything. When the soil has all been scraped off, the ice also gouges up pieces of rock and uses them as chisels with which to scrape still further

fresh material from the solid rock underneath. Thus the *till* or mixed material which an icesheet slowly pushes along underneath itself, and the *moraines* which it piles up in front consist of material of every size, shape, and age. Where the ancient glaciers flowed over level land, as in Illinois, Iowa, and Nebraska, they produced much good clayey soil. In other regions like northern Germany the moraines form a poor, rough region with many sandy plains. Where they scraped over mountains they left rough stony soil, as in northern New England, Wisconsin, and Sweden.

An example of the good effect of glaciation on soil has been described by R. H. Whitbeck. In Wisconsin a sandstone area was glaciated, while the ice flowed around but not over a similar "Driftless" area close by. Where the ice flowed over the sandstone, it deposited a good deal of limestone from regions farther north. Hence it is possible to see how the yield of crops on the sandy residual soil of the driftless area compares with the yield on the mixture of sandy residual soil and transported limestone soil where the ice overrode the sandstone. Here is the result expressed as the average number of bushels per acre raised on each kind of soil:

	Corn	Rye	Potatoes
Driftless counties.........................	21.0	9.6	76.0
Glaciated counties........................	25.3	11.3	107.0

Whitbeck estimates that glaciation makes the crops of Wisconsin worth $50,000,000 per year more than would otherwise be the case. Against this must be set the fact that the value of crops in Maine, for example, has probably been reduced much more than this amount by the icesheet.

Effect of Climate on Soil. 1. *Three Kinds of Soil-producing Agencies.*—Most of the processes by which soil is made are greatly influenced by climate. These processes are of three kinds, mechanical, chemical, and organic. One of the mechanical processes is the cracking of rocks when they are suddenly heated or cooled. In deserts, rocks that have been greatly heated in the sun sometimes snap when a shower falls on them. Another mechanical process is the grinding of rocks or grains of sand upon one another when they are moved by waves, currents, winds, or ice. A third begins with the cracking of the rocks in the long slow process by which they are uplifted, uncovered, and cooled after being far below the surface for millions of years. Although the tiny cracks thus formed are usually invisible, water penetrates them. When it freezes it expands and gradually widens the cracks. Obviously, the heating and cooling of rocks, the strength and frequency of storms and floods, and the occurrence of frost all depend upon climate.

The chemical agencies in the formation of soil work mainly through ground water and air. Even before the rain reaches the ground it may take from the air a little carbonic acid gas that has been given off by a volcano or breathed out by animals. As water seeps through the soil, it dissolves ammonia, humic acid, and other materials from the soil itself, especially from the remains of plants and animals. The oxygen and moisture of the air also help to form soil. Their work in causing decay and rust is seen everywhere. Thus little by little the character of the soil is slowly changed by water and air. The mechanical agents of soil formation are important mainly because they give an opportunity for these chemical agents.

The same is true of the organic agencies of soil formation. A lichen attached to a bare rock or the root of a tree in a crack not only exerts a slight mechanical action, but also provides a little acid. The same is true when a woodchuck digs a hole, or an angle worm makes a meal of earth.

2. *Climate and the Rate of Weathering.*—The rate at which soil grows old depends on the temperature. When water is frozen its chemical activity practically ceases. At higher temperatures the activity increases 6 per cent or more for every increase of one degree Fahrenheit in temperature. If the rocks suffer a certain amount of decay at a temperature of 33° F., about twenty times as much will take place during the same time at 80°. Accordingly soils develop very slowly in cold regions, and very rapidly within the tropics. This contrast is increased by the facts that vegetation is scanty and decays slowly in high latitudes, but is abundant and decays rapidly in low latitudes. Thus soil may be formed hundreds of times faster in the warmest, wettest regions than in very cold regions.

As soils grow older their chemical composition changes steadily. When young they are not good for plants because certain chemical elements have not been set free in sufficient quantities, even if present. Then they pass through a mature stage where the maximum number of useful elements is present in proper amounts. And finally they reach an old stage where many of the elements have been leached away so badly that they are not sufficient for plant growth. How important these changes are may be judged from some experiments by J. E. McMurtrey, of the United States Department of Agriculture. He raised tobacco plants without soil by putting their roots in a nutrient solution which was supposed to contain everything essential for growth. After many experiments he found a solution in which his plants assumed the appearance of No. 6 in A194—fine, sturdy, big-leaved plants. When he omitted one single chemical element from his solution the plants grew very differently and not nearly so well. Thus 1 in A194 shows what happened when nitrogen was omitted, 2, phosphorus, 3 potassium, 4 calcium, 5 magnesium, 7 boron, 8 sulphur, 9 manganese, and 10 iron. Carbon, oxygen, and hydrogen are even more essential, for without them no plant can make any growth whatever, but they are derived from water and air, not from the soil. Thus, in order to insure good growth, plants must not only have abundant air and water but must also be able to get from the soil at least a tiny bit of each of the nine elements whose absence causes the extraordinary

A—The Effect of Depriving Tobacco of Any One Chemical Element.

differences in A194. E. S. Johnston, of the United States Department of Agriculture, found that potato plants pined away and died when unable to obtain boron, but thrived when given an inconceivably small amount, only one part of boron in 2,000,000 parts of the nutrient solution. Too much of certain elements in the soil is as harmful to plants as too little. Thus it is evident that the value of the soil must change constantly and greatly, although slowly, during the long process of chemical metamorphosis to which it is subjected in passing from youth through maturity to old age.

A Cross Section of the Soil from Cold to Warm Regions.—The change in the soil from high latitudes to low is especially evident on the east sides of the continents, for there all latitudes receive a fair amount of rain (Plate II). If all rocks were alike in composition and had been exposed to weathering just long enough to produce a mature soil in middle latitudes, there would be a steady change from infertile young soil in cold regions to fertile mature soil in middle latitudes, and then to infertile old soil in low latitudes. In a general way, this condition actually exists, although with much irregularity. This is clearly evident in Plate II, which should lie open before you as you read the rest of this chapter. Read at once the description of the soil map as given at the left hand end of Plate II.

As a whole the tundra soils of high latitudes (T in Plate II) are pale gray, infertile, water-logged, and young with little humus. Even though the rainfall in high latitudes is always scanty, the soil is usually water-logged. Swamps, such as the "muskeg" of Canada and Alaska or the "tundra" of Siberia with their deep beds of lichens, are extremely abundant. Not only does the low temperature prevent evaporation and keep the lower soil frozen all the time, but frequent freezing and thawing of the upper parts make the ground so rough that the water does not flow off.

Not quite so far north where the swamps give place to coniferous forests the soil improves somewhat, but chemical action is still very slow. One evidence of this is that, in regions like southern Labrador, one can often walk hundreds of yards on dead and fallen trees without setting foot to the ground. The newcomer may wonder whether a terrific storm has recently uprooted them, but many have been lying there for decades. According to H. A. Eidmann, the slowness with which trees decay there renders insects which are decidedly harmful in warmer regions very useful. In Germany the insects spoil freshly cut logs by boring holes and admitting bacteria; in Labrador, if the insects did not do this, fallen trees would keep on accumulating until they blocked new vegetation and almost killed the forest. Because of such conditions the so-called *podzols* or soils of the pine forests are pale, acid, and infertile (Po in Plate II).

In middle latitudes, where deciduous forests prevail, the *humid brownerths* (B_H, Plate II) are browner, less leached, better aerated, and more fertile than the podzols farther north. They are mature specimens of the leached *pedalfer* type with three "horizons" or layers: (1) ordinary soil which has lost most of its lime but is well aerated and contains humus; (2) a lighter, more compact subsoil in which chemicals leached from the soil above have been deposited but are not available for plants because of lack of aeration; and (3) a lower layer which has neither lost nor gained much through the action of water. The prevalence of these mature, mid-latitude brownerths at their best in southeastern Pennsylvania, Japan, Belgium, and northern France, helps to make these sections among the world's richest agricultural regions.

Nearer the equator the proportion of mature and old soils increases, leaching becomes more pronounced, and yellowish, pinkish, and reddish colors prevail. In lower middle latitudes such as our southern states and China the red-and-yellowerths (R, Plate II) prevail on the east sides of the continents. Toward the equator they become more leached and lateritic and gradually merge into the red tropical laterites (L, Plate II). These, in their old state, are the poorest of soils aside from such types as quartz sands, tundra soils, or the saline soils of deserts. Long exposure to rapid decay in warm, wet regions has almost completely disintegrated them into very fine, sticky clay so thoroughly leached as to be the mere skeleton of a soil. Soils which are more or less of this type explain why the level interfluves in many tropical regions support only grass or scanty forest, while the younger and more fertile soils on the slopes are cultivated. Many other tropical soils are very poor because the abundant rain causes them to be water-logged, as in the floodplains of the Amazon and New Guinea.

In spite of their poor quality many tropical soils support magnificent forests. This is possible partly because the trees have become adjusted to a watery environment and require a very small supply of minerals. Moreover, in tropical forests, as we have seen, trees of the same kind rarely grow together in large numbers. This means that no one kind of tree has a chance to exhaust the particular plant foods upon which it draws most heavily. This mixture of all kinds of trees, however, makes it difficult for the native who has to search among scores of species when he is looking for rubber, chicle, rosewood, dyewood, or mahogany.

The poverty of the soil helps to explain why tropical regions are so backward and often so sparsely populated. Climatically the Amazon basin is well fitted for rice, but the great floodplain is so water-logged that proper drainage and aeration of the soil are extremely difficult. The leached quality of the soil fosters the so-called "milpa" system which was mentioned in connection with rubber in Sumatra. This prevails in large sections of South America, the Caribbean region, southeastern Asia, the East Indies, and central Africa. According to this system the natives clear a milpa, or patch of land, let the trees and bushes become dry and burn them off in the dry season. Then, perhaps in holes punched with a pointed stick, they plant corn, pumpkins, "dry" rice, yams, or other crops. One crop, or at most two, exhausts the soil so badly that the fields are soon abandoned and new clearings are made elsewhere. Only by resting several years can the soil recover sufficiently for another crop. The fields that can be cultivated by such a laborious system must be very small. It is difficult to clear the hard-wood trees of the tropics from even an acre of land. So tropical people are not quite so inefficient and stupid as we sometimes think. Their handicaps are tremendous even without the added scourge of tropical diseases and the enervating effect of constantly warm, humid weather.

In limited parts of the tropics the handicap of lateritic soil is removed. For example, for about 2,500 miles near the eastern base of the Andes the tributaries of the Amazon, Orinoco, and La Plata cross a rugged strip where rain is abundant and the slopes are covered with soils which are still young enough so that they are not thoroughly leached into laterites. Sugar, coffee, cacao, and other plantation products grow admirably. Thus far the difficulties of transportation have almost prevented the development of this beautiful Yungas region, but some day it will probably develop rapidly.

Coffee and the Extreme Importance of Soils within the Tropics.— From all this we see why volcanic soils are so important in the tropics. They contain a high percentage of the basic elements which are especially needed as plant food, and they are often young enough to be in their best stage of fertility. As we saw at the beginning of this chapter, Java, with forty million people in an area only as large as Iowa, is able to support such a dense population because of its fresh volcanic soil. In southern Brazil, as P. E. James has shown, the future of the coffee industry depends on the volcanic soils. The early coffee plantations were established on the slopes near Rio de Janeiro. The planters knew nothing about old or young soils, or about leaching, but they did know that coffee does not grow well on the level uplands or in the water-logged valley bottoms. As time went on and the demand for coffee increased, the plantations spread southwestward, and the uplands of São Paulo became the great coffee center. When the plantations became old their yield declined, and new coffee trees did not thrive in them. The soil had become more or less exhausted. Hence the coffee planters went farther into the interior until they found richer soils derived from dark volcanic rocks. There the coffee industry appears to have found a place where it can continue permanently.

Such examples illustrate three great geographic principles: (1) Local variations in the age and character of the underlying rocks reach their maximum importance within the tropics. This is because soils weather so fast in the tropics that, unless they are quite young or contain an unusually high percentage of plant foods, they all assume almost the same poor quality. (2) The differences in the age and quality of the residual soil on slopes of varying steepness are especially important in these same regions. (3) The climate of tropical regions imposes a great handicap through lateritic soil as well as through disease, diet, and its direct effect upon domestic animals and man.

A Cross Section of the Soil from Humid to Dry Regions.—The reader has doubtless noticed that thus far we have spoken only of the pedalfers, or soils from which the lime has been largely leached leaving a great deal of aluminum and iron in the subsoil. Plate II shows that the full sequence of these from tundra to laterite is developed only on the east side of the continents. Accordingly our next step is to study the changes of the soil from the humid east to the dry west. This is best seen in the middle latitudes of the northern United States where the humid brownerths of the region of deciduous forests provide the best soils in our cross section from north to south. Plate II shows that in the United States the soils change from relatively light in the east to dark in the center, and then to light once more. In a previous chapter we saw that the eastern forest gives place to prairie in Illinois because of the growingly continental character of the climate toward the west. It will be remembered that grasses produce abundant short-lived roots which enrich the soil far more than do the long-lived roots of trees which live scores or hundreds of years. This is evident in the contrast between the brownerths of the forests of middle latitudes and the dark *prairi-erths* rich in humus (P in Plate II). These deep soils have an added advantage because they are formed in climates sufficiently dry so that a part at least of the soluble lime is left in the upper soil. The importance of grasses in improving the soil is well demonstrated by comparing A199 showing the yield of corn per acre in Illinois for ten years and A24 showing the distribution of the natural vegetation. In the prairie part of the state where the soil is a fine, dark, rich loam the yield of corn averages 35 to 43 bushels per acre. In the forested southern part where the soil is mainly a pale gray clay, it averages only 19 to 25 bushels. Glaciation has also influenced the soil, for the sharp transition from high to low yields south of the center of Illinois almost coincides with the southern edge of the ancient icesheet. The very best soils arise from a combination of several favorable conditions. The *blackerths*, as they are called (B in Plate II), are found in districts like Iowa and the Black Earth Region of southern Russia which are located near the southern limit of the ancient icesheet and in regions where the optimum conditions along a north and south line coincide with the optimum from east to west. Being unleached, or at least not harmfully leached, and being full of humus, these soils have plenty of lime and nitrates as well as potash, phosphates, and other essential ingredients. Hence they belong to the *pedocals*.

Farther west in the United States, or farther southeast in Eurasia, the drier climate reduces the amount of leaching and the scarcity of vegetation reduces the humus. Accordingly, from western North Dakota to western Texas we find semi-arid *brownerths* (B$_A$ in Plate II) which still retain most of their lime and other soluble basic materials and show little distinction between soil and subsoil. Although these soils have less humus than the black soils they are nearly as rich. Still farther in the interior, where the climate becomes more arid, the materials dissolved by the ground water are carried upward instead of downward. The rain here commonly moistens the soil only to a depth of 2 or 3 feet, and very little seeps away to reappear in springs. On the contrary, much of the water comes up again to the surface through capillary attraction. There it is evaporated and leaves the lime and other materials which it dissolved in the lower parts of the soil. Thus in dry regions we have the *grayerths* (G in Plate II) which display an

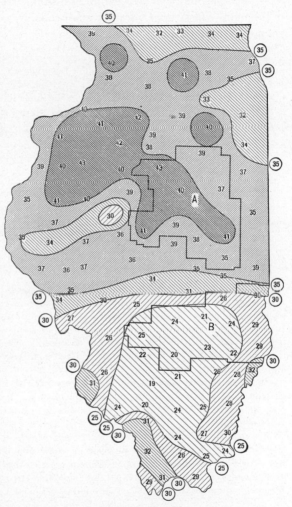

A—Yield of Corn per Acre in Illinois for Ten Years.

accumulation of basic or saline materials in the upper soil in contrast
with the leached acidic character of the soils of humid regions.   In
regions as dry as Utah and Nevada, humus is scarce and the upper
portion of the gray or light brown soil often contains a thin layer of
hard, whitish, more or less saline material, or *hard-pan*, in which lime
is the main constituent.   Many such soils are so full of salts that they
cannot be cultivated even when irrigated.

Exhaustion of the Soil.—If the same crop is cultivated year after year in almost
any soil the yield usually diminishes.   The lower lines in the two parts of A200 show
how the yield fell off at Rothamsted in England when wheat was cultivated year
after year on the same soil with no fertilizer.   The upper line in A shows what happened

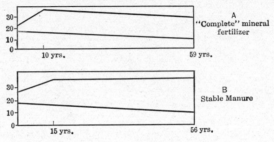

A—Effect of Fertilizers on Yield of Wheat.

when a "complete" mineral fertilizer which was supposed to contain all the elements
needed by the plant was added in suitable amounts each year.   The yield doubled
in ten years, and then declined slowly at the same rate as on the unfertilized plot.
In B the upper line shows what happened under similar circumstances when stable
manure, a more truly complete fertilizer, was used.   The yield increased more slowly
than with the complete fertilizer, but doubled in fifteen years and then retained its
high level steadily.

Such experiments not only demonstrate the extreme importance of fertilizers, but
likewise shed light on the important problem of the historic deterioration of soils.
Such deterioration undoubtedly takes place unless proper care is given to the soil.
It has sometimes been said that in spite of such care deterioration of the soil has been
a main element in the decline of China, Persia, Mesopotamia, Greece, Rome, Spain,
and North Africa, and in the decrease of rural population in New England and
New York.   A contrary view holds that in practically all countries the tracts which
have long been steadily cultivated are still the best.   The Chinese plains, the
Japanese coastal lands, the districts around Naples and Vienna, the Belgian lowland,
the Paris basin, southeastern England, the Connecticut Valley, and the market
garden regions around Boston, New York, and Philadelphia are examples of this in
their respective countries.   This means that cultivation and fertilization may
actually improve the soil.   A201 and the table below it throw light on this question.
They show the average yield of wheat per acre for twenty years.   The left hand end
of the upper line of the diagram represents the yield in Denmark, the best of the
twelve old regions where the yield of wheat per acre is very high.   A step to the
right in this line we find the level of the yield in the Netherlands, and so on down

to France on the right of the upper line. The lower solid line represents the yields of the twelve corresponding states or provinces of highest yield in the parts of the New World where wheat has longest been cultivated, as shown in the middle column of names; the dotted line and third column give the yield in the twelve new regions of highest yield. Irrigated regions like Egypt and Arizona have been omitted.

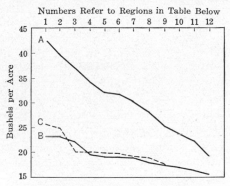

Numbers Refer to Regions in Table Below

A—Average Yield Per Acre of Wheat.

A. Old Regions		B. Older Parts of the New World		C. New Regions	
1. Denmark........	42.4	Maine............	23.1	British Columbia..	25.7
2. Netherlands.....	39.5	Ontario..........	23.1	Idaho............	24.6
3. Belgium........	36.6	Vermont.........	22.0	Wyoming.........	20.2
4. Irish Free State.	34.1*	New York........	19.8	New Zealand......	20.1
5. Great Britain...	31.9	New Jersey.......	19.1	Tasmania.........	20.0
6. Switzerland.....	31.5	Wisconsin........	19.1	Washington.......	20.0
7. Sweden.........	29.7	Nova Scotia......	19.0	Oregon...........	19.1
8. Germany.......	28.1	Pennsylvania.....	17.7	Iowa.............	18.9
9. Norway........	25.1	Michigan.........	17.4	California........	17.3
10. Czechoslovakia..	23.6*	New Brunswick...	17.2	Colorado.........	17.2
11. Japan..........	22.3	Quebec...........	16.7	Manitoba.........	16.7
12. France.........	19.4	Ohio.............	16.6	Montana.........	16.5
Average....	30.4		19.2		19.7

* Ten-year average.

Evidently the old regions raise far more wheat per acre than the newer ones, while in the new regions it makes little difference how long the land has been cultivated. Nevertheless, the yield in the newest regions declined 5.6 per cent from the decade of 1910–19 to that of 1920–29, while that of the older new regions, the middle group in the preceding table, declined only 3.6 per cent. On the contrary, in the oldest regions good cultivation and careful selection of seed *increased* the yield 7.3 per cent.

All this seems to indicate that when soil is not fertilized, especially if the same crop is planted year after year, its fertility usually declines rapidly at first and then more slowly. Thus the soil may ultimately become of very poor quality. A lateritic tropical soil may be exhausted by a single crop. A young volcanic soil, however, like that around Naples, may show almost no deterioration although cultivated without fertilization for many generations. If, however, the land is fertilized and the crops are rotated, and especially if the fertilizer is manure as in Holland, or sewage as in China, the soil may retain its fertility indefinitely, as it does in Japan, Italy, and Belgium.

The Use of Fertilizers.—Man's method of using the soil makes it necessary to use fertilizers. According to nature's method, plants decay where they grow. They return to the soil what they have taken from it, and the leguminous plants like peas and clover add new materials in the form of nitrates. When man reaps the crops he removes materials which nature cannot easily replace. The annual tobacco crop in the United States takes from the soil more than 28 million pounds of nitrogen, 29 million pounds of potassium, and $2\frac{1}{2}$ million pounds of phosphorus. Each year the sewage of the United States carries off to the sea 600 to 1,200 million pounds of nitrogen, 200 to 400 million pounds of potassium, and 80 to 300 million pounds of phosphorus which came originally from the fields.

In addition to these three materials, a good soil, as we have seen, must contain magnesium, iron, sulphur, manganese, boron, and lime. The first five are needed in very small quantities, and have as yet created no recognized problem. Lime is needed in larger amounts and is often absent, but limestone is so widely distributed that lime can commonly be procured without great difficulty. A little silicon, chlorine, and sodium are also taken from the soil by plants, but crops can grow without them. The problem of getting enough phosphorus, potassium, and nitrogen, on the other hand, is extremely important. The following figures give some idea of the rapidity with which these may become exhausted. They show the number of years in which a crop of beets, if planted in the same soil every year without fertilizers, would use up the various elements in an average soil of middle latitudes:

	Years
Calcium in the form of lime	1260
Phosphorus in the form of phosphoric acid	240
Potassium in the form of potash	77
Nitrogen in the form of nitrates and ammonia	47

The Nitrate Fertilizers.—The chief sources of nitrate as fertilizers have long been the manure of domestic animals and the sewage of cities and villages. These are still almost the only fertilizers in less advanced countries like China, and continue to be important in modern countries, although sewage is greatly neglected in the United States. Even during the nineteenth century, however, Chile salt petre became of outstanding importance as a commercial fertilizer, and in later years there has been a tremendous development of the production of synthetic nitrogen. In the few years from 1925 to 1928 the total world output of such nitrogen doubled. The nitrates of Chile are all derived from natural deposits in the Atacama Desert, the narrow stretch between the Andes and the Pacific Coast in northern Chile. For years the British companies that worked these fields not only ruled the world market, but by means of export taxes provided a great part of the Chilean government's income. The moment the value of the deposits was recognized, this once useless desert became the political focus of the three adjoining countries, Chile, Peru, and Bolivia. Chile emerged victorious from the salt petre war of 1879 and has kept this section ever since.

After the World War the increase in the production of synthetic nitrogen threatened to ruin the Chilean salt petre production, but in later years a revival took place. In 1928 about 500,000 tons of Chile salt petre constituted a fourth of the world's commercial production of nitrogen. Since then, commercial agreements that have been made to regulate the relative production of Chile and of the great European manufacturers of nitrates have not proved permanent. Political as well as commercial antagonisms threaten the nitrate trade.

The greatest potential source of nitrogen is the air. Leguminous plants get nitrogen from the air by having on their roots little nodules in which live nitrogen-fixing bacteria. For this reason clover is an admirable crop, not only for forage but to be plowed under as fertilizer. When clover seed is inoculated with the bacteria the large nodules thus produced may make the crop worth more for its nitrogen than for its hay. In the modern synthetic nitrogen industry very strong electric currents are used to fix the nitrogen of the air in the form of ammonia, nitrate of lime, or cyanamide. Germany is here the main producer, with more than a third of the world's entire output. Other European countries, however, try to be self-supporting, and so Europe produces at present 60 per cent, leaving 25 per cent to Chile, while the United States produces scarcely 10 per cent.

Potash.—The greater part (80 per cent) of the world's potash comes from vast deposits deep underground at Stassfurt in Germany. A second productive region, that of southern Alsace, passed from German to French control after the World War. Since 1926 an agreement between these two countries allows Germany to supply about 70 per cent of the world's potash requirements and France 30 per cent. The rest of the world still produces very little. In the United States, which produces only 1 per cent of the potash salts, some is obtained from potash-bearing brines which are pumped from the beds of nearly dry salt lakes in Nebraska and southeastern California. Large amounts have also been discovered in deep-lying desert beds in Texas where oil wells were being drilled. The Dead Sea in Palestine also contains an enormous quantity. The greatest known supply of potash is found in sea-water, but it is so diluted there that it is hard to get. Kelp and other large seaweeds, however, make excellent fertilizers as they contain large quantities of potash.

Phosphates.—The need of phosphorus in foods was demonstrated in Wisconsin by feeding animals with rations deficient in this element. The animals drew phosphorus from their own bones, which became so weak that the animals collapsed. Phosphate fertilizers are derived partly from rocks like apatite and partly from material such as old bones and the slag of iron furnaces. In contrast with its deficit in nitrates and potash, the United States has abundant supplies of phosphates in the rocks of Tennessee and Florida. Phosphates are also produced in fair amount in some European countries, but the supplies there are entirely insufficient to supply the great demand. Nevertheless, the former strong position of the United States as a phosphate exporter to Europe has been successfully challenged by French North Africa, which now produces more than half of the world supply, compared with about a third in the United States.

Distribution of the Use of Fertilizers.—All advanced countries use the manure of domestic animals for fertilizer. One of the reasons for the enormous yield of crops around the North Sea is the large number of cattle which supply fertilizer for the fields. Belgium, Holland, and Denmark each have over 150 cattle per square mile, or three times as many as Poland and Rumania. In our own country the farmers from New England to Iowa and those on the Pacific Coast are greatly bene-fited in the same way. This is very different from the unwise method of many backward countries where manure is used as fuel. In northern India, Persia, Turkey, Egypt, North Africa, and the dry parts of China,

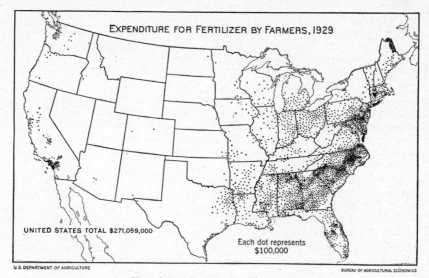

EXPENDITURE FOR FERTILIZER BY FARMERS, 1929

UNITED STATES TOTAL $271,059,000

Each dot represents $100,000

U.S. DEPARTMENT OF AGRICULTURE   BUREAU OF AGRICULTURAL ECONOMICS

A—Use of Fertilizer in the United States.

cakes of manure are plastered against the mud walls to be dried and used as fuel.

Mineral fertilizers are used mainly in the eastern United States and western Europe. A204 shows that in the northern states such use occurs mainly where market gardens are located on sandy soils as on Long Island and in New Jersey, or where special crops are cultivated like the tobacco of the Connecticut Valley and the potatoes of Aroos-took County in Maine. In the South the use of chemical fertilizers is more common than in the North. This is partly because the soil is poorer, partly because cattle are less abundant (A-B415), and partly because of the prevalence of crops like cotton and tobacco which exhaust the soil.

The great use of fertilizer in western Europe as compared with other regions is shown in the following table, which also shows how the relative use of the three kinds of fertilizer varies according to the quality of the soil and the abundance of local supplies.

CONSUMPTION OF NITROGEN (N), PHOSPHORIC ACID (P₂O₅) AND POTASH (K₂O)

(In *pounds* per *acre* of arable land)

Country	N	P₂O₅	K₂O	Total
Holland............................	98	247	225	570
Belgium............................	144	258	122	524
Germany...........................	75	99	143	317
Denmark...........................	43	118	22	183
France.............................	30	101	34	165
Great Britain......................	32	100	31	163
Spain..............................	29	91	6	126
Poland.............................	12	18	18	48

Note the evidence of highly intensive cultivation in Belgium and Holland, where special stress is laid on truck farming. Compare this with the lower intensity in large grain raisers like France and Germany, and in dairy districts like Denmark and Great Britain. In Germany the use of potash is logically very prominent. The table also shows the relative backwardness of southern Europe (Spain) and eastern Europe (Poland). In the advanced countries a recent development is the introduction of compound fertilizers, containing the three chief requisites in practical quantities.

Although the sewage and human waste of cities, villages, and farms are the greatest of all available sources of fertilizer, they are used to only a limited extent. Japan, China, and Java utilize human waste very fully. Only in this way are those countries able to support such dense populations for century after century. The number of animals there is small, and practically all the farm products are consumed by human beings. Thus the waste of the mineral constituents of the soil would be enormous if our methods of disposing of sewage were followed. In the advanced parts of the world, only a few large cities as yet use their sewage for fertilizer. At Melbourne in Australia, the sewage is led some miles from the city and discharged on a large, level tract near the ocean. The Australians dare not use this land for vegetables for fear of disease, but there is really little danger. All the sewage is now used for grass, which grows wonderfully and supports large numbers of cattle. In Paris the sewage is used for market gardens, where the combination of irrigation and fertilization often produces more than one large crop from the same land in a single season.

In large parts of the world, fertilizers are still used very sparingly. In the newer parts of Canada, Australia, the United States, and South America, soil depletion has shown few harmful results as yet, but a serious problem may develop later. In Russia, Africa, and especially India it is one of the great reasons for poverty. One of the main problems of the future is how to find fertilizers for such regions. Another is how to utilize the sewage everywhere.

Effect of the Soil on Social Conditions.—Differences in the soil are associated with marked social differences. This is illustrated in A206, which shows the conditions among the farm population of the counties of Iowa which do not contain towns of 15,000 or more. The counties have been divided into five equal groups according to the value of the land alone per acre without regard to the farm buildings. The upper left hand part of A206 shows that at the last census the average values

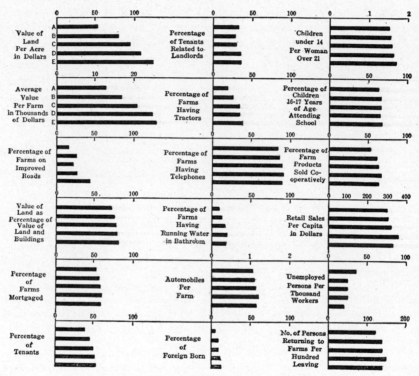

A—Economic and Social Relationships of the Soil in Iowa.

ranged from $57 in the 17 poorest counties to $123 in the 17 richest counties. This difference is largely due to soil, although relief and accessibility to good roads also play a part. The part played by relief is evident from A206, where the counties with the least valuable land (Group A) include the somewhat rougher ones in the northeast, as well as those in the south. The part played by good roads appears in section 3 of A206, where we see that nearly half the farms in the counties with the most valuable land (Group E) are located on hard roads, while in the other groups the percentage is much smaller. This fact accounts for the way in which the counties of Group E fail to show the best conditions in many other respects, being surpassed by the fourth group of counties (*D*), where the land owes its value to its productivity without much regard to transportation.

If allowance is made for the effect of good roads in raising the values in the counties of Group *E* it is very clear that the quality of the soil is closely associated with a large number of economic and social conditions. Since the farms in all sections are nearly the same size, their average value (2 in A206) is twice as great on the best land as on the poorest. No. 4 shows that the farmers on the better land do not put so large a percentage of the value of their farms into buildings as do the

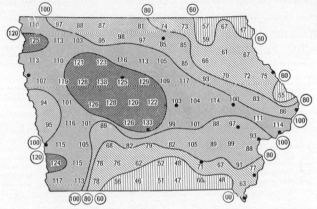

A—Value of Farm Land per Acre without Buildings, and
Cities of over 15,000 in Iowa per 1930 Census.

others. Yet their buildings are actually worth considerably more per farm. But the percentage of mortgages among them (5) is higher than among those on the poorer land. Bankers prefer to lend money on the security of the richer soil. The percentage of tenancy (6) is also high on the good soil. This is common all over the world, for only on good soil can a man's labor produce enough to provide a living not only for his own family, but for at least a part of someone else's. It is interesting to note, however, that on the good land the tendency for the owner to rent his farm to a son or other relative is stronger than on the poor lands (7). Tractors (8), telephones (9), bathrooms with running water (10), and automobiles (11) all become more and more abundant as one goes from the poorer to the better soil. The percentage of foreign born (12) also increases; there are more children per family (13); and a slightly larger percentage of the children continue to go to school after they are old enough to work (14). The larger families are probably due to the fact that the proportion of tenancy on the good land is high.

If we divide the counties solely according to the degree of tenancy the fact that tenancy and large families go together becomes still more evident. When it comes to buying and selling, the same sort of differences are still apparent. The people on the poorer land are less inclined than the others to make use of the farmer's cooperative agencies (15), and they do not buy so much from the stores (16). The people on the most valuable land, however, fail to maintain their position in this respect as well as in many others. But since their land presumably owes part of its value to accessibility, rather than productivity, they probably cannot afford to buy so much as do those in the counties of Group *D* where the land owes its value more completely to its fertility. Or perhaps, being on better roads, the people whose land is held at the highest price are more likely to buy in the cities which are not included in our study. Finally we see in No. 17 that in 1930 during the depression there was less unemployment on the good land than on the poor. Closely related to this is the fact that at that time more people returned to the good land than to the poor (18). A multitude of other relationships like these might be brought out if space permitted and statistics were available. A whole book might well be devoted to studying such aspects of social geography. Here we can merely point out how intimately all phases of life are bound up with the soil beneath our feet.

EXERCISES

1. Find two or more places in your vicinity where the effect of different soils upon vegetation can be seen. In each case describe the color, texture, and depth of the soil and the character of the subsoil. Show how these conditions influence the vegetation.

2. From your own observation, if possible, or otherwise from your reading, describe an example showing the effect of good versus poor soil upon agriculture and upon economic and social conditions.

3. Explain the conditions which have caused the world's largest area of exceptionally good soil, the Black Earth Region, to form a great band extending from northern Rumania through the Ukraine and across southern Russia into Siberia (Plate II). Explain why the average yield of wheat per acre there is low and probably will never be so high as in countries like Denmark.

4. Give reasons for thinking that the soil in certain areas known to you is either residual or transported. What evidence is there as to the agency by which the transported soil was carried?

5. Why is a knowledge of soils often of value to a real estate agent? To a banker? What other kinds of people in addition to farmers might be aided by a knowledge of soil conditions? Tell why in each case.

6. From the maps of soil and population in this book, or in your atlas, what kinds of soils seem to support (*a*) the most dense populations, and (*b*) the most sparse populations? What other geographic factors, however, may be important in determining the density of population?

CHAPTER XI

ECONOMIC, SOCIAL, AND POLITICAL FACTORS IN LAND UTILIZATION

The Balance between Economic and Purely Geographic Factors.— In Chapter IV we saw that regions like southern New England, where the yield of corn per acre is exceptionally high, are by no means the ones where the largest percentage of the cultivated land is devoted to that crop. In Chapter V we also saw that a large part of the world's wheat is grown in relatively unfavorable climates, while some of the best areas like the Middle Atlantic States raise almost none. This same sort of disagreement between possible and actual productivity is evident for many other crops, such as cotton, flax, rye, and rice. A similar condition applies to animals. In regions like England where the yield of both wool and meat per sheep is high, the farmers do not depend upon sheep nearly so much as do those of large areas in countries like Turkey and Persia where the sheep are far less productive. In all these cases the general principle is the same: economic conditions make it less profitable to raise certain products under optimum conditions of climate, soil, and relief than under far less favorable natural conditions. Corn illustrates the matter so well that we shall discuss it in detail. Bear in mind that the general principles which apply to corn apply also to a great many other products.

The Disagreement between the Yield of Corn and the Use of the Land.—We have already noticed that a high yield of corn per acre (B57) does not necessarily mean large total production. The disagreement between yield per acre and total production is still more evident when we study the percentage of harvested land devoted to corn (A210). From Connecticut, with 3 per cent of its harvested land in corn, the percentage increases steadily toward the west until it reaches 43 in Iowa. The yield per acre, however, falls from 46 in Connecticut to 27 in Missouri, although good soil and good climate raise it to 38 in Iowa. South of the Corn Belt the disagreement between the yield per acre and the percentage of harvested land in corn is equally notable. In Kentucky, where the yield is 27 bushels, half the harvested land is in corn, while in Tennessee, Alabama, Georgia, and Florida, the percentages of corn land range from 37 to 44, even though the yield per acre falls to 14 bushels in Georgia and Florida.

The way in which farmers devote much land to corn even when the yield is poor is astonishing. It is especially impressive when we investigate counties rather than states. We then find that the maximum use of the land for corn occurs in certain low southern areas with heavy clayey soils, like those of northern Florida, and in mountainous sections such as the Appalachian highlands of eastern Kentucky and Tennessee. In these areas, three-fifths of the harvested land is used for corn. This is the more remarkable when we recall that land devoted to hay forms

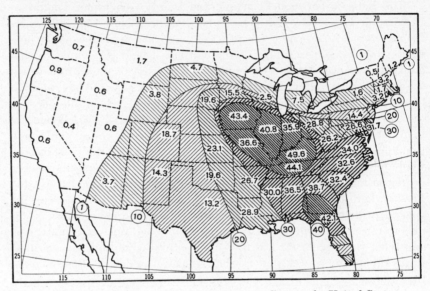

A—Percentage of Harvested Land Devoted to Corn in the United States.

part of the harvested land on which A210 is based. If hay be excluded, the farmers of ten of the poorest counties in the mountains of eastern Kentucky at the time of the last census devoted 72 per cent of their cropped land to corn, while those of ten of the richest counties in the neighboring Blue Grass lowland devoted only 45 per cent. Thus corn is of predominating interest to the farmers of the United States in three regions: (a) the rich, level, central agricultural section where the soil is fertile and the yield per acre high; (b) the poor, mountainous southerly sections where the soil is infertile and the yield low; and (c) the gently hilly Southeast, where the soil is fairly good but the yield low.

The Economic Basis of the Disagreement between Yield per Acre and Land Utilization.—The extensive utilization of the land for corn in these three contrasting areas and the failure to do so in the Northeast illustrate the importance of economic and social factors in problems of economic geography. The principle of geographic distribution here involved is very simple: among the many products which the farmer might raise he chooses those which afford him the greatest satisfaction. Where the farmers belong to a progressive community with high standards of living and a fully developed transportation system, as in Indiana or Holland, the most satisfactory crops are those which afford the greatest net income after allowance has been made for labor, fertilizer, the cost of machinery, and the needs of the soil in the way of rotation of

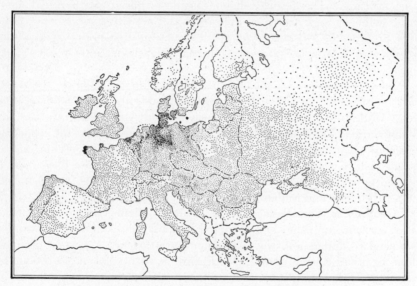

A—Distribution of Swine in Europe before the World War.

crops. In less advanced regions the most satisfactory crops may be those that give the largest amount of food per acre. This is likely to happen where the farmers know little of the markets in other places, or where they do very little planning as to the sale of their crops. It also happens where the farms are small and transportation poorly developed. This is preeminently true in Japan, although the silk raised there illustrates the desire to raise crops that give a good return in money. In most regions the farmer's conduct is also influenced by ignorance and by social customs. His ancestors for many generations have raised certain crops. His family and neighbors are so used to these as food that they prefer them even though other kinds are more healthful. Therefore, he raises them regardless of the fact that modern science shows him new and much better ways of farming. People like that which they are accustomed to, even though it may be far from the best. China with its rice and millet is one of the best examples of this, and so is Ireland, where potatoes occupy 60 per cent of all the land used to raise food for men.

The influence of social customs in the distribution of a product is illustrated by A211, which shows the distribution of swine before the World War. At that time the Russian section of what is now Poland was within the so-called "pale," where Jews had more rights than in other parts of Russia. So they were very numerous and influential, as they still are. The Jewish religion forbids people to eat pork. Therefore, swine are very scarce, as appears from the scarcity of dots in A211. The presence of Moslems, who also look askance on pork, explains the scarcity of dots in the parts of Bulgaria, Yugoslavia, and Greece, which once were part of Turkey.

In very backward regions, especially within the tropics, the most satisfactory crop may be the one which yields the most food for the least work. The people of Uganda in central Africa illustrate this by living largely on green plantains, which are practically the same as bananas. Or again a crop which forms a poor kind of food and has a small yield per acre may be the most satisfactory because it can stand droughts or insect pests better than other crops. This is true of millet in north China and Sudan.

Geographic Variations in Cost of Production.—Before we decide why corn or any other crop is raised in some places and not in others we need to understand the geographic variation in the cost of production, in prices, and in profits. With corn, as with many other products, the regions that make the most profit are those which spend the most to insure good production. A214 is a map of the average cost of producing a bushel of corn during a five-year period when the United States government obtained reports from representative farmers in each of the states. In these reports the farmer's own work is reckoned at a regular rate based on the wages in his part of the country. The same is done for the work of his family and his animals. Each bushel of corn is also reckoned as costing a certain share of the rent of the land. Of course, most farmers own their land and therefore pay no rent. That often leads them to think that they are making more of a profit than they really are, for they forget that if they sold their land they could get quite an income simply by investing the money. When these things, as well as the actual payments for machinery, fertilizer, labor, and other expenses were taken into account, the cost of producing a bushel of corn among these representative farmers varied from 55 cents in Illinois to $1.19 in South Carolina. During the same years the average price received by the farmers was 69 cents in Illinois and $1.03 in South Carolina, as appears in B214. In other words, the average Illinois farmer got a profit of 14 cents a bushel, or $4.90 an acre, on his corn, while the South Carolina farmer lost 16 cents a bushel, or $2.56 per acre (A215). Some of the states from Virginia and West Virginia northeastward made a greater profit per acre than did Illinois. All the southeastern states from South Carolina to Texas, on the other hand, suffered a loss. This seems very strange when we recall that in these states the percentage of harvested land devoted to corn is very high. A survey of 300 farms in Illinois and about 60 in Carolina shows the following reasons for this curious geographical distribution of profit and loss: (1) The average cost of raising and marketing an acre of corn in the two states during these years was almost the same, namely $22, but in Illinois the yield was 35 bushels and in South Carolina only 16. The high cost of labor in Illinois is offset by the much larger amount of fertilizer required in the South, but even this does not make up for the greater fertility of the northern soil, the greater use of machinery, the better plowing, and the more favorable climate in the North. (2) The area devoted to corn on the Illinois farms averages twice as great as in South Carolina. This leads to a considerable reduction in the cost not only of production but of marketing.

Geographic Variations in Price.—Corn affords a good illustration of geographic variations in prices. Since most of the crop is consumed on the farms or in stockyards close at hand, the price is largely determined by the local demand in comparison with the local supply. The resulting prices for a five-year period as shown in B214 have already claimed our attention. B215 shows the yield of corn per farm during the same five years. The two maps are closely similar, although in the South the shading in the map of production is not quite so light as in that of price. Another way of comparing the abundance of corn with the price is seen in the following table where the states are divided into eight groups of six each on the basis of the amount of corn raised per farm:

		Average Yield of Corn per Farm, Bushels	Average Price
Group	I (Greatest yield of corn per farm)	1364	$0.66
Group	II	547	0.78
Group	III	310	0.82
Group	IV	228	0.89
Group	V	164	0.96
Group	VI	130	1.00
Group	VII	75	1.09
Group	VIII	21	1.11

These figures agree with A19 and B57 in showing that where much corn is produced the price is low, while where little is produced the price

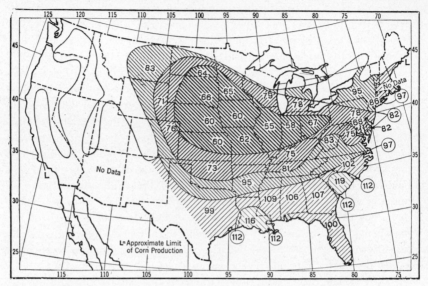

A—Average Cost of Producing a Bushel of Corn in the United States (in cents).

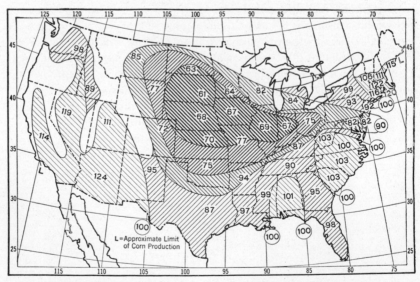

B—Average Price Received by the Farmers of the United States per Bushel of Corn.

is high. A similar law applies to all products, but is modified by the fact that in many cases, such as wheat, the market for a product lies

far from the place where it is raised.   Then the general price level of a
crop is set by production in the world as a whole.   Nevertheless, the

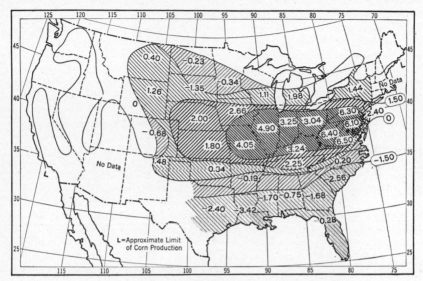

A—Annual Profit or Loss per Acre of Corn in Dollars.

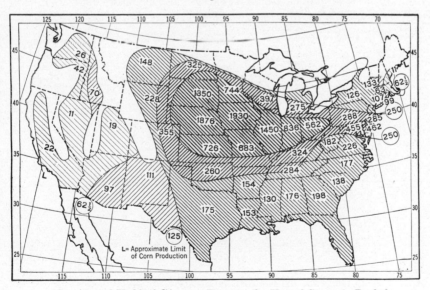

B—Annual Yield of Corn per Farm in the United States in Bushels.

differences in price between one region and another are greatly influenced by the local supply and demand.

Reasons Why the Northeast Raises So Little Corn.—We are now ready to see why corn is not raised in some regions that are very well fitted for it.   The main reason why New England and the Middle Atlantic States raise so little corn is that good land is scarce and the population is numerous and highly prosperous. Under such circumstaces it does not pay to raise much corn, wheat, or any other crop that can easily and cheaply be transported.   This is especially true in the coastal belt of most intensive manufacturing from Portland, Maine, through Boston and New York to Baltimore.   The scarcity of good farm land here, as we have seen, arises partly from the poor quality of the thin, rocky soil in large areas, and partly from the hilly character of the relief.

Since the transportation system of the United States is very well developed, it is not necessary to raise all sorts of products close to this great manufacturing region. To bring a bushel of corn from the Mississippi River to New York or Boston may cost a fifth or even half as much as the value of the corn in Missouri.   But this is a small matter compared with the old days when corn had to be carried on horseback and the cost of a bushel was doubled by transporting it a hundred miles.   Accordingly the crops which pay the farmers best in the Northeast are those that are so heavy or perishable that it costs a great deal to bring them from the Middle West or other regions where good land is abundant.   The large and prosperous urban and industrial population among which these northeastern farms are located is able to buy great amounts of milk, eggs, fresh vegetables, berries, orchard fruits, and even flowers, ornamental shrubs, and hothouse products.   These products command high prices, and the possible profits per acre are far larger than with wheat or corn.   Here are the approximate average values of different kinds of crops per acre for the entire United States or for certain sections during five years according to recent returns of the United States Department of Agriculture.

	Value per Acre in Dollars
Rye	11
Wheat	16
Corn	20
Cotton	26
Sweet potatoes	90
Potatoes	120
Late cantaloupes (New York)	130
Tobacco	150
Early cantaloupes (Lower Valley of Texas)	170
Late cabbage (Pennsylvania)	200
Medium early cabbage (Virginia)	220
Late strawberries (New York)	420
Early strawberries (Florida)	560

The differences are extraordinary.   All the cereals stand low, but corn is worth almost twice as much per acre as rye.   Cotton is worth still more, but its value is small compared with that of vegetables and fruits.   Even the sweet potatoes on an average acre are worth $90, while the strawberries are worth from $400 to $600.   Of course, it costs more to raise and harvest an acre of cotton than an acre of wheat, and still more for an acre of tobacco, cabbages, or strawberries.   In spite of this, the chances of making a good profit are enormously greater with the more expensive crops. From an acre of land devoted to greenhouses the profit may be as great as from a

thousand acres devoted to rye.   Moreover, the comparatively high cost not only
of transporting these more expensive products but also of keeping them fresh, gives
the farmers who live close to the industrial centers two great advantages.   First,
their expenses for transportation are less than are those of the farmers who live
farther away.   Second, when similar vegetables, fruits, or flowers from near and
from remote places are both on sale at the same time, the local product is often
better because fresher.   It therefore brings a higher price.   If meat, milk, and eggs
were added to this table we should find that where there is plenty of rain and a good
market the raising of meat often yields a much larger return per acre than do the
cereals and cotton, but not so large as the vegetables and fruits.   Milk, chickens,
and eggs yield still larger returns per acre.   Thus the kinds of farming that pay
best in the Northeast are dairying, market gardening, poultry raising, and the raising
of fruit and other special crops like the onions and tobacco of the Connecticut
Valley.

Economic Factors in the Utilization of the Land in the Corn Belt.—In the Corn
Belt, especially the western part, geographic and economic conditions combine to
cause a large percentage of the land to be used for corn or else for other kinds of
animal food such as hay and fodder.   Geographically this region which centers in
central Illinois and Iowa lies far enough north so that the climate is extremely healthful for animals as well as excellent for hay and clover.   It lies far enough south to be
within the limits of corn, but on the very edge of the area where that crop will grow,
and thus in the zone of maximum yield per acre.   It also lies far enough east so that
the rainfall, especially in summer, is abundant and reliable.   The excellent effect of
the food and climate on livestock may be judged in part from A218 and B218.
These show that the average weight of the cattle slaughtered here is greater than in
any other part of the country except California, while the hogs are larger only in
New York and New England.   Then, too, this prairie region, as is well known,
possesses vast expanses of level soil which is of the highest quality, so that cultivation
is easy and the yield of crops per acre is high.   Thus it is geographically almost ideal
for raising meat.

Good as these geographic conditions are, they would not foster the raising of
corn and the fattening of livestock on anything like the present scale unless the
location and economic conditions were also favorable.   The central part of the Corn
Belt lies far enough west to be beyond the region where manufacturing is most fully
developed and where the population is very dense.   This fact, together with the
abundance of level and easily used land, means that only a small part of the farm
land is needed for the production of milk, eggs, fruit, vegetables, and the other
products which are so important in the East and also in California.   The climate and
soil are not especially adapted to tobacco growing, and still less to sweet potatoes and
cotton.   If Iowa tried to raise large crops of the other kinds that have a high value
per acre in the table on page 216, she would at once have to compete with regions
farther east which are nearer to the main markets for such products.   Iowa's location, on the other hand, makes corn, hay, and fodder very profitable crops.   Therefore 92 per cent of all the harvested land is devoted to these crops together with oats
which are also fed to animals.   A hog weighs only about one-fifth and a steer
one-tenth as much as the corn that is commonly used in fattening it.   The animals
or their meat can be transported for only a fraction of what it would cost to transport
all their feed.   Therefore it pays to bring the animals to the corn rather than to carry
the corn to the animals.   The location of the Corn Belt is very favorable for this
because large areas of the Great Plains that are too dry for this crop lie to the west,

while the warmer areas to the south do not raise nearly so much corn per acre. Nevertheless, these areas which are not so good for corn have abundant grass which

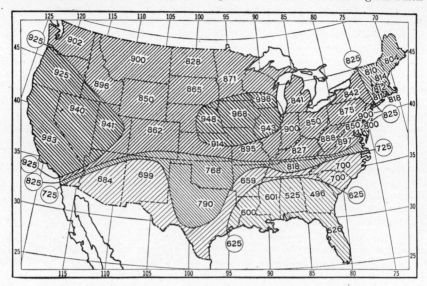

A—Average Weight of Cattle per Head in the United States.

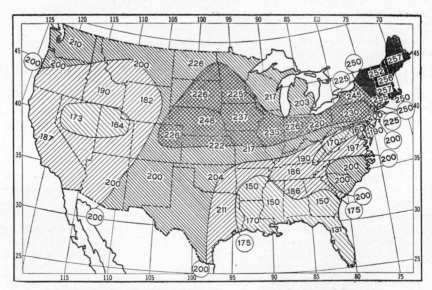

B—Average Weight of Hogs Slaughtered in the United States.

is good for raising animals, but not for fattening them. Thus the dry plains from the western Dakotas south to Texas can raise many cattle and even hogs, but cannot

easily fatten them.   Accordingly it pays to ship these animals to Iowa, Illinois, and
other parts of the Corn Belt.   The animals thus move toward the eastern markets
as well as toward the corn.   The most profitable thing the Corn Belt farmers can
do is to buy them, fatten them, and sell them to be taken East as meat.

Why So Much of the Land is Utilized for Corn in the South.—The surprising
amount of land used for corn in the southeastern states from Kentucky to Florida
(A210) is the next problem that confronts us.   This condition is the more surprising
when we remember that the yield of corn per acre is here much lower than in the
North Atlantic States or the Corn Belt (B57).   In spite of this low yield the farmers
use a third or even a half of their land for corn.   Where cotton will grow, most of
the remainder is devoted to that crop.   A219 shows that more than half the harvested
land is devoted to cotton in a belt extending from central North Carolina through
Georgia and Alabama to Mississippi.   There the belt widens and extends up the
Mississippi Valley to southern Missouri, while westward it expands over much of
Arkansas, Louisiana, and Texas.   In the whole state of Mississippi no less than 60 per
cent of all the harvested land is
devoted to cotton, and over 90
per cent to corn and cotton together.   This is because cotton
gives a larger return per acre
in money than does any other
crop that most of the farmers
in the South are in the habit of
raising.   Some, to be sure, raise
winter vegetables and fruits, but
the areas where this prevails are
relatively small and usually near
the coast (B360).   For the over-

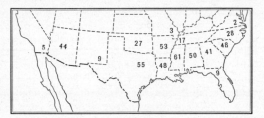

A—Percentage of Harvested Land in Cotton per
1930 Census.

whelming majority of colored farmers cotton is the only important cash crop.   But
cotton cannot be eaten.   Corn, on the other hand, makes good food for both man
and beast.   Although wheat is generally preferred for human use, the warm, moist
climate causes the yield in the South to be so small that the crop is rarely worth
raising.   Therefore, in the old days before railroads and automobile roads made
transportation easy, corn became the staple food product and the staple feed for
animals.   The social habit thus established still persists.   Even among southerners
who can afford wheat or any other kind of food, corn is still eaten by choice to an
extent unknown in the North.   Among vast numbers of the poorer people, especially
the Negroes, money is so scarce that the farmers prefer to feed themselves with their
own corn rather than pay for wheat.   Not only is the farm price of wheat higher
than that of corn, but the farmer who buys wheat flour has to pay milling and
railway charges, and the profits of commission merchants and store keepers.   Except
in favored localities the conditions of transportation also make it difficult to get a
profit from high-priced products like early vegetables and fruit, and correspondingly
profitable to raise food for both man and beast directly on the farm where it is to be
consumed.   The main highways in the South, to be sure, are excellent, but the minor
roads on which a large part of the farmers live are often very muddy and slippery.
Where transportation is particularly well developed and the farmers are especially
progressive, this concentration on corn and cotton does not prevail.   But elsewhere
the farmers must use their land for something, and they are conservative about
making changes.   Corn at any rate furnishes good food for man and beast.   Thus

we see why at least 80 per cent of all the harvested land is devoted to corn and cotton in most parts of the southern states from South Carolina through Georgia, Alabama, Mississippi, Arkansas, Louisiana, and eastern Texas.

Why Mountain Farm Land is Largely Utilized for Corn.—We have already seen that because corn is harvested by hand it is a good grain for slopes. This, in itself, helps to explain why the maximum utilization of farm land for corn is found in rugged regions like the Ozarks and the southern Appalachians. Moreover, corn can be used in the green form as well as ripe; it can be left on the stalk a long time before harvesting; and the stalks make good fodder. Another important fact is that the mountain farms are generally small and their improved land is still more limited. This means that the farmers are poor. Therefore, they are under a special compulsion to raise the crops which will give them the most food, and not those which are more nutritious or appetizing. The fact that the roads among mountains are usually difficult also tends to make the people poor, and this leads again to the use of the crops which provide the greatest amount of food per acre, and in which the use of machinery is not so important as with wheat and other small grains. Corn is also a favorite crop among certain mountaineers because it can easily be converted into whiskey. They speak of the yield of corn in "gallons" per acre. The value of a pound of whiskey is many times as great as that of a pound of the corn from which it is made. Hence whiskey is a profitable product in regions where transportation is expensive. The inaccessibility of the mountains is also a help in this respect, because illicit stills can easily be concealed in remote and forested valleys. In addition to all these economic conditions, the people of remote mountain regions tend to be more conservative than do those of more accessible areas. This in turn tends to perpetuate any old custom such as that of relying largely on a single crop like corn.

Where a Surplus of Wheat is Raised.—Wheat, like corn, affords an excellent example of the effect of economic conditions upon the geographic distribution of crops and prices. It differs from corn mainly in two respects. First, it is so widely raised and so easily transported that the price is greatly influenced by the crops of the world as a whole as well as by the local supply and demand. Second, the methods of cultivation vary far more for wheat than for corn.

The parts of A221 that are most heavily shaded produce a surplus of wheat that can steadily be relied upon. The areas that are lightly shaded with lines produce more wheat than is needed for local consumption, but the exportable surplus is small compared with the population and often disappears in bad years. A comparison of this map with A28 shows that although certain dotted areas like Manchuria, India, France, and Italy produce a great deal of wheat they have little or no surplus. In fact, a *large* surplus which can be relied on year after year for use in other countries is found in only three regions. The most important of these extends from Oklahoma on the south to central Alberta on the north, and reaches westward to Washington and Oregon. It is divided between the United States and Canada, and winter wheat is raised in the south and spring wheat in the north. It ships its wheat mainly eastward via the Great Lakes to the eastern United States and Canada and to Europe, but some goes west to Puget Sound, some south by way of the Mississippi River, and some has begun to go to Europe via Hudson Bay. Nevertheless, this North American wheat area is distinctly a unit. Its surplus is so huge that it not only feeds the United States and Canada, but also furnishes about half of all the wheat that enters into foreign commerce.

Second in importance among wheat-exporting areas comes the South American wheat region, mainly in central Argentina but spreading out into Uruguay. Its surplus for export is often more than half as great

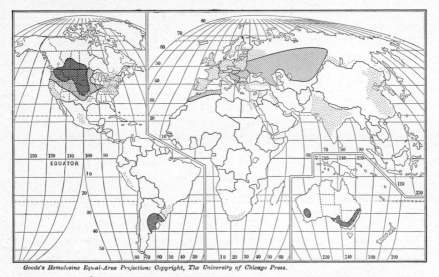

Goode's Homolosine Equal-Area Projection: Copyright, The University of Chicago Press.

A—Wheat-raising Areas. Darkest shading indicates a steady surplus; next shading, usually a surplus; dots, wheat-raising areas with little or no surplus or else a deficit.

as that of North America, but the number of people to whom wheat is supplied locally is only about a tenth as great as in the United States and Canada. The third large and reliable exporter of wheat is Australia, although even there scanty rainfall may cut off much of the export. Most of the Australian wheat comes from a relatively narrow strip in the southeast on the edge of the plateau a little way back from the coast, and from a similar but much smaller strip in the southwest. In New South Wales the surplus of wheat per capita averages about 12 bushels while in South Australia it rises to 48.

The southeastern edge of the great Russian wheat region, west, north, and northeast of the Caspian Sea, may almost be classed with the North American, South American, and Australian wheat regions.

This is the section where the Russians have established their huge new state farms. The surplus of wheat in a section as large as several of our states rises approximately as high as in North Dakota, Saskatchewan, or West Australia. This section, however, grades off into the main wheat area of Russia, that is, into the vast Black Earth or "chernozem" region and its extension of dark chestnut soils extending from Ukraine to Irkutsk (A222). In that area, although a huge amount of wheat is raised, the surplus is relatively small, and almost disappears in bad years. Moreover, the part of Russia where wheat is not raised is so huge and populous that the demand for wheat within the country takes

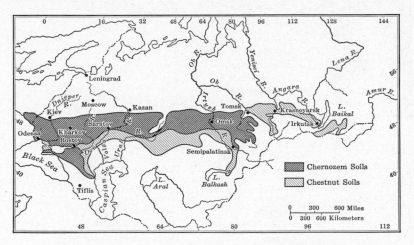

A—Map of the Chernozem or Black Earths of Russia.

most of the surplus in the wheat belt. If Russian industry and prosperity continue to grow at the present rate, it is doubtful whether the increase in wheat production can more than keep pace with the increase in the demand for wheat within the country.

Two other areas also produce a small but fairly steady surplus of wheat for export. One lies in French North Africa, and includes Tunisia, Algeria, and Morocco. The other, in southeastern Europe, includes Rumania, Yugoslavia, and Hungary. Until a few years ago, Manchuria was also supposed to be a great reservoir from which wheat could be drawn for export, but this is fast ceasing to be the case. Not only is the local population increasing more rapidly than the wheat supply, but the farms are small and the methods of cultivation primitive, so that the surplus raised by any individual farmer is small. Moreover, farmers are finding that soy beans pay better than wheat. This is not surprising when one notes how far the heavy summer rains and very cold, dry winters of Mukden depart from the evenly distributed rainfall and mild winters of Belgium (Brussels in A76).

The wide diversity of climates in which wheat can be grown is reflected in a wide diversity of types of wheat. Although regions with warm winters and cool summers like those around the North Sea raise the largest crops per acre, their wheat is comparatively soft and does not make the best kind of bread. In a general way the wheat becomes harder as one goes to regions that are either drier or colder. The hardest wheat of all comes from cold and fairly dry regions like North

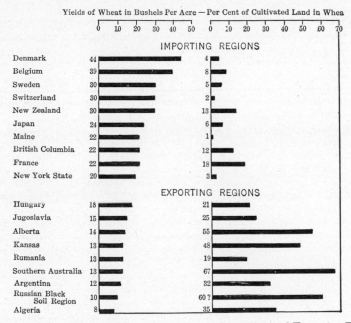

A—Contrasted Conditions of Wheat Production in Importing and Exporting Regions.

Dakota and the Canadian Northwest, and southwestern Siberia. It is in demand in northwestern Europe to be mixed with the softer wheat in order to make bread that rises well. Hence it brings a somewhat higher price than the homegrown wheat there, but not enough to make it anywhere nearly so profitable acre for acre.

Yields of Wheat per Acre in Exporting versus Importing Regions.— The yield of wheat in regions that export wheat is small. Compare the yields in such regions during a recent five-year period as shown in the lower part of A223 with those shown in the upper part for regions which do not raise enough to feed their own people. Then look at the percentages of the cultivated area devoted to wheat in the two groups of countries. The exporting countries have yields of from 8 to 18 bushels per acre. Yet they devote from 19 to 67 per cent of their harvested land to wheat. The importing regions have yields of 20 to 44 bushels per acre. Yet they devote only 1 to 18 per cent of their harvested land to wheat.

Economic and Demographic Factors in the Geographic Distribution of Wheat.— Wheat, like corn, is often pushed out of the regions where it grows best because other crops pay better. The regions that are best for wheat are also good for a great variety of crops such as corn, potatoes, and vegetables. Corn pays so well in Iowa that it would be foolish to devote much space to wheat. In Denmark, oats and barley drive out wheat because they furnish feed for animals just as corn does in Iowa. Germany, Czechoslovakia, and Austria find it profitable to devote at least as much land to potatoes as to wheat. But in Yugoslavia the yield of potatoes is only a third as great as in Germany. Therefore potatoes are not very profitable and the farmers fall back on wheat. Moreover, the climate where wheat grows best is so healthful that the population is generally dense and a large fraction of the good land is used for vegetables, fruits, and industrial crops. Even in new regions like New Zealand and British Columbia, this is fast becoming true.

There are also certain positive advantages which make it pay to raise vast quantities of wheat in the four great areas which produce most of the world's surplus. One of these is the rich, black or dark chestnut soil (Plate II). The great wheat regions of North and South America, Eurasia, and Australia are all located in climates which favor the growth of grass rather than trees. Accordingly all of them have gradually acquired a deep covering of rich, dark soil. A222 and Plate II show the vast extent of this kind of soil in North America and Eurasia. Its distribution agrees quite closely with that of the main wheat areas in both continents. Such soil helps to overcome the handicaps of drought, for it holds water unusually well. It is extremely easy to cultivate, for it breaks up readily under the plow and harrow, and is free from stones.

Another factor in making these three regions great wheat sections is the dry climate (A32). This does indeed reduce the yield of wheat to only 10 or 15 bushels per acre, but on the other hand it much increases the number of acres that any one man can cultivate. It does this by lengthening the period when plowing, and especially harvesting, can be carried on. Where the climate is relatively dry this work is rarely interrupted by rain and mud, as so often happens in moister areas. Nor do weeds make so much trouble when the land is plowed some time before it is planted. At harvest time, wheat in dry climates is in little danger of being beaten down by wind and rain and of having the kernels of grain shaken out by storms. This not only lengthens the period during which harvesting is possible, but lessens the need of tying the cut wheat stalks into sheaves which are piled into shocks in order to let the grain ripen more fully. Moreover, since the grain can safely be left to ripen on the stalk, the dry climate makes it possible to use combines, the huge machines which cut off the heads of wheat, thresh them, and put them in sacks in a single operation.

The levelness of these regions is also a help in making them supply a surplus of wheat. It not only facilitates all sorts of work, such as plowing and hauling, but also makes it possible to use machinery on a large scale.

In spite of all this, such level regions with fine black soil and a moderately dry climate do not necessarily furnish a surplus of wheat. The plains of North Africa, Turkey, Hungary, Yugoslavia, Rumania, the older parts of southern Russia, and Manchuria all illustrate this. These regions belong to a type intermediate between the four great areas which supply a large surplus of wheat and those like France and Ohio where wheat gives a good yield per acre, but not a surplus. The trouble with these places is that they have too many people. Hence the fields are generally small, the methods of cultivation are often primitive, and machinery is rarely used on a large scale. This is well illustrated by the contrast between the southeastern border of the Black Earth region in Russia and the rest of that region. On the border the Russian government has established huge state farms on which much machinery is used and a large surplus of wheat is produced. It was possible to establish these farms because that region is so dry that until machinery was used it did not pay to cultivate the land. Hence the population consisted mainly of nomadic keepers of cattle and sheep, and even now the farming population is sparse. In the long-settled parts of the Black Earth Region, the population is so dense that the amount of land per farmer is small. Often it is scarcely enough to supply food for the farming population alone.

This brings us to the *demographic* factor, that is, the factor of density of population. In some ways the slight density of the population in the wheat-exporting regions is even more important than the rich soil, dry climate, and level plains in permitting these three regions to produce a great surplus of wheat. Because there are few people, the farms are large. This makes it possible for each man's work to produce more than on small farms. On a farm where the fields are only a few acres in extent it is difficult to plow, plant, and harvest with teams of more than two horses. Moreover, on a small farm there is not work enough for more than one or two horses. On a big farm, however, one man can drive six or more horses and go long distances without taking time to turn them around. Thus he can plow three or four furrows instead of one, or cut 30 feet of grain instead of 8. When one man's work accomplishes so much, the farmers on the big farms are able to lay up money, especially if the weather happens to be good at times when it is poor elsewhere, so that the price of wheat goes up. This gives them the capital wherewith to buy machinery. In this way the cost of raising a bushel of wheat can be reduced astonishingly. Here is a table, based on government reports, showing how many hours of work by one man are needed to cultivate an acre of wheat under various conditions:

100 hours or more in places like Turkey or Persia. There, primitive wooden plows are drawn by oxen, the crop is reaped with sickles, tied in sheaves with strings of straw, placed in shocks, carried to a threshing floor on the backs of donkeys, threshed by driving donkeys and oxen around on it, and winnowed by throwing the chaff and grain up into the wind.

60 hours or more in countries like Poland and Yugoslavia, where the small plows are drawn by one horse and the grain is harvested with scythes, tied in sheaves which are carried home in carts, and threshed by hand.

20 to 25 hours in the most advanced European countries like England and in eastern states like New York, Pennsylvania, and Virginia, where good two-horse plows, reaping machines, and power threshing machines are used, but where the large types of machinery are not employed.

15 hours in states like Indiana and Illinois.

5 hours where combines are used on large farms in Kansas, Nebraska, Colorado, and similar states.

2 hours or less on the biggest farms where the tractors and combines travel many miles without stopping or turning.

On one of these largest farms with about 100,000 acres, thirty combines work night and day in the harvesting season, each sacking a thousand bushels a day. The tractors work 2,800 hours per year instead of only 250 as on the average Iowa farm. Two men on tractors and one on a combine do a job which used to require 28 men and 32 horses. In this way, wheat can be raised for about 25 cents a bushel, whereas in the eastern United States it costs at least a dollar a bushel. In eastern Europe and Asia the cost would be much more if wages were reckoned on the American scale. This great difference in cost presents one of the gravest problems of agriculture. The small and backward farms cannot compete with the huge, modern farms, and if the latter raise much wheat or other crops the prices are sure to remain relatively low, and the small farmers can scarcely make a living.

Political Factors in Crop Distribution.—The practical value of our study of geographical and economic factors in crop distribution is often greatly affected by another factor, political in nature. A geographer likes to dream of a world where everything is produced in the regions best suited for it geographically and economically. The politicians spoil this dream by putting strong economic barriers around political units. The idea of such barriers is very old. The entire guild system of the Middle Ages was built on it, and inland trade in that way was greatly hampered. The shipping of products from Italy over the great Alpine-Rhine trade route to northern Europe was hampered not only by fear of bandits, but also by the continuous payment of taxes to one town guild after another. So it is not surprising that the only great trade development in those centuries, that of the Hanseatic League in north Germany, was based on transportation by sea where tax barriers were limited to a few specially favored points like Copenhagen, the gate to the Baltic.

In the nineteenth century the belief in the necessity of protective tariffs broke down under the influence of the Manchester School in England which advocated free trade, and it looked for a moment as if the world were going to develop along natural lines. But the new economic uplift in young countries, a genuine fear of competition, and the desire to promote lines of production, industry, and trade which are not in harmony with the basic geographic factors have once more brought protection to the foreground. This has been especially the case since the World War, and now the world represents a complex structure full of artificial obstructions. Aside from purely political or even personal motives the following are some of the chief reasons for this:

1. The desire to protect infant industries. This point is well illustrated by the attitude of the United States in the latter part of the nine-

teenth century. Being in process of change from a country that exported food and imported industrial products to one where industrial activity is dominant, it imposed high tariffs in order to develop manufacturing possibilities, which were certainly based on geographical facts.

2. As a source of income. When used for this purpose, tariffs lose much of their protective character. Great Britain, until recently the world's great example of free trade, long imposed high duties on a few luxury products, such as wine, spirits, and tobacco. These formed an important source of national income, but did not have any appreciable effect upon the distribution of production.

3. The desire to be self-supporting. This point has become of special interest since the World War. At that time the blockaded Central Powers as well as the neighboring neutral countries experienced the grave disadvantage of insufficient food, fuel, and raw materials for manufacturing. Even the allies felt this, too, especially Great Britain, which was brought almost to collapse by the German submarines. Since the War various countries have tried to reduce these deficits and to make themselves as nearly independent of foreign trade as possible. This is especially the case in respect to food products like grain and meat. Switzerland insists that its farmers shall produce grain in amounts far beyond what is warranted by geographical conditions. France in order to protect her wheat crop regulates the import of grain according to the magnitude of each year's crop.

4. In order to maintain a higher standard of living. This factor is perhaps the most important in explaining the protective policy of the United States. The advocates of a protective tariff claim that free competition with the lower standard in other countries would reduce the American standards. Although this may be true in some cases, many people are doubtful. In former chapters we have seen the geographical reasons for the distribution of production and also of energy. The high American standards of living depend vastly more on very favorable geographical conditions than on any tariff policy. Nevertheless, certain individual industries may be made or ruined by the government's attitude toward foreign competition, especially if forced labor, or subsidies or other aids to their own industries by foreign governments enter into the matter. In 1932, timber from the Soviet States was refused admission to the United States on the ground that it had been cut and shipped by forced labor. Under the present severe state control in Russia, it is very difficult to judge how far this claim is justified. Nor is it at all clear that any possible imports of this kind could have any appreciable effect on American standards.

5. The desire to reduce imports and thus have a more or less bal-

anced trade. Efforts of this kind were especially strong during the world depression of 1929 to 1933, and a large percentage of recent increases in European tariffs can be laid to this cause.

Although a critical discussion of the value of protective tariffs is out of place in a book of this kind, it is desirable to inquire briefly into their relation to economic geography. In view of what we have seen as to the close relation between geography and human activity their influence is apt to be overrated. Nevertheless, political influences seem to become stronger and stronger. Although protection may sometimes be helpful to the countries which use it, at least temporarily, it harms or sometimes almost destroys the economic unity of adjoining regions which ought to be mutually helpful to one another. This evil is exaggerated by the fact that boundaries are mainly political and not based on physical factors. Economic disadvantages of this kind become even more striking when political changes take place or when changes in the tariff threaten ruin to well established business relations.

Political changes were frequent after the World War and often involved a radical change in economic relations. Alsace is geographically a part of the Rhine Graben or depression, and under the German régime it had become economically adjusted to that local geographical base. After the War it lost its connection with its former hinterland. The resulting economic difficulties reacted like a cold shower on the pro-French attitude of the Alsatians. Schleswig-Holstein voted to go back to Denmark, but afterward many voters doubted the advantages of the change, for the former German market was lost and adjustment to Danish conditions was difficult. The Polish corridor separates East Russia from the rest of Germany with which it is economically closely connected. The plebiscite in Silesia broke an industrial unit into three parts, to the great disadvantage of practically all industries. The tariff problem and especially frequent changes in tariffs have strongly influenced the economic relations between Canada and the United States. The dairy exports of Quebec, in the logical hinterland of New York State, are now directed to Great Britain, while under the Smoot-Hawley tariff the lumber industry of British Columbia had to look for new markets.

If we look at the whole world we find an amazing number of political interferences which not only hamper world trade but cause an ever-growing amount of international jealousy and quarrels. Many countries, especially in Europe, do not have the same tariff system for all countries, but try by way of treaties to get from certain countries special favors in return for tariff reductions. International bargaining and the so-called most favored nation clause have been constant sources of economic stress and strained political relations. Tariff increases in one country are followed by reprisals in others; thus protection follows protection, still more endangering the economic unity of the world. Still the geographer does not lose faith, but keeps on dreaming of a future in which the economic development of the world will conform to geographical factors, unhampered by political interference.

EXERCISES

1. Try to ascertain the local price of corn per bushel. How does it compare with the farm price for your state as given in B214? Why does the price vary from state to state? Which section of the table on page 213 does your state fall into (B215)? What geographic and economic conditions mainly determine the price in your local market?

2. What kinds of crops are raised most commonly in the region around your home? How far is this because the climate and soil are better adapted to those crops than to any others, and how far to economic conditions such as are described in this chapter?

3. Explain why both California and Massachusetts raise very little corn although the price there is high.

4. Why do the southern states raise a great deal of corn? Is this because of low costs per bushel? High prices? Explain.

5. If the people of the United States should become vegetarians, how would it probably change the appearance of the five corn maps A–B214, A–B215, and A19.

6. On an outline map of the world, shade lightly the areas where wheat is an important product. (See A28, *Oxford Economic Atlas*, or Goode's *School Atlas*.) Within these areas, shade more heavily the parts that have a surplus for export. What relation is there between the export of wheat and the density of the population? What other conditions help to make an area a wheat exporter? What areas receive the surplus wheat?

7. Explain the contrasted conditions of soil, climate, and distribution of population in three types of regions: (*a*) those which regularly provide a large surplus of wheat for export; (*b*) those which sometimes provide such a surplus; (*c*) those where wheat grows well, but without producing a surplus.

8. Why does the wheat of foreign commerce come almost wholly from regions where the yield per acre is small?

9. On an outline map of the world, shade the areas where the corn production is important. Where does this shading coincide with the shading on your wheat map? Where is this map shaded but not the other? Give reasons in both cases. Is the region of greatest corn production the greatest exporter? Why? In what areas is corn an important food for people? Where is it almost exclusively fed to animals?

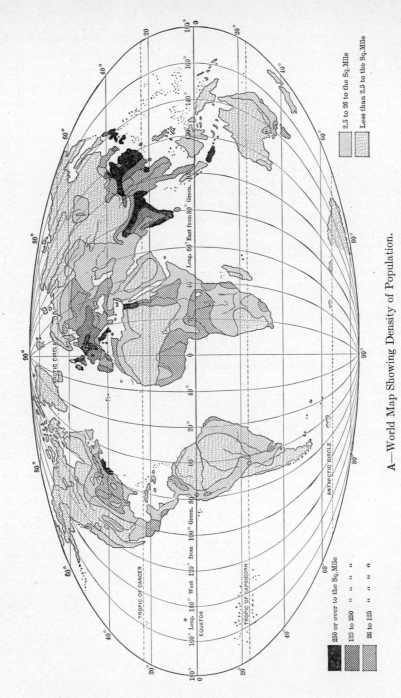

A—World Map Showing Density of Population.

250 or over to the Sq.Mile
125 to 250 " " " "
26 to 125 " " " "

2.5 to 26 to the Sq.Mile
Less than 2.5 to the Sq.Mile

PART II

A SURVEY OF NATURAL REGIONS

CHAPTER XII

NATURAL REGIONS IN LOW LATITUDES

Natural Regions.—A natural region was originally defined by A. J. Herbertson as "an area of the earth's surface which is essentially homogeneous with respect to the conditions that affect human life." Because certain parts of the earth are deserts, tropical plateaus, or temperate river plains, they possess different human qualities. Wherever the general qualities of a given area are fairly uniform, we have a geographic region which may be as large as the Sahara or as small as the Imperial Valley. In it man's activities and modes of life are likely to be fairly uniform. Moreover, wherever any given set of environmental conditions is found, the human activities and modes of life are almost certain to be similar, no matter in which continent the place is located. In this book we have space to discuss only the larger types of natural regions. Therefore the basis of our classification must be mainly climatic, but relief and soil also play important parts. We shall begin at the equator and work poleward, just as in Chapter III. Here, however, we are mainly interested in the effect of the environment on man, whereas there we were trying to get a clear view of the physical principles of climate. Here, too, we are trying to present a short but comprehensive outline of the physical conditions of the whole world as a background for economic and social geography.

In studying each of the natural regions, certain definite steps should be followed. These steps will be described here once for all, but should be repeated with each region. (1) Study the small world map (A233 for the equatorial regions) where the various scattered areas belonging to the region are indicated in black. (2) With the help of Plate I insert these areas on an outline map of the world. (3) Study Plate I in order to see what other natural regions adjoin the one under dis-

231

cussion, and insert their names on your outline map.   (4) Examine the
sample climographs of each region (B233 for equatorial regions) and
write a brief statement of what they show as to (a) temperature,
(b) rainfall, (c) seasonal changes, and (d) degree of approach to the ideal
conditions as indicated by the shaded areas in each climograph.   (5) Prepare one or more climographs of other places within the given natural
region, and compare them with those in the book.   (6) Examine Plate II
and A433 in order to see what kinds of soil and vegetation are dominant.   (7) Keep Plate III, or your atlas before you whenever you are
studying, and note the location of places in relation not only to land
and sea, but to mountains, climate, and types of soil.   (8) Examine
A230 to see whether the population is dense or sparse.

In estimating the qualities of a climate (4, above) bear in mind that
so far as man's own health and vigor are concerned, it is much easier to
correct the harmful effect of low temperature than of any other climatic
deficiency, but it is not so easy to overcome the effect of high temperature.   Therefore, a temperature even a few degrees above the optimum
zone for physical activity, approximately 58° to 72°, retards human progress more than does an outdoor temperature many degrees below the
mental optimum, from about 32° to 46°.   Again, at temperatures above
70° excessive humidity and excessive dryness are both harmful to human
health, whereas at lower temperatures high humidity is an advantage,
provided it does not cause people to get wet and therefore chilled.   In
all the climographs illustrating natural regions, the summer and winter
optima for human health and activity are indicated by the dark shading.   The lighter shadings indicate climatic conditions which may be
excellent for crops, and which are not especially bad for man.   In fact
they may be better than the more heavily shaded types of weather if
they have a more favorable degree of storminess.   The great trouble
with these climographs is that storminess cannot be shown on them.
Nevertheless, the distance of the summer and winter portions of local
climographs from the two heavily shaded areas in the climographs is a
fairly good measure of the quality of a climate.

As for crops, high temperatures do more harm than is generally
supposed because they not only often cause wilting, but foster a great
many parasites, and in the long run sadly impoverish the soil.   Very
low temperatures likewise harm the crops, even though they occur
only in winter.   On the other hand, irrigation, wherever it is possible,
supplies a complete remedy for dryness so far as agriculture is concerned,
but the areas where it is possible are very limited.   Excessive rain at
any season introduces great difficulties in agriculture.

In preparing new climographs of the various regions (5, above) bear

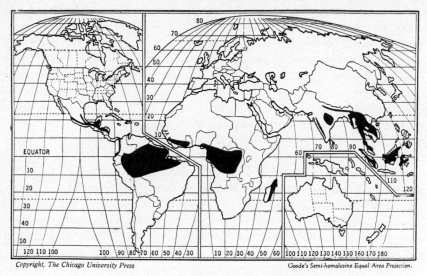

Goode's Semi-homolosine Equal Area Projection.

A—Location of Equatorial Rainforests.

in mind that transitional types of climate are numerous. Those used in the climographs of this book have been selected because they are typical. Others representing places not very far distant may be different because of the relief of the land or the configuration of land and sea.

Equatorial Rainforest.—*The climatic features* of the Equatorial Rainforest (A233 and Plate I) include high temperature, averaging about 80° all the year round at sea-level, very slight seasonal changes, and heavy rainfall (above 80 inches) with no dry season or only a short one (B233). The largest and most typical sections are found in the equatorial lowlands of the Amazon and Congo, in the Malay Islands with their equatorial Monsoon Type of climate, and on the lower slopes of the mountain ranges of India and southeastern Asia where they face

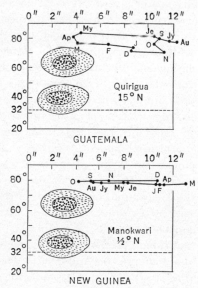

B—Climographs of Equatorial Rainforests.

the southwest summer monsoon.   Other smaller areas are found where
constant trade winds are forced to rise by mountains or highlands, or
where a combination of convectional rain of the equatorial type in summer and of trade-wind rain at other seasons provides the necessary moisture, as in eastern Madagascar, at the eastern base of the Andes, and in
parts of Central America and the West Indies.   In B233 the climograph
of Manokwari in New Guinea almost on the equator is the most typical.
It shows practically no variation of temperature and no month with less
than 4 inches of rain.   Notice that at all seasons it lies well above and to
the right of the optimum for either man or agriculture.   Remember,
too, that high temperature and excessive rainfall are far harder for man
to cope with than are low temperature and drought.   Fire, clothing,
and shelter help to conquer low temperature, while irrigation and wells
greatly reduce the harm done by aridity.   But thus far almost the only
way of combating heat and moisture has been by passive endurance.
B233 shows that Quirigua in Guatemala has a much better climate than
Manokwari, for its drop of temperature to about 70° in winter by reason
of being 15° north of the equator is a great help.   Nevertheless, even
at that season the excessive rainfall is depressing.

Vegetation.—The combination of high temperature and heavy rainfall in the Equatorial Rainforest causes dense vegetation to cover
everything and to be the dominating factor of economic and social life.
Huge trees of great variety spread out their branches in the struggle for
light and sun, and leave the lower parts of the forest half dark.   Passing
through such a forest is difficult: a hothouse climate with water dripping
from the trees, a labyrinth of roots and stems, and everything slimy
and muddy.   Often there is a deathlike silence, broken only by the noise
of rain on the roof of leaves.   Only on top is the forest alive.   There
the trees and the parasitic orchids put forth their blossoms; there the
multicolored parrots, macaws, birds of paradise, toucans, and many
smaller birds flit about; there live the monkeys, whose chattering
resounds far and near when they chase one another at sunrise.   Most
kinds of animal life are rare in these forests; elephants may cross them
and leave wide trails, but tigers and lions keep away as much as
possible.

Human Handicaps.—Equatorial man has never really conquered
this region.   Generally he is dominated by the forest rather than the
forest by him.   In physique he is more or less degenerate, being often
very small, like the African Pygmies.   In childhood and even in maturity
the equatorial tribes are decimated by illness.   Even when in good health
their energy is sapped by wellnigh the world's worst climatic conditions.
Small groups of them, often not more than one family, roam together

through the forests trying to keep alive by gathering fruits and killing animals or fish. Racially primitive, these people of the Equatorial Rainforest are likewise primitive in culture. Superstition and fear take the place of religion. Their dwellings, built on posts or on platforms in the trees, are little more than roofs of palm leaves which serve merely as a refuge from animals and a shelter from rain. No matter whether the people of the rainforest are the Pygmies of the Congo Basin, the Veddahs of Ceylon, the Kubus of Sumatra, the Semang of the Malay Peninsula, or the Indian head hunters of the upper Amazon, they all live the same life, the lowest on earth.

Yet in parts of the rainforest, especially near the borders, better conditions sometimes prevail. Clearings are made by cutting down the branches and burning the trees. At the end of the period of lowest rainfall (B233) columns of smoke show where these more active people are located. In the ashes one or more crops, mostly mountain rice or corn, can be raised. The houses become of a better quality— rude, palm-thatched huts with walls of rough sticks. They may be surrounded by small patches where yams, manioc, taro, or other vegetables grow in a tangle of big weeds. Swine may be kept in order to increase the food supply. Although still almost nomadic, moving on after the soil is exhausted, these people have a higher culture than those who have no agriculture. Trails are kept open, and the people come into contact with more favorably located tribes by means of trade. Their religions, too, contain many well developed ideas.

These better conditions prevail mainly where a dry season diminishes the density of the vegetation. There the forest is more open, the sun penetrates to the ground and animal life is correspondingly abundant. The Moi of Annam, or the Karen of Burma, are good examples of this type of life which rises far above the level of the food gatherers and hunters of the denser forests. Yet even these people are almost incredibly hampered by their environment. They cannot use animals to any great extent. Even such beasts as water buffaloes do not thrive. Not only is the damp, hot climate unfavorable, but the insects are very annoying, and the grasses, where the trees permit them to grow, are extremely coarse and tough. Nevertheless, even in the equatorial forest there are large patches where the soil prevents the growth of trees, but not of grass, and these may support a few poor cattle.

Another great handicap is the quality of the soil. In the flatter areas, such as large sections of the Amazon Basin and the coastal plain of New Guinea, it is water-logged most of the time, and therefore infertile even when dry. Elsewhere it is so thoroughly weathered and leached that one or at most two crops exhaust it. That is one reason why even the agricultural natives are nomadic. They must employ the milpa system, and must make new clearings each year or two where they find some natural opening in the forest, perhaps a place where they themselves lived a few years before and which has only partially grown over. It is easy to build new huts, but very hard to keep down the weeds. Even if the soil were not so poor, the rank growth of weeds, at the rate of three or four feet a month in some cases, would make it very difficult to raise anything.

Another handicap is that nowhere else are diseases so virulent. The natives must contend not only with ordinary malaria and dysentery, but with the more swift and fatal forms of these diseases. Stinging insects are another fearful nuisance, for they make sores which fester and last a long time. Human inertia and disease, poor soil, excessive vegetation, and the difficulty of using animals all unite to prevent Equatorial Rainforests from being of economic importance. A little wild rubber, some wood such as mahogany and rosewood, and the hardened chicle sap from which chewing gum is made, almost complete the list of exports. Only in deserts and very cold regions do we find so little economic development. The products which we think of as typically tropical come mainly from the next of our natural regions. Not a single city of as much as 100,000 inhabitants belongs to this region, although some like Belém in Brazil, Batavia in Java, and Singapore lie on its edges. Manaos on the Amazon is the largest city really within the Equatorial Rainforest, but it has waned greatly since the decline of the wild rubber trade. This agrees with the general sparsity of population (A230).

Regions of Wet Tropical Agriculture. *Climate.*—A look at A237 and Plate I shows the close relation between the Equatorial Rainforest and the Regions of Wet Tropical Agriculture. Climatically the two have much in common, namely, plenty of rain and constant high temture, but B237 indicates that the agricultural regions have the benefit of a longer dry season. Originally the same type of forest covered both, but differences in relief and soil, as well as in the seasonal distribution of rain, have caused a distinct contrast in their present appearance. Few things are more surprising than the change from the dark, moist equatorial forest on the mountains, where man's life reaches its lowest levels, to the carefully prepared rice fields and groves of coconut palms surrounding the villages of the coastal lowlands. Notice in A237 how many parts of this region lie along the coast. Rich alluvial soils, and a tendency toward less rain and a longer dry season as a result of gentle relief, are responsible for this. The coastal plain of southern India, the lowlands of Java, the coastal regions of eastern Brazil, and some of the West Indian Islands are garden spots where rice and corn grow

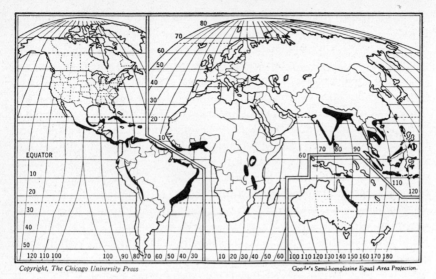

Goode's Semi-homolosine Equal Area Projection.

A—Location of Regions of Wet Tropical Agriculture.

easily and where the villages are hidden in great groves of fruit trees.

Crops.—Some of the tropical crops become of more than local importance. The spices of the Malay Islands were of great value far back in history. They were one of the reasons for the European period of exploration in the fourteenth and fifteenth centuries. Later on, European and American companies became interested in the production of tropical crops for the world market. In some regions the natives were encouraged to increase the planted area, and contracts were made to buy all that they could raise. In others, plantations were established and production was brought under direct foreign control with natives working under white supervision. Most of the present colonial possessions

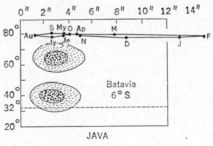

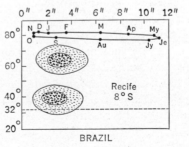

B—Climographs of Regions of Wet Tropical Agriculture.

of European countries are the result of the work of such trading companies. The companies gradually assumed political power and then the home governments came in and took the political control away from the companies. In our day the banana plantations of the Caribbean region, the cacao groves of Brazil and the Guinea coast of Africa, the oil palm forests of Nigeria, the copra production of the Malay Islands, the tobacco fields of Cuba and the Philippine Islands, and the sugar cane of Cuba, Java, Brazil, and Natal, have become important factors in world trade and commerce. Rice, the great food crop of these Regions of Wet Tropical Agriculture, also enters into world trade. From the delta plains of southeastern Asia with their summer floods, millions of tons go yearly to the overpopulated regions of India, Java, and China.

Economic and Social Life.—In spite of the white man's interference, the economic and social life of these regions is still decidedly native. It follows lines which have been developed in the hundreds or thousands of years during which the cultivation of rice, bananas, or corn has been the chief occupation. Rice has been by far the most important. It has helped greatly in giving to southeastern Asia a degree of native culture unrivaled in other tropical lowlands. If people are going to cultivate rice of the ordinary irrigated type, they must live in permanent villages. They have to cooperate with one another in turning the water supply into canals and in dividing it among the various fields. They have to work hard and steadily in planting and harvesting their rice. They also have to be always on the job in order to make sure that the little dykes which surround their rice fields are kept in order. Carelessness for a few days may mean that the water flows away from the rice and the entire year's crop is lost. Thus among the rice-raising villages the spirit of democracy, self government, and cooperation is quite highly developed. What harms one, harms all. With this goes evidence of progress in other respects. The bamboo houses standing among irregularly placed fruit trees show a great advance over the rude huts of the Equatorial Forest. They do more than merely shelter the inhabitants. They show a tendency toward comfort, ornamentation, and even some luxury. Of course, life is still very simple and people do not work hard. The way in which the climographs of these regions depart from the optimum (B237) shows that we should not expect any great amount of energy. Trade is not active. The native farmer gets most of his food from his rice field, but supplements it with fish or chickens, coconut oil, and a great variety of garden fruits, such as the big red and orange mango, the mangosteen with its delicate white and pink flesh, and the bad smelling but delicious durian. Another way in which the people of the Wet Tropical Agricultural Regions in southeastern Asia and the East Indies are ahead of the forest people, although far behind those of cooler regions, is in the use of animals. This does not mean, however, that the fields are large; in fact, they are very small, for the farmer follows the impulses aroused by the climate and spends a great deal of his time resting under the shady roof in front of his house.

Present and Past Communities.—The larger villages in the parts of this natural region lying in southern Asia and the East Indies often have a central square built around a huge banyan tree. Here are the main buildings: a mosque, a temple, or a Christian church, the house of the village chief, the school, and the local store. In the latter an enterprising merchant, often a Chinese in the Malay Peninsula and the East Indies, or even in Central America, offers for sale a surprising number of world products, ranging from California raisins and Canadian salmon to German bottled beer, Japanese toys, and Chinese fireworks. The villages stand close together, for rice produces a great amount of food per acre so that the country can support a dense population.

A similar density of population and a still higher state of culture prevailed in former centuries whenever a strong government ruled. This is evident in the wonderful specimens of ancient architecture seen at such places as Angkor in Siam, Burubudur in Java, and many temples of southern India. The Khmer Empire of Indo-China and the Moghul Sultanate of the Ganges plain are examples of the highest cultures that have prevailed in the Regions of Wet Tropical Agriculture. In America the Maya Empire of Guatemala and Yucatan with its magnificent ruins illustrates similar conditions in a civilization based on corn. In Africa the Haussa states of Nigeria and the Uganda Empire in the center of the continent are modern examples of the way in which a relatively high civilization grows up where wet tropical agriculture is at its best. In the Haussa states, millet and cattle were the chief agricultural reliances. In Uganda, the banana is the chief crop. There a village normally consists of a great number of banana patches, each with a neat grass hut in its center. When a banana patch is once established it forms a permanent and highly valuable possession, just as does a grove of oil palms in Nigeria, or the terraced rice fields in Burma. The necessity of maintaining and guarding such permanent possessions has been one of the great reasons why these people under favorable conditions of tropical agriculture have gone so far ahead of the wild tribes in the Equatorial Rainforest. The contrast between the two groups is perhaps as great as the contrast between the more progressive tropical type and ourselves.

Increase in Population.—Since the white man came to these Regions of Tropical Agriculture there has been a tremendous increase in population.   In Java the population has grown from about 5,000,000 in 1800 to approximately 40,000,000 today.   Only in parts of the plains of China and India do we find so dense an agricultural population.   This growth of population is partly due to the fact that the white man's rule has brought peace.   It is also due to the fact that he has brought modern transportation, the possibility of intensive commerce, better hygiene, and lower taxes.   This has resulted in certain difficulties.   One is that the population has outrun the local food supply.   This is beginning to be the case in the parts of India where there are plantations and still more so in Ceylon and Java.   Cuba is so largely devoted to raising sugar for consumption in the United States that it does not raise much more than half of the food needed by its own people.   In this respect it resembles the northeastern United States and northwestern Europe. The great staple food crops do not pay so well as do more specialized crops like sugar and tobacco, or what we may call the luxury crops such as tea, coffee, cacao, and spices, or even the industrial crops such as jute, manila hemp, sisal, and cotton.   Moreover, contrary to common supposition, the yield of crops per acre in the Regions of Wet Tropical Agriculture is not high compared with that farther north.   Thus the rice production of Java per acre is less than half as great as that of Japan, and we have already seen how small is the corn production in the tropical regions compared with those farther north.   Thus many sections of the Wet Tropical Agricultural Regions show a marked tendency to be no longer self-supporting but to rely on cooler climates for staple articles of food.

Transitional Areas.—Between these highly developed and densely crowded Regions of Wet Tropical Agriculture and the primitive, sparsely populated Equatorial Rainforests there are a great number of transitional types.   Often it is difficult to decide whether a region belongs to the Equatorial Rainforest or to the Regions of Wet Tropical Agriculture. The tropical coastal lowlands of Central and South America, although sometimes very dry as in Venezuela, are more often swampy and unhealthful.   Under these conditions the life of the Indians remains primitive and economically unproductive.   The Indians in most of the regions of the old Mayan civilization in the forests back from the Yucatan coast and southward to northern Honduras are of this type.   Yet formerly a highly developed agriculture prevailed here.   It is in such transitional areas between fully developed equatorial forests and regions of comparatively easy tropical agriculture that the white man's work becomes of outstanding value.   Mainly for the sake of bananas the land is drained, the forest is cut, roads are made, and the villages of the plantations show the way to more advanced economic and cultural conditions.

From the coastal lowlands where wet tropical agriculture prevails, the modern type of economic life is beginning to extend over the adjacent mountains and plateaus, and wherever possible these are also made productive.   Volcanic or other soils of special fertility, higher elevation, lower temperature, and a moderately dry season all unite to make it possible to raise crops which are of outstanding value to the world market.   Thus rubber forests cover great sections of the Malay Peninsula, Java, and Sumatra; coffee plantations are the backbone of Brazilian prosperity; tea estates dominate economic life on the mountains of Ceylon, Assam, and Java; cacao groves, often shaded by taller trees with dainty pink blossoms, mantle the slopes in regions like Trinidad, western Ecuador, eastern Brazil, and especially San Thomé, a Portuguese island in the Gulf of Guinea; and quinine trees display their red and green leaves 6,000 feet above the sea in Java.   These upland crops, together with the lowland crops of rice, bananas, sugar, manila hemp, sisal, and jute, make the tropical regions the source of a great deal of the world's raw material as well as of its supply of foods that are more or less luxuries.

Cities.—A dense population and abundant valuable products cause the Regions of Wet Tropical Agriculture to be well supplied with cities. Eighteen have populations of over 250,000.   As one gets away from the Equatorial Rainforest the size of these cities increases.   Thus the seven within 12° of the equator (Singapore, Colombo, Batavia, Surabaya, Belém, Recife, and São Salvador) average about 350,000 inhabitants; the four between 12 and 18° (Madras, Rangoon, Bangkok, Manila) average about 410,000; and the seven in higher latitudes (Bombay, Calcutta, Hongkong, Canton, Habana, Rio de Janeiro, and São Paulo) average over a million and none has much less than 600,000.   It is interesting to note that, aside from Bombay in latitude 19°, these larger cities all lie close to the tropics at latitudes of 22 or 23°.   The fact that the lowest latitudes do not favor the growth of large cities becomes still more evident when we note that Singapore, Hongkong, and to a less degree Colombo, owe a large share of their growth to the fact that they are way stations on great routes between more active parts of the world in higher latitudes.

One of the most noteworthy facts about these eighteen tropical cities is that all except São Paulo are seaports.   This is partly because the Regions of Wet Tropical Agriculture lie mainly along the seacoasts, as is evident in Plate I, but it is also because the cities in this part of the world are almost purely commercial and governmental with very little industrial, financial, or cultural activity.   Many are closely associated with the export of some particular product; Calcutta with jute; Bombay with cotton; Bangkok and Rangoon with rice; Manila with manila hemp; Surabaya, Habana, and Recife with sugar; Singapore and formerly Belém with rubber; and São Paulo and formerly Rio de Janeiro with coffee. Although São Paulo is not a seaport, Santos, its port, may almost be counted as a distant suburb of this rapidly growing coffee city. São Salvador in Brazil is quite a cacao port, although other products like sugar and hides are also important. Bananas are the only main product of tropical plantations not represented in this discussion of cities. They are so perishable that they cannot be collected at any one great port, but must be picked up from many small ports close to the plantations. Batavia, Canton, Hongkong, Madras, and Rio de Janeiro do not specialize in definite products so much as do most of the other cities in regions of this type. All except Hongkong have grown large because they are centers of both trade and government for large numbers of people.

Manufacturing is of minor importance in the Regions of Wet Tropical Agriculture. São Paulo, with its textile and other factories, comes nearer than any of the other cities to being a manufacturing center. This is just what would be expected, for São Paulo lies not only about 2,400 feet above the sea, but on the very border of the tropics so that it has quite cool winters and very comfortable summers. Bombay comes next as a manufacturing place, but its cotton mills give occupation to only a small part of the population, and have been a minor factor in the city's growth. In the other cities there is a certain amount of simple manufacturing in the way of preparing raw materials for market. Many people likewise engage in primitive industries which they carry on in their homes or in the little shops of silversmiths, embroiderers, coppersmiths, wood carvers, ivory carvers, shoemakers, and the like, who lend to the bazaars of such cities a large part of their charm. Moreover, in these modern days the community industries in these tropical cities include not only primitive bread-making, carpentry, and mason-work but the supplying of electricity, gas, and transportation according to European methods. Yet in spite of all this, there is little real manufacturing. Hence the trade of all these tropical cities consists mainly of the export of plantation products, or in some cases of hides and forest products, and the import of machinery, cloth, motor vehicles, and in some instances cereals from regions in higher latitudes.

The White Man.—Except in the more temperate regions of southern Brazil and Natal where the white man forms an important part of the population, the white man's task in wet tropical agriculture is mainly one of supervision. His numbers, therefore, are very small compared with the native population. But even for this work of supervising he often needs fresh vitality, for the warm, monotonous climate saps his energy. He can get this temporarily by going up into the mountains where lower temperatures prevail, but to escape the monotony he has to go back to the area of cyclonic storms. So one of the rules for the white employees of private concerns as well as governments is that regular and frequent vacations shall be given.

An exceptional situation in respect to white men in the Regions of Wet Tropical Agriculture is found in northern Queensland. There about 200,000 white people from the races of northern Europe do all sorts of work under more or less tropical conditions. Protected by law against labor competition from colored races, these people are carrying on a unique experiment in colonization. Although the cost of production along almost every line is considerably higher than in tropical regions with colored labor, the results have been fairly successful. The health of the people is quite good. The death rate, which is generally high in tropical regions, is here remarkably low, and the people work with considerable energy. This is explained partly by the fact that many of the white people live on the uplands where the climate is cooler than at sea-level. Another highly favorable condition is that with a white population it has been possible to apply modern hygiene in such a way that the dangerous tropical diseases have been largely kept out. Still more important perhaps is the fact that people rarely migrate to an area where the climate is known to be so difficult unless they have unusual energy and good health. Moreover, if other types migrate to such places, the weaker and less successful generally move out again, leaving a group of outstanding energy and enterprise. Thus although the climate continues to be a burden on man's energy, the selection of the population allows a progressive community to maintain itself. This does not prove that the white race can retain its full energy in the Regions of Wet Tropical Agriculture. But it does show that if the tropical diseases are eliminated, if the right kind of people are chosen, and if the white people live apart from the natives and maintain their own cultural and moral standards, they can get along in these regions much better in the future than heretofore.

Wet and Dry Low Latitudes. *Climate.*—(Read pages 231–232 again and review Chapter III. Study A244 and A245.) We are now dealing with a climate characterized by convectional summer rain and hot dry winters, as appears in A245. Plate I shows that these Wet and Dry Low Latitudes are transitional between the Equatorial Rainforest and the Desert. Therefore the climatic conditions vary a great deal. They range from a rather long wet season and fairly humid conditions on the equatorial side to a short wet season and semi-arid conditions in higher latitudes. The winters are uniformly dry. The temperature drops somewhat during the months when the sun is lowest, but early in the spring it is already very high. At that season everything is bleached and burned. The grass, often tall enough to conceal a herd of elephants, is brown; most of the trees and bushes are leafless or have only dull, dusty leaves. The soil is often broken by deep cracks, most of the rivers have dried up, and a thick layer of dust covers everything. The temperatures at this time are among the world's highest, frequently rising above 100° every day for months. Even the deep wells often go dry; in fact, the difficulty of getting water has had a great deal to do with preventing large

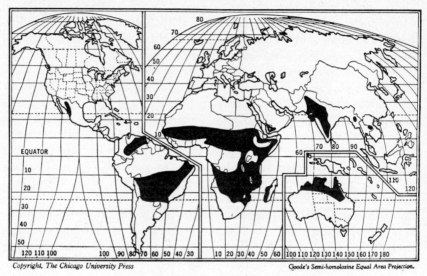

Copyright, The Chicago University Press   Goode's Semi-homolosine Equal Area Projection.

A—Location of Wet and Dry Low Latitudes.

sections from becoming populated. In summer the equatorial rains arrive in the wake of the vertical sun.   Rain falls each day in heavy afternoon showers, the dry soil turns to mud, the rivers are swollen, and great sections flooded.   Nature awakens from its long sleep, and under the clear blue morning sky everything looks inexpressibly green and beautiful.   Farther from the equator the rainy period is short, and the showers become more rare until finally they fade out entirely.   The large swampy areas in summer not only make transportation extremely difficult, but offer a serious threat to the health of both men and animals. They breed malarial mosquitoes by the million.   Here, too, is the place of the tsetse fly, which excludes practically all domestic animals except the donkey from large areas. Because of it, large sections of central Africa, once productive and with a comparatively dense population, are now deserted and avoided. Ticks are also a terrible scourge, bringing great irritation as well as deadly fever to cattle and even to human beings.

Dry Tropical Forest and Savanna.—The vegetation follows the climate closely. Except in the moister valleys it is the kind that can stand a long dry season. On the borders of the Equatorial Rainforest, or of the Regions of Wet Tropical Agriculture, we find an open forest in the midst of heavy grass 6 to 10 feet high. In the African part of the Wet and Dry Low Latitudes small, umbrella-shaped, thorny acacia trees are especially characteristic, as are occasional great baobabs, curious trees with short stubby trunks ten or twenty feet in diameter which end in a point amid a whorl of branches. In less rainy regions this scrubby forest gives place to genuine park-like savanna with only scattered trees. This gradually merges into immense treeless grasslands broken only by narrow strips of dense gallery forest along the rivers where abundant moisture supports a growth like that of the Equatorial Rainforest. Finally on the outer margins where the climate becomes semi-arid the grass becomes very short or else gives way to thorny scrub. The surface in these regions is generally rather flat, for where there are

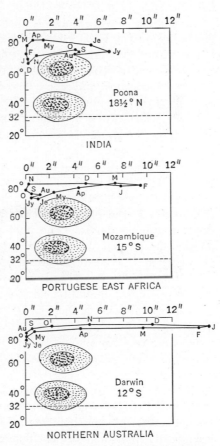

A — Climographs of Wet and Dry Low Latitudes.

mountains more rain falls and the vegetation is more dense. Thus the main impression given by the Wet and Dry Low Latitudes is one of rolling or mildly hilly grasslands interrupted more or less by trees or scrub. In South America much the same kind of vegetation is found. In the dry region near the São Francisco River in Brazil, for example, the scrubby "coatinga" forest is full of thorny little mimosa trees corresponding to the acacias of Africa. In the Gran Chaco the quebracho tree with a bark full of tannin is one of the few resources of a similar open forest. A traveler who was there in the wet season calls the Gran Chaco a "green Hell." Perhaps Bolivia and Paraguay might not have thought it worth fighting for if Pilcomayo and Paraguay rivers did not offer Bolivia an outlet to the sea.

Animal Life.—The grassy plains and hills of the Wet and Dry Low Latitudes are the El Dorado of animal life, especially in Africa. The tall and abundant grass supports millions of herbivorous animals such as antelopes of all sizes from little creatures no bigger than a cat up to the great hartebeest and gnu. These in turn provide food for thousands of flesheaters, including the lion in Africa, the tiger in Asia, and the jaguar in South America. Here roam enormous herds of striped zebras, and long-necked giraffes among which ostriches with waving plumes may often be seen. The dangerous African buffalo charges the hunter suddenly out of a screen of grass. Elephants, in spite of the ivory hunters, can still be found in large numbers. Along the rivers the hippopotamus divides his time between land and water, and crocodiles sun themselves on the banks. Jackals and vultures live on the bodies of dead or dying animals. The photographs taken by men like Martin Johnson prove that the extraordinary big game stories of explorers and travelers from Livingstone to Roosevelt are not fantastic.

Leached Soils.—Many soils of the Low Latitude Wet and Dry Regions are disappointing in quality. From the amount of rain and the cover of grass one would expect them to be good, but they are too badly leached by the heavy rains in summer. Infertile laterites are common, but in some sections, like the northern Deccan, where the rainfall is more favorable, dark soils of high fertility are found, the so-called "regur" or cotton soil.

Responses of Man.—In a general way, the responses of man to this environment everywhere follow the same lines, but differ considerably in their grade of development. Nowhere, either now or in the past, has a really high stage of development been reached. The handicap of an extremely hot and prolonged dry season appears to have been fatal to rapid progress. The lowest stage of development is seen among the primitive "Black Fellows" of northern Australia. They still live in the Stone Age. Being too poor to buy knives, they often chip arrow heads out of glass bottles thrown away by white men. When left to themselves they go largely unclothed and have no shelters beyond the flimsiest little huts of sticks and grass. They are not food producers but hunters, gatherers of insects, and collectors of wild seeds, nuts, fruits, and succulent plants. They represent a type of human culture developed in a very unfavorable climate with the further handicaps of no native animals fit for milking and for draft, no native grains fit for cultivation, and no contact with other races from whom they might learn new ways. The white man has indeed introduced sheep on the Barkley Uplands in the northeast and cattle on the uplands of the northwest, but the greater part of northern Australia is still empty and unproductive.

In *South America* the degree of progress in this climatic region is only a little greater than in Australia. Before the coming of the white man the Indians there never went beyond the hunting stage, although game is far less common than in Africa. White men then introduced cattle, and cattle-raising has become the main source of income. Villages are very small and scattered. Most of the inhabitants are Indians who lead a semi-nomadic life, moving with their cattle to the better-watered areas in the dry season, but getting away from the mud and insects of those areas when the rains arrive. Then they go to higher, drier sites where fresh grass is sprouting. They cannot stay there when the rains are ended, however, because of the scarcity of water. The villages consist of brush huts. They are found on moderately elevated areas near permanent sources of water and are surrounded by a few fields planted chiefly with corn and pumpkins. Even cattle-raising has not been very successful. The coarse grass does not provide good pasturage except when it first sprouts. The dry season often brings suffering or even death from lack of water. Ticks and other insects not only impair the health of the animals, but injure the hides by making sores which leave holes or weak spots in the skins. Transportation is also difficult because of the mud in the wet season, the scarcity of water in the dry season, and the absence of good roads at all seasons. Thus the Llanos of the Orinoco, the Gran Chaco in Paraguay and Bolivia, the uplands on the gentle western slope of the plateau of eastern Brazil, and the great central Brazilian Campos or Matto Grosso are still wide open spaces waiting for development.

In *Africa* the economic and cultural development of the Wet and Dry Low Latitudes reaches a higher level than in Australia or South America. This is especially true north of the Equatorial Rainforest which borders the Guinea coast. In the low plateau extending from Senegal to Upper Nigeria crops are raised as far north as the rainfall is adequate. In spring the air is full of smoke where the dry grass is being burned to clear the fields. Millet, cotton, and peanuts are the main crops. Senegal is a great exporter of peanuts, which go to Europe and especially Marseille for the extraction of the oil. Large villages of conical grass huts protected by mud walls show the relatively high level of native culture. Farther north where the climate becomes drier, stock-raising takes the place of crops, houses made of mud replace the grass huts, and finally the nomadic life of the Desert becomes dominant.

A peculiar condition often prevails along the edge of the Wet and Dry Low Latitudes near the Desert. The nomads are bold, hardy people while the settled villagers, although having a higher culture and greater wealth, are by no means so warlike. So the nomadic tribes often conquer the others, and take possession of the land. Then they live as a ruling class, making the sedentary people work for them. The combination of the forceful nomads and the more industrious villagers often helps to make such marginal areas the most highly developed parts of the Wet and Dry Low Latitudes. This is especially noticeable in the remains of former and higher types of civilization such as are found in India.

In east Africa it is often difficult to separate the Wet and Dry Low Latitudes from the Regions of Wet Tropical Agriculture and from the Cool Tropical Highlands. Sharp local differences are common, especially where higher elevation brings lower temperature and consequently less aridity. Thus Uganda, with its dense population and its bananas, millet, and cotton, displays many features which ally it with the Cool Tropical Highlands and the Regions of Wet Tropical Agriculture, as well as with the Wet and Dry Low Latitudes. But conditions typical of this latter environment prevail once more in the southern part of the Egyptian Sudan as well as in Somaliland and Eritrea away from the hot, desertlike coasts.

In the Nile Valley of southern Sudan the cattle-raising, nomadic life persists within 10° of the equator. There the enormously tall, slender Shilluk and Dinka Negroes wander stark naked with their cattle. No man considers it proper to appear abroad without a spear, but clothing is of no importance. This is not surprising, for the heat here attains wellnigh the greatest extreme known upon the earth's surface. Except for their use of cattle these people are scarcely higher in civilization than are the aboriginal Australians, but farther to the north toward Khartum, where the heat is less constant and summer humidity not so high, the stage of culture rises.

The life of the nomads a little south of Khartum well illustrates the general mode of life in the drier grasslands on the cooler borders of the Wet and Dry Low Latitudes. In the dry season these cattle keepers build huts of grass and of grass matting beside the rivers which do not dry up, or in low places where water can be procured by digging wells. Just before the rains begin in the spring, the nomads burn off the dry grass and the weeds. Then when the rains begin they plant some millet.

After that they wander about setting up their huts wherever the grass looks richest. The cattle get water from the juicy fresh grass, and the people drink milk. When the grass becomes scarce or too dry the Sudanese return to harvest their millet and store it in little grass huts with pagoda-shaped grass roofs. Ashamed of manual work, good fighters but poor workers, they dominate the more industrious but less warlike farming people and make them do the manual work. In former years they withstood the white man's invasion longer than anyone else. The memory of their Mahdi who defeated the English at Khartum still lingers.

In the great southern grasslands of Rhodesia and Angola similar conditions prevail. Poor conditions of health join with local wars and raids of slave-dealers to cause the population to be sparse. The Hereros of Southwest Africa who chose starvation in the desert rather than German rule, and the Zulus of southeastern Africa who established a military kingdom in the nineteenth century before their defeat by the Boers and English, are geographically similar to the Sudanese warriors. The semi-independent British Colony of Basutoland is a lingering remnant of their power. From the south, Boer cattle-raisers have migrated into southern Rhodesia and even Angola. On the Rhodesian uplands, which because of their elevation belong really to another climatic region, white farmers helped by black labor raise cattle, sheep, corn, wheat, and cotton. Here, as in all parts of this climatic region, the summer rain may be late or scarce, thus bringing disaster.

In *Asia* this type of climate covers most of the Deccan Plateau in India, besides smaller regions in Burma and Siam. Here the level of human progress rises higher than in other sections where the Wet and Dry Low Latitude climate prevails. One reason is that the climate and relief are better for agriculture than in most of the other sections, and extensive irrigation from small ponds, called "tanks," is employed. In the Deccan the climatic conditions are slightly different from those of South America and Africa. Here we have a monsoon type of rainfall brought mainly by winds from the southwest and hence diminished in the interior by the mountain wall of the Western Ghats. Therefore the summer rains and floods are not so overwhelmingly heavy as in the corresponding parts of South America. Here, too, the presence of the ocean not far away on both sides makes the distribution of rain more uniform from month to month than in Africa. Khartum, for example, gets three-fourths of its rain in the two months of July and August. At Mysore in the same latitude on the east coast of India a similar percentage of the total rainfall is distributed over six months. Even at Poona, farther north on the western edge of the central part of the

Deccan Plateau, it takes over four months for three-fourths of the rain to fall. Again Khartum has nine months with an average rainfall of less than half an inch, while Masulipatam and Patna each have only four. This diminishes the difficulties due to floods. It also improves the conditions of health because the rainy season in this type of climate is usually more healthful than the dry season with its great heat and blowing dust. Moreover, such conditions of rainfall prolong the season when the crops do not suffer from either drought or flood. They join with the relief in making it relatively easy to practice irrigation, for little dams can be built which hold the water for months. The "tanks" thus formed do indeed increase the ravages of malaria, but they make life far less uncertain for the farmer, and permit a far denser and more prosperous population than would otherwise be possible. So although the Dravidian people of southern India are desperately poor and ignorant, and very deficient in energy, they have at least developed a kind of civilization a little higher than that of other parts of the Wet and Dry Low Latitudes.

The Dravidian farmers of the Indian peninsula combine cattle-keeping with crop-raising. Where water is available, rice is raised, but jowar, a kind of millet, covers a far greater acreage and forms the main part of the diet in the form of bread or porridge. Indian corn, pulses, which are legumes resembling peas, and in the north, wheat, are the other main food crops. A rainfall of approximately 40 inches is sufficient for those crops if it comes at the right times, but failure of the rains is very common. Terrible famines are the result unless food can be brought from more favorable sections, as is now done by the British government. Only a few fruits like the mango are raised, and vegetables are rare. Livestock of many kinds, including cows, buffaloes, swine, chickens, and even sheep and goats, plays an important part in the scheme of land utilization. Yet most of the animals are of very poor quality. The cows give so little milk that they are called "tea cup" cows. They are used mainly for plowing. When they are too old for that their meat is extremely tough. The usefulness of the cattle for plowing is probably one reason why the Hindu religion prohibits the use of meat. The hens, too, are small and lay very few eggs; the sheep are thin and hairy. In the fertile soils of the northwestern and western Deccan, cotton is the main industrial crop and is exported in great quantities from Bombay. Here, just as in the rice-growing lowlands of Bengal, the village with its grass-thatched huts is the nucleus of a very mild industrial life, in the form of home industries like weaving, pottery making, and basket work.

The picture of the Wet and Dry Low Latitudes in Asia is completed by the dry belt of central Burma with its millet, sesamum, cotton, and peanuts, and by the cattle-raising Korat Plateau in Siam where the permeability of the soil makes it too dry for agriculture, even though the rainfall is sufficient.

Taken as a whole, this type of natural region stands between the Equatorial Rainforest and the Regions of Wet Tropical Agriculture in density of population, degree of progress, and variety and value of products. The rest of the world gets from it some cotton, a poor grade of hides, gum arabic from the bushes of Sudan, and a few other things. These are negligible compared with the tea, coffee, cocoa, sugar, spices, bananas, quinine, kapok, copra, palm oil, jute, manila hemp, and rubber of the much smaller areas of Wet Tropical Agriculture. India is the only part of the Wet and Dry Low Latitudes where there are either large cities or any appreciable industrial development. Hyderabad, Poona, Ahmadabad, Delhi and Lahore range from nearly 250,000 to 400,000 inhabitants, but there are no cities above half a million. They have a fair number of cotton mills, especially at Poona and Ahmadabad, and a few other factories, but they are not industrial cities in the European or American sense. Moreover, none of them are seaports, and the entire Wet and Dry Low Latitudes have no seaports of any great magnitude. This is partly because this climatic region is often cut off from the coast by a more rainy section where the trade winds or monsoons create conditions fit for wet tropical agriculture. But cities and especially seaports are also scarce because the Wet and Dry Low Latitudes produce so little that serves the needs of other regions.

Cool Tropical Highlands and the Great Value of Small Differences in Temperatures (A252, A253, and pages 231–232).—The contrast between tropical highlands and lowlands is due largely to temperature. This is seen in the high plateaus of the Andes, Mexico, Rhodesia, Tanganyika, Kenya, Ethiopa, Yemen in Arabia, and Yunnan in southern China (Plate I). It is also highly important in lower tropical plateaus such as those of southeastern Brazil, Central America, Uganda, Madagascar, and the peninsula of India. Within the tropics the temperature usually declines approximately one degree Fahrenheit for every 300 feet of altitude, although there is much local variation. Nowhere else are human health and activity so greatly influenced by differences of altitude. We have seen that an average temperature of 60° to 70° for day and night with a fairly high humidity is the optimum for health and physical activity. Temperatures only 10° higher, averaging 80° or more, are uncomfortable and debilitating. If the humidity is also high, they cause most people to be listless or at least disinclined to work.

Near the equator the temperature along the seacoasts averages approximately 80° the year round, while in the interior at low altitudes it runs still higher—from 80° to 83° at Manaos on the Amazon, for example. Even at the tropics the temperature on the coast averages above 70° at least half the year, while at low altitudes in the interior such temperatures may last nine months and the warmest month may average as high as 85°. Such conditions are among the chief causes of tropical inefficiency. They not only favor the development of parasites such as the hookworm and the anopheles mosquito which causes malaria, but also reduce people's power to resist diseases in general, and above all diminish the desire to work.

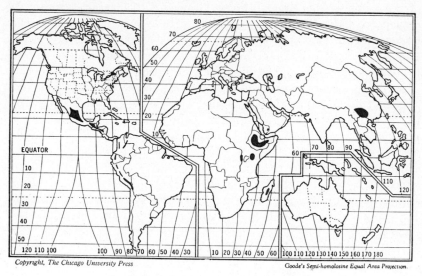

Goode's Semi-homolosine Equal Area Projection.

A—Location of Cool Tropical Highlands.

From all this we see why a rise of a few thousand feet in tropical regions is extremely beneficial, even though it brings only a little of the variability which is so important as a stimulant. A rise of only two or three thousand feet brings the temperature close to the optimum. Thus at La Guaira on the coast of Venezuela the monthly average ranges from 78° to 83°. This is not so bad if one has nothing to do except drink lemonade. But it is very debilitating, and slows up people's work enormously, especially when the vertical sun brings calms and high atmospheric humidity. Not far away at Caracas, an altitude of 3,300 feet reduces the temperature to 64° in the coolest month and 69° in the warmest. Such temperatures are delightful, and are not uncomfortable even when the air is moist. At Quito, close to the equator, but 9,000 feet high, no month averages below 54° or above 55°. At Nairobi, the capital of Kenya, on the equator at an altitude of 5,500, the sun is very hot, but the nights are pleasantly cool. Rio de Janeiro, where the coolest month averages 69° and the six humid months 74° to 79°, does not grow so fast as São Paulo, 2,600 feet higher on the edge of the plateau. There average temperatures of 58° to 69° join with the coffee industry in producing one of the most energetic and progressive cities in South America.

Rainfall and Vegetation in Cool Tropical Highlands.—When the midday sun approaches the zenith a rainy season generally begins in Tropical Highlands. The rains increase in intensity for two or three months (A253), because the equatorial zone of rising air, calms, and showers follows the sun in its movements northward or southward. When the vertical sun is farthest away, however, in June or December according to the hemisphere, one of the trade-wind belts, or even the desert belt of descending air, reaches the plateau. Then there is little or no rain. Nevertheless, on the windward slopes, where the trade winds are forced to rise and give up their moisture, rain is common at all seasons, and the vegetation takes the form of a dense tropical forest such as we saw on the east slope of the Andes (page 152). On the plateaus, where the dry season is usually well developed, grassland is often interspersed with forests.

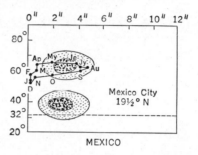

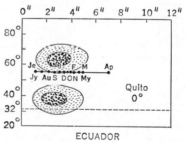

A—Climographs of Cool Tropical Highlands.

In parts of the Guatemalan Plateau one rides among pine trees and blackberry bushes. Around Mexico City, where the monthly average temperatures of 54° to 65° are almost ideal, the surrounding mountains reduce the rainfall so much that dry grasslands prevail, together with irrigation, adobe houses, and miles of hedges made of the desert-loving agave or century plant. In Kenya, at heights of 8,000 feet, broad grassy slopes alternate with thick bamboo jungles. Higher still in Ecuador or Colombia the more level parts of the Andean Plateau look much like the eastern United States or western Europe. They afford charming landscapes with fields of green grass, corn, and potatoes, and many green trees, cattle, orchards, blueberries, and soft, fleecy clouds. In the little parks or squares of the towns, flowers which come with us at various seasons from early spring to autumn—violets, tulips, primroses, daffodils, columbines, roses, and fall asters—are all blooming at once. In the orchards the same tree may carry buds, flowers, and both green and ripe peaches, apples, or plums. Unfortunately the fruits and vegatables of cooler regions are usually of poor quality when raised in the tropics. They need a winter in order to do their best.

Temperature and Crops.—Bogotá, Quito, and especially La Paz are so high that they are often uncomfortable. The morning sun is hot, but in the afternoon the wind may chill one to the bone, and the evenings make one shiver. Out-of-doors one wants to be like the Indians and wear a poncho, or woolen cape with a hole in the center for the head. In the house a fire soon makes the air too warm, and it is hard to get the right temperature. The low temperature at a height of about 10,000 feet near Quito has a curious effect on the corn crop. The temperature at night is so low that this crop needs six months to mature. On clear nights when the sun is either farthest north or farthest south frosts may occur. Hence the only way to raise corn is to plant it just before one frosty season, and harvest it just before the next. The seeds germinate while there is danger of frost but the sprouts do not appear above the ground. Then the plants have just time to mature before frost comes again.

In Kenya at altitudes of 7,000 to 9,000 feet, one sees a curious mixture of tropical and temperate conditions. Wild African black people dressed in cattle hides and loaded with anklets, armlets, necklaces, and huge earrings of copper wire and beads live near recently arrived white settlers. The natives support themselves by means of cattle on the upper grasslands and by raising corn and bananas lower down. The white people have plowed up huge fields where they raise soft wheat at the higher levels, soft white corn with huge kernels lower down, and coffee still lower at altitudes of about 5,000 feet. Close to an English home, almost naked black "boys" are driving long teams of oxen which pull the white man's plows. Across a bushy little gully the tracks of an elephant that came last night form big holes among the plum and apple trees of a European orchard.

Highland Civilization.—This close juxtaposition of different civilizations is characteristic of Tropical Highlands. In the Andes and Mexico, before the coming of the white men, the rulers were the descendants of invaders who had conquered but not displaced the earlier owners of the land. The Spaniards followed their example, finding the country good because it was so cool and free from disease. But the old civilization still persists beside the new. Four centuries of life with the Spaniards have altered the Indians' mode of life very little.

In Africa the contrast between the lowlands and the central plateau is almost startling. We have already seen that in southern Sudan the Shilluks and Dinkas of the Nile lowland are among the most backward people in the world. They cake their naked bodies with ashes to keep off insects. They rarely plant fields, but wander about with their cattle. Houses are replaced by flimsy shelters from the sun, made by tying together the tops of enormous grasses ten feet or more in height, and spreading the bottoms in an arc. At a height of 3,500 to 5,000 feet in the Uganda Plateau a little farther south the relative coolness and the favorable distribution of rainfall throughout the year have helped to develop the most advanced of the native people of the great equatorial belt of Africa. Long before the white man came they lived in villages where neat grass huts were hidden among banana patches surrounded by small fields of peanuts, yams, and manioc. They had learned to make cloth out of bark, and to build round huts that are spacious, dry, and pleasing to the eye. They had organized a real government with a king surrounded by vassals. Their ability is illustrated by the railroad to Kampala, their chief town. When this was planned, the British officials intended to use foreign laborers. The native chiefs thought this would be bad for their people, and so asked the British to let them do the work themselves. When their chiefs called upon them the Baganda, as the Uganda people are called, did the work "as well as Chinese would have done it," according to a British official, and finished it three months ahead of time. The naked cattle people of the hot lowland would never have energy to do such a thing. At a still higher altitude ten or fifteen thousand white settlers are holding the highest, coolest parts of Kenya in the midst of two and a half million black people. About twenty-five thousand Hindus and others from India have also immigrated thither. By serving as artisans, small business men, and clerks they create great jealousy, for they take the jobs which are wanted by the abler natives on the one hand and by the less able whites on the other.

The great reason for this mixture of civilization is that the highlands, especially the lower ones, are the best of all tropical regions. They supply not only valuable metals as in Peru, Bolivia, and Colombia, but most of our tea and coffee. In southern Brazil the plateau and the coffee have attracted energetic Italians and Spaniards to São Paulo where they challenge the power of the Portuguese and Negro elements of Rio de Janeiro and the north. This has led to frequent revolutions even in the present century. In similar fashion the people who live high up in Arequipa, Quito, and Bogotá are scornful of their more dusky compatriots down below at Lima, Guayaquil, and Cartagena.

Yet in spite of these advantages the Cool Tropical Highlands can boast of only one large center of population, Mexico City. The ruggedness of the plateaus, their remoteness from the sea, and the small size of the territory that is naturally tributary to any one center, hamper the growth of cities. Mexico City has attained its present size largely because it lies in an unusually wide and fertile basin which has easy access to other parts of the plateau farther north and south.

EXERCISES

1. Select some area lying within the Equatorial Rainforest. Look it up in the encyclopedia, in textbooks, and books of travel. Write a sketch of its economic and social geography, paying especial attention to conditions which agree or disagree with the description of the Equatorial Rainforest in this chapter.

2. Do the same thing for the Region of Wet Tropical Agriculture, but pick out some crop or city for special description.

3. Look up the maps mentioned in the index of this book under the heading: "Maps: World." What products come in appreciable amounts from the Wet and Dry Low Latitudes as compared with the Region of Wet Tropical Agriculture? Explain the difference in both the kind and amount of production.

4. What part of the Wet and Dry Low Latitudes is especially productive? Explain the relation of this fact to continentality and relief.

5. If you were going to raise cattle within the tropics, in which of the four natural regions discussed in this chapter would you locate yourself? Before deciding, tabulate the advantages and disadvantages of each region. What other considerations beside climate would influence your choice of a location?

6. Look up the Incas, and show how this chapter helps to explain why the Spaniards found so high a civilization and so much valuable loot among them.

7. On an outline map of the world, indicate the tropical areas that are high enough to be occupied advantageously by white men. What drawbacks in the way of climate have these areas as compared with the United States?

8. Make a list of the large cities of the natural regions discussed in this chapter. Discuss their location in respect to rainfall, products, and coasts.

CHAPTER XIII

DESERTS AND GRASSLANDS

Deserts. *Their Vast Extent.*—In Plate I, Deserts occupy more space than any other natural region—about a fifth of the earth's land surface excluding Antarctica. They extend from near the equator in Africa and South America to latitude 50° in Central Asia. From Spanish Morocco they stretch through the Sahara, Egypt, Arabia, Irak, Persia, Afghanistan, and Baluchistan to western India. Farther north another desert band runs from the Caspian Sea through Turkmenistan, Uzbekistan, and other parts of Asiatic Russia to Sinkiang and Mongolia. Smaller deserts lie in the southwestern United States and northern Mexico, while the narrow desert strip along the Pacific Coast from Ecuador through Peru and Bolivia to Chile is one of the world's driest places. Its southward counterpart east of the Andes in Argentina extends in mitigated form to Patagonia. Southwest Africa displays similar features in its Kalahari Desert, while a large part of Australia in these same latitudes is also desert.

With one exception no desert reaches the eastern coast of a continent. Trade winds and monsoons make this impossible. Africa from Egypt through the Anglo-Egyptian Sudan to Eritrea and French, British, and Italian Somaliland forms the exception. But northern Africa as far south as the Strait of Bab el Mandeb is not really a separate continent, for it has no broad ocean on the east—only the hot Red Sea. Thus, except for Somaliland, where the hot coast is dry because it runs parallel to both the trade winds and the opposite monsoon, deserts are unknown along the thousands of miles forming the east coasts of the continents.

The Temperature of Deserts.—The range of temperature in deserts is very great (A259). In northern Peru all months are warm with averages ranging from 63° to 78°. At Urga in Mongolia the January average is −15° and that of July 64°, a difference of 79°. At In-Salah in the Sahara and at Jacobabad in India an almost unendurable average of 98° is recorded for the hottest month, but January sinks to 54° in the Sahara and 57° in India. Such high temperatures almost drive white people crazy. In view of its latitude (43°), the depression of Turfan,

257

below sea-level in Central Asia, is one of the most extraordinary deserts. It illustrates the fact that in deserts the range of temperature is extreme not only from season to season, but even from day to night. At Lukchun in Turfan the monthly averages range from 13° in January to 90° in July, and the range is still greater at the bottom of this depression 300 feet below sea-level. The daily range is still more extraordinary. At sunrise on March 5 the authors of this book saw the thermometer at −2° F., and in the middle of the same day it stood at 54° in the deep shade of a cliff. The desert air is so clear, and so little heat is lost by evaporation, that the unbroken sunshine warms the earth

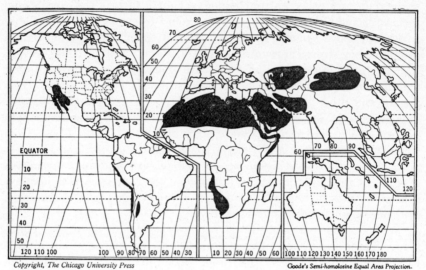

Goode's Semi-homolosine Equal Area Projection.

A—Location of Deserts.

very rapidly by day and in summer, but the clearness also allows the air to cool off with equal rapidity at night and in winter. Hence Bertram Thomas, the first man of European race to cross southern Arabia, speaks of frosts at a low altitude only 20° from the equator. Yet the Arabs there muffle their heads to keep out the heat which rises to 120° or 130° by day in summer. In still lower latitudes in the Australian desert the unclothed natives have been described as being sometimes so benumbed by the cold nights that in the morning they lie about as if drugged until they are thawed by an hour or two of sunlight.

The Rainfall of Deserts.—Although many deserts have no rain for years at a time, all deserts may have showers of great intensity when the rain finally comes. In Arizona the authors of this book once crossed a dry stream channel at noon, but on trying to return the same way a few hours later found a raging muddy river two hundred feet wide. They camped there until the river flowed by next day. In Egypt they saw the desolate site of a village which was foolishly located on an alluvial fan at the mouth of a gorge leading down through the cliffs that border the Nile Valley. A recent heavy shower on the mountains, like the one which caused the river in Arizona, had sent down the first flood within

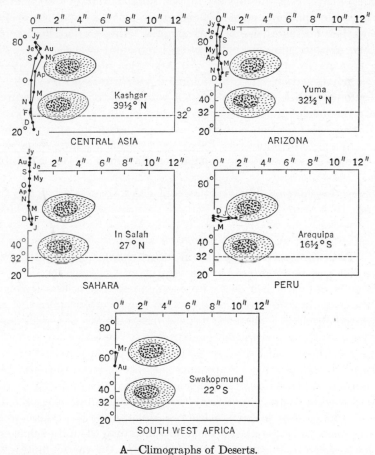

A—Climographs of Deserts.

the memory of living men, and washed away the whole village. Sometimes the floods in deserts last a considerable time. In 1912 a large party of geographers from many countries was held up three days because of rain at the Roosevelt Dam in Arizona.

The seasons of desert rainfall vary according to the causes of the deserts. In latitudes below 20° the main deserts (A258) are due to the trade winds which have blown across mountains or broad stretches of land where the air loses its moisture. Such deserts get a little rain in summer when the edges of the equatorial rain belt swing farthest north or south. In latitudes 20° to 30° or 35° the deserts are due partly to the trade winds, but also to the fact that this is the zone where high atmospheric pressure causes the air to descend and therefore become warm and dry. Such deserts get a little summer rain of the equatorial type on their equatorial edge as at Khartum and a little of the cyclonic type on their northern edge as at Alexandria. Intermediate regions, like southern Arizona, may get both kinds of rain, and thus have two short rainy seasons six months apart. In Argentina and Utah the deserts arise largely because neither the dominant west winds of these latitudes, nor cyclonic storms with their varied winds, bring much moisture so far into the interior. The deserts in Asia are of vast area largely because the size of the Eurasian continent causes winds from every direction to lose most of their moisture before penetrating so far. What little rain they do get comes mainly in summer when the monsoon winds blow inland.

Desert Vegetation.—The vegetation of deserts varies much less from latitude to latitude than does that of more humid regions. This is mainly because the relatively high summer temperature and great dryness cause intense evaporation no matter what may be the desert's latitude. Thus the greatest contrast in desert vegetation is not between equatorial and temperate or arctic forms, but between the deserts of the New World with their abundant cacti and agaves, or century plants, and those of the Old World where these families were unknown until introduced by man. The most typical desert plants are small bushes with various devices to prevent evaporation. The leaves are sometimes very small, thick, and hairy; or perhaps plump and watery with skins that prevent evaporation. Sometimes they are reduced to sharp spines or little bracts. Other plants are leafless, but have chlorophyll, or green matter, in their stems. Another device is fat stems full of water. One form of this is seen in certain leafless Mexican bushes whose round, plump stems can be cut like cheese, and which drip when broken even in the driest, hottest weather. Another is seen in the cactus family with its fleshy, thorny stems and leaves. In all cases the object is to reduce evaporation to the lowest limits and store up water which cannot easily get out. In many deserts no vegetation at all is visible for long distances; often an occasional little bush a foot or two high is seen at intervals of scores or hundreds of feet. Such bushes can live without rain for years. In other deserts the bushes are fairly numerous and there is also an annual cover of sparse short grass which becomes dry and brittle soon after the end of the rainy season so that much of it is blown away by the wind. On the edges of deserts there are very beautiful areas where the whole country is covered with bushes or smaller herbage. In southern Arizona creosote and mesquite bushes, many kinds of cacti with brilliant flowers, and feathery grasses in isolated clumps make the desert most attractive. In southeastern California, Syria, and the interior of eastern Australia the ground after a rain is sometimes covered with a green carpet on which are great patches of brillant flowers, bright blue for a mile, then yellow, red, pink, white, or flaming orange. Even in the driest deserts a single shower may cover the land with a superbly flowered carpet of grass a foot or two high. On the Peruvian coast this happened in 1925. In March of that year 15.5 inches of rain fell at Trujillo in contrast to only 1.4 during the previous 7 years. No heavy rain had fallen since 1891. The seeds must have lain dormant many years.

Oases.—Well-watered spots called oases are a feature of all deserts. There one finds a great variety of wild plants like those of the neighboring more humid regions outside the desert. When these are added to the true desert species the total number of kinds of plants in deserts is greater than in the neighboring humid regions. The same is true of crops, for in many oases any crop which can stand the temperatures can be raised no matter what its requirements for water. The oases of Tadjikistan (Russian Turkestan) and Sinkiang (Chinese Turkestan) in Central Asia, for example, produce not only all manner of cereals, vegetables, and fibers, but most superb grapes, melons, peaches, and other fruits. Turfan is so cold that the grape vines have to be buried deeply under mounds of earth in winter. Yet its small, seedless grapes make such plump delicious raisins that in former days a caravan used to make the three months' journey to Peking each year in order to supply the Chinese Emperor's table. In the driest and hottest deserts the palm tree is the dominant plant. This is partly because it yields such abundant food with so little care, but still more because it grows well not only in intense heat but in soil that is more or less saline. Egypt, with its abundant cotton, sugar, and cereal crops, and its millions of date palms, is probably the most famous of all oases. Some of the world's largest sugar plantations are located in the oases of Peru where small rivers debouch on little plains at the western base of the Andes. Yet in spite of their fertility oases take little part in world trade. For the world at large, the cotton of Asiatic Russia, the Indus Valley, Egypt, and the part of the Sudan where the Blue Nile and the White Nile meet is the most important product. Dates, camel's hair, wool, and some hides are more characteristic but less important exports from deserts.

A Typical Desert Basin.—Most deserts contain many basins enclosed by mountains through which the rivers find no outlets. This is because the water supply is not enough to fill the basin with a lake that overflows and thus cuts a valley through the surrounding mountains. Hence all the water and all the gravel and mud washed down from the mountains are deposited in the bottom of the basin. The water forms a lake which in time becomes salty. Thus dry regions tend to be lake regions, as is readily apparent on a good map of our southwestern states, Persia, or western Argentina. All running water carries at least a little saline material in solution. Since all the water of these lakes is evaporated the salt remains behind and the lakes grow more and more salty. Great Salt Lake and the Dead Sea are so saline that the swimmer there floats with his head and shoulders well above the water.

The gravel and silt brought down by the streams are deposited at the base of the mountain in low, flat alluvial fans, or else are laid down in the lake, thus raising its bed and making it very shallow. In many basins the change of climate since the glacial period has caused the lakes to disappear, leaving great deposits of salt, as in Death Valley. Such salts are among the most valuable assets of deserts, especially if they contain potash, as at Searles Lake in California. The potash in the water of the Dead Sea is worth billions of dollars.

The topography of a desert basin is very different from that of ordinary humid regions. A typical desert basin consists of a series of concentric zones. On the outside lie rough mountains so bare of vegetation that the wind and the occasional rains have swept away practically all the finer materials from the lower slopes. Then comes a broad band of piedmont gravel, coarse near the mountains but finer farther out. In Sinkiang, Persia, and Arabia such gravels often form smooth, barren expanses like vast beaches from one to a hundred miles wide. Next comes a zone of finer material with more sand and silt. Here the water which has sunk into the gravel near the mountains often stands near the surface and may even flow out in springs. This gives rise to a zone of oases. Still farther down the very gentle slope of the plains in a desert basin lies another zone where floods have deposited still finer clayey materials. This, as well as the other zones, is often swept by strong winds. These carry away so much material that the pebbles in the gravel form a smooth pavement devoid of fine material, while the clays are cut into fantastic tables separated by aisles and hollows. The finer dust, as we have seen, is carried away to form loess. The large sandy particles are heaped in a zone of sand dunes. In Central Asia and Arabia these are often hundreds of feet high and very hard to traverse. They are brownish or yellowish on the edges of the larger deserts, but pinkish far out in the centers. Sandy ripples and little dunes of every size are superposed upon one another and upon the big dunes in a superbly beautiful fashion. The last zone is the dry part of the lake bed. Part may be clayey, but the newer portions almost invariably consist of highly saline material and perhaps of pure white salts.

The People of Deserts.—The people of the oases are very different from those of the real desert. The oasis folk are likely to be quiet, plodding, cowardly people like the Egyptian "fellahs," or peasants, the Chantos of Sinkiang, and the Sarts of Tadjikistan. The vast majority of them cultivate their fields and orchards, care for a few sheep and perhaps a donkey, feast on sour milk with melons and grapes, or dates, according to how far north they live, and know almost nothing of what happens outside their own oasis. The real desert people are nomads who depend on their sheep, goats, horses, and camels for a living. They are obliged to be nomadic, for there is rarely enough grass or water in any one place to support them for long. They live in tents which can easily be packed on their animals. No one can live in luxury, for it is impossible to carry many goods from place to place. Moreover, at any time, a drought or a raid may reduce even the richest to poverty. Then, too, the work of all, rich or poor, is the same. Hence the democratic spirit is strong among desert nomads.

Other qualities are also fostered by their mode of living. In times of drought or distress the only feasible way to add to the resources of a family is by robbing someone else. Thus raids on other tribes have become not only allowable, but highly honorable. On such raids the power of leadership, the ability to obey directions faithfully, the power to endure hunger, thirst, and weariness without complaint, and above all bravery in making an attack are absolutely essential to success. The young men who fail in these qualities cannot get wives, and often are driven out of the camp and have to take refuge in the oases. Thus for generations the desert nomads have acquired the ability to lead, to follow a leader, and to fight, but not to work with their hands. When they leave the deserts they often become merchants if they go peacefully, or an aristocratic ruling class if they go out as warriors. Turkey, Egypt, China, and Persia have all been dominated during a large part of their history by people whose ancestors acquired the power of leadership in the desert.

Towns in Deserts.—Almost every oasis has a village, town, or city. The size of these depends largely on the size of the streams that water them. Thus Egypt with the huge Nile River has two big cities, Cairo with over a million people and Alexandria more than half as large. The Euphrates and Tigris Rivers provide so much irrigation that Baghdad on the Tigris has over 250,000 people. The Rimac coming down from the high Andes provides enough water to make Lima and its port of Callao a metropolitan district considerably more populous than Baghdad. The melted snows of lofty Mount Demavend seeping along through piedmont gravels do the same for Teheran in Persia. The Indus River also supports a number of cities, among which Karachi with over 200,000 is the chief, but here the city is by no means so large relatively as is the river. Finally there is one great desert city of nearly half a million people which owes its existence not to water but to oil. Baku on the western side of the Caspian Sea is perhaps the most oily city in the

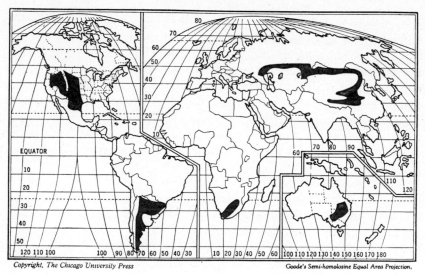

Goode's Semi-homolosine Equal Area Projection.

A—Location of Temperate Grasslands.

world. It is not a pleasant place in which to live, and the proportion of men there is very high compared with women and children. Aside from Baku the desert cities are mainly commercial centers dealing in the agricultural products of their oases and the imported manufactured goods for which these products are exchanged. Nevertheless only Alexandria and Karachi are genuine seaports, although Baku may be called a lake port, and Lima is so near to Callao that the two belong together more fully than do Los Angeles and its port San Pedro. Baku is the only one of the desert cities which does much manufacturing. The rest, however, have great numbers of artisans who carry on hand trades and do all sorts of little jobs to supply local utensils, furniture, clothing, and food. All of these desert cities contain vast numbers of one- or two-story houses built of adobe. In the better quarters these are whitewashed and appear quite attractive; in the poor quarters they are left in their original yellowish-brown mud color. In the better quarters there are also many plaster houses which are often tinted pink, red, blue, brown, or green, making the streets quite gay. Dust and dirt are common in these cities. The air is so dry that people get the habit of throwing garbage and other refuse into the streets where it either dries up or is eaten by packs of ownerless dogs. Whenever the wind blows the dryness permits a great amount of filthy dust to be blown into the air. Such conditions, combined with poor sanitation, or none at all, make the death rate very high in the great majority of oasis cities. Cairo has one of the highest death rates in the whole world.

Temperate Grasslands. *Climate.*— This climatic region is less definite than most of the others, as may be seen from the different forms of the climographs in A266. Yet it has certain climatic characteristics which give all parts the same general type of vegetation and the same kind of value for man. It differs from the grasslands of the Wet and Dry Low Latitudes in having lower temperatures, especially in winter when frosts or even severe cold are the rule. Although the precipitation is heavier than in deserts it is so scanty or so poorly distributed throughout the year that the vegetation consists of grass with only scattered trees in some parts. The Temperate Grasslands, however, range from almost

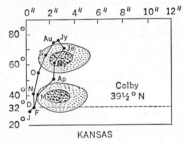

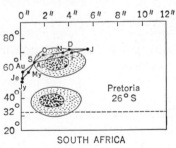

A—Climographs of Temperate Grasslands.

desert conditions to beautiful areas with tall grass and a good many trees. The grass is less coarse and of much better quality than in the Wet and Dry Low Latitudes.

The rain in most of the region comes in summer as the result of winds that blow inward toward the interior of the continents. The dryness, which usually prevails in winter, is largely due either to a location far in the interior of a continent, or to protection from the prevailing oceanic winds by mountains. Such conditions account for the immense grassy plains of North America, the so-called Great Plains, extending westward towards the Rockies from about the one hundredth meridian and southward into Mexico. A similar type of country is found west of the Rockies in the Basin and Range region. In South America it occupies a large part of Uruguay and Argentina, aside from the section surrounding the lower La Plata. The western part of the latter country displays the alkaline soils and saline swamps characteristic of semi-deserts. The high veldt of South Africa with its rolling grasslands also belongs to this type, as do the great steppés surrounding the deserts of Central Asia. There the grasslands extend from the borders of Turkestan through Mongolia and then southward and again westward in eastern Tibet. Finally the better pasture lands of the interior of eastern Australia should also be mentioned. In the southern part of this last region, however, the influence of the Mediterranean Climate with its winter rain is recognizable. Where two distinct types of rainfall thus cooperate we get a fairly even distribution of rain throughout the year as in New South Wales. The broad pampas of Argentina extending down into Patagonia show a similar seasonal division of precipitation, although still with a summer maximum. The interior basin of the Columbia River, on the other hand, is so much influenced by the more intense cyclonic control in winter that it then gets the maximum of its sparse rainfall.

The predominance of summer rain is a decided advantage from the standpoint of human utilization. The combination of warmth and moisture, even though the moisture is not abundant, gives a considerable growth of vegetation in regions that would be almost deserts if the precipitation came in the cold season when plants cannot grow.

Farming.—The *soil* in the temperate grasslands is not unfavorable except when excessive aridity increases its alkali content. The abundance of grass has caused these grassland soils on the whole to be so dark colored and fertile that they would be of great value if they had water enough. Their good qualities are one of the conditions that have stimulated *dry farming* on their moister edges. Wheat is the chief crop thus raised, although barley, oats, flax, and even corn are also raised in some places. In the western parts of Kansas, Nebraska, and the Dakotas, as well as in Colorado, Wyoming, Montana, eastern Oregon, and some of the other drier states, it is a common practice to plow the fields after the rainy season and then leave them unsown. The dry, dusty soil on top of the fields acts as a blanket to prevent evaporation. The plowing kills the weeds. Hence growing plants take very little water out of the soil, even though no new supplies of rain arrive for nearly a year. Thus when the next rainy season arrives the ground is in good condition to be plowed once more and sown. In other words, dry farming helps to give these dry regions the kind of advantage which the more favored parts of the world get by having favorable rainfall in winter and spring as well as summer. Dry farming doubles the amount of work required in planting the fields. Therefore it is practicable only in level regions where big machines can plow, plant, and reap the crop very cheaply. The need for such machines in this type of climate is one reason why they have been so highly developed in the United States. In Russia there was practically no agriculture in the sections belonging to this climatic type until recently. All the land was devoted to stock-raising. That made it easy for the Russians to establish their large state farms. The largest of these, called the "giant" and located north of the Caucasus Mountains, contains 427,000 acres.

These Russian farms, like the dry farms in other regions of this same climatic type, suffer from another handicap. The rainfall is so variable and unreliable that even with the most careful plowing the crop may be very scanty or even fail. In Russia the Soviet government was jubilant over the big crops during the first years of the state farms. A few years later, however, it began imposing penalties on the workers because of the scanty yields. The workers doubtless grew careless, but part of the trouble came from the scarcity or poor distribution of the rainfall. Similar conditions in New South Wales have caused the yield per acre to vary from 17 bushels per acre in good years to 3 in poor years; in Argentina, even when all parts are taken together, the variation is from $15\frac{1}{2}$ to $4\frac{1}{2}$. In the parts where the climate makes it necessary to use dry farming methods the variations are still greater, for the crop may fail completely.

Stock-raising.—The dominant type of land utilization in the Regions of Temperate Grasslands is stock-raising of the *extensive* rather than the intensive type. This means raising big herds of beef cattle, sheep, or even swine, as happens in New Mexico. The animals forage for themselves and receive very little care. The *ranchers* who carry on this work may try their hand at dry farming when the prices of grain are high, but this is a side issue.. They are also likely to raise a few crops by irrigation if possible. This provides good alfalfa hay for the work animals and dairy cows. If the rancher is fortunate he may also raise alfalfa to tide his "range cattle" over a dry season. In Asia, where the degree of progress in this climatic region is less than in the other continents, most of the inhabitants are genuine *nomads* like the Khirghiz.

The great *western plains of North America* form a vast flat expanse broken only by a few island-like hills or mountains. They are treeless, except along the rivers or where trees have been planted and irrigated by man. Toward the wetter east they pass by a very gradual transition into the prairies where the rainfall is more reliable, but on the west the Rockies form a great wall separating them from a region where man's economic responses are very different. The grass varies according to the rainfall. It is tall and deep-rooted in the fairly humid east, but short and surface-rooted in the dry west. Huge farms are necessary to provide a living for the ranch owner. Not only must the good years take care of the losses of the lean, but each cow requires a large area. In A268 notice how rapidly the number of acres of pasturage required to support a cow increases from Iowa where one or two acres are needed to the region west of the Rockies where no less than 75 acres are required. In Wyoming, 25 per cent of the farms have an area of over 1,000 acres.

A large and well managed cattle ranch usually has a center which is

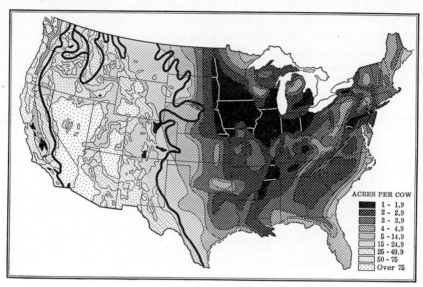

ACRES PER COW

	1 - 1.9
	2 - 2.9
	3 - 3.9
	4 - 4.9
	5 - 14.9
	15 - 24.9
	25 - 49.9
	50 - 75
	Over 75

A—Acres of Pasture Required per Cow in the United States.

almost a little village. There one finds houses for the families of the rancher and his men, a garage and a place where a blacksmith can work, stables for the horses and a few dairy cows, barns for alfalfa, a chicken house, a few acres of irrigated fields, some shade trees, a little orchard, and, above all, a reliable supply of water, which may come from a running stream or be pumped from the ground. If there is much water for irrigation, sugar beets and fruits on a commerical scale may be raised, but this leads to the village type of life and is not the custom on ranches. In various directions at a distance from the central ranch house, windmills, or in these days pumps run by electricity or gasoline, pour water into troughs so that the animals can always get a drink without going far. Close by there may be sheds where the animals can take shelter from the blizzards which are a feature of this region. Perhaps the sheds contain a supply of wild hay which is cut nearby in years of good rainfall and stored for use in dry seasons. Of course, the population under such conditions is very sparse, but in dry weather the dirt roads are good enough so that it is easy to drive 20 or 30 miles to the village. Yet in many cases the living conditions on the cattle ranches are quite primitive, especially where there is no irrigation (A270). There the people often have no dairy cows and live on canned milk as well canned vegetables and fruit, and it frequently is difficult to send the children to school.

As a general rule, sheep and cattle are not kept on the same ranches. Sheep prefer short grass which they crop very closely. Therefore they do best in the drier western sections. Cattle prefer longer grass and thrive best farther east. In Texas, on the Edwards Plateau, a rather unusual condition exists, for cattle, sheep, and goats are run simultaneously on the same range. The cattle eat the grass, the sheep eat the weeds, and the goats browse on the leaves of the scrubby bushes. By regulating the proportion of animals, a vegetable balance is maintained, according to O. E. Baker. The island mountains, like the Black Hills, if high enough, have more rain than the plains, and the mode of life is different. They are often forested, the grass remains green much longer than on the plains, and mining camps add to the variety of the economic use of the land.

In the entire area of Temperate Grasslands in North America, Denver is the only city of over 250,000 people. It owes its growth to mining quite as much as to cattle ranching and to the irrigation which supports many smaller towns at the eastern base of the Rockies. Spokane, Salt Lake City, and El Paso are smaller cities which owe their growth mainly to agriculture. All of these cities of the grasslands have the usual industries of highly progressive regions, but none of them make many elaborate manufactured goods to be shipped far and wide.

The *Great Basin*, or Basin and Range Region between the Rocky Mountains and the Sierra Nevada, belongs mainly to the Temperate Grassland Region. In the south, however, it is too dry to belong to this type of natural region, while in the north (eastern Washington) it is rainy enough for wheat without dry farming and so belongs to the Cool Continental Agricultural type. In most of the Great Basin, as in the semi-arid plains east of the Rockies, great flocks of sheep are found. In summer they climb the slopes of the many mountain blocks where the rainfall is fairly abundant and grass continues to grow throughout the summer. Dry farming is of local importance, but irrigated sections like those near Salt Lake City and on the Snake River are much more

so. Here, just as in the many irrigated areas along the eastern base of
the Rocky Mountains (A270), the village type of life has developed very
pleasantly. In the irrigated sections the farms are small, for the type
of farming is intensive. One man can cultivate only a few acres of fruit
trees, berries, vegetables, sugar beets, or even alfalfa when the crop has
to be cut five or six times in a season. This causes many farmers to

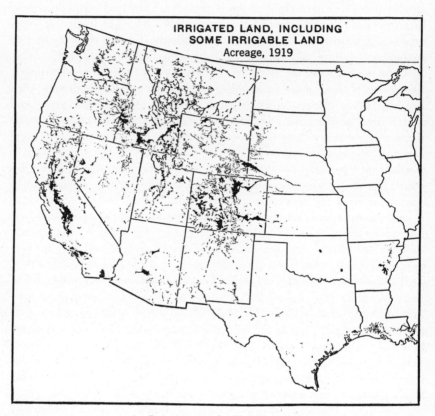

A—Irrigation in the United States.

live close together and makes it easy to maintain schools, churches,
lodges, and other forms of social life. The alfalfa raised in the irrigated
tracts is often used for stock which are pastured most of the time on
the dry land round about.

The *South American* dry plains of the Temperate Grassland type
extend from the borders of the Gran Chaco through the typical pampas,
with their tall, plumed clumps of grass, to the Strait of Magellan and
even Tierra del Fuego. Except in the green oases along the eastern

base of the Andes and along the rivers, extensive stock-raising prevails almost everywhere. Scrub vegetation called "Monte" dominates in the north. This, as well as the warm climate, makes the country especially fit for goats, but cattle are also kept. The goats are not herded in large flocks but are kept in groups by Italian and Spanish families. The standard of living is very low, and the disorderly little huts of the inhabitants are scattered in irregular groups in the great scrubby plains. In some sections, especially near latitude 30° S., salt plains prevent practically all economic activity. Sheep prevail farther south in the Patagonian part of the pampas. They are especially abundant where the bushy vegetation is replaced by a moorland vegetation of grass, moss, ferns, and lichens as a result of much lower temperature and more rain. In the warmer northern section the sparsity of feed obliges people to keep sheep of a widely ranging type and to practice transhumance, moving to the lower slopes of the Andes during the dry winter and back when the rains come in summer. In the south, however, grazing is possible the year round. The wool here is of excellent quality, a fact which has encouraged the growth of vast holdings (estancias) under English or other foreign control.

The Temperate Grasslands of *South Africa* are found on the eastern and southeastern uplands and are bordered by the Desert on the west, the Wet and Dry Low Latitudes on the north, a well watered coastal zone on the east and the Mediterranean "Kaap" or Cape region on the south. Elevation is here the great factor in making the land suitable for white men. The Boers, who are the main element among the white farmers, have large holdings on which most of the work is done by colored native labor. Cattle are here the main stock, but their numbers fluctuate because of drought. Sheep do better in the drier parts. Goats, raised for mohair, are also of importance. Toward the wetter eastern divide, such crops as corn and wheat become more important, but the weather often interferes with successful production.

The *Australian* part of the Temperate Grassland Region includes the rather level and westward sloping uplands west of the isohyet of 15 inches of rain which marks the border of the zone where wheat is raised and where sheep are numerous. The vegetation consists of grass and isolated eucalyptus trees in the east, changing to a dry scrub in the west, where grass appears only after the occasional showers. The land is utilized for sheep, which are fairly numerous in the better areas but very sparse farther inland. Frequent artesian wells and tanks or ponds near the houses help to maintain the sheep and also often nourish a home supply of fruit and vegetables. In this wide, open land, where roads are mere trails, where kangaroos still hop around and dingos are eager to attack sheep, the "squatters," as the big land owners are called, ride around their "stations" on horseback to see if the fences are still intact and the animals safe from dingos.   Rabbits are another serious pest.   Since their introduction from Europe they have multiplied until they sometimes starve the sheep and cattle by eating all the grass. Thousands of miles of wire fences and millions of dollars spent in killing the animals have brought little relief.

The last and largest section of the Temperate Grasslands is in *Asia*. Here man's economic response varies according to the local environment.   Stock-raising is predominant so far as area is concerned, but the irrigated areas support far more people.   Nowhere is the nomadic life more fully developed.   Most of our domestic animals, the horse, sheep, goat, camel, donkey, and yak, were probably first domesticated in this region or on its mountainous borders.   Beginning with the Russian Tartars, Kalmucks, and Kazaks on the west, we find the Khirghiz, Buriats, and Mongols on the north of the deserts of Central Asia; then, as we swing around to the south and again to the west in Plate I, we find more Mongols and then the Tibetans, as well as many minor tribes. All these many races are much alike in habits.   They live in tents, most of which are circular structures made of thick felt with round holes at the top to let in light and let out the smoke.   Their furniture consists of little except bags, ornate boxes, saddles, churns, beautiful rugs, and a few cooking utensils.   Their clothing is made partly of imported cotton goods and even silk, but mainly of wool which is spun and woven by the women.   They wear high leather boots reaching to the knees; they shield their hands from the cold by means of long sleeves that often hang down a foot below the hands.   Sour milk, hard sour cheese, and butter form the staff of life, with some bread and meat, but not so much of the latter as might be expected.   Vegetables and fruits are almost unknown.   Migrations are the rule, but they are of a much more regular type than those in the real desert.   The commonest form of migration is from lowlands in winter to the moister, cooler highlands, or from the edges of a plain where there are permanent supplies of water out to the center where water is found only in the wet season.   Aside from hides and wool, such people have nothing to send to foreign countries, but they supply the irrigated tracts with meat.

The irrigated tracts in this part of Asia are of large size because many great rivers come down from the snowy Tien Shan, Altai, and Hindu Kush Mountains and the Pamirs, the loftiest of all plateaus. Famous cities like Samarkand, and Tashkent, the only city of over 250,000 aside from Denver in all the Temperate Grasslands, are supported by the trade of the people who live in the irrigated tracts.   Shady

streets with a canal and a row of tall poplars on each side are bordered
by walls of yellowish mud behind which rise fruit trees of many sorts.
Whatever land is cultivated yields abundantly, for it has plenty of
water. The people lead the pleasant, comfortable, but not exciting
life which we have already discussed in talking of the desert oases and
the irrigated tracts of the United States. But they do not engage in
raids or even in long and arduous journeys from lowlands to high mountains as do the nomads in the surrounding grasslands. Their work does
little more than supply their own needs. They do indeed produce some
cotton and fruit, and also some unusual kinds of silk goods to send to
other countries, but that is about all. They are not especially energetic,
and there is so little cultivated land in proportion to the population that
they do not have a large surplus to exchange for the goods of other
regions.

EXERCISES

1. On an outline map of the world, color the Deserts in yellow and the
Temperate Grasslands in light green. Summarize the reasons for the light
rainfall or the aridity of each area.

2. Write the names of the continents in order according to the percentage
of their area which is desert, putting the highest percentage first. Why have
the continents near the end of the list such small desert areas?

3. In what situations are most oases formed? Name the different sources
of the water used in oases.

4. Read about deserts in some book like *Arabia Deserta*, by Doughty; *Arabia
Felix*, by Thomas; or *The Pulse of Asia*, by Huntington. How do the deserts
there described differ from the typical deserts described in this chapter? Make
an outline for a theme on life in the desert.

5. Explain why deserts have larger cities and more of them than any natural
region thus far studied except the Regions of Wet Tropical Agriculture. Would
you prefer to reside in a city of the Desert or of the Regions of Wet Tropical
Agriculture? Why?

6. Study a world map of vegetation (A433 in this book, or Plate 6 in the
Oxford Economic Atlas) and determine the natural regions within which grasslands are located. Why are the grasslands divided among so many natural
regions? How do those of the various regions differ in economic value and in
the mode of life of the people?

7. The people of grasslands and deserts depend mostly on animals. Do the
maps in this book indicate that these are the regions where animals are most
abundant? Explain.

CHAPTER XIV

MEDITERRANEAN AND MILD EAST COAST REGIONS

Cyclonic Winter Rain versus Monsoon Summer Rain.—In this chapter we shall discuss the latitudes where the differences between the east and west sides of the continents are most extreme. In latitudes 30° to 40° the west side is everywhere dry in summer, but gets rain from cyclonic storms in winter, thus giving the Mediterranean Type of climate. On the east side the summers are always rainy by reason of inblowing monsoon winds; the winters may be dry or may get cyclonic rain. In these latitudes, more than in any others, the huge size of Asia and the consequent scarcity of cyclonic rain on the east side bring intense human suffering. Here, too, the west sides of the continents get the twofold advantage of cyclonic storms in winter and of oceanic conditions which bring relatively cool summers, at least near the open ocean. In harmony with this contrast, civilization ranges from a very high type in such a region as California to a type that is terribly handicapped in China.

Mediterranean Type (A275, B275, see page 231). *Climate.*—This is the world's most advertised climatic type. In winter, when the zone of cyclonic storms moves south, blue sky and warm sun alternate with heavy showers to make nature look fresh and charming. Temperatures averaging around 60° are cool enough to be invigorating but not to harm vegetation. In summer, however, the poleward migration of the belts of tropical high pressure brings heat and drought, and for months the sun burns down from a pale blue sky through a dust-laden atmosphere. Only near the coast do sea breezes temper these conditions. Where the ocean temperature happens to be abnormally low, however, because of the rising of the water from great depths, as happens in California and Morocco, the onshore winds may make the summers delightful. The dryness, to be sure, continues to be a handicap, even though tempered slightly by heavy coastal dews, or still more by fogs. On the Pacific Coast of the United States from about latitude 35° northward the coast for a few miles inland is shrouded with fog much of the time in summer. Westerly winds over the main body of the Pacific become saturated with moisture. As the winds pass over the strip of cold, upwelling water near the coast they are chilled and

274

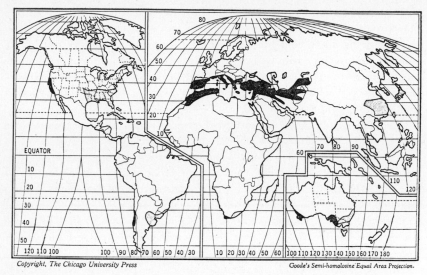

Goode's Semi-homolosine Equal Area Projection.

A—Location of Regions of Mediterranean Type (solid) and of Warm Temperate Humid Regions (dotted). Note how the two types balance one another on opposite sides of the continents.

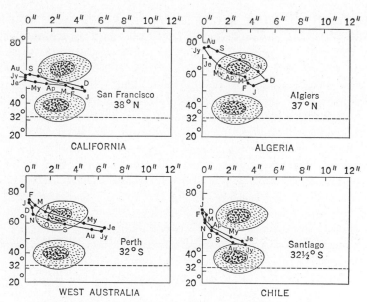

B—Climographs of Regions of the Mediterranean Type.

their vapor is condensed into fog. In the mornings, especially, this blows over the land, thus lowering the temperature not only because the inblowing air is cold but also because the sunlight is kept out. The coolness, humidity, and variability thus introduced are important elements in making this coastal climate healthful and invigorating. Nevertheless, people sometimes deliberately go inland a few miles in order to find sunshine and warmth.

Relief.—Relief is an important factor in limiting the area of the regions under the control of the Mediterranean Type of climate. The Sierra Nevada separates a rather narrow coastal zone from the dry interior plateaus and basins that extend from eastern Washington to Arizona. Even to the west of the main mountains the coast ranges largely shut out the influence of the ocean from the great California Valley and the Willamette and Puget Sound Valleys. In Chile, the Andes, the Central Valley, and Chilean coastal ranges provide conditions closely similar to those in California.

In South Africa only the extreme tip of the continent comes under control of the cyclonic storms which give the Mediterranean Type of climate its winter rain. In Australia again the western edge of the plateau of Western Australia and the Flinders Range in South Australia limit the zone of winter rain considerably. On the other hand, in southern Europe, North Africa, and the part of Asia known as the Near East, the Mediterranean climate expands far to the east. In winter the relatively warm Mediterranean Sea acts as a low-pressure area attracting cyclonic storms and even originating some. The variable winds that thus arise bring considerable precipitation along the shores of the many mountain-bordered peninsulas and islands, especially on their west side. Under favorable conditions the cyclonic storms continue far eastward, being helped locally by the fact that in winter the Black and Caspian Seas tend to form minor local areas of relatively high temperature and low pressure. In this way the rainfall in the Near East is under Mediterranean control. This type of control extends southeastward beyond the Persian Gulf and eastward along the Persian and Afghan Mountains even into northern India and Turkestan. Away from the west coast of Asia the rainfall decreases very rapidly except for heavy rains on the south shores of the Caspian and Black Seas, but this does not alter the general rule of winter rains and summer droughts.

Vegetation.—One of the most typical features of this whole region is a type of vegetation adjusted perfectly to the long, hot, dry summers. It lacks entirely the character of a dense forest such as hides every rock in the equatorial regions. Instead it forms a sort of thin veil of green, often interrupted by colorful rocks which are especially beautiful where they rise steeply beside the deep blue sea. Two types of vegetation prevail: the bush type, or "maquis" called "chaparral" in California, and the open forest. The maquis is a growth of hard-stemmed bushes which cover the lower slopes of mountains or hills and often replace ancient forests which have been cut for timber. It is of great botanical variety, green and even blossoming in winter, and beautiful because of the color of the flowers, which often have a strong perfume. In summer, however, it looks desolate and dead.

Many of the trees of the open forest keep their gray-green foliage throughout the year. The laurel and holly are famous trees of this kind. Venerable live-oaks provide acorns for people as well as swine. In Spain and Portugal the cork oak adds a tinge of red to the landscape where its thick sheets of bark have been removed from the trunks. Umbrella-shaped pines are a typical feature of the rocky coasts, and majestic chestnut trees on the higher slopes provide not only shade and beauty, but a valuable supply of food. Around the houses, walnut trees, or in the drier regions almonds, provide still other valuable tree crops. So important are these that J. Russell Smith believes that nut trees may some day become one of the world's best and cheapest sources of food. Such trees can grow on land that is too steep or stony for ordinary crops. Once planted they grow for generations with almost no care. Aside from the pines, good trees for lumber are not common. The poplars which grow in long rows beside thousands of irrigation ditches are used for this purpose all over the lands around the Mediterranean Sea. Tall eucalypts provide a great source of timber in the Mediterranean parts of Western and South Australia as well as in other parts of the continent. They have been introduced in large numbers in California and Chile and even in the high plateaus of Ecuador and Peru. But California does not need to rely on these poorer kinds of timber, for in spite of rapid lumbering large sections of its high mountains are still shrouded in a superb forest of pines and other conifers. Its giant sequoias or Big Trees are near cousins of the famous cedars of Lebanon which rival them in size and age high on the Syrian mountains back of Beirut.

Fruit Trees.—The most valuable of the Mediterranean trees is the olive, a native of this climate. Italy has 5,000,000 acres of olive trees; the Peloponnesus in Greece probably has at least 20 olive trees for every inhabitant. The blue-black fruit is mainly used for the extraction of olive oil, a basic material of the Mediterranean kitchen. Two other kinds of essentially Mediterranean plants are of world importance—the vine and the citrus trees. The dark red and orange Mediterranean wines have more than local fame, although mainly used for local consumption. Fresh grapes are exported from Spain (Almeria) and California (Sacramento). Dried grapes in the form of raisins are exported from California (Fresno) and Asia Minor (Smyrna). Under the name of dried currants they are one of the important exports of Greece. Unfermented grape juice is a popular beverage in South Africa and America. Citrus fruits have had a boom since the importance of vitamins was realized, especially here in the United States. They are a typical product of the Mediterraean climate, although they grow also on the southern edge of the Warm Temperate Humid Region in places like Florida, China, and New South Wales. Italy (Sicily) and Spain (Valencia) were for centuries the main producers. Until the present century was well under way, oranges brought from a distance were a luxury and not as now almost an essential part of the diet. Spain and Italy still produce large quantities of oranges and lemons, and also of tangerines named after Tangier in Morocco, but strong rival producers have sprung up, as in Palestine, and especially California, where the expansion of orange culture under irrigation has been sensational.

The Mediterranean climate is favorable to a great variety of other fruits, for instance, grapefruit and pomegranates, both of which belong to the citrus family; figs for which Asia Minor is famous; the dates of northern Africa and Mesopotamia which have already been mentioned; peaches and plums like those from which prunes are made in the Santa Clara Valley of California. In many ways orchards, vineyards, and other forms of fruit-growing are man's most outstanding response to this climatic environment. They are more important here than in any other natural region. Vegetables, too, are important in a minor way, and in places like California and Algeria the raising of early vegetables for shipment to cooler climates becomes an important occupation.

Wheat and Other Crops.—Fruits and vegetables are not the only things which grow in the Mediterranean climate. *Wheat*, the chief grain, originated near the Mediterranean. Everywhere it grows well, although the yield per acre is scarcely half as much as in the Marine Cyclonic Region farther north. Planted in the fall, it is ready to harvest at the beginning of the dry season. It is grown *intensively* with plenty of fertilization on some of the lowland plains like the Po Basin where high yields can be obtained because of the relatively favorable rainfall and temperature and the consequent efficacy of fertilizers. It is grown *extensively* without much preparation of the soil, or else is replaced by barley, in dry sections where the yield is lower and very few other crops can be raised. Wheat fields are found in the coast range valleys of California, in the coastal zone of Morocco, in the valleys and uplands of Palestine and Syria, and on the basin-shaped plateau of Anatolia.

A real wheat belt runs through southwestern Australia between the isohyets of 25 and 15 inches of rain, and wheat is the main crop of Chile. Corn partly replaces wheat only where there is some summer rain and plenty in spring and fall as in the Po Basin, but such places are on the margin where the Mediterranean Type of climate merges into the Cyclonic Type. Where irrigation can be practiced, the Mediterranean Type of climate permits a great variety of crops like rice in the Po Basin and California, cotton in the Cilician Plain of southeastern Asia Minor, and even sugar cane on the south coast of Spain. Irrigation is also used a great deal in raising fruit. It has been practiced since ancient times in spots where water and level land are available.

Land Utilization.—In most of the regions where the Mediterranean Type of winter rain prevails, only a small percentage of the land is cultivated. In most sections, mountains occupy a great deal of space. Then, too, the long, hot summers make the growing season unduly short in many places where the soil dries quickly because it is thin or sandy or slopes toward the sun. Moreover, the sparsity of vegetation in such places during the dry summers has allowed a great deal of soil to be washed away by the heavy winter showers, thus leaving bare rock or only scattered pockets of soil as on many of the hills of Palestine. A diminution of storminess and the occurrence of periods of extreme drought during historic times seem to have increased this tendency.

Such conditions, joined with the short, nutritious, winter-grown grass, and the favorable conditions of temperature, have led to the extensive use of sheep and goats, and to a fairly widespread use of cattle. Throughout the whole Mediterranean area from Spain to Palestine and on to Persia almost every village has flocks and herds which are driven out to pasture each day, often under the charge of boys or even girls. The milk of goats and sheep, as well as cattle, is widely used, but generally in the sour state or as cheese rather than as fresh milk or butter.

The combination of a mountainous environment and a Mediterranean climate has also fostered a great development of transhumance in the form of seasonal migrations. During the winter the flocks and herds find plenty to eat close to the villages. When the dry summer arrives the supply of fresh grass soon disappears and all the dry grass is soon consumed. But among the mountains the heavier rainfall and lower temperature not only have produced a heavy growth of unused grass by this time, but they cause the grass to keep on growing during much of the summer. So from thousands of villages the flocks and herds are driven up to mountain pastures where they stay for several months each summer. Even in new regions like California and Chile transhumance is common in a modified form.

These same conditions of rugged relief, eroded slopes, and dry summers during which the water supply is greatly reduced cause the economic and social life of these regions to be greatly concentrated in valleys, coastal plains, mountain-girt basins, and the borders of the larger plains. These larger plains are indeed well populated, but away from the mountains large sections cannot support many people because of lack of water in the dry season. This is seen in the Syrian plain near Aleppo, on the great central plain of Anatolia, and in much of the Great Valley of California. Other sections are swampy and malarial as in Bœotia in Greece or in the coastal plain of western Italy. There, for fear of malaria, the farmers dare not sleep at their fields, but return to their villages on the lower slopes of the neighboring hills, even in the busy harvest season.

Social Conditions.—From the social point of view, Mediterranean life has always had decided advantages, which it still retains. Although village life predominates in most parts of the world, aside from the English-speaking and Scandinavian countries, it is peculiarly developed around the Mediterranean. This is partly because of the necessity of gathering close to the most permanent supplies of water and of sharing the water fairly when it is used for irrigation. The mild winter temperature and the freedom from storms for many months in summer tend to encourage outdoor life the whole year round. This is doubtless one reason why the Spaniards, Italians, and Greeks throng into the village streets in such numbers at sunset and in the evening, and are such lovers of crowds and haters of solitude. The houses do not have to be heated, and the Roman type built around a fountain in a square, open courtyard or atrium is still typical in many sections. The concentration of the people on the coast and the great length of the winding coastline are good for health as they give many people the advantage of cooling sea breezes in the hot summer. These conditions also encourage fishing, sailing, and trade by water, thus making the people internationally minded. This is most conspicuous in Greece with its many colonial ventures far back in history, but it is also true of other Mediterranean lands to a less degree. Even now a peculiarly large percentage of the Greeks are engaged in trade and transportation (A281).

Although the Mediterranean climate permits the raising of a great many kinds of food, the long summer droughts and the consequent scarcity of vegetables limit the diet somewhat. For the bulk of the people of southern Europe the diet is still essentially the same as during the Roman period, with fruit, fish, wheat in the form of white bread or macaroni, olive oil, goat's milk, and cheese as its basic factors.

Cities.—On the whole, the regions with the Mediterranean Type of climate are fairly densely populated, but not to such a degree as the Regions of Wet Tropical Agriculture, the Warm Temperate Humid Region, and the Chinese Monsoon Region. They supply a considerable amount of material for world trade in the form of fruits, olive oil, wheat, wool, hides, and lumber. In some sections they also supply metallic ores and petroleum, but none of them are well supplied with coal. Large cities are fairly numerous: Lisbon in Portugal; Seville, Madrid, Valencia, and Barcelona in Spain; Marseille and Nice in France; Genoa,

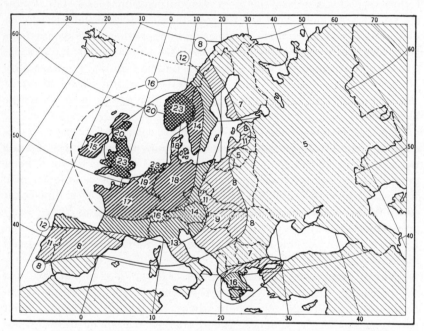

A—Percentage of European Men Engaged in Trade and Transportation.

Florence, Rome, Naples, Palermo, and Catania in Italy; Athens, with Piraeus, in Greece; Istanbul and Smyrna in Turkey; Tiflis in the Caucasus; Beirut in Syria; Algiers in Algeria; San Francisco, Oakland, and Los Angeles in the United States; Santiago and Valparaiso in Chile; Capetown in South Africa; and Adelaide in Australia. Note that only six—Seville, Madrid, Florence, Rome, Tiflis, and Santiago— are inland cities. The remaining twenty are all seaports. Only two— Rome and Los Angeles—have over a million inhabitants. These cities carry on a considerable amount of complex manufacturing. Yet only a few like Barcelona can be classified as primarily industrial rather than commercial.   On the whole, the Regions of the Mediterranean Type import manufactured goods far more than they export them.

This last condition is in part associated with the fact that although the winters with their cyclonic storms are sufficiently cool, humid, and unstable to be highly invigorating, the hot, dry, monotonous summers remain a heavy handicap except in favored locations like the California coast.   To understand the concentration of the highest ancient civilization in this climate rather than farther north we need to recall that even as recently as the time of Christ man had not yet learned to live comfortably in what are now the most stimulating climates.   At that time the Cyclonic Regions were great forested areas which could not be conquered until man knew more about using iron, beasts of burden, methods of making clothing and shelter, and the use of many other later inventions.   Thus in those ancient periods, even if we overlook the possibility of some change of climate, the Mediterranean region offered the best climate among the parts of the world which man has hitherto been able to conquer.

A recent economic asset of many regions with a Mediterranean climate is their attractiveness not only for tourists but for people who want to settle down in a pleasant climate.   California offers a most interesting example of the way in which climate can be commercialized. Thousands of people go there every year to find a pleasant place in which to spend their declining years.   The Rivieria in Europe has a similar attraction, but its proximity to the great manufacturing area of Europe makes it possible for most of the winter guests to go north again in summer.

Warm Temperate Humid Regions.   *Rainfall, Temperature, and Continentality.*—Regions of this type lie on the east side of the continents in latitudes 25° or 30° to about 38° (Plate I).   They differ greatly from the corresponding Mediterranean regions on the west side in similar latitudes.   The chief difference is that they have abundant summer rain in contrast to the long droughts of Mediterranean lands. All of the Warm Temperate Humid Regions also have a fair amount of winter rain—in some cases as much as or more than in summer.   In the southern hemisphere the very small tract of this kind at the southern tip of Africa, and the larger tracts centering around Sydney in Australia and around Buenos Aires and Montevideo in South America, have almost the same amount of rain at all seasons (A302).   In the northern hemisphere, the large Warm Temperate Humid Region in the southeastern quarter of the United States shows a moderate excess of summer rain, while southern China and Japan show a marked excess.   This contrast between the two hemispheres is mainly due to continentality.   The

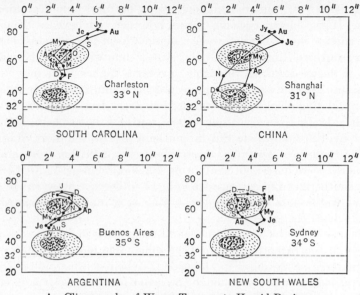

A—Climographs of Warm Temperate Humid Regions.

effect of continentality is especially clear in the temperature, as appears in the following table, where six places, all lying on the seacoast and in practically the same latitude, are arranged in the order of their temperatures during the coldest month.

Place	Country	Latitude	Temperature		Rainfall	
			Coldest Month	Warmest Month	Total, Inches	Percentage in Warmer Half Year
Shanghai..........	China.......	31 12N	38°	80°	44	66
Kagoshima........	Japan.......	31 35N	45	80	85	66
Savannah..........	U. S.........	32 5N	52	82	49	64
Rio Grande do Sul..	Brazil.......	32 10S	55	74	47	47
Port Maquarie.....	Australia....	31 25S	55	73	61	58
East London.......	South Africa.	33 0S	58	70	26	50

In this table the summer temperatures fall in the inverse order of the winter temperatures, cold winters being associated with hot summers. Thus central China has fairly cold winters with a good deal of frost, but its summers are very hot. Being also humid they are debilitating. Southern Japan is not quite so cold as China in winter, and gets only a little frost, but its summers are as hot and humid as those of China. It gets enough cyclonic storms, however, to relieve the monotony of the climate somewhat and to be a distinct asset to health and energy. In the southern United States the winter temperature at Savannah, about a degree north of Shanghai, averages higher than in southern Japan, but cyclonic storms are more prevalent and bring more frequent and stimulating changes. In winter they carry frost clear to northern Florida. In this same latitude in the southern hemisphere, as represented by Rio Grande do Sul in southern Brazil and Port Maquarie north of Sydney in Australia, the seacoasts are free from frost, and yet the summers are not so hot as to bring much discomfort. East London, at the southern end of Africa, with only 12° difference between the coldest and warmest months, has one of the most uniform climates anywhere outside the tropics.

The rise in winter temperatures and the decline in summer temperatures from top to bottom of the preceding table mean that the places there named are arranged in the order of their continentality. Shanghai and Kagoshima, even though the latter lies on the southern end of an island, Kyushu, are dominated by the alternating monsoon winds which blow outward from the cold fastnesses of inner Asia in winter and inward from warm ocean currents in summer. Savannah is similarly, but less markedly, influenced by outblowing and inblowing winds, owing to the size of North America. The smaller bulk of South America and Australia, and especially of the portions in latitudes higher than the Warm Temperate Humid Regions, has only a mild effect in causing contrasts from season to season. At Rio Grande do Sul and Port Maquarie it permits a close approximation to oceanic uniformity. East London is dominated by the ocean rather than by Africa, which lies wholly to the north.

In the preceding table the rainfall shows the effect of continentality less clearly than does temperature, because rainfall is greatly influenced by local relief. Yet on the whole it is greatest where the continental indraft is greatest, and diminishes where this almost dies out in South Africa. Moreover, the percentage of summer rain is greater where the continental indraft is strong in summer. Nevertheless, the noteworthy fact about the rainfall is its distribution in moderate amounts throughout the entire year.

Vegetation and Agriculture.—This distribution of rain is highly important for vegetation. It means that in a state of nature the Warm Temperate Humid Regions are well covered with broadleaved forests (A433). Japan is densely forested; few countries give a greater impression of cloudiness and universal greenness, as is evident in Japanese art, with its trees and mountains rising out of mist. In many parts of southern and central China the trees have indeed been largely cut off by man, but many mountains are well forested, and when a tract is protected, as in certain enclosures near Amoy and Swatow, big trees grow rapidly. The mountains near Foochow carry pine forests. In Australia the eucalypts in the southern part of the Warm Temperate Humid Region attain enormous size. In the United States the southern states contain the finest hard-wood forests of the continent, as well as splendid pines on the sandy tracts.

The abundance of rain at all seasons also means that agriculture thrives, and that a dense population can be supported. Southern China and Japan are so densely populated that the farmers are forced not only to carry cultivation far up the slopes of the mountains, but to be content with only two or three acres of cultivated land per family. Even in the United States, the South contains the densest agricultural population of the country, especially in the sections where the percentage of Negroes is high. In the southern continents the density is not so high, but, in proportion to the level land available, it is higher than in almost any other sections of which the white man has recently taken possession.

The crops in the Warm Temperate Humid Region vary according to the density of population and standards of living as well as rainfall and temperature. In southern China and Japan, great density of population, low standards of living, high summer temperatures, and heavy summer rain cause rice to be overwhelmingly the most important crop. Sweet potatoes and beans are secondary food crops of considerable importance. Fruits do not grow well because of the excessive summer rain. Tea, raised mainly on the hillsides, is the great luxury crop. In China it formerly furnished a fair amount of cash as an export crop, but the foreign market was lost because the great plantations in Ceylon and elsewhere pay far more attention to quality and grading than do the individual Chinese farmers. The most important industrial crop in China and Japan is mulberry leaves for silkworms. The long, warm, wet summers are ideal for this tree, which often sends out two or three sets of new leaves after the preceding crop has been stripped off for the worms. Accordingly most of the world's silk is raised here, and cocoons furnish the main source of ready money. Cotton is also raised in considerable quantities in the Yangtze Valley.

In the Warm Temperate Humid Region of the United States, corn takes the place of rice, partly because of a difference in climate, and partly because the old way of raising rice demanded so much hard labor. Silk and tea are not raised, for similar reasons. Perhaps they might be profitable, if machine methods of raising them could be devised, as has been done for rice. Cotton, however, has been so profitable that other crops have been neglected, and this region has become the world's main source of that crop. Hence it gives a name to one of the chief agricultural regions into which the United States is divided. A55 shows these regions and should be studied in connection with the other natural regions discussed in this chapter and the next. Cotton, like silk and tea, requires a great amount of cheap labor. Many people doubt whether it would ever have become of great importance here had it not been that the climate fits not only the cotton plant but also the Negroes who were introduced from Africa. It is noteworthy that on the western edge of the Cotton Belt, where white farmers predominate, great efforts have been made to devise mechanical cotton pickers. Success appears to have been attained, but only in the relatively dry sections where the bolls of cotton can be left on the plants until all are ripe without danger of their becoming discolored, and where the cotton plants are short enough so that the machines can drive over them.

In the Warm Temperate Region of Argentina and Uruguay, corn and cattle are the chief products, although wheat is of great importance in the south. In Australia the lower temperature and rainfall of the plateau which forms the main part of the Warm Temperate Humid Region cause wheat and sheep, with some fruit, to be the main standbys, though mining is of some importance.

Culture and Habits. *Australia.*—The character of Australia as a whole is well typified in New South Wales, which forms the central part of the Warm Temperate Humid Region in this continent. Along the coast lies a narrow plain fringed with winding bays where the land has been drowned a little. General farming and dairying give this plain a pleasant, fruitful appearance, but agriculture is a small matter compared with the great city of Sydney and its beautiful suburbs scattered along many miles of winding water front. Each evening tens of thousands of workers hasten to the ferry landings, much as they do to the famous bridge over the Golden Horn in Constantinople, in order to take boats to their suburban homes. Sydney and also Brisbane, which lie close to the Wet Tropical Agricultural Region, are not only European but British to an extraordinary degree. Yet the social and moral tone is lighter and more buoyant than in England. Horse races and betting at all seasons, and innumerable picnics and parties, as well as a very high degree of comfort and assertiveness are some of the evidences of this. These qualities are partly due to the relatively adventurous and unconventional character of the immigrants who have chosen to come to this distant land. They are also due partly to the great economic possibilities of a new continent with great mineral wealth, abundant land, and vast opportunities for raising wheat, wool, and cattle. In spite of the recurrent years of drought, people can prosper greatly here because the population is sparse and the farms therefore large enough so that the good years tide over the bad ones. Then, too, the scarcity of laborers has permitted the working people to insist on high minimum wages, short hours, and other advantages such as old age pensions, allowances for babies, and assurance that their jobs cannot be taken from them suddenly. Hence there are few poor people in Australia, and a large percentage even of the poorer classes have homes of their own. Such conditions not only allow time for pleasure and for incessant tea-drinking, but give a certain freedom of spirit which makes people gaily enjoy the good things of life. The climate helps in this respect, for temperatures like those shown above for Port Maquarie, and a moderate but well distributed rainfall, make outdoor recreation pleasant at all seasons.

A little way inland from Sydney the sharply and deeply dissected escarpment of the plateau forms a rough tract which to this day is almost uninhabited and quite wild. At its top the plateau, cooler and more bracing than the coastal plain, stretches away to the west in a succession of green rolling hills covered with wheat fields interspersed with patches of gray-green eucalyptus trees and occasional orchards and vineyards. Farther west, where the rainfall is less, still larger farms support huge flocks of sheep, like those of the adjacent Temperate Grasslands. This pleasant region of comfortable farms and small but prosperous villages illustrates the main source of the wealth which enables so many people to get a living in the cities. If its farms should be broken up into smaller units, as many people desire, the surplus available for the support of Australia's high standards of living would diminish. Yet here, as in many other farming districts, a great many people are eager to get away from the farms and live in the city.

Argentina, Uruguay, and Southern Brazil.—The South American part of the Warm Temperate Humid Region resembles the Australian part in being thoroughly European in racial composition, in having a gay and pleasure-loving population, and in being highly urbanized, as appears in the two great cities of Buenos Aires and Montevideo, as well as in smaller cities like Rosario. Another resemblance is that the wealth which supports the magnificent cities is derived largely from wheat, sheep, and cattle which thrive in outlying regions and are shipped through the great ports. The minerals of the Australian region, however, are replaced by corn in Argentina. This is the natural result of the fact that the South American plain extends far inland, thus giving warm and fairly moist summers over a large area. Socially the difference is greater than economically. Although the wealth of Argentina, Uruguay, and the extreme southern tip of Brazil rivals that of Australia, it is distributed far more unequally. The farms are even larger than those of Australia, and the owners rarely work them themselves. Even more than the Australian land owners they congregate in the great cities. In the past this has given the cities a relatively large number of idle and wealthy people whose mode of life has created the feeling that work is undesirable and that the thing to aim at is a streak of luck by which one gets rich. Labor has not been so scarce as in Australia and has never succeeded in organizing itself and getting privileges like those of the Australians. Accordingly in the cities we find a great number of comparatively poor people and few of the middle class. On the farms there is a corresponding body of poor peons who either work for the large land owners or get a living on farms of their own so small and poorly equipped that they cannot maintain the unequal fight against the frequent crop failures. This development of an upper and lower class with only a small middle class has arisen partly because most of the earlier settlers here were Spaniards, and the later immigrants have been more largely Italians, both races bringing with them a social system different from that of England.

The Southern United States.—Coming to the northern hemisphere we find that the warmer summers have fostered a social system quite different from that of either Argentina or Australia. The warm summers favor corn, tobacco, and cotton, but give people from northern Europe a distaste for outdoor work on the farms. Moreover, the opportunities for manual labor in the cooler North have led laboring people to migrate there rather than to the South. Hence Negro slaves were imported, and in time became such a force that a white man who worked with his hands was considered of a decidedly inferior class. Since the Civil War this idea has gradually weakened, but it must still be reckoned with. The result is that today we have in the South a large number of white people, mainly of British descent, who compare favorably with those of Australia. Some live on farms or in villages and run plantations where they employ colored people or rent land to them and supervise their work. Others live in attractive villages, towns, and small cities, and carry on all kinds of work except pure manual labor, which is left to the Negroes. But in addition to this the South has the problem of "poor whites," people who have not succeeded well in competition with the cheap labor of the colored people, or who have been forced in one way or another onto farms too small or unproductive to support the usual white standard of living. The Negroes, too, show a wide range of character. One type is self-respecting, industrious, and intelligent, although often handicapped by the small size of their farms, or by the limited kinds of work in which colored people are welcome. Another type comprises a large number of rather shiftless, happy-go-lucky people, the kind of Negroes who live in small dilapidated shanties and work only when absolutely necessary.

The South has another economic and social feature unknown in the corresponding regions of the southern hemisphere. This is a well developed and growing cotton-manufacturing industry. Australia, to be sure, is making an increasing proportion of its own manufactured goods, but it manufactures very little for other people. The South, on the contrary, does not make any great assortment of manufactured goods, but manufactures a huge amount of cotton cloth which it sends away in exchange for other kinds of manufactures.

All these conditions, taken together, have retarded the growth of great cities. Although the South has five times as many people as Australia, it has no city of a million inhabitants in contrast to two there. New Orleans, the largest southern city, has about half a million people; Atlanta, Birmingham, Dallas, Houston, and Memphis, have over 250,-000. Aside from Birmingham, all of these are primarily centers of commerce, although all carry on active local manufacturing. Birmingham with its iron, on the other hand, together with smaller cities like Columbus, Augusta, and Charlotte with their cotton mills and Durham with its tobacco factories, provide a type of strictly manufacturing city almost unknown elsewhere in the Warm Temperate Humid Region except in Japan.

Japan.—Climatically southern Japan comes closer to the southern United States than to any other section of the Warm Temperate Humid Region. These two differ from the three in the southern hemisphere in having not only warmer summers, averaging about 80° instead of a little above 70°, but also colder winters (page 283). They differ from these and from South China in having fairly abundant cyclonic storms and abundant rainfall at all seasons. Japan, however, is more humid than our South. In relief, on the other hand, Japan, with its ubiquitous mountains, has more resemblance to South China than to New South Wales with its plateau, or to Argentina and our South with their plains. As a result of its humid climate Japan is not a good place for the cotton, corn, wheat, cattle, and sheep which are the standbys of the sections of the Warm Temperate Humid Region thus far discussed. It is excellent, however, for rice as the main reliance for food, silk for cash, and tea for drink. The most typical scene in Japan includes misty mountains swathed in dark forests, watery rice fields in which barefooted men and women are bending over to set out rice plants, and narrow pathways which are too small for carts and are often merely the tops of mud dykes between rice fields. Such a scene also includes villages where houses with flimsy paper walls are topped with a thatch of rice straw, heavy enough to withstand typhoons. These cyclonic storms start as westward moving hurricanes in the tropical Pacific and swing northeastward up the coast. The villages usually stand on the drier, poorer, sloping land on the edge of the rice fields. The slopes above them usually show innumerable terraces, which often bear mulberry trees that have a bushy look because they are constantly pollarded to get leaves for the silkworms. In other regions the terraces are beautified by the soft, round green balls of the tea bush, or are devoted to little fields containing green vegetables, as well as wheat and barley which are cultivated almost like beans, being sown, weeded, and reaped by hand.

Everywhere there is evidence of an enormous density of population and of an immense amount of work expended upon very tiny plots of land. One wonders whether Australia, Argentina, and our South would ever become like this if the agricultural population kept on growing denser for centuries. In such a country the greatest problem is bound to be poverty. Although the Japanese are exceedingly industrious they find it difficult to raise food for their 65 or 70 million people, let alone a surplus of any great size. So the Japanese are looking restlessly for new opportunities. They have pushed their sway over Chosen, Taiwan, and many islands, and have made themselves the real masters of Manchuria. But these places afford little chance for Japanese colonies, for they are already well populated with people whose standards of living are even lower than those of the Japanese. They do, however, afford some opportunities for trade and for getting raw materials in exchange for the goods which Japan manufactures. But the population of Japan is growing so fast that something must be done. North America and Australia are closed by law to Japanese as well as Chinese immigrants. Brazil is almost the only suitable place now open, but only a few Japanese have gone there.

Being an energetic people by reason of the combined effects of race, culture, and climate, the Japanese are meeting this situation by improving their agriculture and by trying to develop manufactures. In this last they have followed almost the same course as our South. They have developed a huge textile industry which began with silk, but in which cotton imported from the United States, China, and India has now become the chief factor. They have developed a small iron industry, and they have begun to make a good many kinds of more complex goods. They even send to the United States such things as toy footballs, electric light bulbs, and Christmas cards. Yet all this amounts to relatively little compared with what is done by countries like Germany, or with the needs of Japan. Perhaps the greatest economic problem of Japan is that she has no great facilities for manufacturing in the way of fuel and raw materials. Moreover, she has come into the industrial field so late that she has to compete with very strong rivals like the United States and Great Britain.

In Japan, as elsewhere, the cities give a clue to the activity of manufacturing as compared with trade. Tokyo with over 5,000,000 people in the central city and suburbs, and Yokohama with more than 600,000 are parts of a great metropolitan district which is surpassed only by New York and London as a *conurbation* or city group. There are many factories here, but trade and minor handicrafts carried on at home or in tiny shops occupy the people far more than does factory work in our sense of the word. Because human labor is still so cheap, while machines are expensive, the day of the labor-saving machine has only dawned in Japan. Osaka with 2,500,000 people and its neighbor Kobe with 800,000 form another huge conurbation which is decidedly more industrial than Tokyo. If Kyoto, not far away, with its commercial and handicraft population be added, we have a conurbation which ranks with those of the great manufacturing regions of Great Britain and northwestern Germany. Nagoya, with over 900,000 people, is a thorough-going manufacturing city which has grown mostly within the last two generations. Since the only other city of over 250,000 is Hiroshima, it is clear that most of Japan has not yet reached a high stage of industrialization.

South China.—This region, like Japan, is occupied by a homogeneous native population which has been there so long that the land has been divided and subdivided interminably. The plains of the Yangtze in the northern part of the Warm Temperate Humid Region and the great mass of mature mountains extending southward to the Si Valley are alike in one respect. Wherever one goes, all the good land, all that is not too steep, too thinly clad with soil, too water-logged, or in other ways unfit, is carefully cultivated. Even in the mountains, villages of mud or stone with roofs of tile or heavy thatch are extraordinarily numerous. In the plains, just as in Japan, innumerable people swarm everywhere, bending over their work or staggering under heavy loads suspended from the ends of poles. Each plot of land is weeded again and again, and a single acre receives work enough to cultivate five acres. Very few domestic animals are kept in proportion to the number of people, for human muscles can dig up the fields, and the land needed to support a single ox will produce almost enough food for a family. Some animals can be fed on the fallow fields, on slopes too steep for cultivation, and on the edges of dykes and paths, but the rice straw which is so abundant is poor fodder, and the hot, humid summers are bad for animals.

The economy of the Chinese is astounding. Human waste, decayed weeds, and every other bit of organic matter that can be made into fertilizer is saved to enrich the fields. Marvelous economy is exercised in the use of fuel and raw materials as well as food. Wood, for example, is extremely scarce even though the climate favors the growth of trees. Wherever people are numerous the slopes have been denuded for generations. Hence no wood except small sticks is used for fuel, and when good wood is needed for houses and boxes it is rarely available. The scarcity of wood in contrast to the abundance of labor is reflected in the way in which the Chinese will spend days or months in beautifully painting and enameling boxes made of wood so thin that it breaks under the least strain. In the same way the women put beautiful embroidery upon the cheapest kind of cloth.

Even where the average person is so poor, the energy and thrift of the Chinese make trade much more active than in tropical countries. The city markets present scenes of fascinating activity with their open-fronted shops, gay paper goods, curious and innumerable kinds of food, street vendors, beggars, and softly trotting porters. Transportation is limited to man-power even more than in Japan, where jinrikishas and man-drawn carts are far more numerous than automobiles, and horse-drawn vehicles are a rarity. In many of the Chinese cities a large part of the streets are so narrow that even jinrikishas have difficulty in passing one another, and practically all the traffic is carried by men. Yet many of the larger cities like Shanghai, Changsha, and Foochow have modern quarters and foreign sections, quite different from the main sections. These cities, and others such as Chengtu, Chunking, Nanking, Ningpo, and Soochow, are perfect hives of industry and skill, for they are filled with thousands of craftsmen skilled in weaving silk, working metals, carving wood, and preparing foodstuffs. But practically none of the workers use machinery run by anything except human power, and real factories are almost unknown. Yet Shanghai has begun to follow the example of Japan in establishing cotton as well as silk factories, while Hankow is following Birmingham in making the rougher forms of iron goods. The most interesting Chinese cities in the Warm Temperate Humid Region are of the Hangchow type, where the commercial center of a rich agricultural section is also a center of wonderful art and architecture handed down in the Buddhist monasteries.

Political instability rivals overpopulation in determining the economic and social status of China as well as of the South American sec-

tion of the Warm Temperate Humid Region. Few parts of the world
have suffered so frequently and severely as China from civil war, banditry, and general misgovernment. Throughout the country's history
these factors have again and again brought needless misery in addition
to that which arises from chronic poverty and recurrent bad crops and
famine. Often the distress arising from bad crops is the cause of rebellion and banditry, but these in turn upset the usual routine so much
that they are again the cause of famines. Thus China is caught in a
vicious circle, and throughout most of the present century has been
chronically in a state of war in one section or another.

North China Summer Monsoon Region. *The Unfavorable Climate.*—
Asia contains one natural region which has no parallel in the other continents. This is found in North China and extends in modified form
into Manchuria and Chosen. Here the vast size of Asia produces a
tremendous effect in creating violent seasonal contrasts in rainfall and
temperature. Here are some figures for Peiping (Peking) corresponding to those given on an earlier page for various places in the Warm
Temperate Humid Regions:

Average temperature of coldest month........... 24°
Average temperature of warmest month.......... 78°
Total annual rainfall........................... 25 inches
Percentage of rain in six warmest months........ 92

From November to April the total rainfall at Peiping (A293) amounts
to only 2 inches; the winter temperature is too low for either health
or the highest mental activity; and
worst of all the air is very dry and
the northwest winds very strong. The
winds cause the temperature to feel
lower than would be indicated by an
average of 24° in January. They
fill the air so full of dust that one
can often feel the grit between his
teeth. May normally has nearly as
much rain as the preceding six
months, but even that is far too little
to prepare the ground for planting,

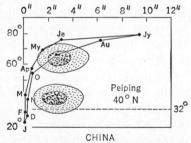

A — Climograph of North China
Monsoon Region.

after its long parching through the winter. Only in June can a good
rainfall of 3 or 4 inches be expected. During the next two months the
opposite extreme prevails. Not only is the temperature almost as high
as in South or Central China, but the rain falls in torrents, a third of
the year's supply coming in July, and the air is very humid. The climo-

graph in A293 makes it clear that only in May, June, and September does the weather approach closely to the optimum conditions for either agriculture or human health. The situation is rendered still worse by the fact that the stimulus of cyclonic storms is largely absent, while the variability in the rainfall from year to year is extreme. As a result of all these conditions the climate of North China appears to be the worst among those of well populated lands outside the tropics.

Droughts, Floods, and Famines.—Many of the most undesirable effects of the North China Monsoon climate arise through famines. The nature of the relief joins with the climate to cause a combination of droughts and floods which is peculiarly disastrous. Where the winters are so dry, and where even in April the normal rainfall is less than an inch, a failure of the rains in May and June is extremely harmful. The ground has no stored-up moisture with which to start the crops, and if they do not get started until July, very few will mature. Unfortunately, failures of the rains in May and June are very common and sometimes are repeated for several years in succession. This in itself would lead to dire famine at frequent intervals, at least among the farmers who cannot rely on irrigation. But the irrigation farmers are not much more fortunate than the others. Most of them live upon alluvial plains which are extremely flat and which often lie below the level to which the rivers have raised their own beds. The summer rains, as we have seen, are very heavy. After a drought they are especially likely to fall with such intensity that the flat fields become water-logged and are sometimes converted into lakes over which people have to travel in boats, even though the rivers do not overflow. But another feature of the topography adds to the misfortunes of China. North of the plains rise steep mountains where man's age-long search for wood joins with the dryness of the long winters to cause trees to be scarce. The inblowing monsoons drench these mountains with rain in July and August, and this flows off in tremendous floods unhampered by forests. So the rivers overflow, breaking their dykes and engulfing thousands of square miles of land. The case is like that of the Mississippi River in 1927, but vastly worse. At such times not only the fields, but all except the most elevated of the villages, are swamped, and thousands or even millions of people are rendered homeless as well as absolutely without means of getting food. Worst of all, the land is so flat that in many places the water stands for months on the flooded fields and does not even disappear in time to allow a crop to be planted the spring after the flood.

Such combinations of drought and flood give North China the worst and most frequent famines of any part of the world—even worse than those of India. On an average a famine of some sort occurs somewhere in China, but mainly in the north, at least once every two or three years, and perhaps oftener. A big famine involving anywhere from ten to fifty or a hundred million people and killing them by the hundred thousand or million comes every ten years or so. But between the famines the productivity of the land is so great that the population constantly replenishes itself and becomes extremely dense. Thus the number of people who suffer from famine is enormous, and the standards of living are kept down to the very lowest level. Hence North China is poorer than its neighbors—poorer probably than the home of any other large body of people unless it be India where famines of similar type, but less severe, combine with tropical inertia and extreme density of population to create similar dire poverty.

Famines, Migrations, and Human Character.—Many people believe that the Chinese famines have much to do with Chinese character and with the fact that, contrary to the general rule in low and middle latitudes, the warmer part of China is more progressive as well as more prosperous than the cooler part. Some of the most widely spread Chinese characteristics include economy, thrift, ability to live on a minimum supply of food, inertia, conservatism, indifference to suffering, and absorption in their own personal affairs with little thought of others or of the public welfare. Of course there are many notable exceptions— Chinese who vie with the people of any other land in high abilities and high ideals—but we are talking of the poor peasants who comprise by far the greater part of the Chinese. When droughts and floods bring famine it is evident that thrifty, economical people, who have saved in the past and who now use their resources frugally and wisely, are much more likely to survive than are those who have been wasteful in the past and who now eat up their food without planning for the future. Thus for ages the people who were weak in thrift, economy, and forethought, and also those who were constitutionally unable to endure privation, must have been eliminated. We know that among animals the constant elimination of certain types gradually changes the biological character of a herd. Many examples, such as the Parsees of India and the Icelanders, seem to indicate that the innate mental abilities of people may also be altered in the same way. This is what seems to have happened in China.

This selective process appears to have worked in various ways. For example, the family which is kind-hearted and shares its food with its poorer neighbors is more likely to perish than is the selfish family which keeps its food to itself. Again, in times of famine it is a common practice to commit suicide. The ones who do this are generally those who are more sensitive to privation or who are ashamed to become mere beggars. Then, too, in famines the children are frequently sold, especially the young girls, in order to get a little money wherewith to keep the rest alive. If parents are sensitive and heed the pleadings of their little daughters, a family which might otherwise survive is likely to perish. Thus many conditions combine to favor the preservation of those who are hard-hearted and callous to the sufferings of others or to the welfare of any except their own immediate group. Again, if a family group sticks together and cooperates it is more likely to survive than if each one fends for himself. Thus it is often said that there is a selection not only of certain types of individuals, but of certain types of social institutions, such as patriarchal families and ancestor worship, which happen to be especially fit to cope with famines.

Migration plays a prominent part in Chinese famines. Where the famine is due to drought the people generally stay at home until their resources gradually give out, and then drift away in groups to neighboring regions where the famine is not so bad. If the famine is due to flood, the people of thousands of villages may all become wanderers at once. It often happens that the families which are most gifted with forethought and energy are the first to migrate, or else go farthest away, even if they start with the rest. They are the most likely to see that their chances of finding work and getting a living are best if they go far ahead of the main crowd or far beyond it, and thus reach places where normal conditions prevail. They are also likely to be the ones who have the means to do this. Moreover, such people are far more likely to become well established in their new homes. Hence many stay there when their less efficient relatives and neighbors go back to build new houses, make new furniture, and reclaim land that has been injured by standing water or by sand brought by the floods. Thus for hundreds or thousands of years the human stock of the famine districts has suffered loss through the slow outward movement of people with more than average ability. The movement has been mainly toward the south, since deserts and mountains lie to the north and west, and the sea to the east. Missionaries say that often in the villages of the Yangtze Valley, for example, the leaders seem to be largely from the north. In such a village one man says, "I came during the famine twenty years ago." Another says that his father, grandfather, or great-grandfather came in such and such a famine. Thus the famine districts permanently lose many of their ablest people, while the regions farther south are the gainers.

Such conditions, joined with the hardships and disease which depress the vitality of people who endure the northern famines, seems to account for at least part of the lesser activity, energy, and progressiveness of North China compared with South China. They also help to account for the fact that most of the Chinese who migrate to other lands, aside from Manchuria, come from the South. So, to a surprising degree, do the higher officials. Hence it is not strange that the leadership in China's reform movements comes largely from the Warm Temperate Humid Region and not from the North China Monsoon Region. Similar conditions account in part for the backwardness of Chosen. They help to explain why China's incipient industrial development centers in the Yangtze Valley rather than farther north. They throw light on the almost incredible poverty of scores of millions of people who live in mud villages all over the north. The migration of ten or twenty million northern Chinese from Shantung and Hopeh to Manchuria, the land of wheat and soy beans, during the present century, shows how great is the pressure upon these conservative, home-loving people to get away whenever transportation, economics, and politics make it possible. If China could be free from the curse of famine, almost every phase of life would be profoundly altered. China might then become a great contributor to the commerce, industry, and political control of the world instead of one of the smallest contributors in proportion to the number of people. Of course the Chinese are so numerous that their aggregate purchasing power and influence are considerable. Nevertheless the influence of the North China Monsoon type of climate does much to render the average Chinese not one-tenth, perhaps not one one hundredth, as influential in world affairs as the average Swiss or Dane.

In spite of all this suffering, poverty, and migration, the North China Monsoon Region, including Manchuria and Chosen, has a considerable number of cities. The old capital, Peiping, and Tientsin are the only really large ones. Among the others, Antung, Kiaochow, and Tsingtao are seaports, but Harbin, Keijo, Mukden, Sianfu, and Tsinan all lie inland. The comparative scarcity of seaports is significant of the low rank in international commerce which is imposed upon this region by the extreme continentality of its climate.

EXERCISES

1. Run through the maps of products, activities, and human conditions in this book (see Index under "maps"), or in your atlas, and classify them into three groups according to whether the regions of the Mediterranean Type are highly important, moderately important, or of little or no importance. Discuss the significance of your results. (See Exercise 3 below.)

2. How do the large cities of the Mediterranean Type compare with those of the Regions of Wet Tropical Agriculture in number, size, and location with respect to the sea?

3. Make a map study of the Warm Temperate Humid Region like that of regions of the Mediterranean Type described in Exercise 1 above. Tabulate and explain the difference between the two.

4. Read H. King's *Farmers of Forty Centuries*, or J. H. Buck's *Chinese Farm Economy*, and compare the agriculture there described with that of the wheat farms of Australia, Canada, and the United States.

5. Make a tabular outline showing ways in which the crops, animals, industries, commerce, social conditions, institutions, and other conditions of the Mediterranean and North Chinese Monsoon Regions are different. Show how these differences are related to the location of the two regions in respect to land and sea.

6. If you had a suitable income and wished to retire, which of the natural regions discussed thus far would you choose to live in? Why?

7. What advantage of geographical location has the region about the Mediterranean Sea over other areas of Mediterranean Climate? Explain.

8. Make a study of famines. Prepare a map showing parts of the world where they occur (*a*) frequently, (*b*) occasionally, (*c*) almost never. On the basis of this, arrange the natural regions in the approximate order of their liability to famine.

CHAPTER XV

NATURAL REGIONS IN HIGHER LATITUDES

The Region of Marine Cyclonic Storms (A300, A301, and page 231). *Climate.*—Westerly winds and eastward-moving cyclonic storms are the outstanding features of the climate of this region. Although mountains limit the region to a coastal strip in North America, South America, and Australia, it goes far inland in Europe and includes the whole of western Europe. Even there, however, it extends farther from north to south than from east to west. From above 60° of latitude on the Norwegian coast it extends through the three Scandinavian countries, the two Low Countries, Germany, Great Britain, Ireland, and France to nearly 40° of latitude in the northern corner of Spain. Switzerland, western Czechoslovakia and Austria also lie on its edges, and the Po Valley of northern Italy is a transition region of only a slightly different type. The outstanding human feature of this region is its economic and social leadership. Only the Continental Cyclonic Region in the eastern United States rivals western Europe in these respects. The fact that both regions are called "cyclonic" indicates their most distinctive geographic characteristic. The main climatic difference between the two is found in a different base for the cyclonic control, marine for one, continental for the other. This means that while both regions have a constant succession of storms, the extremes of temperature from season to season and also from one phase of a storm to another are less marked in the marine region than in the continental.

Since the Marine Cyclonic Regions lie on the western edges of the continents the dominating westerlies carry oceanic influences inland. Mild winters and cool summers are the inevitable result (A301). Where the coastal waters are exceptionally warm, as on the west coasts of North America and especially Europe, the marine control is correspondingly intense in winter, so that mild winters prevail on the coast as far north as the Arctic Circle.

One reason for this winter warmth is that oceans always cool off more slowly than land. Another is that the ocean surface in these regions consists of water that has drifted northeastward from low latitudes near the equator. This remains warm until it has traveled so far

that it cools down to the average for the higher latitude.   This explains
the warmth of the Japanese current on the Alaskan coast of the Pacific
and the still greater warmth of the Gulf Stream and its continuation in
the North Atlantic Drift which crosses only a narrow oceanic basin
before reaching Great Britain and Scandinavia.   The absence of corresponding warmth in the southern oceans arises from the fact that there
the eastward-moving currents travel thousands of miles in the same
latitude before reaching Chile or New Zealand.

In summer the westerly oceanic winds which blow over the Marine
Cyclonic Regions cool the land instead of warming it.   This is because

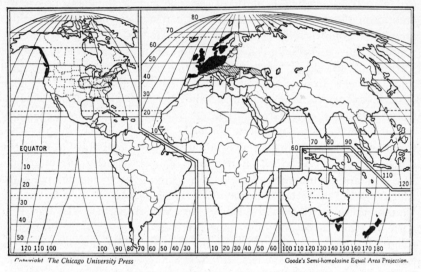

Goode's Semi-homolosine Equal Area Projection.

A—Location of Three Types of Cyclonic Regions: Marine (solid), American Continental (fine dots), European Continental (lines).

the water in the oceanic "drifts" moves very slowly, taking the better
part of a year to get from low latitudes near the East or West Indies to
high latitudes near Alaska or Norway.   Hence when it gets so far its
temperature is only a few degrees above the average for those latitudes.
This means that the water is cool compared with the summer temperature.   In summer any region in middle or high latitudes is cooled by
winds from the open ocean because the sun raises the temperature of
land much faster than that of water.

Besides causing mild winters and cool summers the westerlies bring
oceanic moisture to the land.   This gives the Marine Cyclonic Regions
high humidity, cloudy skies, and heavy precipitation when the air is
forced to rise on the westward side of the mountains, or when it encoun-

ters land that is cool because the sun is low in winter. The mountain
ranges running parallel to the coast limit such precipitation to a narrow
coastal zone in North America and Chile, and greatly diminish the area
in Scandinavia, Tasmania, and New Zealand. Where there are no barriers, however, as in west central Europe, ocean moisture is carried far
inland.

The Function of Cyclonic Storms.—In this climatic background,
cyclonic storms bring two great advantages, as we have already seen.
First, they cause the moist oceanic air to rise and become cool, thus
producing rain at all seasons (A301). The value of this to agriculture
can scarcely be overestimated, as we
saw when studying corn. Abundant
rain at all seasons is a rare condition
(A302). In the second place, the
cyclonic storms supply the variability
which we have seen to be so valuable.
A brilliant morning may change into a
dreary afternoon, or after a day of rain
the wind may chase away the clouds,
bring out the sun, and cause the kind
of drop in temperature which does so
much to restore health and stimulate
activity. In the Marine Cyclonic Regions, clouds are as typical as is the sun
in the Mediterranean Region. In their
various forms and colors they are an
essential part of the landscape. But
the chief importance of the instability
of cyclonic weather is that it increases
the energy, vitality, and health of the

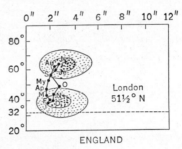

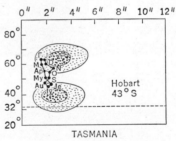

A—Climographs of Marine
Cyclonic Regions.

inhabitants and has much to do with
their great economic, social, and cultural activity. Other factors like
the small size of a country, isolation, or lack of innate ability, may
hamper production, and still others like coal, iron, good harbors, racial
ability, and the advantages of past successes may increase it. The point
is, however, that only where the climate is favorable do we find the
highest levels of modern development.

Vegetation.—Forests once covered practically all parts of the Marine
Cyclonic Regions except the cool, wet, upland moors and the swamps.
In Europe the ancient Roman legions were checked by the thick German
forest. In Washington, Oregon, and southern New Zealand much of
the forest still persists and is very dense and tall. In Europe, however,

most of the forest has disappeared in the search for arable land. It persists only on the mountains, on patches of poor sandy soil, in special reservations or parks, and in park-like groves with rows of trees set out by the hand of man. Lowland countries like Holland and Denmark have very little real forest, although trees are abundant along the roads and canals and around the individual farm houses, while the villages are hidden in their foliage. On the mountains, however, the forest still stands in its old glory. Oaks and beeches are the most typical trees in the deciduous type of forest which occupies the warmer sites and better soils. On the higher slopes and on sandy soils coniferous trees replace

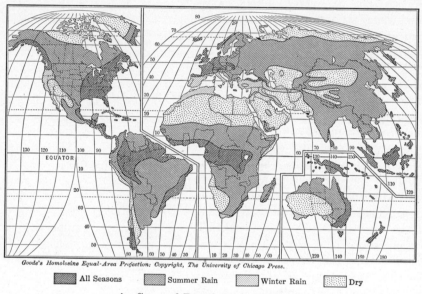

Goode's Homolosine Equal-Area Projection: Copyright, The University of Chicago Press.

All Seasons   Summer Rain   Winter Rain   Dry

A—Seasonal Distribution of Rainfall.

these broadleaved species. Forestry is more highly developed in the Marine Cyclonic Region of Europe than anywhere else in the world, but it cannot prevent a large timber deficit (see page 439). Along the upper limits of the forest, alpine meadows with their brilliantly colored flowers extend to the upper limit of vegetation. Along the west coasts in many places and on some uplands strong winds and frequent, prolonged drizzly rains prevent the growth of trees, and cause the marshy type of vegetation so typical of the moors of the British Isles.

Poor Soils.—As might be expected from the climate, the Marine Cyclonic soils are constantly leached and are not especially good (Plate II). The gray *podsols* of the north, being acid as well as leached, are poor and unproductive. The most typical kind, however, is the brown forest soil. Although this is somewhat leached, its moderate humus content shows the influence of the deciduous forests. Peaty soils on the swampy lowlands and on the marshy, rain-drenched uplands of the western coasts complete the main soil divisions. Locally these unfavorable conditions of the soil are ameliorated by mixed glacial soils produced by the icesheet which covered great areas in the Ice Age. Another relatively good kind of soil is the loess which was deposited under dry conditions by winds blowing out from the icesheets over great wastes of débris laid down by ice and water. This often forms a fertile blanket over the limestone soil of France and Belgium. Fertile clays have also been recovered from the ocean. This is due partly to a slight rising of the land which has exposed much of the best land in Scandinavia. It is also due to human action in the Low Countries where the Dutch have been especially active in dyking and draining the land of their "polders." Alluvial river deposits also provide small areas of good soil not only in ordinary floodplains, but in structural depressions like the Willamette Valley in Oregon, and the Rhine *Graben*, or depressed segment of the earth's crust, which is divided between Germany and France. Nevertheless the average soil is far from ideal.

Methods of Land Utilization.—In spite of the poor soil the Marine Cyclonic Regions show a very high type of land utilization. As C. F. Marbut well shows, this takes place in spite of the soils and not because of them. Two geographical conditions make it possible. One is the fact that we have here the optimum climate for a great number of crops. The optimum, it will be remembered, includes not only mild winters and moderately warm summers but rain and humidity at all seasons. The other is the fact that the climate is nearly perfect for both the physical well-being and mental activity of people who have risen to a stage of culture where they can easily protect themselves against cold and rain. Former chapters have shown how the high yield of grains obtained in these regions is a response to climate, how the cows give more milk and a greater percentage of butter fat than anywhere else, and how the hens lay more eggs. The fact that man here has good health and a surplus of energy of both mind and body has increased these advantages.

The results of this mental activity are very clear in agriculture. Man's keen mind has found out how to improve the soil with fertilizers. It has carefully worked out the principles and practice of crop rotation. It has also increased the yield of crops by the selection of good seed and the crossing of different types, and by detailed studies of what kinds of crops suit the local soil. The desire to maintain high standards of living in spite of the growth of population has stimulated the production of crops which yield the greatest value per acre, thus emphasizing those which have to be raised near the market because of being perishable. Along with this has gone a constantly increasing tendency to import the kinds of food which can easily be brought from a distance. Thus there has been a constant shift away from the grains towards vegetables and fruit. Truck gardens of great size surround all the cities and are also located in other favorable spots. Every day, long trains with vegetables run from Holland to the industrial regions of Germany. Millions of acres are used for potatoes, and a meal in western Europe is scarcely complete without them. Orchards of apples, peaches, pears, plums, and cherries cover large sections of Oregon and central Tasmania, and these fruits, especially apples, appear in the markets all over the world. In May the rounded hills of the Swiss plateau are white with fruit blossoms. Grapes are by no means so important as in the regions of the Mediterranean Type. Nevertheless they continue northward so far as to make France the world leader in the production of high-grade wines.

Industrial crops as well as grains have declined in importance, as the Marine Cyclonic Regions have taken up more intensive agriculture. Even the large sugar-beet production in the zone extending from France through Belgium and Holland into Germany, Czechoslovakia, and Poland has a hard battle against the equatorial cane-sugar production. On the other hand, such extremely specialized and valuable crops as those of the Dutch bulb fields and nurseries are of steadily growing importance. They send their products all over the world.

In spite of all this the *grains* are still important, especially where the soil is less favorable for more intensive production. Although wheat has its highest yields farther north in Denmark, it assumes the greatest importance to farmers in the more sunny fields of France. Oats, in spite of the fame of the Scottish oatmeal, are mainly raised as feed for horses and other stock. Rye, which can stand low temperatures and poor soil better than wheat, increases greatly in importance in Germany. There dark rye bread replaces the white bread of the French and English. Barley is much raised for swine, especially in Denmark. With hops it forms the basis of an important beer industry, especially in Germany.

Cattle and Dairying.—The natural tendency towards the growth of a short, soft, nutritious kind of grass in the Marine Cyclonic Regions, and the fact that the mild winters keep such grass green most of the year, have invited the raising of stock, especially cattle on the lowlands and sheep on the uplands. This has been particularly true of the more marine western sections of Europe, where the green meadows of Ireland,

Great Britain, Brittany, Normandy, Holland, and Denmark are unsurpassed for dairy products. The British highlands and New Zealand are
among the world's greatest sheep regions, for the animals there excel
in both wool and mutton. The same is true of western Oregon
and Washington, and of the small section of southern Chile which
falls in this climatic zone. But one sees now a tendency, wherever
possible, towards replacing the meadows by fields of clover, turnips,
the beets called swedes, and grains like barley and oats which are cut
while green. These are fed to the cattle in the barns. With such
crops not only is the yield of milk higher per acre than with pasturage,
but the milk contains a higher percentage of fat. It even pays to import
cattle feed such as cotton-seed cake and bean cake from other parts of
the world. Thus butter and cheese are increasingly important products
of all the Marine Cyclonic Regions. Swine grow fat on the skimmed
milk, while chicken farms complete the picture of intensive animal
production. The perishability of dairy products and the alertness of
the farmers in the Marine Cyclonic Regions have stimulated the development of farmers cooperative movements. Such movements have
spread to other products, especially fruit and early vegetables. Denmark is the outstanding pioneer in this respect, but New Zealand and
the Pacific Coast of the United States are following close on her heels.
In Denmark nearly everything connected with the economic life of the
farmers is carried on cooperatively.

Fishing.—Still another result of the warmth brought to high latitudes by the ocean currents is the extensive fisheries off the coasts of
Marine Cyclonic Regions. The coasts of Norway and the North Sea
form the world's greatest fishing region. The Pacific Coast from
Oregon to Alaska with its abundant salmon as well as other fish also
ranks very high (A429).

The Dominance of Manufacturing.—Although vegetables, fruit,
grain, livestock, and lumber provide most of the economic wealth of the
part of the Marine Cyclonic Region located outside Europe, these are
overshadowed in Europe itself by manufacturing. Smoke from chimneys hanging low over the industrial regions of western Europe makes
the face of nature grimy and unpleasant. Long freight trains haul
heavy loads away from the factories. Huge, unattractive cities have
spread over the land so rapidly that the industrial parts of Britain,
Belgium, and Germany (A489) have become a great, dirty conglomera-
tion of factories, houses, and people. Power, in the form of coal, is the
main reason why the *form* but not the *degree* of human activity is so
different in these industrial regions from what it is in the agricultural
parts of the Marine Cyclonic Regions like Denmark, New Zealand, and

Washington. The presence of a dense population which is ready to work in factories has been another favorable condition for manufacturing. And so has the presence of abundant iron ore and an advantageous position in respect to transportation by land and sea.

But the *élan vital*, the spirit of eagerness, which has been the driving force in the modern development of manufacturing, has been the energy of the population. Long before the steam engine was invented this same spirit made the Marine Cyclonic Regions lead the world in home industries, in exploration, in foreign trade, and in military and political prowess. Then when the time was ripe, as we shall see more fully later, they used the existing home industries and the old commerce as a base for the development of a new system founded on machinery. In some ways the system was not really new. Cotton, wool, and linen had been manufactured before in the same places where the new development took place. Iron tools had for centuries been famous products of local districts such as Sheffield which now have become agglomerations of big steel plants. In the eighteenth century more ships sailed from the harbors of western Europe than from any others, and more wagons and carriages drove over the roads there. The only things that have changed are the speed, the form, and the magnitude of human activity. The kind and relative degree of activity compared with other parts of the world are still the same. Other regions like China with great supplies of power, raw material, and labor might have done the same. They failed to do so not merely because bound so closely in an ancient social and political system, but also because the requisite stimulus to mental activity and the indispensable inventive alertness were lacking, even though the necessary inherent ability may have been present. There seems in this way to be a strong relation between high crop yields and highly complicated factories. Neither of these is a necessary result of the cyclonic type of climate, but both are more easily produced in cyclonic regions than elsewhere because of climatic conditions close to the optimum. The great industrial sections of England, France, Germany, and Belgium, and the smaller but more specialized industrial areas of Switzerland, Sweden, northern Italy, and Holland, are examples of what keen, inventive minds can do under the most favorable combination of environmental conditions.

Trade.—Food must be shipped in large quantities from the rural districts to the manufacturing cities, and manufactured products must be sent back. A constant surplus of one kind in one region balances a constant deficit of the same kind elsewhere. A dense railroad net, navigable rivers, numerous canals, and well-built roads, besides airplane lines, provide the routes of traffic. But note that ease of traffic by no means depends wholly on favorable conditions of relief and waterways. Where people are active they insist on good means of transportation. It is vastly easier to travel in the Alps than in the plains of Siberia. Portland, Oregon, a hundred miles inland, has dug out its river and is a vastly better port than the finest harbor along the drowned coast of Celebes. In New Zealand, in spite of the small population and high mountains, the roads, railroads, and airplanes make all parts far more accessible than is the Sinai Peninsula close to the Suez Canal.

Trade is more than local. Its interests go all over the world. Food and raw material come to Europe in exchange for finished products or capital, and the whole development of Europe's colonial empire is a result of the energy and vitality of its inhabitants. Great harbors, especially near the mouths of rivers, are one result of this trade. And the trade in turn, by its world-wide quality, makes those cities international meeting points.

Modes of Life.—In the Marine Cyclonic Regions the modes of life reflect not only the great variety of nationalities, but likewise the dual form of economic development. The straw-covered homes of the Irish, where acrid peat smoke hangs over the valley; the charming English cottages in gardens of sweet peas and roses; the stately, red-roofed, cleanly washed farm houses of Holland; the dull, gray, square peasant homes of France; the picturesque architecture of the ancient German villages; and the attractive wooden cottages or châlets of the Swiss with their long balconies represent only a few of the many different types of rural settlement. Such differences largely disappear in the cities, especially where factories are dominant. Some of the cities of historical and political fame have still a "soul" of their own, as Count Keyserling says, but others show the regular combination of official buildings, dreary factories, and great, stupid tenement houses far neater than the slums which they replace, but desperately uninteresting. Even in England where the many-storied tenements are replaced by endless rows of two-story houses packed wall to wall, the effect is only a little better. Factory smoke and grime reduce everything to the same dull color, and the main impression is dreary and ugly. Yet among all this one finds many of the world's most beautiful old cathedrals, town halls, and other stately buildings whose beauty and charm vie with those of the castles out in the country. Moreover, no part of the world can boast of nobler modern museums, opera houses, churches, government buildings, and homes of wealthy citizens.

Social and Cultural Features.—These likewise show the influence of the cyclonic climate. Death rates are low, with New Zealand and the state of Washington in close competition for the world's lowest record.

Scandinavia and Holland are not far behind (A123.) Cultural standards, such as attendance at schools and universities, are high (A136).
Each of the different nationalities, as Keyserling well sums it up, has a
culture of its own resulting from its own environment and historical
development. But all vie with one another in intellectual standing, and
constant rivalry keeps them alive and vital. The German philosopher
Spengler predicted the "decline of the West," the breakdown of western
civilization. Even though that may occur temporarily, the nature of
the geographical environment suggests that such a breakdown will
always be followed by a new rise. The Marine Cyclonic Regions seem
to be geographically predestined to be highly productive and to occupy
an outstanding position in the world's economic life.

Abundance of Cities.—The great number and large size of the cities
also bear witness to the dominance of the Marine Cyclonic Regions.
Among the world's cities of over 250,000 inhabitants no less than
56, or approximately 28 per cent, belong to this one type of region.
Among these are London, Berlin, Paris, Hamburg, Glasgow, Birmingham, and Melbourne, all with over a million inhabitants. Nearly half
(24) of these great cities are seaports, but in this region the sea is relatively less important than in many others as a factor in determining
which settlements shall grow into great cities. The reason is that here
for the first time in this study of natural regions we come upon great
inland cities which owe their growth almost entirely to manufacturing
rather than to commercial and political conditions. How important
such cities are may be judged from the third column on page 309.
All the cities in the other columns, no matter whether seaports or inland
centers of commerce and government, also possess important manufacturing industries. In fact, the outstanding characteristic of the cities
in the Marine Cyclonic Regions is the great amount of complex manufacturing which they carry on in order to supply not only their own
needs, but also those of regions far away.

The American Continental Cyclonic Region. *Resemblance to Marine
Cyclonic Regions.*—The American Continental Cyclonic Region, which
appears only in the northeastern quarter of the United States (Plate I),
resembles the Marine Cyclonic Regions in many respects. The most
characteristic resemblance is that the weather in both regions is dominated
by a fairly regular succession of cyclones and anticyclones which move in
general from west to east, bringing a constant alternation of clouds,
rain, and variable winds during the cyclones, and sunshine, fair weather,
and westerly winds or calms during the anticyclones. The cyclones and
anticyclones move faster and are more intense and numerous in winter
than in summer, and their paths swing farther south. At all seasons

CITIES OF OVER 250,000 INHABITANTS IN MARINE CYCLONIC REGIONS

A. Seaports	B. Inland commercial and political centers	C. Cities owing their growth almost wholly to manufacturing
Amsterdam	Berlin	Birmingham (England)
Antwerp	Cologne	Bochum
Belfast	Dresden	Bradford
Bordeaux	Frankfort	Chemnitz
Bremen	The Hague*	Dortmund
Bristol	Hannover	Duisburg-Hamborn
Brussels	Leipzig	Düsseldorf
Copenhagen	Lyon	Essen
Dublin	Magdeburg	Gelsen Kirchen
Edinburgh	Munich	Leeds
Glasgow	Nuremberg	Manchester
Hamburg	Paris	Mannheim
Hull	Prague	Nottingham
Liverpool	Stuttgart	Sheffield
London	Vienna†	Stoke
Melbourne	Zürich	West Ham
Newcastle		Wuppertal
Oslo		(Elberfeld-Barmen)
Portland (Oregon)		
Rotterdam		
Seattle		
Stettin		
Stockholm		
Vancouver		

* Although close to the sea and having a little harbor for fishing boats The Hague can scarcely be called a seaport.

† Vienna is on the border between the Marine Cyclonic Region and the Continental Cyclonic Region.

the cyclones provide sufficient rain, and in large sections the rainfall in all months is practically the same (A310). Few other parts of the world enjoy such regularity of rainfall not only from season to season but also from year to year (p. 70). This assures the farmers of a reasonably good yield per acre except in rare instances. It thereby encourages them to make improvements and helps them to produce the surplus which is necessary if commerce and manufacturing are to flourish. For this reason the farm population is well spread over the whole of both areas except where the land is too rugged (B310). The storms also provide conditions of atmospheric humidity and variability which are excellent for health and activity among both animals and man.

The seasonal changes approach the optimum, the summers being not far from the physical optimum and the winters from the mental optimum. Hence these regions are the most healthful and active parts of the world. Their death rates average 11 or 12 per thousand people compared with twice as much in tropical and oriental countries. Add to all this a favorable location in respect to other productive natural regions, together with abundant local supplies of coal and iron, and it is not surprising that the Cyclonic Regions carry on by far the greater part of the world's manufacturing, especially in its more complex forms, and have in their hands a similar share of the world's wealth, political power, and culture.

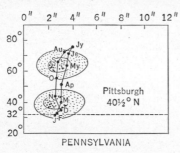

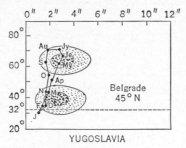

A—Climographs of American and European Continental Cyclonic Regions.

Differences between Continental and Marine Cyclonic Regions.—In spite of these similarities the two types of Cyclonic Regions differ more than is usually realized. We saw this difference very concretely in previous chapters where we found that the Marine

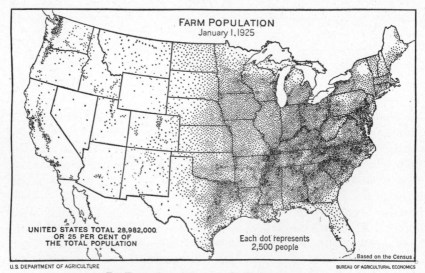

B—Farm Population in the United States.

Cyclonic Regions provide the optimum conditions for wheat, whereas the Continental Cyclonic Regions provide the distinctly different optimum for corn. Nowhere in the Marine Cyclonic Regions does corn really thrive, and nowhere in the Continental Cyclonic Regions does wheat come anywhere near the standard set by the North Sea region. The difference between these two optima is as important for man as for crops. The first factor in causing this difference is latitude. The Continental Cyclonic Region in America lies 10° nearer the equator than does the Marine Cyclonic Region in Europe. Hence the sunshine is much more intense. In four cities near the edges of the American region, July averages about 10° warmer than in four corresponding European cities, as appears in the following table.

Continental Cyclonic Region	July	January	Marine Cyclonic Region	July	January
Milwaukee..........	70°	21°	Oslo...............	63°	25°
Boston.............	72	27	London............	63	39
Baltimore..........	77	34	Berlin.............	66	32
St. Louis...........	79	31	Bordeaux..........	68	41

In spite of vacations, fresh air funds, refrigeration, and municipal and state sanitary services, the death rate rises ominously, and human efficiency is correspondingly lowered, when the temperature rises to high levels, as we saw in Chapter VI. Even the normal summers of this area are too warm for the largest output of potatoes, milk, eggs, and other products. Their heat on the other hand is excellent for corn and tobacco, although even for corn such temperatures as prevail in Baltimore and St. Louis are too high.

A second factor in making the American cyclonic area different from the European is its position on the east side of its continent instead of the west side. This means that when westerly winds blow, as they do predominantly, the American area gets temperatures resembling those of the interior, whereas the European area gets those of the sea. This is one reason for the high summer temperatures in the American Cyclonic Region. It should be noted, however, that along the Atlantic Coast a narrow strip from Boston even as far south as Baltimore is much influenced by the ocean. Hence it is cooler in summer and warmer in winter than the regions farther inland. Some especially oceanic places like Mount Desert, Newport, Nantucket, and Atlantic City have climates which approach that of the Marine Cyclonic Regions, but are probably more stimulating.

In winter the continental effect is even greater than in summer, for the tendency toward strong west winds is reinforced by the tendency for strong winds to blow outward from the interior of a cold continent. Hence in the table given above the four American cities average 6° *cooler* than the four European cities in spite of their more southerly position. This causes a high peak in the death rate at the end of the winter with a corresponding drop in efficiency. It appears to be the main reason why the yields of wheat per acre, even in our eastern sections, are so much lower than those of the North Sea Region. In addition to this, although the rainfall is greater in the American Cyclonic Region than in the European, the relative humidity is lower. This is because our westerly winds blow from the dry interior whereas those of Europe blow from the ocean. Hence Europeans are often greatly impressed by our bright blue skies in contrast with the haziness of their own. In similar fashion the North Sea Region has more rainy days than does the northeastern quarter of the United States, but not so much rain per day. This is because their rain is brought by westerly winds and that of the eastern United States by easterly winds. In winter a corresponding condition gives western Europe short cold waves due to easterly winds, while the northeastern United States gets more frequent and severe ones due to westerly winds. All these conditions are disadvantages to both people and crops in the United States.

The Restless Activity of America.—To make up for these disadvantages, the changes of weather in the Continental Cyclonic Region in America are more frequent and pronounced than in any of the Marine Cyclonic Regions. This is true also in the American Region of Cool Continental Agriculture in contrast with the corresponding area in Europe and Asia. This variability of the weather arises from the fact that in North America the cyclonic storms not only swing far to the south, but are more frequent and active than in any other region unless it be around Antarctica. This makes the American climate not only healthful but peculiarly bracing and stimulating. Each storm with its changes of wind, sun, rainfall, atmospheric humidity, sunshine, and especially temperature brings with it a spur to activity. It is generally recognized that in the United States we *do* more, but perhaps *think* less, than in Europe. Our children are more lively and boisterous and much harder to restrain. Our young people demand and receive greater freedom and are "on the go" far more than young people elsewhere. Our older people throw themselves into both work and play with a vim that is unique. As people grow old in this part of the world they want to keep on working instead of retiring comfortably as in Europe. In countries like Turkey, India, and China, people often give up their work twenty years younger than we do.

How much of all this is due to climate and how much to other conditions is a matter of great dispute. There is good reason to believe that on the whole the people who migrate to new regions differ in temperament from those of the same social class who stay behind (page 296). Other things being equal, the migrants tend to be of the more alert, active, adaptable, and adventurous type, especially if the migration involves danger, risk, hardship, and new conditions of life. On the other hand, those who stay behind generally include the most thoughtful and successful as well as the more conservative and unadaptable types. In addition to this there can be no doubt that new circumstances, the wealth and opportunities of a new land, and the necessity for building up a new country act as powerful stimulants to activity and invention. The automobile, the movie, and other modern innovations and ideas stimulate incessant activity, especially among our young people. Thus biological inheritance and the economic and social conditions of a new and rich country clearly cooperate with the climate in producing the peculiar alertness, activity, impulsiveness, and lack of poise which are characteristic of America and especially of the Continental Cyclonic Region where dwell a large fraction of the people of the United States.

In this region, then, we find a very healthy and active people who are always seeking for something new. They display a passion for bigness, speed, and energy. As a result they have very fully utilized the coal, iron, cotton, corn, and other resources which lie within their borders or close by, and have built up a manufacturing industry which finds no rival except in the Marine Cyclonic Region of Europe. They have also carried crime, moral reforms, religious activity, and universal education to levels almost unknown elsewhere. Moreover, the degree of wealth is much greater than in the European region, as is inevitable where people of the finest racial stocks find themselves in a highly stimulating climate with all the stored-up culture of the Old World behind them, and with an abundance of fertile land, vast forests, and untold mineral wealth before them. The astounding feature of all this is not that the Continental Cyclonic Region of North America has attained such power and wealth, but that a more or less accidental chain of circumstances should have caused so many and such great advantages to focus in one region. The way in which the Marine Cyclonic and the Continental Cyclonic Regions stand out upon map after map in this book (A134, A136, A478, A489, A526, etc.) as well as upon dozens of others showing other features of human activity and progress, is in many ways the dominant feature of the whole science of economic geography.

Types of Cities.—Here, too, just as in the Marine Cyclonic Region, large cities are numerous in proportion to the population, and many owe their growth primarily to manufacturing. In the following table the cities of over 250,000 inhabitants are divided according to their relation to important navigable waterways, and after each city is given the percentage of its men who are engaged in what may properly be called manufacturing, that is, in industrial pursuits other than the building industries.

Seaports		Lake Ports		River Ports		Not Ports	
Baltimore	34	Buffalo	40	Cincinnati	37	Akron	57
Boston	26	Chicago	36	Kansas City	25	Columbus	30
Jersey City	33	Cleveland	45	Louisville	34	Indianapolis	35
New York	32	Detroit	54	Pittsburgh	37		
Philadelphia	38	Milwaukee	51	St. Louis	37		
Providence	45	Rochester	46	Washington	15		
Newark	40	Toledo	43				
		Toronto	—				

Among the 24 cities in this list all but 3 are ports of some kind, and in all except Washington at least a quarter of the men are employed in manufacturing. But note that although some of the coast cities, such as Providence, are so highly industrialized that nearly half their men are at work in factories, the industrialization of the lake cities has gone still further. Even in a place like Chicago, where commerce plays a great rôle, 36 per cent of the men are in factories, and in Detroit this rises to 54 per cent. Only in the Marine Cyclonic Region of Europe do we find any other group of cities where manufacturing is so dominant.

The European Continental Cyclonic Region.—This region differs from the American Cyclonic Continental Region sufficiently to justify separate treatment. Shut off from direct Atlantic influences by the Alps on the west, it is bordered on the south by the typical Mediterranean region and on the north by a region of lower temperatures, especially in winter. In general the temperature quite closely resembles that of the American Continental Cyclonic Region, both regions having winter temperatures near the freezing point or lower, and summer temperatures between 70° and 80°. But differences appear in the rainfall. The western part of the European region, the Po Basin, comes nearest to the American figures, although it lacks the American uniformity from season to season, and has pronounced maxima in fall and spring caused by the Mediterranean neighborhood. Toward the east the European zone becomes rapidly drier, Milan having 40 inches of rain.

Belgrade 24, Bucharest 23, and Odessa 16. Moreover, dry winters and a maximum of rain in summer prevail. A still greater factor is the great variability of the rain. The departure of the annual rainfall from the average increases from 10–15 per cent in the west to as much as 20–25 per cent in the east. This fact, in conjunction with the low rainfall, means that the danger of poor crops increases rapidly toward the east to the great detriment of human prosperity. The importance of this appears in the fact that in spite of intensive cultivation the yields of corn, even at the maximum in Italy, averaged only 22 bushels per acre during a twenty-year period, or half as much as in Connecticut, while the maximum wheat production per acre is not half so much as in Denmark (A78).

The Po Basin.—A brief description of the four sections of this European Continental Cyclonic Region will show how rapidly the conditions of life change from east to west. The four are well separated by mountains which increase the diversity. Rather mild winters and warm summers, young alluvial soils, a fair rainfall during the entire year, and water for irrigation from the glacier-covered Alps make the Po Basin the granary of Italy and the best section of southern Europe. Intensive land utilization with fairly good yields per acre is the result. Wheat and corn fields cover much of the area, rice is raised in easily irrigated sections, and dairy cattle are kept in large numbers on the marsh lands bordering the Po River. Rows of mulberry trees along the boundaries of the fields are used for silkworms, and wherever there are slopes, vineyards are plentiful. In this essentially agricultural area manufacturing flourishes far more than in any other part of Italy. It is based on water power and supplies the needs of the dense population of a vigorously growing nation. In contrast to the less active Mediterranean population farther south, the inhabitants of the Po Basin show great energy. This is often said to be the result of migration from the north, but it is only what would be expected in a climate which is not only the stormiest in Italy but very fine in its seasonal range of temperature. Thus it is not surprising that in many ways this is one of the world's highly productive regions and plays an important rôle in the political history of Europe.

The Danube Basin.—This mountain-girt second section of the European Cyclonic Continental Region is much more continental than the Po Basin. Its winters are colder and drier, and its summer rains more variable. Nevertheless the conditions for raising grain are good, compared with most parts of the world, for dark soils formed under grass prevail, the summer temperatures are favorable and rain fairly abundant. When the authors traveled from Vienna to Bucharest and farther south in July, the flat plain seemed like one huge field of wheat and sturdy corn, and the many villages with their whitewashed houses suggested general prosperity. Nevertheless there is a pronounced change for the worse, for although Austria, western Hungary, and western Yugoslavia have the aspects of western Europe in many respects, the poorer eastern parts begin to suggest the Orient. Since the factors which foster the intensive development of manufacturing are missing, except at Vienna, and prosperity depends mainly on the crops, the variability in the yield from year to year becomes a disturbing element. The frequent recurrence of poor crops makes it hard for the small farmer to get a living. In 1920, for example, the Yugoslavian farmer got, on an average, only 54 bushels of wheat on land that yielded 100 in 1928. In the Netherlands, on the other hand, in the worst year during this same period, the farmers got 77 bushels on land which yielded 100 in the best years. Moreover, during this whole period the Yugoslavian farmers averaged only one bushel from an area which gave 2.7 in the Netherlands.

Because of such conditions the land here in this European Cyclonic Continental Region has tended to fall into the hands of large owners. With their big holdings such owners can stand bad times better than small owners, but such conditions hamper the higher cultural development of the population. In the post-war reorganization of society the government forced the division of the large holdings into small units which are now owned by the farmers themselves, but this is not in accord with the climatic conditions and can be successful only when backed by government credits in bad times. Such economic conditions promote political instability, and this is increased by the constant friction of one country with another over tariffs. An attempt to solve this latter difficulty is seen in the present tendency towards an economic Danube confederation.

The Rumanian Section.—The third section of the European Cyclonic Continental Region embraces much of Rumania, especially *Walachia*, or the plain of the lower Danube. Here the disadvantages just discussed are even more pronounced than in Yugoslavia. Fields of wheat and corn cover the lowlands, but the chance of crop failure is an ever-present menace. In 1928 the Rumanian farmers got only 43 bushels of corn from land that gave 100 in 1926. In Connecticut, on the contrary, the worst year between 1910 and 1930 gave 72 bushels for every 100 in the best year. Even as far west as Iowa the corresponding figure is 61. Unfortunately, the regions with the greatest instability in their crops are also those where the people depend most completely on agriculture. In Yugoslavia about 67 and in Rumania 71 men out of every hundred are engaged in agriculture, whereas in the Netherlands the corresponding number is 26, and in Connecticut 7.   Where the crops are so variable and so large a part of the people are farmers, the majority of the people are almost sure to stand on a low cultural level.   With this, so long as our type of social organization prevails, there is almost inevitably a great contrast between rich land owners and half-starved peasants, and between luxurious cities like Bucharest and peasant villages where the people live in whitewashed little mud houses and the whole family crowds into two or three rooms with mud floors.

Southern Russia.—Except near the Caucasus, where rainfall is more plentiful, southern Russia, the last of our four sections of the European Cyclonic Continental Region, is still more handicapped by drought.   As one proceeds eastward into drier areas, corn is replaced by wheat and barley.   Then, in spite of fertile soils which are chocolate brown in the south and darker in the north, the type of cultivation approaches more and more to dry farming.   Finally, near the border of the continental grasslands (Plate I), cattle replace crops just as on the great American plains.   The density of population is low and the peasants are poor.   The Soviet policy of replacing the former large land holdings of this region by great government farms is wholly in harmony with the character of the climate, for the small cultivator is unable to solve the problem of climatic instability.

Cities.—Large cities are not numerous in the European Continental Cyclonic Region.   Budapest, however, has a million inhabitants, while Vienna with nearly twice as many lies close to the border between this region and the Marine Cyclonic Region.   The cities, like the farming, show a rapid change of quality from west to east.   Vienna is strongly west European, with important manufactures of many complex types. Budapest, although magnificent, begins to show a hint of the east, especially in the simple quality of its factories which turn out a far greater value of flour than of machines, and plain cotton cloth, leather, and beer rather than automobiles.   In the Po Basin, Turin and Milan are like Vienna in being manufacturing centers of the active west European type, but Venice and Trieste begin to show the eastern simplicity in their manufactures.   Farther east there are only a few great cities—Belgrade, Bucharest, Odessa, and Rostov.   All of them are commercial centers and seats of government rather than centers of manufacturing.

Cool Continental Region.   *Climate.*—This region differs from the preceding region because of a cooler summer, but principally because of a much colder winter.   It includes a considerable area in both of the northern land masses.   In North America it lies north of the Corn Belt and the American Continental Cyclonic Region, and stretches from the coast of northern New England far into the plains of Alberta and

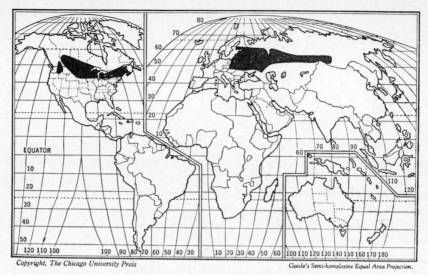

A—Location of Cool Continental Regions.

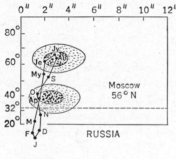

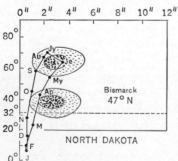

B—Climographs of Cool Continental Regions.

Saskatchewan. In Eurasia it lies east of the Marine Cyclonic Region and tapers down to a narrow strip which extends far into Siberia, and ends only at the high uplands and mountains of eastern Siberia. The American and the Eurasian parts have enough in common so that they are here grouped together. Yet they differ in the same way as do the two Continental Cyclonic Regions and might reasonably be treated separately.

Both regions consist largely of vast plains, and only in limited areas like the Adirondacks, the White Mountains, and the Urals is the relief important. Monotonous lowland plains, where glacial moraines often form the only break in the flatness, are typical, although in the eastern part of North America a rolling dissected upland takes the place of the lowlands. In both the American and Eurasian regions, warm but short summers and cold, long winters dominate man's life both economically and socially. In both the rainfall decreases from the coast inland. (B318.)

The American Portion.—The differences between the two regions can be best described by giving a more detailed picture of each. The climate of the American part of this region is greatly modified by cyclonic storms and large lakes. The cyclonic control means that even in winter the cold periods are interrupted by southern winds, bringing warm air not only from the Atlantic and sometimes the Gulf of Mexico, but even from the Pacific Ocean. The hot spells of summer are also broken by cooler days more often than in the cool continental interior of Eurasia. The cyclonic control also means that the rainfall in the American region is sufficient for crops clear to the Rocky Mountains, although decreasing toward the west. The rain is rather evenly distributed throughout the year in the east, while in the west a summer maximum is noticeable, although the winters also have a fair amount of snow. The lakes reduce the severity of the climate in the adjoining regions, especially where the prevailing westerly winds bring the winter warmth and summer coolness of the water to the eastern shores. The natural vegetation follows the climate. In the east the evenly distributed rainfall permits forests to cover the land that is not cleared for crops; farther west, prairies prevail (A433). The soils vary similarly, being light colored and leached in the forested east, and dark and fertile in the grassy west (Plate II). The farmer in North Dakota faces long, cold winters with strong blizzards and long interruptions of communication because of snow. January averages 3° at Devil's Lake. Frosts may occur in May, and the average frostless season is only 125 days. Nevertheless the early summer rains, the long, warm summer days, and a drier late summer favor the growth of grains, especially wheat, but not many other crops. Hence one-crop agriculture, with its attendant difficulties, is dominant (p. 219). The extreme variability of the climate, however, is detrimental. Sometimes the rainfall is too scanty or comes too late; sudden hail storms may in a single hour destroy crops that the farmer has nursed for months; late frosts in the spring or early autumn frosts may prevent the grain from ripening properly. Hence the yield of crops in both the Canadian and American parts of the Cool Continental Region varies greatly from year to year. This means that the average yield per acre is relatively low; hence very large farms, averaging nearly 1500 acres in North Dakota versus only 55 in Mississippi, are needed to maintain the American standard of living. It also means that periods of prosperity and stringency alternate rapidly. This is also true to a less degree along a north and south strip extending all the way from Manitoba to Texas (A320). The difficulty of such periods is increased by the fact that this region is far from large markets. This increases the effect of the variability in encouraging radical tendencies. The race and training of these western farmers, as well as the energizing quality of their cyclonic climate, do not permit them to submit to misfortune in the apathetic fashion of the Russian peasants. Hence they turn to political agitations, such as those connected with the Grange in the 1870's, then the Farmers' Alliance, the Populist Party, the Free Silver Movement, and in later days the Non-Partisan League and the Farm Bloc. In times of stress it becomes popular to

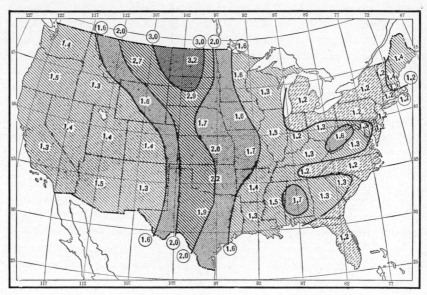

A—Relation between Average Value of Crops per Acre in Best and Poorest Years from 1910 to 1919. The number 2.0, for example, means that the value per acre in the best year was twice as great as in the worst.

denounce old methods, organize non-partisan leagues, advocate state operation of grain elevators and banks, and vote for the cancellation of debts and reimbursement to losers in closed banks by the state. But good crops come again, prosperity returns, the depressed prices of agricultural products rise, and the people become more conservative.

In the eastern part of the Cool Continental Region in America, the more stable and less extreme climate and the modifications due to the Great Lakes and the ocean make life less strenuous than in the west. Although the growing season is short the crops are by no means so variable as in the west (A320). The more abundant and regular rainfall enables potatoes to thrive wonderfully (A87); Michigan raises sugar beets, and in large sections many other vegetables and fruits grow excellently. The eastern shore of Lake Michigan shows a long zone of peaches, cherries, and other fruits. Apples of the finest flavor are raised in huge quantities in northern New York and the Annapolis Valley of Nova Scotia. Nevertheless, such conditions are typical of only a small part of the Cool Continental Regions. Still more important is the fact that the cool, moist climate makes grass grow excellently, and promotes a large yield of milk and butter fat (A102). Hence from Wisconsin and Michigan eastward through Ontario, Quebec, northern New England, and the Maritime Provinces dairying is the dominant method of land utilization. Cattle, especially black and white Holsteins, are a typical part of the landscape. Frosts do less harm to cattle than to grain, for the forage crops to which the farmers devote their main efforts are not injured so easily as cereals. Then, too, the proximity of this region to the great manufacturing area of the Continental Cyclonic Region and to the waterways of the Great Lakes, the St. Lawrence, and the ocean makes it easy to find a market not only for potatoes and apples but also for milk and its products. Wisconsin cheese and Vermont butter are widely familiar, and ocean liners from Montreal on the St. Lawrence carry dairy products to Europe.

The forest cover also helps the farmers of the eastern part of the Cool Continental Region, not only by providing abundant firewood, but by furnishing a winter occupation as well. Similar regions in Russia cannot so easily profit by shipping out lumber, pulp wood, and pulp because of remoteness both from waterways and markets. The great manufacturing district just south of the American region also provides a ready outlet for surplus labor, and many people take advantage of this in winter, returning to the farms in summer. The forests, together with the rolling terrain, the mountains, and the abundant glacial lakes and winding rivers, also make this eastern part of the Cool Continental Region very attractive for summer tourists, and thus still further stabilize the income of the farmers. Nevertheless many farms have been abandoned in northern New England and New York, but only where poor soil and rugged relief make it unprofitable to raise vegetables, apples, or dairy cattle. And finally the glaciated mountain topography with its lakes, rapids, and waterfalls combines with the regularity of the rainfall to make the development of water power easy and profitable.

When conditions like these cooperate with a stimulating although somewhat rigorous climate, a high degree of progress and some important cities may be expected. The number of large cities is not great, to be sure, although it is fairly large in proportion to the population. Montreal is the only one with over a million inhabitants, St. Paul and Minneapolis form a large metropolitan district, and Winnipeg is growing rapidly.   Milwaukee might also be reckoned as belonging to this region, although on page 314 we have put it in the Continental Cyclonic Region.   All these cities are engaged in active manufacturing, much of which is such work as flour milling or the preparation of other local products for market.

The Eurasian Portion.—Very different is the development in the Eurasian Cold Continental Region in spite of a similar range of temperature and the same general flatness.   The difference lies mainly in a weaker cyclonic control in Eurasia, greater dryness in the south, and greater isolation.   The lack of stimulating cyclonic control is especially visible in winter.   Then the huge size of Asia leads to such low temperature and high atmospheric pressure that the outblowing winds almost exclude cyclonic storms from the interior.   Hence in the Soviet Union from the borders of the Baltic States and Poland *eastward* the winters are colder, drier, and less broken by warm periods than are the corresponding portions of the American Cool Continental Region from southeastern Canada *westward*.   In summer, on the other hand, a fair number of storms penetrate the continent, and the precipitation is largely concentrated within a few warm months.   It is worth noting that the Baltic States which Russia lost in the World War are the part of this natural region most closely resembling the more favored parts of the American region.   Note also that whereas in the American region the main contrast is between the east and west, in Eurasia there is a contrast between north and south.   In the northwest of the Eurasian area, near the Baltic Sea, we find the best seasonal distribution of rainfall, the finest forests, the easiest access to the world's main markets, the most leached soils, the best of the grassy meadows, and the greatest development of dairying. Toward the southeast, although the summers are warmer, the rainfall is more concentrated in a few months, thus increasing the danger of crop failures;   grass takes the place of forests, the "chernozem" soil is dark and fertile, and cereal crops largely replace cattle.   The colder northern section with its less fertile soil is used for rye, potatoes, and flax; but in the southeast the fertile black soil supports a wheat belt which runs far into Siberia.   There, even more than in the corresponding part of America, the lack of snow in winter and the uncertainty due to both drought and frost cause the yield of the crops to vary greatly.   So serious is this that even within the present century this section of the Soviet Union has several times suffered badly from shortage of food and even starvation.

The character of the Russian peasants seems to reflect these environmental conditions.   One of the most noteworthy features of the Soviet

Union is that among its peasants at least a hundred million live in almost the same fashion.   This is possible because here, as nowhere else, climate and relief provide uniformity over an enormous area. One of the outstanding characteristics of these peasants is their passive submission to authority.   Formerly they lived under a rigid village system or under landlords who had almost complete power; now they live under the equally rigid control of the Soviet government.   It concentrates some of them as laborers on state farms, it lets others live in their old villages as members of great cooperative farms or "collectives" which are dominated by a handful of leaders; and it demands absolute obedience from all.

The fact that these hundred million peasants submit so easily may be partly racial and partly due to a long series of historical events, but the geographic environment seems also to have been important.   From the geographic point of view one of the most potent features of peasant life in Russia is the long period of idleness in winter.   Near Moscow, for example, the ground usually freezes in mid-October and soon the men have practically no work.   Only a little firewood has to be cut because the houses are very small; everyone crowds into one room, and the animals, which are often kept within the same walls as the people, help to provide heat.   The care of the animals takes very little of the men's time, for the women do most of it.   Moreover, the average Russian peasant has never had more than one or two horses, three cattle, a pig, and perhaps ten hens.   Contrast this with the three horses or mules, nine cows and calves, twenty pigs, and eighty hens on an average farm in Indiana.   In the past the men have not known how to read, their houses have been very badly lighted, and there has been little in the way of handicrafts.   Since the Russian peasants all live in villages, the men have not had to clear the snow from the roads to town nor go to town to do errands and get the mail.   Nor have they had much of the stimulus to both health and activity that comes from cyclonic storms. What wonder then that in winter they often spend sixteen hours in bed, and the rest of the time do little except huddle over the fire, eat, drink and talk.   Not till April does the frost leave the ground at Moscow, and then for several weeks mud prevents plowing and other outside work. Thus for practically six months each year the Russian peasant has lived in enforced idleness.   Then when the spring work really begins the men are so soft from lack of exercise that they become terribly tired even though they cultivate only small tracts.   Such a life is a potent instrument in deadening initiative and promoting inefficiency.   It appears to be one of the main reasons why it has been so easy for a few forceful people to dominate the vast peasant population.   The rapid increase of education and the more frequent exchange between the farming and industrial populations may change all this, but even so there will still be an important difference between the American and Eurasian portions of the Cold Continental Region.

In the past the cities have shown this difference very clearly. Warsaw, Moscow, and Leningrad are all huge cities with over a million people, while Lodz, Breslau, Königsberg, Kiev, Kharkov, and Rīga are important. Yet none of them has hitherto been a manufacturing city to any such degree as Montreal, Milwaukee, and Minneapolis. For the most part they are centers of trade and of the smaller and simpler kinds of manufacturing. Lodz, to be sure, is one of the most thorough-going manufacturing cities in the world, for it does very little except make cotton cloth. Moreover, the Russian cities are making strenuous efforts to reach the industrial level of the European and American Cyclonic Regions. Nevertheless, they will have to be multiplied threefold in size and five- or sixfold in productivity before they are as important in proportion to the whole population as are the great cities of the American Cool Continental Region.

Cool Forests. *The Dominant Forest.*—An immense, dark green coniferous forest, the Taiga as the Russians call it, is the dominating factor in this region. The glacial lakes and waterfalls, the broad, slow rivers, the occasional fields of crops, the scattered pastures where cattle are grazing, and the clearings where sawmills are located are mere trifles in this universal mantle of green trees. From Alaska and the Laurentian Upland one can follow these forests to Labrador. In the Old World they extend from Norway, Sweden, and Finland through the great plain of northern Russia and west Siberia, the central Siberian Plateau, and the East Siberian mountains to the Pacific Coast. Many species of spruce, fir, and pine are represented in different regions, but the character of the forest is always the same—the great coniferous forest with its acid podzols (Plate II). Larches which lose their needles in winter, and hardwoods like the ash, elm, and above all the birch, are intermingled with the evergreens, but are scarcely more than insignificant details drowned in the great dark green uniformity. On the north the forest is bordered by the Tundra with its ever-frozen subsoil. On the marine western side, except where high mountains cause a southward extension in North America, the forested zone is rather narrow. It widens toward the east where it includes the mixed forests of the Amur region and Karafuto in Asia, and offshoots in the Adirondacks and New England in North America. The southern limit is partly climatic, but depends also on the degree to which man has destroyed the dominance of the forest. A great part of our Cool Continental Region and some of the Marine Cyclonic Region once belonged to the Cool Forests.

Human Responses.—Man's activity in this great forest region is greatly limited. The climate is not attractive, especially in the north. The winters are long, cold, and dark, and the very low temperatures

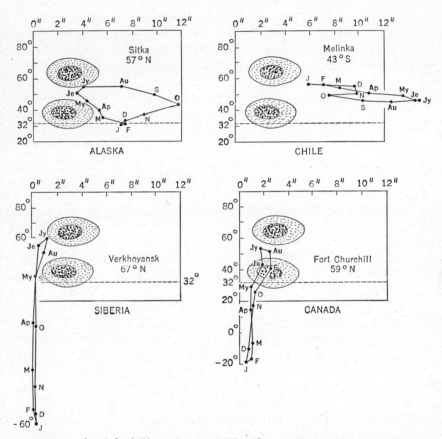

A—Climographs of Cool Forest Regions—West Coasts above, and Interior Regions below.

would be unendurable were not the atmosphere so calm most of the time. The snowfall is light except near the sea. In the spring a great deal of heat has to be used in thawing the snow and the frozen lakes, rivers, and soils before the land can grow warm. As a result the summers, although surprisingly warm, are very short and the prospects for agriculture discouraging. So the native Indian and Mongoloid tribes live chiefly by hunting and fishing, and hence follow a migratory mode of life which does not favor an advanced type of civilization.

The thickness of the furs needed to protect the animals from the cold winters has brought white men here as traders or even as hunters and introduced a wholly different type of culture.   As J. Russell Smith puts it: "At the trading post the two cultures meet, the white man of the complicated life of books, machinery, and wide knowledge of many things, and the red man and the half breed, of simple life, bookless, but with profound knowledge of the things of the forest."   Each fall the native families still start out from the Hudson Bay Company posts on a great migration in search of furs.   They endure the almost incredible hardships of the climate and the dangers of hungry wolves in order to bring back furs for the great southern markets.   The fur trade was once a fundamental part of the business of the old Hanseatic League in western Europe; and the Hudson River Valley was then the great entrance gate to the Canadian hunting fields.   Even now, in spite of the competition of well organized fur farms, the Cool Forests of Canada and Eurasia still furnish the main fur supply.   Fishing rivals hunting as the main source of food for the natives, and where this region joins the Tundra the keeping of reindeer may provide meat not only for local use but also for the dense population much farther south.

Challenging the Forest.—Two other factors tend to produce a slight increase in the white population of the northern forests; the *search for timber* and for *minerals*.   Here is the world's greatest supply of soft wood, both for timber and pulp.   The timber camps of Washington and British Columbia and the big pulp mills of Ontario and Quebec, the well organized timber industry of Norway, Sweden, and Finland, and the newly revived activity in northern Russia around the Dvina River illustrate the matter.   Mountains and glacial topography offer water power for the sawmills.   Millions of trees are transported by railroad, as in the American Northwest, or float down the rivers to the sawmills and pulp factories.   Temporary and in some places permanent settlements bring modern activity and noise into the silence of these cool forests.   Mining likewise brings first the geologist and then the mining camp, which, if permanently successful, may result in a real city.   The Swedish iron ore cities of Kiruna and Gellivare near the Arctic Circle are like oases in the northern forest where formerly only a few Lapps, who depend on reindeer, represented the human element.   Railroads, necessary for transportation of the timber and mining products, open the land for the settler who logically follows the lumbermen and miners in order to produce at least a few crops and sell them at huge prices.

At the same time temperate agriculture enters the forest from the south and forces its edge farther north. Thanks to the long summer days and the consequent abundant insolation, crops can be raised much farther north than was formerly expected. Isaiah Bowman in *The Pioneer Fringe* points out that north of parallel 55° along the Peace River Valley in Canada the invasion of the Cool Forest is in full swing so that the population increased from 2,000 in 1911 to 60,000 in 1931. Besides the typical subarctic crops of barley and oats, both of which

mature rapidly, spring wheat is raised. If it does not ripen, it is used as fodder in the dairy industry. Ranching, in spite of the long winters, which make stable feeding necessary, moves northward as far as grass grows, to be finally replaced by reindeer herding on the Tundra. In Russia, cultivation around the White Sea has reached the Arctic Circle, and in Sweden and Finland it nearly comes up to that line. The long, narrow Siberian crop belt running eastward from the Urals to Lake Baikal, and continuing along the Amur Valley, consists largely of territory that once belonged to the Taiga, especially in central and eastern Siberia. Along some of the Siberian rivers cultivation reaches much farther north.

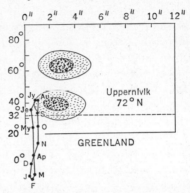

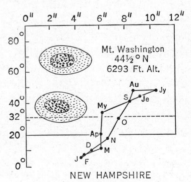

A—Climographs of Tundras and High Mountains.

Thus the great belt of forests does not stand unchallenged, but taken as a whole, the changes in its boundaries are relatively small and do not seriously break the immense uniformity of the Cool Forests. A product of the climate, it will probably continue to exist as a timber reserve for a world in which the other timber areas may continue to decline.

The southern part of the coast of Chile belongs to this same type of region. The forest there is somewhat mixed in character, but agrees with the northern type in dominating everything. Swept by the wind and often showing the effect of this by its brushy form, the forest covers the mountain slopes up to the alpine meadows and glaciers. Practically untouched by man, it waits for some future day to be included in the economic realm where man is dominant.

Tundra and High Mountains.—Tundra borders the region of Cool Forests towards the Arctic. Here the low temperature forbids the growth of trees, and the land presents a desolate picture of low scrub, mosses, and lichens (A327). The winters are so long and have so little snow that the subsoil remains permanently frozen. Consequently, when the surface thaws, the water cannot sink away underground, and swamps prevail almost everywhere. Traveling is unpleasant for this reason and also because of the great swarms of mosquitoes which make life miserable. Great, slow rivers wind northward through the Tundra. They are frozen in winter, but flood great areas in summer because the snow melts along their upper courses while the ice still forms a barrier lower down. Nevertheless the summers are not entirely unproductive. Reindeer herds graze on the lichens; many fur animals and birds come from the southern forest to feed on the berries of the shrubs and herbs that grow among the gray lichens. Hunters follow the game, fishermen seek salmon and sturgeon, and lumbermen accompany rafts of timber down to Hudson Bay and the Arctic Ocean. But the season of activity starts only in June, and in September the Tundra is again deserted and desolate.

Similar conditions are found among high mountains, especially on the uplands of western and northern Tibet. One author (Grenard) remarks that even the Gobi Desert looks fertile when compared with the bleak, saturated basins of the highest plateaus in Asia. But even here mosses and lichens and even small patches of grass with flowers appear in favorable spots. Huge yaks and herds of mountain sheep and antelopes roam this area in summer in search of food, and sometimes Tibetan herdsmen can be found here with their stock. But winter comes early, and most of the year the land bears an aspect of complete worthlessness.

EXERCISES

1. Compare the utilization of the land in the Marine Cyclonic Region and in the Wet and Dry Low Latitudes, and show why there is such a difference.

2. On outline maps of the continents locate all the cities mentioned in Chapters XIII–XVI, using symbols to indicate the following sizes: below 250,000; 250,000–500,000; 500,000–1,000,000; over 1,000,000. Insert on your maps the boundaries of the natural regions. Then discuss the location, size, and kind of activity in the cities of the Cyclonic Regions compared with those of the rest of the world.

3. Let a group of students cooperate in going through the maps of products, activities, and other human conditions in this book or in your desk atlas (*Oxford Economic* or *Goode's*) and make a table showing the status of each product or activity in each of the natural regions. Use four grades: (A) very well developed, (B) well developed, (C) poorly developed, (D) absent. Insert these let-

ters after the name of each product in the column devoted to each natural region. Count the A's, B's, etc., in each column and discuss your results.

4. Look up central Siberia in books and magazines, and compare it with the Canadian provinces of Manitoba, Saskatchewan, and Alberta. On maps of rainfall (A32) and temperature (A30, 31) see how the two regions differ in these respects. If you have an *Oxford Economic Atlas* consult the continental climatic maps. Write out your conclusions as to the physical and human differences between the two areas.

5. What topographic conditions have caused the Marine Cyclonic Region of Europe to be so much more important than that of North America? If there were no mountains in North America west of the Rockies, would the Marine Cyclonic Area there be as great as that of Europe? Why? Is the relatively sparse population of the Marine Cyclonic Region of North America due to climate? Explain.

6. In your imagination take two airplane trips: (1) from Florida to Labrador following the coast; (2) from Southern California to Alaska. In each case note what the people are doing for a living in different latitudes as seen from the low-flying plane and place the results in two columns. Compare and discuss.

PART III

CHAPTER XVI

FORAGE, CEREALS, ROOT CROPS, AND SUGAR

Factors in the Distribution of Crops.—The distribution of crops depends not only on variations in plant resources from place to place, but also on differences in human activities and tastes. Looking at the matter from the standpoint of both plants and man, the main physical factors in crop distribution are: (1) climate; (2) soils; and (3) relief. The main economic factors are: (4) value of the crops as food for man, feed for animals, or raw material for manufacturing; (5) productivity as measured by the yield per acre or the results of a given amount of work; (6) ease of preparation for market, keeping qualities, bulkiness, and other conditions which influence transportation; (7) accessibility of markets; (8) relation to other crops and animals as to profit, space required on the farm, demands for fertilizers, and the amount and season of labor. The main human factors are: (9) health and energy; (10) density of population; (11) stage of culture; and (12) habits, customs, and prejudices, including such conditions as tariffs.

The importance of these factors has been discussed in previous chapters. Some are emphasized below in relation to particular products, but all should be borne in mind. Accessibility to markets perhaps needs further emphasis. Dairy centers, for example, can sell fresh milk only as nearby population increases, or as transportation facilities are improved. Farms near dying mining centers in Colorado have been abandoned, as were many in central Pennsylvania when the lumber industry collapsed a few years ago. Many of the Pennsylvania farms, however, were taken up again after the state built good highways into the formerly inaccessible but fertile valleys.

The Main Types of Crops.—All the world's great crops and many minor ones of only local importance are treated in the following pages. They are divided into the following groups, each with its own distinc-

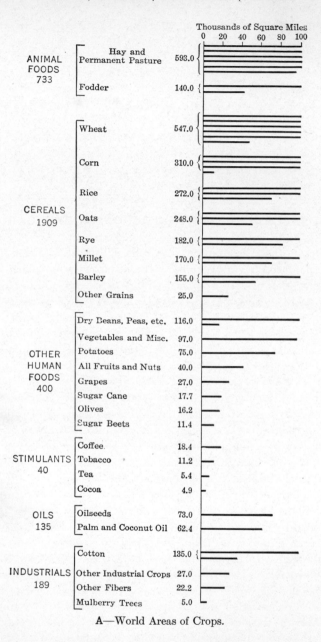

A—World Areas of Crops.

tive geographical distribution: (1) feed for animals; (2) food for man; (3) spices, stimulants, narcotics, and drugs, all of which are taken into the human body, but are not properly foods; (4) vegetable oils, partly for food and partly for raw materials; and (5) raw materials for industry and commerce. The groups overlap somewhat, for crops like corn, barley, and turnips are used for both man and animals, and some like potatoes are used also as raw materials for manufacturing. In the fourth group, certain oils, especially olive oil, are used almost exclusively as food, and some, like tung oil, wholly as raw materials. The fifth group is called raw materials for industry and *commerce* because it includes articles, like cut flowers and nursery shrubs, which are sold for use in their natural form. Many of the products listed under stimulants, narcotics, and drugs might also be placed under raw materials,

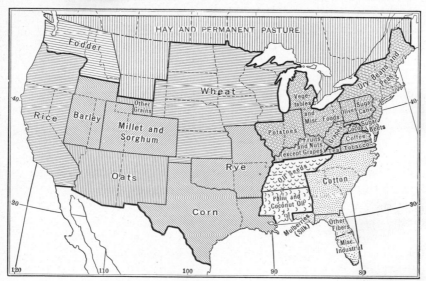

A—Total Area of Harvested Land in Whole World Superimposed upon the United States and Southern Canada.

for such things as tobacco and quinine have to be manufactured quite elaborately. The alcoholic drinks also form an exceptional group, since they are manufactured products based on one or more crops which are described elsewhere. The following descriptions begin as a rule with the tropical products of each main type, but there are exceptions, especially where a product is very widely raised, or where several products are much alike.

How the Earth's Good Land is Divided among Crops.—The relative amounts of land given to different kinds of crops are shown in A333. The parts of the earth's surface used for crops of all kinds are only as large as the United States and the inhabited southern part of Canada.

In A333 the different shadings indicate the area which each major crop, or group of crops, would cover if all of it from all over the world were raised in one part of the United States. The positions of the crops on the map have no significance. In the north and northwest a heavy line surrounds an area equal to that occupied by all the world's cultivated grasses, forage crops, and improved pastures. All these together occupy an area no larger than the states of Washington, Idaho, and Montana, and the inhabited southern part of Canada. West of the Mississippi an area equal to that occupied by seven main cereals and a group of minor cereals is surrounded by another heavy line. If all the world's grain fields were moved to America they would cover a solid group of states equal to practically the whole of the United States west of the Mississippi River. The West North Central States would almost suffice for the entire wheat crop, provided the soil, relief, and climate were such that every bit of land could be used. Corn would need only Texas and Louisiana; rice would require Oregon, California, and part of Nevada; oats would cover only New Mexico and Arizona with a little in Nevada; rye would need Missouri, Arkansas, and Oklahoma; and millet most of Colorado and Utah. We think of potatoes as a great crop, but the world's entire supply is raised on an area smaller than Indiana and Illinois. The fresh vegetables, root crops, and miscellaneous crops like spices cover.an area smaller than Ohio and Michigan.

The fruits and nuts shown in A333 occupy an area equal to that of Kentucky together with the addition of West Virginia for grapes. Sugar, which is raised on an area as large as Maryland, Delaware, and a third or more of Pennsylvania occupies far more land that all the tropical fruits together. The stimulants of all the world grow on an area only as large as Virginia. It seems hard to believe that all the tobacco fields in the world, if collected into one place, would be only one-fourth as large as Virginia. But bear in mind that the area devoted to a crop is a very imperfect measure of the crop's value. The silk crop of the world, reckoned at the prices given as most typical in the Statistical Yearbook of the League of Nations, has a value equal to about half that of the barley crop. But barley occupies about thirty times as much space as the mulberry trees used for silkworms. An acre or two of mulberry trees in Japan is enough to keep a whole family busy far into the night during the time when the worms are feeding.

Crops Used for Animals.—The true grasses are the most important food crops for animals, but various cereals which are fed either as green fodder or as grain press close upon them. These, too, are grasses from the botanical point of view. Next in importance as animal food come the legumes such as clover, alfalfa, and beans. Far in the rear, but highly important in many regions, come tubers, such as potatoes, and roots like the turnip and carrot. In the world as a whole, as appears in A332, hay and permanent pasture occupy nearly 600,000 square miles, which means that grass receives more space than any other kind of cultivated plant. Fodder crops which are sown every year and cut green occupy somewhat less than one-fourth as large an area.

Taking the world as a whole, grasses and fodder crops probably occupy about 18 per cent of the entire area of improved land, although the statistics are very inadequate. In the United States, however, they occupy no less than 23 per cent, or more than any other crop except corn, which is practically the same (A335). Hay is usually

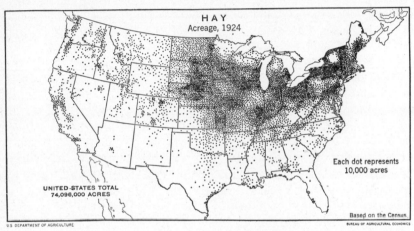

A—Hay in the United States.

one of the first three crops in value (page 53). If we include also the areas where corn, oats, barley, and other crops which might serve as food for man are raised as feed for animals the percentage of crop land devoted to animals in the United States rises close to 60. In Europe this percentage is much smaller. The density of population there permits only a small part of the cultivated land to be used for animals, and the consumption of meat, milk, and eggs per capita is far lower than in the United States. The percentage of land devoted to animal crops varies greatly, however, being above 70 in Denmark and almost zero in Greece and eastern Russia. In the rest of the world only a few places like southern Canada, New Zealand, and Argentina have large percentages. Where the population is sparse and the climate not too moist and tropical, many animals are indeed supported upon rough, unimproved pastures, as in Australia, Argentina, northern India, the steppes of Central Asia, the savannas of the Sudan, the Orinoco plain, and other tropical sections. In many other regions, especially in large parts of India and China, the population is so dense that domestic animals are scarce compared with people. They get their food mainly by browsing beside the roads or in the fields after the crops grown for human use have been harvested.

Grasses.—In tropical countries the native forage plants, though often rank and succulent, generally lack the nutritive value found in the grasses of cooler climates. This is one great reason for the scarcity of good domestic animals there. Certain tropical grasses, however, make such good fodder that they are being widely introduced elsewhere. Guinea grass is perhaps the best of these. It grows luxuriantly, is rich in sugar and proteins, and has no hard fibers although often reaching 12 feet in height. Moreover, it has a very heavy yield—20 to 30 tons per acre on an average, against only one or two in most hay fields of the United States and three or four for alfalfa. There are other cultivated tropical grasses, but practically all of them are rather tough. Moreover, unless they are carefully weeded and often renewed, most of them are soon displaced by some of the poorer types.

As one goes from the tropical savannas toward the belt of deserts, the grasses become smaller and more nutritious. On the south side of the Sahara, for example, the grazing is much better than in regions like the southern Sudan or the llanos of the Orinoco. Farther from the equator in subtropical climates and in the Temperate Grasslands the grasses are still better, but neither here nor in the savannas are they cultivated to any appreciable extent. Only in the cyclonic regions or their immediate neighborhood does one find any great abundance of cultivated grass, but there, far more than in tropical countries, grass becomes a great crop. Temperate as well as tropical grasses illustrate the way in which good plants, no matter where they originate, are being introduced all over the world. Agricultural experts say that if we improve grasses as much as we have improved the cereals, we can double or treble the number of cattle that we can keep on an acre of land.

Legumes as Forage.—Although *alfalfa*, or lucerne, is grown in parts of the drier tropics, it is chiefly important in arid and temperate areas. It is found in the heat of the Imperial Valley and in the cool, dry climate of Saskatchewan, but not much in humid regions like Great Britain. Its 15-foot tap roots enable it to withstand summer droughts and make it an excellent crop for irrigated areas, where one watering often suffices to produce a cutting of hay. In the United States it thrives best in the warmer southwestern states. In Europe it has been grown for centuries and is widely dispersed in the southern half. The *clovers*, especially red clover, are also valuable and widely used forage plants of the legume family. They are much used in crop rotation, and like alfalfa are beneficial to the soil because of their power to fix nitrogen from the air.

Crops Raised as Food for Man.—Among the crops raised for human food the cereals occupy an overwhelming proportion of the land. A332 shows that the world's acreage of wheat is almost equal to the space occupied by all non-cereal food crops combined. A337 shows how widely it is spread in the United States. Next in importance, so far as area is concerned, come corn, rice, oats, rye, millet, and barley.

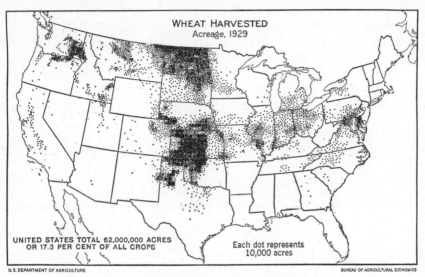

A—Wheat Production in the United States.

Wherever civilization is even moderately advanced, one of these seven cereals is usually the most important food crop. The ease with which they can be raised, their good keeping qualities, and the large number of calories of heat which they furnish all combine to this end. Yet after civilization reaches a certain stage the importance of cereals in the diet declines. They provide too much starch. The roots and tubers, especially potatoes and yams, err in this same respect, and so does sugar, although there the starch becomes sugar. Because of their many good qualities people often choose cereals instead of other crops that are more healthful, but such people also need nitrogenous foods or proteids, as well as carbohydrates. So without knowing just why, they cultivate beans and other legumes, which are potent agents in fixing nitrogen (page 187). Thus in China, India, Japan, and many tropical

countries, vast quantities of beans, gram, and other legumes are cultivated along with rice, millet, or wheat. More fortunate nations, which
live where grass grows well, also get abundant proteids from milk, meat,
and eggs. But a good diet needs also vitamins, acids, and salts. Vegetables, especially the leafy ones and those the seeds of which are eaten
in the green state like fresh peas and young sweet corn, are excellent
sources of vitamins. Fresh fruits also furnish vitamins and are the best
sources of acids and certain other valuable ingredients of a diet. Hence
advanced nations, understanding the value of modern discoveries as to
diet, have greatly increased their consumption of fruits and fresh vegetables. The whole situation is that among primitive tropical people
there is often far too great a reliance on green stuff, especially bananas;
among people in a medium stage like the Chinese and Hindus, and even
among more advanced people like Russians, Rumanians, Italians, and
some of our own groups, there is far too much use of cereals; and
finally among the most progressive people the use of cereals declines while
that of fruit and vegetables, as well as of meat, milk, and eggs, increases.

The Distribution of Cereals.—Some idea of the relative productivity
and value of the most important cereals may be obtained from the following table based on the ten countries or states with the highest yield
of each crop:

Crop	A. Approximate yield per acre in pounds	B. Value per acre in the United States includ- ing stalks, straw, etc. (Averages of 1909, 1919, 1929)
Rice	3,000	$59.03
Corn	2,500	25.19
Wheat	2,000	18.98
Barley	1,900	16.53
Millet	1,700	14.54
Oats	1,600	15.91
Rye	1,500	11.83

Because of the economic conditions discussed in earlier chapters,
the high value of the rice crop per acre would presumably cause that
crop to be the farmer's first choice if all the cereals could be grown in
a given region with equal ease. The next choice is corn and then wheat
with barley, oats, millet, and rye following behind. So far as climate
and soil permit, this appears to be nearly what happens. Many factors do indeed make it desirable for the majority of farmers to cultivate

a variety of crops including two or three cereals. Nevertheless, wherever rice can be grown easily it generally gets most of the space, unless it competes with a still more profitable crop like sugar. Where corn yields good crops, but rice will not grow, corn tends to get the lion's share of the land devoted to cereals; where neither rice nor corn is profitable, farmers generally give first choice to wheat, provided it will grow well. We shall discuss these cereals individually, omitting corn and wheat because they have been discussed in previous chapters, and beginning with rice because it is the most tropical.

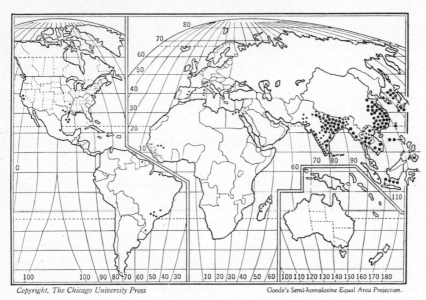

Goode's Semi-homolosine Equal Area Projection.

A—World Production of Rice. Each large dot indicates one per cent of the world production, each small dot one-tenth of one per cent.

Areas of Rice Production.—Although rice has too much starch and too little proteid to be as good a food as wheat, it probably forms the staple food of more people than any other crop. Furthermore, among the great crops, it is the surest and most regular in yield. Since most of the people in the main rice regions, the heavily dotted parts of A339, are poor, an enormous number make rice their almost exclusive diet. Rice is probably of tropical origin; and most of it is raised where abundant rains accompany high temperature and at least four months have an average temperature of 75° F. (A30). Nevertheless, rice culture reaches 35° of north latitude in California, northern Japan, and Manchuria, and 45° in northern Italy. Rice, like many other plants, has innumerable varieties, a few of which may be raised in areas considerably cooler than those which produce the greater proportion of the crop.

The world's great rice region is found in southeastern Asia from India to Japan including the East Indies Islands. Here the heavy monsoon rains of summer on the mainland and in Japan, and the tropical rains of the more equatorial regions, give plenty of water. High mountains lead to great condensation of moisture, thus feeding thousands of small streams as well as large rivers, like the Ganges, Brahmaputra, Si, and Yangtze. The waters of these are diverted over terraced slopes or spread over vast plains covered with dyked fields. Such conditions of water distribution are found in the less important and cooler rice regions mentioned above and in the minor rice areas of the far south like Natal and southern Brazil, as well as in Egypt and along the lower Mississippi. As population increases, rice tends to replace other crops wherever possible, because it will support more people. Many tropical floodplains, especially river deltas, may perhaps become great rice regions when they have a larger population or their people acquire greater industry and intelligence. Borneo, New Guinea, central Africa, and the basins of the great rivers of South America contain large areas of this sort, but the water-logged soil in many such regions presents great difficulties.

There are two main types of rice—the wetland, called sawah or paddy, and the upland, mountain or dry kind. Probably 75 per cent of the world's rice is the wetland type. This is generally raised in level, dyked fields where water stands most of the time for months, thus killing most of the weeds. This kind of cultivation usually requires much cheap labor, for the seeds are planted in beds, the young seedlings are set out in the mud by hand, and later the ripe heads of rice are reaped by hand. Nevertheless, rice is also planted and harvested with machines, in much the same manner as other small grains, as happens in Louisiana and Texas. Mountain rice is planted in terraces on slopes and is naturally irrigated when the heavy rains form temporary ponds behind the dykes on the terraces. It is grown up to an altitude of 8,000 feet in the Himalayas, but important production of wet rice is generally limited to elevations of 3,000 or 4,000 feet.

Relative to its great production, rice does not enter largely into the commerce of the world. In some of the chief producing countries, such as the main part of British India and the Philippine Islands, the dense population demands so much food that there is little surplus, and China, Japan, and British Malaya are actually notable importers of rice. The chief exporting areas, Burma, Siam, and Indo-China, raise their rice in the deltas of three great rivers—the Irrawaddy with Rangoon as its port, the Menam with Bangkok, and the Mekong with Saigon.

Rice and Human Progress.—It is commonly believed that rice-growing, in the tropics at least, is associated with wretched economic conditions and that it is carried on by people who are scarcely more

than serfs. It is true that the bulk of the world's rice is grown where
the people are generally poor. But, on the other hand, the production
of rice is not the business of the truly destitute. The rice-grower is apt
to be his own master and in this respect is superior to the laborer on a
plantation. The investment in rice lands and the immobility of this
investment tend to bind the people to the soil and prevent their migration. Such people tend to be peaceable and conservative. We have
already seen that they have to adjust their needs for water to those of
their neighbors very carefully. Moreover, they have to take the utmost
care in keeping the dykes of their little fields in constant repair and in
watching to see that the rice is neither unduly flooded nor too dry.

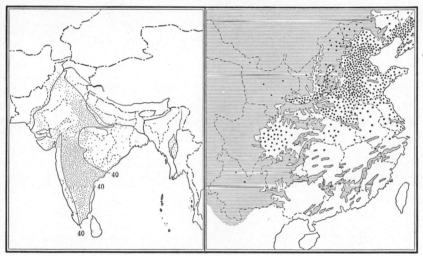

From *Asia* by J. L. Stamp.

A—Millet in India and China.

Thus rice culture by the paddy system of southeastern Asia not only
often underlies and explains great density of population, but has also
helped greatly in developing the peaceful, conservative civilizations of
India, Java, southern China, and other neighboring regions, and in
making the people the most industrious of those in tropical climes.

Millet and Sorghum.—Millet is poor food, but can be grown where drought and
heat ruin other grains. Hence it is of major importance in the drier parts of India,
in northern China, southern Manchuria, and in a strip across Africa south of the
Sahara (A341). It is especially important in the parts of the Wet and Dry Low
Latitudes and of the Asiatic Monsoon Regions which are low enough to have very
high summer temperatures and where the rainfall is less than 40 inches. It can be
grown without irrigation even where the rainfall is as low as 20 inches, for when once
sprouted it grows very rapidly and can stand dry weather. In India it is notably
important in the Deccan plateau, but tends to disappear where the rainfall exceeds

40 inches.   It occupies about 65,000,000 acres of land in India, or more than twice as much as wheat.   In China under similar conditions of summer rain, but with lower winter temperatures, it is estimated to occupy 35,000,000 acres, or almost as much as wheat.   Near the houses in both regions little enclosures are often fenced with the stalks of the larger millets which are like corn stalks.   The name millet is used rather

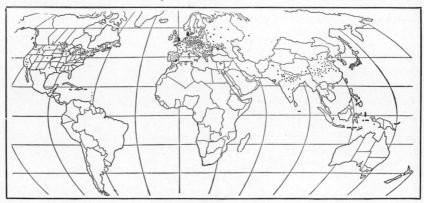

A—World Map of Barley.

carelessly and may embrace a considerable number of grains, especially of the sorghum family.   The millets produced in the United States are used mostly for forage and hence are not classed as cereals.   They are grown largely near the eastern edge of the Dry Plains.

Barley, the Cereal of Great Range.—In very ancient times, barley was in many

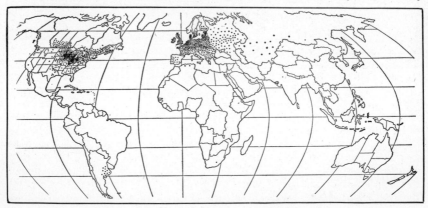

B—World Production of Oats.

places the chief source of bread.   This may have been partly because its yield per acre in the drier kind of Mediterranean area like Morocco is greater than that of wheat.   Moreover, it thrives in a wide range of climates and soils.   It does best where wheat flourishes, but it matures more quickly and hence is better able to withstand low temperatures and dryness.   (See Chapter II, page 28.)   Thus it is raised at a height of 14,000 feet in the Himalayas, north of 70° in Norway, and almost within the desert in North Africa. It is used as bread, though not so much as formerly; as feed for animals; and especially as a source of malt from which beer is obtained by fermentation and whiskey by distillation.

B342 shows that, in its wide distribution in practically all countries outside the tropics, barley is like wheat except that its range is a little wider and very little is grown in the southern hemisphere. The chief producers are Russia, the United States, Germany, Canada, Rumania, Spain, Japan, Poland, and Czechoslovakia. Formerly Russia exported enormous amounts, and Germany and the United Kingdom were great importers. In later years the United States, Canada, Rumania, and North Africa have shared in the export trade and the United Kingdom has surpassed Germany in importation.

Distribution of Oats.—The distribution of oats is (B342) much like that of horses (A410). In a few northern countries, like Scotland, where other grains do not thrive, oats form a significant article of human food. Elsewhere, although

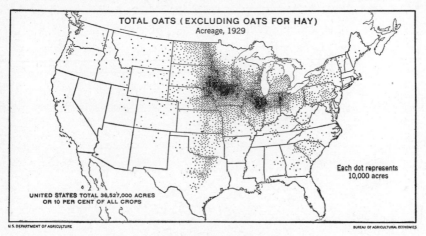

A—Oats in the United States.

used as oatmeal porridge and oat cakes, they constitute only a small percentage of the diet. This is partly because their bulk and poor keeping quality make it hard to ship them, thus keeping them out of foreign trade. Yet, in their relative proportions of carbohydrates and protein, oats are the best of all grains. They are such good feed for cattle and especially horses that the crop is sometimes the world's greatest when measured in bushels, but in weight it does not rank so high.

Oats are especially adapted to cool, moist climates and do not thrive where the climate is warm. Hence the great centers of production are in northwestern Europe, where the summers are a little cooler than the optimum for wheat and more humid than the optimum for rye, and in the northeastern United States and southern Canada, where the climate is similar except that the summers are warmer and the winters much colder (B342). In this latter area the heaviest production is found in the Middle West, where the summers are considerably warmer than the optimum for oats. This affords still another illutration of the effect of economic factors on crop distribution. Here horses are still very numerous, in spite of the automobile, and hence the demand for oats is great, although less than formerly. In proportion to their size, Denmark, Belgium, and the Netherlands are great producers of oats because their climatic conditions are almost ideal for this crop, which is utilized in the dairy industry.

Rye and the Soil of Europe.—People who live in wheat-eating countries, like the United States, do not realize the importance of rye as a staple food among the peasants of large parts of northern Europe (A344). In the United States some rye is produced in North Dakota and neighboring states, but production declined when the use of the crop for liquors as well as stock feed fell off. Central Europe illustrates the fact that rye is the cereal of poor soils in cool regions. A344 shows what enormous quantities of rye are raised in Europe, where over 95 per cent of the world's total crop is produced. The cool summer climate is in part the reason for this concentration of effort on rye rather than other cereals. But A28, B342, and A342 show that

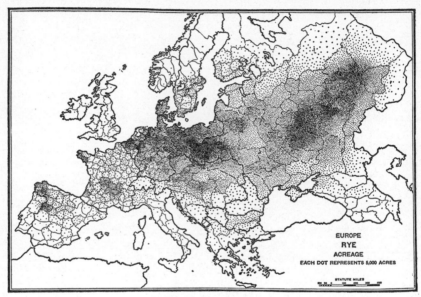

EUROPE
RYE
ACREAGE
EACH DOT REPRESENTS 5,000 ACRES

STATUTE MILES

A—Rye in Europe.

wheat, oats, and barley are all raised in large quantities in parts of Europe having climates fully as cool and unfavorable as those where much of the rye is raised. The fact is that, in the parts of Europe where rye is chiefly cultivated, the soil, as C. F. Marbut of the United States Bureau of Soils puts it, is mainly light in color, low in organic matter and lime, and low to medium in potash and phosphorus. It also has a poor structure or speedily develops such a structure so that it soon loses its organic matter. Its light color causes it to fail to utilize the full force of the sun's rays in storing up heat. A country with such soils may indeed produce large yields of wheat. Germany, for example, averages 27 or more bushels per acre, but that is because the climate is very favorable and only the better land is devoted to wheat. This does not mean that this wheat land is good compared with the black earths of Russia and Dakota, but merely that it is better than most of the German soil. As a rule the soil is so poor that Germany gives to wheat only about the same area as to barley, which is less than half as much as to oats, and a third as much as to rye. The people of Germany, Poland, and much of Russia, aside from the southeast, eat rye bread mainly because the soil beneath their feet is poor.

Buckwheat.—Although classed with the cereals, buckwheat is really an ally of some of the weeds. It is another crop that is often sown on poor soils in cool climates. The name, meaning beech wheat, is appropriate because the little triangular fruits (the so-called seeds) are shaped like beechnuts. The chief uses are for buckwheat cakes in the United States and Canada, as food for poultry, especially pheasants, in England, and as a source of honey for bees; grown on the poorer soils of Russia, it is used also for human food.

The Pulses.—In southeastern Asia from India to Manchuria the pulses assume great importance as part of man's diet. This is mainly because meat is scarce there and the pulses supply a high percentage of protein. They are plants like peas and beans, which bear seeds in pods. The most tropical of the pulses is the *chick-pea* or *gram*. In India it occupies two-thirds as much space as wheat and one-fourth as much as rice, and is eaten roasted or ground to flour. In Turkey it is often boiled, coated with sugar, and sold like peanuts. In southern Europe it is used mainly as an ingredient of soups. The *lentil*, another pulse, has served as human food ever since the Bronze Age. It probably formed the pottage for which Esau sold his birthright. The lentil is a small plant, 6 to 18 inches in height, having a very small pod with two seeds. The *soy bean*, a native of southeastern Asia, has been cultivated since prehistoric times in China and Japan. It is probably the most important legume grown in those countries today. The principal producers are China, Manchuria, Japan, Chosen, and the United States, where the acreage has increased more than fivefold in a decade. Soy beans can be grown in climates suitable for corn and cotton; the plant may be used as hay, pasture, or silage, and the seeds may be made into oil and meal, or prepared in various ways for human food. Manchuria exports two or three million tons of beans each year as well as three or four hundred thousand tons of oil. The oil is good for cooking, and is also used in the preparation of soap and certain kinds of paint. Dry *edible beans* of numerous varieties form a considerable portion of man's diet in many parts of the world. In the United States the production is greatly localized, especially in western New York, Michigan, and California (A346). Dry *peas*, or field peas, in distinction from green peas, cow-peas and chick-peas, grow well only in the colder parts of the temperate zone. In the United States they are important in Wisconsin, Michigan, and the high San Luis Valley of Colorado. In northwestern Europe they are important enough to enter into foreign trade. Other pulses such as *vetches*, *lupines*, the *carob*, and *mesquite* are used mainly as fodder for animals.

Roots and Tubers.—Roots and tubers are heavy products which generally have a high yield per acre. For this reason only a small proportion of the land is usually given to them, and it rarely pays to transport them long distances. Hence they play little part in world trade. In the tropics many people rely on one or another of four root crops—sweet potatoes, cassava, yams, and taro. The *cassava*, or manioc, a widely spread native of South America, is a shrubby plant 5 to 8 feet high with roots which swell out into large tubers. These contain abundant starch, which can be converted into mandioca flour for bread, as well as into tapioca and other products. Cassava is a chief food product of Brazil and a staple food in many other parts of Latin America, tropical Africa, and the East Indies. Brazil and neighboring areas export large amounts of mandioca meal, but the bulk of the tapioca comes from the East Indies.

The *sweet potato* was found among the Indian crops when Brazil was first visited by Europeans.   It was soon carried to Spain and introduced into Europe long before the white potato.   It is now cultivated in practically all the warmer parts of the earth, and is popular as a rotation crop in various rice-growing areas.   It supplies considerably more calories of heat energy than does the white potato, and in some countries is recommended as a promising source of alcohol (35 gallons per ton). Sweet potatoes are often sliced and dried for future use, and many millions of bushels grown on the sandy soils of the southeastern United States are canned.   In southern China a purplish kind with pale flesh is often finely shredded and dried for winter use.   It is called "poor man's rice" because it is not only cheap but insipid and unappetizing, as the Chinese cook it.

The *yam* rivals cassava and the sweet potato as a tropical standby.   Like the sweet potato, with which it is often confused, the yam is more nutritious than the common potato.   It appears to withstand droughts better than do other tropical

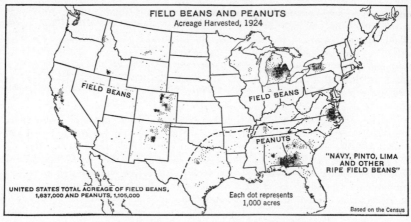

A—Beans and Peanuts in the United States.

root crops.   The *taro*, of China, Malaysia, and smaller islands of the Pacific, was long the principal food of the natives of Polynesia, and was commonly eaten with breadfruit.   In some parts of the West Indies a variety of taro is known as dasheen. Less widely distributed, but still of importance, is the *arrowroot*, from which is made a white, tasteless, odorless, powdery starch that is used for children and invalids.   It is prepared from the small tubers or rhizomes of a reed-like plant generally under 3 feet in height.   St. Vincent, in the West Indies, is the chief source of the prepared product, which averages about 5,000,000 pounds annually.

Passing now to cooler latitudes we come to several bulbs containing the strong flavor and nerve-stimulating substance known as allyl sulphide.   The best known of these, the *onion*, *leek*, and *garlic*, are grown in subtropical areas and often well into the cooler regions.   Bermuda and Teneriffe produce onions for the early market in the United States.   Our commercial crop centers in southeastern Texas, northern Illinois, Indiana and Ohio, California, New York, Colorado, and the Connecticut Valley of Massachusetts.   Onions are also important in Europe, Holland being an important exporter.   The leek is more tolerant of temperature than the onion and can be raised over wider areas, but in this country there is small demand for it.

Leeks are important in many countries of Europe, particularly in Wales, but cannot be stored or transported as easily as onions and hence are not generally so popular. Garlic, with its much stronger odor, is in less favor although much used in cookery by many of the people of Mediterranean lands, India, and other warm countries.

In temperate regions, *radishes*, *garden beets*, *carrots*, and *parsnips* are among the most widely grown and typical root crops. They do not thrive in tropical regions, partly because some species, at least, need considerably more than twelve hours of sunshine to induce flowering and seed production. Radishes reach their greatest use in Japan, where a long white variety sometimes as big as a man's forearm is pickled. Beets, because of their sweetness, have been developed until sugar beets are one of the world's greatest crops. They are treated later under sugars. The carrot was formerly considered fit only for horses, cattle, and the very poor. In Holland, according to an old custom, a guest who had outstayed his welcome was served with carrots as a hint that supplies were getting low. Today carrots are so highly esteemed that in the raw state they are recommended as promoters of proper nutrition and good complexions. Radishes, beets, and carrots all have the best flavor when young. They also stand transportation easily. Hence they find a place among the early vegetables raised in the South and in California. A thousand or fifteen hundred carloads of young carrots are sometimes shipped out of Texas in a year, and still more from California. One year the Netherlands actually sent us almost five million pounds of carrots. Parsnips are peculiar in that they do not develop their best flavor until frozen. The *Jerusalem artichoke*, an insipid little tuber, is a plant just good enough to be cultivated a little, but is not of much value.

Turnips and Rutabagas (Swedish turnips) are other root crops that fill an important place in many kitchen gardens of cooler regions, and are also grown as forage crops. *Mangels* are a similar kind of root grown almost entirely as forage for cattle. The use of all three of these root crops is largely concentrated in northwestern Europe, and to a less extent in the northern United States and Canada.

Economic and Social Significance of Potatoes.—The *white or Irish potato*, or *the* potato, as the people of the United States and Europe commonly call it, belongs to cooler latitudes than any of the roots thus far discussed. Because of its nutritive qualities and huge yield per acre, it is by far the most important of the so-called vegetables. A pound of potatoes, to be sure, supplies scarcely 300 calories of heat in contrast to 1,000 or even 1,200 for wheat after deductions have been made for the bran, oily kernels, and coarser grades of flour that are mainly fed to animals. But even in France, which in parts is quite warm for potatoes, an average acre yields about 6 times as many bushels of potatoes as of wheat; the corresponding figure stands at 7 in Germany, England, and the United States, and rises to 10 or 11 in Norway, Lithuania, Poland, and Canada. Potatoes may not be such good food as wheat, but they provide two or three times as many calories per acre.

Another important quality of potatoes is that the ordinary variety, being derived from the constantly cool, moist highlands of the Andes, thrives best in climates too cool for corn and too moist for the most profitable wheat culture. It also does well in rather poor soils, provided they are light and friable. The combination of such soil with cool, moist summers accounts for the fact that the potato, although Ameri-

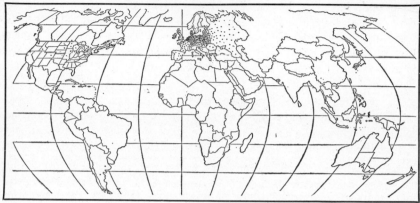

A—World Production of Potatoes.

can in origin, is now mainly produced in Europe, which raises about 90 per cent of the world's crop, as appears in A348 and the following table:

APPROXIMATE PRODUCTION OF CHIEF CROPS BY CONTINENTS IN MILLIONS OF POUNDS

	North America	Europe	Asia *	South America	Africa	Australia
Rough rice........	2,100	2,200	280,000	2,400	5,300	65
Wheat..........	78,000	120,000	70,000	17,000	7,000	9,000
Corn............	158,000	39,000	11,000	26,000	10,800	520
Oats............	92,000	92,000	5,300	2,500	540	680
Rye.............	3,300	96,000	?	380	45	4
Barley..........	19,000	46,000	21,000	1,700	5,000	340
Potatoes.........	29,000	360,000	17,000	4,000	4,800	1,100

* Including rough estimates for China.

The introduction of potatoes has been an important factor in permitting Europe to have such a dense population. In Germany the importance of potatoes is even greater than in Europe as a whole.

Potatoes would doubtless be raised far more widely, were it not that (1) they are especially likely to be spoiled by prolonged rain; (2) they suffer badly from disease and insects in some areas; (3) they do not keep well in comparison with grains; and (4) their weight and bulk make transportation costly. Wherever the climate is right, however, they are widely distributed. Except in the South and in the drier parts of the West, scarcely a farmer in the United States fails to raise a few for his own use.

Potatoes, Famines, Migration, and Prosperity.—Ireland once suffered terribly because the farmers relied too much on potatoes. A century or more ago, Ireland was in trouble because much of its land was held in large estates by absentee landlords who lived in the cities or in England. At the same time the population was increasing rapidly and the peasants' land holdings were decreasing in average size. Consequently the peasants more and more substituted potatoes for wheat and other crops, as is natural, where many people must be supported on a small area in such a climate. This was favored by a series of relatively dry, warm summers which gave this moist, cool island a long succession of abundant potato crops. Thus in 1845 Ireland was supporting 8,300,-000 inhabitants, which is twice as many as now. Then a series of wet, cool summers ruined one potato crop after another. Famine ensued. Two or three hundred thousand people died of starvation and fever, even though the British government provided work for 200,000 people at one time, and supplied food to over 3,000,000. Another result was a very rapid migration, mainly to America. This, together with the deaths, reduced the population to 6,600,000 in 1850. In the 'eighties of the last century, bad crops again produced similar conditions on a milder scale. This illustrates the dangers of one-crop agriculture. If the Irish had been raising a wide diversity of crops, it is not probable that all would have failed at the same time. But unfortunately Ireland is a *marginal* land, with such cool, moist summers that potatoes are one of the few crops that grow well. A similar reliance on wheat is one of the great dangers of North Dakota, Saskatchewan, and their neighbors. The reason is the same, namely, that few other crops grow well. The southern states also suffer similarly from too great reliance on cotton.

The commercial production of potatoes in the United States is greatly concentrated, as shown in A350. This is due in large measure to the location of the crop where it can take advantage of cool summers, friable limey soils, and markets. The advantages of climate and soil prevail over those of good markets in cases like Idaho, central Wisconsin, and especially Aroostook County in northeastern Maine. In Maine there is an astonishing contrast between the scrubby forests, and widely scattered, poor little farms on the thin, sandy soil of the upper Penobscot region north of Bangor and the gently rolling, richly cultivated great farms on the limey loam of Aroostook. There almost every farm has a big hay barn, a large, half-buried potato storehouse, a

comfortable dwelling house, and in many cases a silo, and all the buildings are well painted. This illustrates still another phase of one-crop
farming. The Aroostook farmers do not generally suffer so much
because their potato crop fails as because potatoes are sometimes so
abundant elsewhere that the price is too low to pay for carrying them
to the distant markets. Then the farmers may get almost nothing for
their crop, and have to rely on their cattle. Nevertheless, they profit
so much from years of good prices and from selling seed potatoes that
they can tide over the bad years and have a high degree of prosperity.
Thus one-crop farming may bring more wealth than any other kind, as

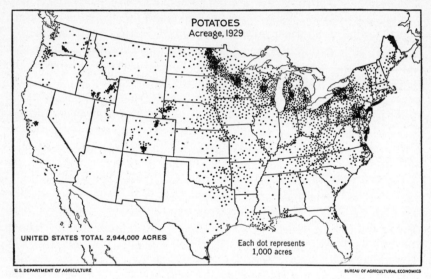

A—Potatoes in the United States.

happens here and among the Dakota wheat farmers, but it is almost
always accompanied by great dangers. In Germany, where the largest
of all potato crops is raised, the price does not fluctuate so widely as in
the United States. This is partly because the Marine Cyclonic climate
is not so variable as ours, and partly because potatoes there have a
wider range of uses than with us, including stock feed, flour, alcohol,
and starch. Hence when potatoes are scarce the amount fed to stock,
for example, can be reduced without greatly changing the price.

Although the potato is native to South America, the production is
unimportant in the southern hemisphere. The temperate areas there
are sparsely populated, and in the tropical highlands there is little arable
land and only a few million people. Hence the total production is
small, although on some of the plateaus potatoes of every shade from

purple and red to pink and yellow form a considerable part of the food of the inhabitants. The potato has never been much improved by selection in the region where it originated. In fact, most of the Indians, who are the chief potato raisers, eat the big ones, and keep the little ones to plant.

Sugar, the Great Carbohydrate Crop.—Sugar is probably the most widely used of all food products. Vast areas get along without potatoes or rice, and almost without wheat, but except among the lowest savages practically no part of the world is without sugar. Yet sugar, like corn and potatoes, is a comparatively new crop for the world as a whole. The desire of ancient people for sweets was satisfied by fruits and honey. In the Middle Ages, to be sure, the Arabs had learned to make sugar, and the ruins of old sugar mills are found in Palestine. But only within the past three hundred years has sugar become common. During that time its use has increased with great regularity until now it is one of the most important articles of diet in all civilized countries. Nearly all sugar is obtained from the juice of two plants, the *sugar cane*, which is essentially tropical or subtropical, and the *sugar beet*, which is temperate.

Sugar supplies the same human needs as potatoes, and produces even more food per acre. Measured in calories, a pound of sugar is equivalent to nearly 6 pounds of potatoes. In the United States the average yield of beet sugar per acre amounts to about 3,000 pounds and that of potatoes is 7,000. In Europe, aside from Russia, where it is much smaller, the yield of beet sugar is about the same as in the United States, but that of potatoes is about twice as great. Thus in the United States the calories per acre are two and one-half times greater from sugar than from potatoes, and in Europe about 30 per cent greater. The production of sugar per acre from cane is often much greater than from beets. In Hawaii and Java it amounts to nearly 12,000 pounds, or at least four times as many calories as from the correspondingly good potato areas of Belgium and Maine. It falls, however, to about 4,000 in Cuba, 2,300 in India, 1,800 in the Philippines, and only 1,500 in Louisiana, where the temperature is relatively low. But even in Louisiana, sugar gives more than twice as many calories and a higher money value than potatoes. In Hawaii a yield as high as 12 tons of sugar per acre has actually been obtained. Naturally, then, sugar is the sort of crop which receives the utmost attention, is planted on the land best adapted to it, and is given the greatest political protection. In one of its two main forms it is raised in most of the well inhabited countries (A352).

Sugar Cane.—The greatest source of sugar is a perennial grass much like corn in appearance, with stalks generally 1 or 2 inches in diameter and 8 to 12 feet high. Although sugar cane is raised in minor subtropical areas like Louisiana, southern Spain, and southern China, it is essentially tropical. The plant does best in a hot, moist climate with some periods of dry weather. These periods of dry weather during the ripening of the cane greatly increase its sugar content; in wet weather the sap is watery. With the exception of the irrigated areas the great producing regions have high atmospheric humidity, an annual rainfall of over 40 inches, entire freedom from frost, and a temperature of at least 80° during the warmest month. The cane will grow

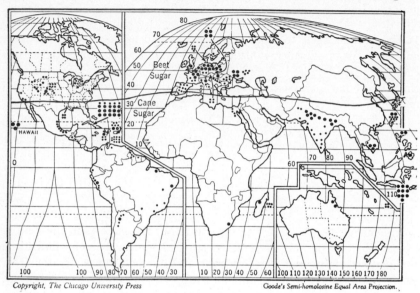

Goode's Semi-homolosine Equal Area Projection.

A—World Production of Sugar. Each large dot indicates 1 per cent of the world production, each small dot one-tenth of 1 per cent.

upon a great variety of soils, but is most productive on the rich and comparatively young soils of the rather low, level lands near the sea. The leading producers are Cuba, British India, Java, Hawaii, Formosa, the Philippines, Puerto Rico, and Australia (A352). The chief exporters are Cuba and Java. The most important importers are the United States and the United Kingdom. Today more than two-fifths of the world's cane sugar is produced in the western hemisphere, and about one-third in the Caribbean area alone (A352). Although India is one of the greatest producers of cane sugar, it is also the third greatest importer, ranking after Great Britain and above Japan.

In the most favorable tropical lands, as we have seen, sugar cane is so profitable that it often replaces cereals like rice in Java and corn in

Cuba, especially on the level, well watered lands near the seacoast. In Java the danger of reducing the supply of staple foods through the exportation of sugar is so great that the government does not allow more than a third of the land in any given area to be devoted to sugar. Nevertheless, Java has to import rice. In Cuba so much of the good corn land is given up to sugar that the island imports more foodstuffs per capita than almost any other country. Sugar is the one basic food-stuff, as distinguished from luxuries like tea and coffee, that is exported in huge quantities from tropical to non-tropical lands.

On the mainland of the United States sugar cane can be profitably grown on only a small area. Production is confined chiefly to the lower delta of the Mississippi River in Louisiana. Here winter frosts often damage the stubble, and the best yields are obtained only by the expensive process of planting annually or biennially. It is doubtful whether much cane would be raised here were it not for a political factor in the form of a high tariff on foreign sugar. Cuba pays a lower rate than other countries, but enough to keep the Louisiana industry and the American beet-sugar industry alive. Nevertheless, Louisiana suffers in competition with Puerto Rico, Hawaii, and the Philippines, which send large amounts of sugar to the United States free of duty. These other regions would also suffer if they were not possessions of the United States and thus provided with a favored market.

The Sugar Plantations of Cuba.—The sugar industry in Cuba illustrates not only the general principles of plantation agriculture, but the dangers of one-crop agriculture and of political uncertainty. This one relatively small producer of sugar cane supplies one-sixth or even one-fifth of all the world's sugar, including both beet and cane. This means the development of enormous plantations and an immense investment of capital. Excepting some of the smaller Caribbean islands, no other area is so largely given over to sugar production as is Cuba. The prosperity and political stability of this island republic, as well as the well-being of its people, are bound up in this one crop.

The laborers who work on the sugar plantations rarely raise more than a small fraction of their own food, nor do other farmers in Cuba raise a surplus sufficient to feed them. Hence, Cuba imports large quantities of food in exchange for her sugar. Each year, as a rule, Cuba sends to the United States sugar worth $80 or even $100 per Cuban inhabitant. At least a third of this, and often more, goes to paying for food, which many people believe the Cubans themselves might easily raise. Because Cuba is so dependent on imports, she is vitally interested not only in the price of corn, wheat, and pork in the United States, but in the success of the Newfoundland fisheries, which supply the Cuban tables, especially on Fridays, and in the troubles of the Texan and Mexican oil fields whence comes fuel for her tractors, and in the strikes of the Pittsburgh district whence comes heavy machinery for the centrals, or sugar factories, and rails for the tramways that ramify widely in the cane fields. She is still more vitally interested in the recent revival of the sugar-beet industry in Europe, and in changes in the American tariff.

Variations in the price of sugar from year to year have a great effect on Cuba. During the World War, competition from the beet sugar of Europe and from the sugar regions of Asia was largely cut off. This caused a period of high prices in Cuba, with resultant prosperity and great expansion of the industry. Money was spent lavishly; many fine houses were built, and others were started only to be left uncompleted when the inevitable slump arrived. Then beet sugar came back into the market, other areas like Java became serious competitors, and the United States tariff was raised. The people of Cuba suddenly found that from a standard of living that was very high for tropical people they were thrown down to a condition of poverty and misery. Political discontent broke out, and there were signs of rebellion. Such conditions are apt to be found in areas which depend too largely upon a single crop. If only a quarter, instead of five-sixths, of Cuba's exports consisted of sugar, that island would be much happier. Nevertheless, if the demand for sugar should continue to increase, as it has in the past, Cuba is likely to continue to raise sugar, for few places are better adapted to this crop not only in climate but also in location near a huge market.

The Consumption of Sugar.—The following table gives samples of some of the greatest and some of the smallest consumers of sugar per capita.

Country	Pounds per capita per annum
Australia	128
Hawaii	121
Denmark	112
United States	112
Cuba	97
Great Britain	92
Canada	90
Switzerland	86
Italy	20
Egypt	18
U. S. S. R.	18
Haiti and Santo Domingo	9
China	6

These wide fluctuations depend mainly on economic conditions, but also in part on local customs and the abundance of local supplies of sugar. Consumption is high in all the countries which fall within the heavily shaded portions of our maps of climatic energy, manufacturing, and use of automobiles (A119, A489, A134). It is also high in places like Hawaii and Cuba where much sugar is produced and the people are generally fairly prosperous, at least for their latitude. It is low in countries like Italy and Russia which produce little or no sugar and cannot afford to import much. It is also low in Egypt, Haiti, and Santo Domingo, where people cannot afford it even though much sugar is produced locally. Southern China, where sugar cane is raised, is similar, but northern China, together with India, contains tens of millions of people to whom sugar is a rare luxury.

Sugar Beets.—Out of the thirty million or more tons of sugar produced in the world each year, beet sugar forms about one-third. In 1913, government subsidies of various kinds in Europe had raised beet sugar to over 45 per cent of the total, but the World War reduced this to only 20. Since 1920 there has been an increase to somewhat more that the pre-war amount, but as cane sugar has increased by ten million tons, nearly doubling itself since 1913, the beet percentage is much below its old level.

The sugar beet, as we have seen, is a temperate crop grown under conditions very different from those of cane. It requires deep, fertile, well-drained, loamy soils with a fair proportion of lime. Since the crop is an exhausting one, fertilization is generally required annually. The climatic requirements are also rather restrictive. The young plants are sensitive to frost, but the best growth seems to require temperatures of 60° F. to 73° F. for about three months of the summer. Thus far, large-scale production of the sugar beet has been restricted to Europe and the United States (A352). In addition to favorable soil and climate a plentiful supply of labor is needed. Climatic conditions are such that white labor may be used, but only under certain limited economic conditions can such labor be obtained cheaply enough. In some European areas like the central parts of France, Germany, Czechoslovakia, Poland, and western Russia, farm labor is cheap enough for this. Elsewhere, especially in the United States, Great Britain, and the low countries, good beet areas are located near industrial centers and members of the family not engaged in manufacturing may be employed in the careful weeding and thinning required when the beet plants are small. In the United States the difficulty of getting suitable labor is serious, and the growers often resort to the employment of whole families on the contract system.

Even under the best of natural and economic conditions the sugar beet finds it difficult to compete with sugar cane, which has the advantage of easier culture and richer yield per acre, although giving only half as much per ton of raw material. Sugar cane has the further advantage that it is grown in tropical and subtropical areas where labor is very cheap. The disadvantages of sugar beets are partly offset by other factors. Sugar beets are grown where the population is dense, which gives a local market. Here also sources of fertilizer are more abundant. Capital is more readily obtained and good machinery can easily be used. Furthermore, the refuse material and by-products have greater value.

In spite of these favorable factors, the sugar-beet areas would probably be very limited if it were not for artificial and largely political conditions. Many nations of the temperate zone feel that there is danger in depending on the tropics for their sugar supply. They also desire to encourage a variety of useful occupations at home. Hence they have encouraged the growth of sugar beets by subsidies or bounties and protective tariffs. Another kind of interference with the natural or purely geographical distribution of sugar production is typical of a strong modern tendency. After the World War, as we have seen, the resultant high prices stimulated not only the revival of the beet-sugar industry but a great expansion of the tropical sugar industry. Hence prices fell very low. Accordingly, after long deliberation the three main exporting groups outside the United States, namely, Cuba, Java, and the European beet producers, accepted a scheme of cooperation in order to control the world market and raise prices. Although heralded as the first step in world cooperation the plan has not fulfilled expectation.

Minor Sugar Plants.—In addition to cane and beets, a vast number of plants carry sugar in their sap and a few of these are used locally. O. W. Barrett estimates that one billion pounds of sugar are made annually from various types of *palm trees*. At first thought this seems a staggering amount, but compared with 60 billion pounds of cane and beet sugar, it is small. Some authorities estimate that if all the palm trees were properly tapped, they would yield more sugar than is now produced from all sources. In some areas, especially the southern United States from Oklahoma eastward, a big species of *sorghum* with stalks like corn is grown for sugar or more often for syrup. In Vermont, New York, Ohio, and neighboring parts of the northeastern United States and southern Canada considerable sugar is obtained by tapping the trunk of various kinds of maples, especially the *sugar maple*. Because of the marvelous flavor, both maple sugar and maple syrup bring a high price. Unfortunately the supply is diminishing with the ever-lessening number of trees. The total industry amounts to only five or six million dollars in normal years.

EXERCISES

1. Compare the rice map (A339) with the maps of seasonal rainfall (A50), temperature (A30–31), climatic energy (A119), automobiles (A134), seaports (A591), foreign trade (A597), population (A230), and education (A136), and write a statement as to the relation of rice to climate, prosperity, and progress.

2. Discuss the relation of the soil to the raising of cereals, basing your work not only on this chapter but also on preceding parts of this book, on Plate II, and on any other maps that you find in your atlas. Show which cereals can stand poor soils, which ones usually get the best soils, and why.

3. On the basis of the data given in this chapter and near the end of Chapter XV, together with some reasonable estimates as to the cost of transportation, prepare a statement showing why you think that certain changes in the sugar industry would occur if free trade prevailed everywhere, and there were no political interference. Take account not only of agricultural and industrial results, but of commercial and social results as well.

4. In this chapter and elsewhere, especially in Chapters XI, XV, and XVIII (see Index), search for data as to one-crop agriculture. Make a list of crops and regions where it prevails, and discuss its dangers and advantages.

5. Discuss the political relations of sugar and explain why they are so important. Find out about the tariff regulations as to sugar in the United States and elsewhere. What connection is there between sugar and our political relations with Hawaii, Puerto Rico, the Philippines, and Cuba? What other nations get their sugar largely from their colonies? Do they produce much sugar at home? How do such conditions influence the attitude of Germany toward the League of Nations?

6. From this chapter and others, especially Chapters II, IV, VI, XVI, and XIX (see Index), make a list of crops and animals in which there is a distinct superiority on the coldward margin. Discuss the causes and significance of this and its relation to commerce.

7. Contrast the labor requirements and the available types of labor in the sugar-cane and sugar-beet industries.

8. Would you expect people on a wheat diet or on a potato diet to make more progress? Why? Can you name any nations that tend to prove or disprove your belief?

CHAPTER XVII

GREEN VEGETABLES, FRUITS, AND NUTS

Green Garden Vegetables and Garden Fruits.—The use of green vegetables and of the fruits commonly grown in gardens is widespread, but less important than is generally supposed. In some slight form it is almost universal wherever agriculture is practiced. Yet India, Russia, and other countries contain hundreds of millions of peasants who rarely use these products. In the Mediterranean lands of Turkey, Greece, Spain, and North Africa almost as unfavorable conditions prevail. The Japanese suffer seriously because their diet contains so much rice and so small a percentage of these vitamin foods. Similar conditions are found elsewhere. In Buenos Aires or Rio de Janeiro the city markets are well supplied with vegetables, but the peons on the farms rarely use them. Even in China, among the "farmers of Forty Centuries" as King calls them, where many authors rightly expatiate on the abundance and variety of vegetables and where the city markets are full of them, the ordinary peasants use them sparingly. They have to, because they need their small bits of land for crops which produce a greater number of calories of heat. On the 2,900 farms studied there by J. L. Buck, 3 per cent of the land devoted to raising human food is indeed given to green beans, but less than 1 per cent goes to other green vegetables and fruits. In the United States, when only the human food of the country itself is considered, disregarding animals and exports, 6 per cent of the land is devoted to green vegetables and garden fruits. In California and New York the percentage rises to 10. In Europe the corresponding figure falls to less than 1 per cent in Poland and Finland. It increases to about 2 in Germany and Belgium, 3 in France, 4 in Italy and Great Britain, and reaches a maximum of 10 or more in Holland. The really abundant use of fresh vegetables is restricted to two main centers, the United States and western and central Europe with northern Italy, while the Sino-Japanese area holds an intermediate position. Elsewhere, vegetables are common only in the cities and among the more prosperous and intelligent people. In other words, the free use of fresh vegetables is one of the luxuries which highly advanced and prosperous people enjoy because they have so much surplus energy and wealth, or

357

else it is the result of high industry among poor people like the Chinese and Japanese whose climate permits them to raise green vegetables after or with the more important crops that supply the body with heat and energy.

Growth of Truck Farming.—In the United States, western Europe, and the other progressive parts of the earth the use of fresh vegetables has greatly increased in recent decades. This is illustrated by the following figures showing the increase in acreage of certain commercially grown crops in the United States between 1918 and 1929 before the great depression which diminished people's buying power.

| | Acreage | |
Crop	1919	1929
Asparagus	30,000	99,000
Beans (snap or string)	72,000	134,000
Cauliflower	7,000	25,000
Lettuce	22,000	141,000
Peas (for fresh use)	6,000	67,000
Spinach	10,000	73,000
Strawberries	119,000	199,000

The increase thus shown is due to a combination of economic and social reasons. One of the economic reasons is the rising price of meat and milk. Therefore, people resort to vegetables rather than increase their consumption of starchy grains and tubers. Another economic reason is the immense improvement in methods of canning, preserving, and drying. A third is the development of cold-storage methods which not only allow fresh vegetables and fruits to be preserved a long time and transported without spoiling, but preserve the vitamins and flavor to a surprising degree. Still another is the great improvement not only in refrigerator cars, but also in trucks and roads. Freshness is so important a quality in vegetables that it pays to send them directly from farm to market in trucks not only locally, but even over considerable distances. It is estimated that within 100 or 150 miles of New York City at least half of the shipments of fresh vegetables to the city's wholesale and jobbing markets are carried by motor trucks.

The main social reason for the growth in the use of fresh garden vegetables and fruits is the increasing recognition of their importance as sources of the vitamins which are so essential to health. Millions of intelligent people have learned that it pays to have these in their food at all seasons. Another social factor is the rise in the standard of living and the consequent change in the variety and attractiveness of the fresh foodstuffs in the consumer's market basket. Still other factors are increased realization by farmers that it pays to satisfy the consumer's more expensive needs; continued improvement in grading, packing, and handling; better local distribution of fresh foods through chain stores; and more general and attractive displays of vegetables and fruits in stores.   This combination of economic and social conditions has greatly stimulated the growth of communities whose main business is to furnish fruit and garden produce to city markets.   Such farming is called market gardening when carried on close to the cities, and truck farming when carried on farther away, and hence less intensively.

Localization of Truck Farming.—Fresh vegetables yield much food and a high value per acre; they are bulky; they deteriorate rapidly; and they require relatively large amounts of labor.   For these reasons they tend to be raised on the land best adapted to them, and as near the centers of population as possible.   Hence, they tend to displace the cereals, potatoes, and even dairy farms.   The land best adapted to vegetables is not necessarily the same as that best adapted to field crops.   Thus the warm, light, sandy soil of Long Island, and lower Florida, though not good for wheat or corn, is good for crops whose high value warrants intensive cultivation and large expenditures for fertilizers.   Again, the optimum climate for vegetables, so far as the truck gardener is concerned, may not be the optimum in the ordinary sense, but the one that enables him to get his crop to the market at the most profitable season.   The desirability of planting vegetables as near the centers of population as possible is due to the advisability of having the gardens near a supply of labor, as well as near the market.   These two conditions, together with the high value of the crops per acre, are the main reasons why the farmer puts his vegetable garden on the best bit of land he can find, and yet as near the house as possible.   They are also the reasons why the densest shading in B360 clusters around the main cities and in California and along the Atlantic Coast from New York southward.   They also explain why the cultivation of vegetables for the winter market has increased with great rapidity in Florida, where the acreage of vegetables was 6 times as great in 1929 as in 1899, and in California, where the corresponding figure is nearly 13.

Modern transportation, refrigeration, and packing facilities have so extended the vegetable-raising areas that in one part or another of the United States fresh products are almost always ready for shipment to distant centers with less favorable climates.   As soon as cold weather drives homegrown green vegetables from the northern markets, those from the South take their places.   This is illustrated in A361, where the shipments of tomatoes in carload lots during a typical year are illustrated.   Similar diagrams might be drawn for almost any vegetable.   The prices

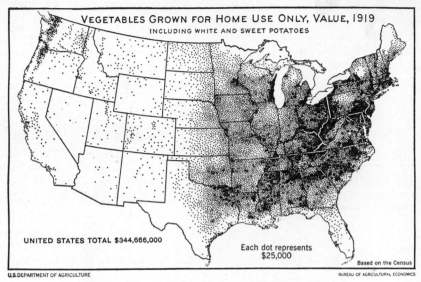

A—Vegetables in Home Gardens in the United States.

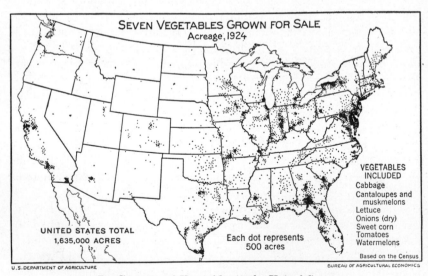

B—Commercial Vegetables in the United States.

of the vegetables vary according to the distance and scarcity of sources of supply. Thus in Chicago the wholesale price of strawberries per quart ranged as follows in a typical season: March 51 cents, April 35, May 27, and June 12.

In Europe similar conditions prevail. London, Paris, Berlin, Rome, Naples, and even Constantinople and Moscow are surrounded by areas devoted largely to vegetables. Much of Holland is a vast vegetable garden. Unusually warm places like the so-called English Riviera on the south coast of Devon and the real Riviera on the southern slope of the Alps in France are full of truck gardens to serve the early market in the great cities. Algeria and Tunis are more and more becoming important sources of winter vegetables for the great manufacturing area surrounding the North Sea. With the march of the seasons the centers of vegetable production swing back and forth from North Africa to Sweden just as they do from Florida and Texas to Canada.

Leaves and Stems.—The most common source of vitamins is leaves and stems. In tropical regions, people often get these from wild products, especially *palm buds* and bamboo shoots; the palm buds, cut from the tree tops, suggest celery, although less stringy and with a different flavor, and are sometimes known as "palm salad," "palm cabbage," or "palmetto." The soft, succulent *bamboo shoots* are often served like asparagus. They are also salted, pickled, or candied, and eaten with rice, especially in Japan and southern China, where they grow as well as in the tropics. If earth is heaped over the

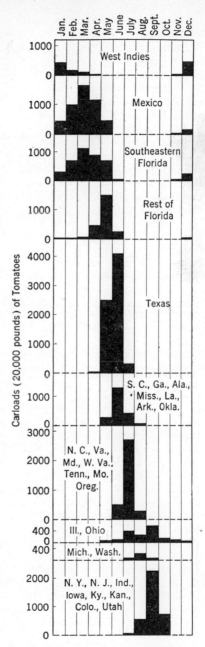

A—Seasonal Changes in the Regions from which Tomatoes are Shipped by Rail or Steamship for Consumption in the United States.

sprouting bamboo roots, the sprouts can be kept soft and white longer than otherwise, just as with asparagus.

Many of the leafy temperate vegetables are grown in the outer tropics and subtropics during the cool season or at an elevation. The quantities are usually small, however, unless the product is to be shipped to early markets in cooler regions. The artichoke, sometimes called the *globe artichoke* to distinguish it from the small and rather tasteless tuber known as the Jerusalem artichoke, is one of the few vegetables which belongs primarily to the Mediterranean Type of climate. The part that is eaten suggests a spineless thistle bud surrounded by a thick head of fleshy leaves.

Although *celery* is grown extensively in Florida and California, it is also a profitable crop in cooler states like Michigan and New York, and is often grown on land from which some early vegetable has been removed. It generally brings a good price but requires much labor and more skill than many other crops. The edible shoots of *asparagus* spring up after the plant has rested during a cool interval. The plant flourishes best in regions which have a decidedly cold season, but half of the production in the United States comes from California, Georgia, and South Carolina and half from northern states, especially New Jersey. *Rhubarb* is also a perennial stock. It develops early stems which are prized for pies and sauce. Because of their valuable vitamins, *Swiss chard* and especially *spinach* have grown rapidly in use, so that spinach is widely grown all over the country, but Texas supplies half the commercial crop. *Parsley* is grown mainly near great cities like Chicago and New York, for its leaves are much used as a garnish and not eaten. *Purslane* illustrates the force of custom in determining people's diet. Its small fleshy leaves are used in Europe, but in the United States it is such an annoying weed that when a New England farmer considers a thing especially bad he calls it "meaner than pusly."

The *cabbage* family, like the onion, bean, and turnip families, illustrates the fact that man uses only a very small percentage of the plants around him, but when he does find a plant group whose individual flavor and odor he likes, he is apt to use a number of different species. Turnips and radishes are closely allied to the cabbage. The cabbage itself is grown in the temperate areas of all continents and invades the subtropics in the cool season. The map of its production shows concentration around cities, for cabbage is difficult to transport but quite tolerant of soils. The large buds of *Brussels sprouts*, which are like tiny cabbages, have a more delicate flavor than cabbage. They are more often grown in Europe than in the United States. *Chinese cabbage*, another relative, is a rapid grower and somewhat more tolerant of heat than is the common cabbage. In China one sees it carried in huge loads on men's backs to the city markets in the fall. The *cauliflower*, which Mark Twain called a "cabbage with a college education," resembles *broccoli* in that the flower is the part that is most edible. Its production is rapidly increasing. It grows mainly in our northern states and in the Mediterranean Type of climate. It is a great favorite in Australia. With these leafy vegetables one may also put *kohlrabi*, which belongs to the closely related mustard family. It stores up food in a round expansion of the stem. On many tables, *lettuce* is used more often than any other vegetable except potatoes. Because of the steady demand all winter, it is one of the most common greenhouse products. *Endive*, more bitter than lettuce, receives more attention in Europe than in the United States. It is more tolerant of both heat and cold.

Garden Fruits and Seed Vessels.—The next group of garden crops to claim our attention consists of those in which the useful part consists of short-lived fruits like the tomato and strawberry, or seed vessels and green seeds like snap (string) beans, peppers, and sweet corn. We begin again with low latitudes. The fruit of the *pineapple*, a native of tropical America, stands upright in the center of a group of leaves with sharp points, and may rise 2 or even 4 feet from the ground. It is usually grown where there are 50 inches or more of rain. Unlike most fruits it does not develop its full flavor when picked green. Hence its transportation offers a difficult problem. The United States is largely supplied from Florida, Hawaii, and the West Indies; Europe is partially supplied from the Azores and Canary Islands. Canned pineapple is more important in international trade than the fresh fruit, Hawaii distributing over 90 per cent of it. One cannery there has the largest output of any fruit cannery in the world.

Another common tropical garden product is the *chayote*, a pear-shaped, one-seeded fruit which tastes like a squash and is similarly used. This perennial creeper is a native of the West Indies. The gourd family with its wide-spreading vines is another of those which supply numerous useful fruits, especially in middle latitudes. The *gourd* itself, with its tough, thin, stiff rind, provides a very valuable substitute for cups, bowls, jars, water pipes, and other utensils all the way from Spain to Japan. Melons are the most familiar edible members of the gourd family. Although the *watermelon* is a native of tropical and southern Africa, it has spread to practically all warm temperate areas. Ancient Egyptian paintings show that this refreshing fruit was known when the pyramids were built. It is now grown widely both in home gardens and commercially in China, India, southern Russia, southern France, Egypt, South Africa, and the southern United States—the leading states being Georgia, Texas, and Florida. The *muskmelon* originated in southern Asia, where it grows spontaneously in India, but is now grown in nearly all tropical and warm temperate areas. The enormous number of varieties indicates how popular it is. In Turkey and Persia each district has its own particular kind, and the expert can tell at a glance, or even by taste and smell, where a melon comes from. In the United States the well-known canteloupe, casaba, and other varieties grow best in the South and above all in the hot Southwest in places like the Imperial Valley. The golden *pumpkin*, first cousin to the melon, was used by the Indians from Central America to New England before the arrival of the white man. In early colonial days, when baked, boiled, or made into luscious pies, it rendered such valuable service that it vies with turkey and cranberry as the most famous Thanksgiving dish. The *squash* is merely a variety of pumpkin and has much the same uses. It is more delicate, however, and more nearly limited to cooler regions, thus illustrating the general law that crops are of better quality near the cooler margin of their habitat. The larger and coarser types of both pumpkin and squash are raised in great quantities as fodder for cattle and pigs, being often planted among the corn. In some countries like Russia roasted pumpkin seeds are a favorite delicacy.

The *cucumber*, another close relative of the melon, probably originated in northern India. Its popularity both as a fresh vegetable and preserved as a "pickle" has caused it to be grown widely throughout the warmer portions of the temperate zone, for it can be grown on any good soil.

Today the *tomato* is one of the most widely used garden products. The Spaniards brought it from South America, and its use both fresh and canned has spread all over the world. In Turkey and other lands with hot, sunny Mediterranean summers, it is often dried on the flat housetops for winter use with rice or parched wheat in the dish known as "pilaf." The leading producers in the United States are Florida, Mississippi, New Jersey, California, and Maryland.

The large, shiny, pendent egg-shaped fruit of the *eggplant* is another tropical vegetable whose center of usefulness has gradually been pushed northward. Originally probably a native of southern Asia, it is now used chiefly in the warmer part of the temperate zone. In the southern United States it is extensively grown as a kitchen-garden vegetable and has considerable value as a market crop.

The kind of *"pepper"* grown in vegetable gardens is the fruit of a species of capsicum. As the term is generally used it applies to two different types, the red pepper which properly belongs among the spices on page 392, and the large sweet pepper which is used as a vegetable. The latter has only recently begun to be used much in the United States. In the past it was imported from Bermuda, the Bahamas, and Cuba, but it is now grown in the South.

In colonial America the pioneers were very fond of green corn either boiled or as "roasting ears." The field variety then used, however, was not nearly so palatable as the *sweet corn* now so popular in the United States either "on the cob" or canned. Sweet corn, like the squash, is an especially palatable variety of a plant which was of tropical origin, but which has been developed by selection and crossing on the coldward margin of the crop's habitat. Thus its distribution is very limited, and it is little used outside the northeastern quarter of the United States. Most Europeans have never seen it, and think our way of putting the whole of a great buttered ear up to our mouths quite barbarous. Since sweet corn is used almost exclusively in the unripe state, crops of very high quality can be grown in regions so cool that the seed does not mature. The commercial production of sweet corn, in distinction from the widespread production in home gardens, is concentrated in a few counties. This is usually the result of proximity to cities, or to the fact that because the crop grows well in these places canneries have been established. The canneries make it possible for a state like Iowa, with no large cities, to be one of the largest producers of sweet corn. Illinois, Maryland, Ohio, New York, Pennsylvania, Indiana, New Jersey, and Minnesota are also important producers. It is notable that Maine and California, though producing little field corn for grain, have a considerable acreage in sweet corn.

Green or snap beans, which many people call string beans, are grown in practically all the gardens of the United States, and there are very numerous varieties. Western seed is preferred as it is freer from the diseases which affect the green beans of the East. For commercial purposes the leading states are Florida, New Jersey, Louisiana, and California. *Green peas* are grown in general in the states farther north than those where green beans are found, as the plants are less tolerant of heat. They are grown largely in the same areas as sweet corn and are localized, principally for the same reasons, near cities or canneries. The strength of custom is shown in the growth of green peas for the market. Large and sweet peas have been developed, but the public associates smallness with sweetness, and the canners hesitate to try to overcome this long-established prejudice.

Most gardens of any extent contain at least a small *strawberry bed*. The wild strawberry is widely distributed in temperate regions and in the cooler elevated portions of the tropics. Women and children with strawberries for sale are a common sight at railroad stations as far apart as the Peruvian highlands and Finland. A great number of domestic varieties have been developed in order to increase yield, develop larger size, and retain as much as possible of the superior flavor of the wild variety. Particular varieties have been developed for special purposes: one with tough skins for long-distance shipping; a deep red acid variety for canning; a light red tart variety for preserving; and a sweet, highly flavored variety for eating fresh out of hand. Commercial production of strawberries in the United States is greatly concentrated in a few centers such as southern New Jersey, southern Delaware, the eastern shore of Maryland and Virginia, eastern North Carolina, western Tennessee, southwestern Missouri, and northwestern Arkansas, one parish in Louisiana north of New Orleans, one county in Florida, Hood River Valley in Oregon, and the Willamette and Puget Sound Valleys. In the last few years a remarkable development has occurred in Louisiana and Florida, perhaps owing to the creation of an earlier market than formerly. Oregon and Washington have increased their production for the late market.

The consumption of edible *mushrooms*, as well as of *seaweeds*, illustrates how man's use of natural resources extends far down to the lower orders of plants. One of the innumerable species of mushrooms has been selected as the best for general cultivation. It grows naturally in rich, open, breezy pastures among short grass. When cultivated commercially, it is usually grown in large, dark barns where shelf after shelf holds a few inches of rich, highly manured soil, and where both light and temperature can be easily controlled. Since fresh mushrooms cannot stand much transportation the crop is raised mainly near large cities, especially in southeastern Pennsylvania and northern Delaware. From here, regular lines of trucks supply not only Philadelphia but even New York and more distant cities. Near some cities the problem of getting stable manure for the mushroom barns is serious because of the increasing displacement of horses by automobiles. In western Europe, mushrooms are used more than in America. In Paris many are produced in mile after mile of underground cellars or passageways at depths of 60 to 160 feet, where the temperature and humidity remain all the year at the right level for mushrooms. In Russia, during the frequent times of shortage in the grain crops, wild mushrooms are an important resource.

Fruits.—The fruits used by man appear to be distributed over the earth more uniformly than the vegetables. Nevertheless, there are enormous differences between well supplied areas like the Wet Tropical Agricultural Regions or the Mediterranean Regions and the poorly supplied regions of the Wet and Dry Low Latitudes or the Cool Continental Interiors. Where the summers are cool and yet of sufficient length, most farmers have at least a few apple trees. The same is true of peaches, pears, berries, grapes, oranges, and especially bananas in their respective climates. Only rarely, however, do fruits or vegetables really compete with cereals for space, for the areas devoted to them are generally insignificant. Another noteworthy fact is that the commercial production of both vegetables and fruits tends to be highly localized. The commercial production of apples is largely concentrated in limited sections where oats are a great crop, as in the Annapolis Valley of Nova Scotia, northern New York, western Washington, and southwestern British Columbia. The grape attains a similar importance in somewhat warmer regions with drier summers. France, Italy, and central California are good examples, as are certain cooler regions where the frost-free season is prolonged by the presence of a body of water to windward, as on the southern and eastern shores of the more southerly Great Lakes. Farther southward, in regions which are generally free from frost but have a decided contrast between summer and winter, the orange is the great fruit, as in limited sections of southern California, Florida, Spain, southern Italy, Palestine, and southeastern Australia. Finally, in Regions of Wet Tropical Agriculture, banana plantations are concentrated, mainly in a few places around the Caribbean Sea.

Tropical Fruits.—The *banana*, a native of India and southern China, is without question the most important of tropical fruits and perhaps of all fruits. One evidence of this is the extraordinary rapidity with which its use has increased in the generation or two since it was introduced into the diet of temperate regions. Another is the fact that the banana probably forms a staple article of food for more people than does any other fruit. Outside of the larger cities, nearly every inhabitant of the Regions of Wet Tropical Agriculture and of the more favored parts of the other natural regions in low latitudes has a few banana plants as part of the chaotic mixture of trees, bushes, and crops that surround his house. Some of these are banana plants in the ordinary sense and supply fruit that is eaten fresh, especially by children. More of them, especially where this fruit is a main reliance, are plantains, that is, species of the banana genus which need to be cooked, but the terms banana and plantain are used with a variety of meanings. In tropical regions the cooked fruit, usually baked or steamed, but sometimes fried, is far more important than the raw. The banana is also preserved sometimes in the form of flour, or as "figs" made by slicing a peeled ripe banana in halves and drying it. Millions of people in Latin America, Africa, southern Asia, and the East Indies think that something is radically wrong if a bunch of green bananas is not hanging in the hut. More perhaps than any other plant the banana makes life easy in the tropics, while at the same time it ties people down to permanent residence in one place. Thus it has had much to do with developing, encouraging, and perpetuating the inert and careless temperament of tropical people.

The banana is a treelike plant 4 to 25 feet high with large, glossy leaves 2 to 6 feet long and a foot or two wide. Each stalk bears a single bunch of bananas composed of from 6 to 14 "hands," as the smaller groups of a dozen or more fruits are called, but bunches with less than 9 hands have little commercial value. Because of its long cultivation only a few of the many varieties now produce seeds, and the plant is propagated by cutting off sections of the root with some of the buds, which spring up in large numbers. The banana is at home wherever the climate is always warm and there is rain enough to produce tropical forests. It is found in a belt reaching entirely around the central part of the earth, including places as far north as Madeira and as high as 6,000 feet near the equator. All the important commercial plantations are found at low elevations, but this is mainly because of the need of ocean transportation. Nowhere do people rely on the banana more completely than in the plateaus of Uganda, Urundi, Kenya, and others in central Africa at elevations of 3,000 to 6,000 feet. After the shoots have been set out the banana needs little care, and will produce fruit in 12 to 14 months, although at higher elevations or on the edges of the tropics it may require nearly three years. The yield per acre is enormous, varying from about 200 to 300 bunches per year. Of course there are some hazards. Dry seasons reduce the yield very greatly and sometimes cause famines in central Africa. Commercial plantations suffer not only from hurricanes, but from diseases also, especially banana wilt, or Panama disease. These disadvantages are of minor importance compared with the nutritive qualities and high yield of the fruit, and with the fact that bananas can be picked quite green and yet ripen without loss of flavor or nutritive value. This gives time for transportation and allows machinery such as moving belts to be used in handling the bunches.

The great area for commercial production of bananas centers around the Caribbean Sea. Here the climate is right, and there are large unused areas that can be turned to banana production. The United States is close at hand to supply not only a large market, but also men with capital and initiative to start plantations. Hence over 60,000,000 bunches of bananas come to us annually, half from Honduras and Jamaica and the rest from lesser producers of the Caribbean area. Banana plantations have not developed on a large scale south of Europe because the areas in the same latitude as the Caribbean are largely desert and the good banana areas farther south in Africa are much farther from Europe than is the Caribbean section. Fast vessels carry bananas from the Caribbean to Europe as well as to the United States. It is interesting to note, however, that the banana, like every other crop, shows a tendency not only to be raised as near its market as possible, provided other crops are taken into account, but to move toward cooler regions. Plantations have been established in French North Africa, in the warm, low valley around the Sea of Galilee five or six hundred feet below sea-level, and also along the Syrian coast as far north as Beirut in the latitude of Wilmington, North Carolina.

The entrance of the banana into foreign trade has done its share to alter the life of the tropics, especially around the Caribbean Sea. Vast capital has flowed into the region; forests have been removed, wet areas drained, railroads built, workers' homes and hospitals erected, and whole fleets of swift ships constructed to move the bananas promptly to market. This has brought about a considerable shifting of population. It has also brought a revival of economic life where other products such as cacao were on the decline, as in Ecuador.

Many other tropical fruits are important in low latitudes, and especially in the Regions of Wet Tropical Agriculture, but are not well known elsewhere. The *avocado* or *alligator pear* is one of these which is fast becoming better known. It is the fruit of a tree which has become almost universally distributed throughout the tropics and part of the subtropics. The dark green fruit, 5 to 12 inches long with a big stone in it, weighs 1 to 4 pounds, and may be spherical, oblong, or pear-shaped. The yellowish green flesh contains 15 to 30 per cent of fat. This makes it so nutritious that it is of great value in areas where fruit is the main diet. With us it is used mainly as a salad. Because of its relatively high cost it is not yet sold in any considerable amount in temperate regions. Nevertheless, commercial avocado orchards have been planted in Florida and California, and chain groceries are handling the fruit.

Another tropical fruit, the delicious mango, a native of Asia, is sometimes called the apple of the tropics, for it is eaten fresh, stewed, or made into jellies or marmalade. There are also the delicately flavored and beautiful *mangosteen*, the well-named *custard apple*, the *breadfruit*, the great, finely flavored *durian* with its wretched smell, and the cloyingly sweet *zapote* which grows on the tree that furnishes chicle gum. Generally these grow in hit or miss fashion around the thatched native huts of the Regions of Wet Tropical Agriculture. None, however, are articles of commerce in any quantities, for they do not stand transportation well and have not been improved as have the more desirable fruits like the orange and banana. In fact it is usually difficult to buy them even where they grow in abundance. The *papaya*, which is a genuine tree melon, has hitherto belonged to this same class of tropical fruits, but some people think that it bids fair to attain a considerable place in the markets of the world. As a result of recent improvements it not only retains its original flavor and its full content of vitamins A, B, C, and D, but has acquired shipping qualities which may allow its advent in northern markets. Its supply of four vitamins gives it excellent medicinal properties useful in curing digestive troubles. It furnishes an interesting example of possible tropical additions to our diet. Different from any of the other fruits thus far mentioned is the common or lemon *guava*, for it enters into commerce in the form of a jelly which is a highly prized dessert. The manufacture of guava jelly is a considerable industry in Hawaii, Cuba, Puerto Rico, Florida, and elsewhere.

Desert Fruits.—Certain fruits of deserts and arid regions play an important part in the life of the scanty population. Many cacti have edible fruits which were a main source of food among the primitive Indians of an earlier day. The *prickly pear* is the best known of these. This red or yellow fruit is sold on the streets in Greece and other Mediterranean lands where the cactus has been introduced from America. In a trice the skilful vendor slices off the skin with its little bunches of spines so that the purchaser eats the slightly acid but rather insipid fruit in comfort. Nevertheless the difficulty of keeping the small spines from becoming mixed with the fruit is a decided deterrent to its utilization. Therefore the cactus plant is mainly useful for hedges and as food for cattle and horses, especially in the dry season. In Australia, where the prickly pear was introduced as a forage plant for cattle, it has become almost as bad a pest as the rabbits. Where the climate is near its optimum it forms almost impenetrable thickets of great extent.

The *date* palm is one of the most useful of trees. It is essentially a product of the hot desert, but grows only in oases where there is sufficient ground water. All the way across North Africa, Arabia, Persia, and the dry part of India, it grows wherever there is sufficient water, even in places where the water is a little saline. Large parts of the Nile Valley and of the Tigris-Euphrates plain near Baghdad and Bosra seem like enormous groves of date palms.   In Algeria and Tunis there is more than one date palm for every person, and in Egypt, Iraq, and Arabia this proportion may be exceeded.   Dates of excellent quality are raised in Arizona, New Mexico, and California, but the United States still imports about 50,000,000 pounds each year.   The dates used in the United States and Europe are an important article of export from Persia, Iraq, Morocco, Algeria, Tunis, and some other areas around the Mediterranean.

Although important as an export, the date plays its chief rôle in the home economics of the dwellers in the smaller oases and in the desert itself.   In many of the smaller oases of the Sahara, Arabia, and Persia, there is no running water for irrigation.   The only available supply is under the ground, for the oases are often hollows where the surface dips so far that it approaches the level of ground water.   Often this water is somewhat alkaline or brackish.   In such cases it is of little use for ordinary crops even when it is laboriously lifted out of a well by a camel pulling a leather bucket by means of a rope running on a pulley.   But palm trees thrive on such water, and if they have enough of it, seem to benefit from the most extreme heat.   So the oasis people often live on a diet consisting more of dates than of anything else.   The nomads of the surrounding desert want the dates, too, and often make raids to get them.   But the nomads cannot get dates unless there are oasis people to care for the trees.   Hence the surrounding nomads often protect the oases from marauders, and in return peacefully take a share of the dates.

Citrus Fruits.—Among the fruits grown in both tropical and subtropical areas some have reached such great commercial importance on the cooler margins of their habitat that we think of them as primarily subtropical.   Among these are the citrus fruits such as the orange, lemon, lime, grapefruit, tangerine, kumquat, and citron.   These are of tropical origin and are killed by frost.   Nevertheless, the usual development of better types on the coldward margin of the habitat has resulted in commercial production in a few places, such as parts of California and southern Texas, where frosts are not unusual in winter.   In such areas artificial protection is usually afforded.

The *orange* is the best known and most important of the citrus fruits. Originating in China, it found its way into Europe by the Middle Ages and is now grown in many places in both the tropics and subtropics. In most of the tropical areas the oranges are of relatively poor quality, being somewhat acid and often greenish even when ripe.   They are there grown mainly for local consumption, although a good many are exported from Brazil, and river steamers carry thousands of boxes down the Paraná River from Paraguay to Rosario, Buenos Aires, and other cities.   The oranges grown in the southern hemisphere often command a high price, as they appear in Europe and other northern areas as an off-season product.   This has helped to stimulate production in Brazil, South Africa, and Australia.   But in general the world's major supply of oranges comes from the subtropics of the northern hemisphere either in humid east-coast areas like Florida and Japan, or drier west-coast regions like California and the Mediterranean lands.   The delicious flavor and relatively good keeping qualities of the orange are enough to insure a growing market for this popular fruit, but recent discoveries as to the value of its vitamins, both for general health and for the teeth, have greatly increased the demand.

In spite of the expense of irrigation, orange culture has made by far the greatest growth in the Mediterranean Type of climate.   Omitting the tropical product, which has little commercial importance and for which no data are available, Spain alone produces nearly a third of the world's oranges, while California produces nearly as many.   Italy is the third largest producer, although it raises only about a sixth or a fifth as many as Spain or California.   Other large producers with the Mediterranean Type of climate include Syria and Palestine, Algeria and Tunis, South Africa, and Australia.   On the other hand, Florida, with about a third as many oranges as Spain, is the only really large producer in a climate with summer rains, although Mexico, Japan, and Uruguay also deserve mention.   Altogether the countries with summer rain produce only about a sixth of the recorded orange crop;   and even if data were available for genuinely tropical countries this would not be greatly increased. It would be increased a little, however, if we included bitter oranges which are good for canning and preserves, but not for eating raw.   Japan raises many more bitter oranges than sweet ones.   Hot summer sun and dry weather seem to be needed to make the fruit sweet.   Regions like Florida, Uruguay, and northern Mexico with only moderate summer rain seem to meet this requirement, and also to be relatively free from the diseases which frequently afflict the orange tree where the summers are humid.

In the United States, frost is a great enemy of the orange crop.   This is specially true in Florida, because that state lies on the east side of the continent and hence gets strong outblowing northwest winds from the high-pressure area which develops over the continent in winter. Florida began to ship oranges to the North about 1875 after the East Coast Railway was completed, but severe frosts in 1886, 1894, and 1899 ruined about three-fourths of the groves in the northern part of the state. This caused new plantings to be made farther south, and at the same time gave a chance to California. In 1922 a frost again spoiled half of the crop in Florida and killed many trees, thus giving the industry another shove to the south. Nevertheless other conditions such as relative freedom from pests and the quality of the northern fruit lead people to plant new groves even in areas that have suffered from frost. Thus oranges illustrate the way in which the limits of many crops move backward and forward in response to cycles of weather. In this case, frost is the dominant factor, just as is drought in causing the limits of corn cultivation to swing back and forth in western Kansas. In California the frosts are less harmful than in Florida because the westerly and northwesterly winds come across the ocean and hence cannot become very cold in winter. Cold northeast winds, on the other hand, are much less common than northwest winds, and they are warmed somewhat by crossing the Sierras and giving up their moisture before they descend to the coastal section of California. Nevertheless they sometimes bring frosts. Generally the danger of freezing can be overcome, for the Weather Bureau gives warnings which enable the growers to build smudgy fires and create a smoke screen in the orange groves.

In California the rapid and intensive development of the orange and other fruit industries, together with the great distance from the large eastern markets, has confronted the fruit growers with a very perplexing problem as to marketing their products. Being an alert set of people, like most of those who have migrated long distances, they formed the California Citrus Fruit Growers Association, one of the pioneer cooperative organizations. This takes care of collecting, grading, and selling the fruit, and of the many other activities involved in handling the thousands of cars of oranges that are shipped to the East every year.

The *lemon* is slightly more susceptible to damage by frost than the orange and hence is grown commercially in the warmer parts of the regions with a Mediterranean climate. Where lemons and oranges are produced in the same locality the lemon is usually given the more favorable position on the slopes, where there is less danger of frost. Although lemons are grown in all the continents, the great commercial production is centered in the Mediterranean area, particularly southern Italy and Sicily, and in California, which supplies the demand in the United States. Important amounts of citric acid and lemon oil are marketed as by-products of the lemon.

Limes are even more sensitive to low temperature than lemons. Hence they are found mainly in the tropics and the warmer parts of the subtropics, especially the West Indies and particularly Dominica, and only to a slight extent in Florida, California, and the Mediterranean areas. The by-products of the lime are imported in varying amounts as citric acid, lime oil, and lime juice.

The *grapefruit*, also known as the pomelo or chaddock, grows on a somewhat larger tree than the lime. Although this fruit is well known in the United States and is common in our cities, it is little used elsewhere. It has been perfected only recently and hence is raised in the newer fruit lands of Florida, California, and South Africa rather than the older citrus areas of the Mediterranean. Florida has been by far the largest producer, but the production in southern Texas has increased so fast that that state now competes with California for second place, and bids fair to rival Florida.

The *citron*, often 6 to 10 inches long, grows on a small tree in the tropics and to a small extent in Florida and California. Its main commercial importance arises from its thick peel which is dried and candied, and exported from the western Mediterranean area.

We come now to two other citrus fruits, the *kumquat* or *loquat*, and the *tangerine* or *mandarin*, which are better adapted to climates with wet summers than are the orange and lemon. The kumquat grows on a bush 6 or 8 feet high. This small fruit, about an inch in diameter, often has such a pretty golden orange color that it is used for decorations. The pulp is somewhat acid, and the rind has such a sweet aromatic taste that the entire fruit is often eaten raw or preserved. The tangerine, larger and more spherical than the kumquat, resembles a small, sweet, reddish orange with a skin that is almost completely separated from the pulp. It is used somewhat in this country, but the production is not large. In Japan and parts of China, on the other hand, it is the most abundant of all fruits, exceeding even the persimmon. Its name comes from Tangier in Morocco, and the fruit is common in North Africa.

Persimmon trees are of two general types, native to North America and Asia. The American type is found wild in the central and southern states. The yellowish fruit of this tree is sweet and delicious when ripe and especially when touched by frost, but it is very astringent when green. The fear of biting into a green persimmon tends to bring this fine fruit into disfavor so that even where it grows abundantly, it is often used mainly as forage for pigs and other animals. In China and Japan the Asiatic persimmon is very abundant in the autumn although it cannot be kept long. It is also grown widely in the tropics and to some extent in the southern states and California. In recent years these persimmons have become familiar in our city markets, where they have met with considerable favor. They are not so astringent when green as our native fruit, but neither are they so sweet when ripe. The Asiatic persimmon is much larger than the native variety and much brighter in color, often attaining the size and having the color of our common red tomato.

The *mulberry* goes with the mandarin and persimmon as a fruit which is especially adapted to the Warm Temperate Humid Region of southern Asia, although it is also raised in the regions of the Mediterranean Type. Although it is generally known that vast numbers of mulberry trees are grown to provide leaves as food for silkworms, it is not so well known that mulberry trees are also cultivated on a large scale for their fruit—white, red, or purple berries about the size and shape of a blackberry. The white kind is the best for general use although rather insipidly sweet and lacking the luscious, mildly acid quality of the darker kinds. It is the only one used to any great extent in Mediterranean lands. The trees are easily raised and bear so prodigiously that the ground beneath them is often carpeted with fruit. In Turkey during the short bearing season in the early summer both dogs and beggars sometimes take up their abode under the trees and live on the berries for weeks. In China and Japan the berries are equally prized, although the trees are cut back so much to get leaves for silkworms that the great majority bear little fruit. In some regions, especially those of the Mediterranean Type with long, dry summers, mulberries are often dried to be used later in some other form. In the United States, the trees are grown mostly in our southern states to produce berries as forage for pigs. It is believed by some that mulberries might profitably be raised on a large scale as food for animals.

Let us turn now to certain fruits which join with the orange and lemon in making regions of the Mediterranean Type the parts of the world where the most varied and delicious assortment of fruits is produced. The *fig* is a native of Turkey and some other Mediterranean lands. It is grown quite widely in some tropical and subtropical regions, including our southern states and California. The tree attains a large size. It can perhaps be cultivated over a wider range than the orange, but figs are produced for export mainly around the eastern Mediterranean, particularly Asia Minor, where the Smyrna figs are famous. They are shipped mainly to Great Britain and the United States. Palestine, Greece, and Italy also produce fine figs, and this fruit is mentioned in the Bible and in Greek and Roman literature. This is not merely because the fresh fruit is so delicious, but because it can be easily dried in the sun, and then preserved a long time. California has made rapid strides in fig production, especially since the introduction of the fig wasp and the wild or Capri fig. Like the grape, banana, rose, and many other plants that have long been cultivated, the fig is usually propagated by cuttings, and its power to produce seed has thus been diminished. Accordingly better fruit is produced if flowering branches of the wild trees, or Capri figs, are placed among the cultivated trees. The fig wasp then carries the wild pollen to the cultivated figs, thus producing better fruit. Old Greek and Latin books tell about this process. It is one of many cases where man owes a great deal to insects. We are so troubled by the destruction due to insects that we often forget that a large share of our crops would fail if deprived of certain beneficial insects. Of the two principal types of figs one is the Smyrna type, which is dried for market. It is grown in semi-arid or typical Mediterranean lands and needs wasp fertilization. The other, or Magnolia type, is preserved in thick syrup. It is grown in regions of summer rain such as the coast of the Gulf of Mexico where Texas is a large producer. It does not require wasp fertilization.

Apricots, another typical Mediterranean fruit, are a yellow or golden-yellow peach-like fruit grown for the most part in the warmer areas of Europe, in the Levant, and in California. It is often said that the apricot is to Syria what the fig is to Smyrna and Ephesus. California exports its apricots both in cans and dried; the other important commercial areas—Syria, Asia Minor, and Caucasia—market only the dried fruit. The kernel of the apricot seed is also valuable, as from it is extracted an oil which is sometimes used as a substitute for almond-oil or cottonseed oil.

The *pomegranate* is still another typical Mediterranean fruit. It is relatively unimportant in trade, but the red pulp that surrounds its many seeds makes a delicious drink like lemonade. It is also raised in southern Asia and other semi-tropical and subtropical regions. In the United States it is chiefly grown in California and the South and often as an ornamental tree as well as for fruit.

Two Great Mediterranean Crops.—For thousands of years the *olive* has been recognized as one of the most valuable crops. It is used mainly for oil, but is also of enormous importance as a fruit to be pickled. In Mediterranean lands, innumerable people eat nothing but bread and pickled ripe olives for meal after meal. The pickled green olives that we use are rarely seen among the people who raise most of the olives. The olive is a native of Asia Minor, and is strictly limited to the Mediterranean Type of climate. It can stand temperatures of 20° or lower, and a rainfall as low as 15 inches. It can also be grown where the topography is rough and the soil stony. Accordingly it is suitable to considerable areas around the Mediterranean which otherwise would be of little value. Then, too, the olive is easily propagated and lives to a great age. It does not bear fruit until after many years of care, but then it bears profusely and steadily. Hence, on all sides of the Mediterranean Sea, gray-green olive orchards cover innumerable hillsides which would otherwise be left bare. In parts of southern Spain the whole landscape for mile after mile seems to consist of olive groves. Nevertheless in other regions with the Mediterranean Type of climate olives are of minor importance, although some are raised in California and Australia.

Another reason for the scarcity of olives outside the regions near the Mediterranean is the labor required in the commercial production. The trees must be tilled, pruned, and grafted, and the harvest period is short, requiring concentration of labor. If the fruit is to be pickled green the olives are picked by hand when fully grown but before any color appears. For ripe pickles or oil, the olives are taken from the trees when they have turned dark but not black. Much labor is also involved in preparation of the pickled olives and in extracting the oil. Around the Mediterranean, plenty of cheap labor is available for this work, but in the new lands with the Mediterranean Type of climate, labor is scarce and expensive. So it only pays to produce the expensive pickled green olives. Moreover, in these new lands the standard of living is so high that butter and meat are used for carbohydrate foods, and olive oil is not in great demand. Accordingly, Spain and Italy are the great producers of olives, with Greece, Tunis, and Portugal important but trailing the two leaders by a wide margin.

From the standpoint of historical development and importance in economic geography the *grape* surpasses even the olive. It probably originated in western Asia or southeastern Europe. From the earliest times its value both as food and as a source of wine appears to have been known. The Bible speaks of it continually. "And Judah and Israel dwelt safely, every man under his vine and under his fig tree." "I am the true vine, and my Father is the husbandman." Among the Greeks the wine god, Bacchus, was a great favorite. Today the grape is cultivated wherever the climate permits, which means in Mediterranean, Desert, and large parts of Cyclonic Regions.

It requires well drained land with a sunny, warm season. Too much rain makes the grapes watery, and a mean temperature below 60° F. during the month of ripening is detrimental, but prolonged heat is also harmful, especially if accompanied by much moisture. The vine can withstand rather severe summer droughts because of its long tap root. The restrictions imposed by temperature, moisture, and sunlight, however, concentrate the most important production in the world's five areas of Mediterranean climate. Nevertheless the culture of the vine extends considerably beyond these areas. In Europe for instance it extends to about $47\frac{1}{2}°$ N. in western France and even 53° N. in Poland but is limited to an area much farther south in southern Russia. Similar conditions are found in North America, but the limits are farther south with few exceptions—in California about 37° N. and in Ontario 42° N.

Local factors as well as general climatic conditions play an important part in vine culture. Vineyards are usually placed on slopes because

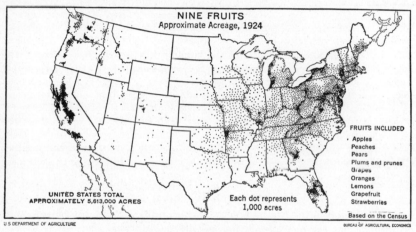

A—Fruit in the United States.

the roots there find better drainage, cold air blows away to lower levels, more sunlight can reach the fruit, and the level land can be more profitably used for crops that require plowing, planting, and reaping after the fashion of grain. Soil conditions are also extremely important in producing some especially prized flavors of fruit or wine. Around the Mediterranean Sea, the climatic conditions, the rough topography, the soil, the taste developed by the people, and their skill in growing the vine and preparing its products combine to make this area the world's center of grape culture. France and Italy are the outstanding countries, but Spain, southern Russia, Algeria, Greece, and western Asia are very important. Other areas of importance are California, the lakes region of the United States, parts of Argentina, Chile, Australia, and South Africa (A375).

Grapes are marketed in three forms: fresh as table grapes; dried as currants or raisins; and as grape juice or wine. Table grapes are grown throughout all the areas of Mediterranean climate, including many places where they will not make good wine. California and Spain are especially noted in this respect, but Algeria, Portugal, Germany, and other regions help to supply Europe, and many table grapes are grown around the lakes and in local areas in the eastern United States. As might be expected, the most delicious of all grapes are those grown farthest north. In Holland, for example, the summer temperature out-of-doors is too low for grapes, but a little additional heat through protection in greenhouses enables that country to export great, round purple grapes whose delicate flavor almost surpasses the imagination.

Dried grapes are an important article of international trade. The bright, sunny, cloudless days where the Mediterranean climate prevails fit these regions for the production of dried fruits. Greece has practically a monopoly on *dried currants*, the *raisins* made from a small, specialized seedless grape. The soil around the gulf of Corinth is especially favorable for this grape, and the name "currant" is a corruption of Corinth. *Raisins* are produced in all areas of the Mediterranean climatic type, but in recent years the San Joaquin Valley in California has become the greatest producing center. Here water can be supplied by irrigation and the sunlight is abundant, the temperature high, and the humidity low—at harvest season. The advantages of these physical conditions are supplemented by the activities of cooperative associations in marketing and advertising. "Have you had your iron today?" is a well known slogan designed to indicate the healthful quality of raisins. They are healthful, although iron has very little to do with the matter. The cultivation of grapes for table use or wine is more important than for raisins, but that will be discussed under stimulants.

Temperate Orchard Fruits.—The common orchard fruits are generally grown in higher latitudes than the citrus group, but quinces, nectarines, and peaches are better adapted to Mediterranean conditions than are the more strictly cool temperate fruits such as apples, pears, plums, and cherries. However, peaches are often grown in cool temperate areas and plums and cherries flourish in Mediterranean lands. The *quince* is the fruit of a small tree or shrub. Outwardly it resembles a yellow apple but has many seeds and the flesh is hard and acid. It is used in marmalades, jellies, and preserves but is not of great importance in trade. The *nectarine* is a smooth-skinned, green and red variety of peach which is only locally of commercial importance. *Peach* trees are less hardy than apples and bloom earlier. Thus cold weather is likely to injure the trees in winter and the blossoms in spring. The southern states with their mild winters are more important in peach cultivation than the northern states. Three major centers of peach culture are found in the United States: the early peach district of central Georgia; the late peach district along Lake Ontario in New York; and the canning and dried peach district in California. There are several minor centers as in New Jersey, eastern Tennessee, western Maryland, east of Lake Michigan, southern Illinois, western Arkansas, and northeastern Texas. Scattered orchards are found elsewhere both in the South and North. Some of the northern areas of cultivation are near tempering winds of the ocean or bays, to the lee of the Great Lakes which keep the air cool and prevent blossoming until after danger of frost is past, or on slopes in locally protected valleys. The peach is grown to some extent in all temperate areas of the globe.

The *pear* is a native of southern Europe and Asia but is now grown in temperate areas in all continents. Pear trees can grow farther north than peaches. In some parts of the United States, especially the Gulf Coast States and California, the pear orchards have suffered from a severe blight. In the United States the important centers of production are central and southern California, the Yakima Valley in Washington, the Rogue Valley in Oregon, southwestern Michigan, the shore of Lake Ontario in New York, the Hudson Valley, and the coastal plain of southern New Jersey, Delaware, and eastern Maryland.

The many varieties of *cherries* fall into two general types—sweet and sour. The sweet cherries are grown in the Far West, centering in the lower Sacramento Valley and the corresponding north–south valleys of Oregon and Washington. Some sweet cherries are grown in the Hudson Valley, western New York, and western Michigan. The commercial cherry of most of the East, however, is the sour or "pie" cherry which is widely scattered in farmers' orchards and in small commercial orchards. The cherry tree is rather easily cultivated and may be grown in a climate colder than is suitable for pears or peaches. The cherry trees that line the roads in Czechoslovakia illustrate this, but the cold winter of 1929–30 is said to have killed a million trees there.

The *plum*, of which there are a great many varieties, has a rather wide climatic range. Some are grown in practically every state in the Union. The ordinary plum seems to do best in the Mississippi Valley. West of the Rockies a variety of plum with a higher content of sugar predominates. When dried it is known as the *prune*. This requires a longer season and more sunshine than the ordinary plum; it also needs considerable water. Hence it is admirably adapted to the irrigated valleys of the Pacific States.

The *apple* is the leading fruit crop of the United States. Of the the normal yield of about 200 million bushels in this country and Canada, less than half is shipped to distant markets. The farms and villages of the United States are the great centers not only of the production but likewise of the consumption of apples. The continent of Europe is also important as an apple producer. England raises a good many, but also imports them from the continent, Canada, the United States, and Australia. Apples are also produced in eastern Asia, South Africa, and Chile, but not in large quantities.

Apples are grown in practically all parts of the United States, except the Far South and the coldest parts of the northern interior. This is in harmony with the fact that the apple has so wide a range as to climate and soil that the area adapted to apple growing appears to be at least fifty times as great as that needed to supply the probable demand. The favorite areas of concentration are the slopes of the hills and mountains of New England and the Appalachians, the rough lands near portions of the Mississippi and Missouri rivers, the Ozarks, the lake shores especially that of Lake Ontario, and the irrigated valleys of Washington and Oregon. New York is the greatest producer, followed by Washington and Virginia. In a recent year the West produced one-fourth of the apples on only one-seventh of the acreage of bearing trees. Western growers are better organized and hence have better methods of marketing than their eastern competitors. This fact coupled with the bright colors of many western apples allows the western fruit to invade the city markets of the East, though the eastern fruit generally has an excellent flavor.

Hundreds of varieties of apples are grown in the United States, but five represent almost half of the total production. Different varieties are popular in different cities, so that custom and tradition play an important part in determining what kind shall be sold. The proximity of the areas of production is important, but this cannot account for the city of New York demanding so large a percentage of McIntosh apples and Philadelphia insisting on Staymen Winesaps up to one-third of the city's supply.

Bush berries is a term applied to various types of small fruits. There is a great number of different kinds, but the best known are raspberries, blackberries and dewberries, gooseberries, currants, blueberries and huckleberries, and cranberries. *Raspberries* are grown in temperate regions generally but mainly in Europe and the United States. In this country two well defined varieties are used—the red and the black, although there are many types of each. Raspberries do best on deep, sandy loam in a cool, moist climate. However, since they are usually marketed fresh, proximity to cities is an important factor in location.

Blackberries and dewberries grow wild over much of the United States and in many other parts of the world. Both do well on deep, sandy loam, but the blackberry prefers a heavier soil than the dewberry. They are easily reproduced, easily cultivated, and in most sections are a very profitable crop.

Gooseberries and currants have been familiar in gardens from the earliest times. Hence their production is widely scattered, although there is concentration in a few areas near markets. Goosberries are usually harvested when green and used for pies and preserves. Currants from the garden bush are not to be confused with the small, dried grape previously discussed. Garden currants may be red, black, white, or purple when ripe. They are used mostly for jellies.

Blueberries and huckleberries are in great demand to be eaten fresh or in pies and similar confections. Most of the demand is supplied from wild sources, for many varieties are found both in the marshes and on the thin soils of the highlands of New England, New Jersey, the Appalachians, the Great Lakes States, and the Far West. Only recently has there been an attempt to cultivate these bushes for commercial purposes.

The production of *cranberries* is almost exclusively an American industry. Although in a few areas cranberries may be picked from wild bushes the commercial crop comes from cultivated areas. The cranberry requires a cool climate, an acid peat soil, and plenty of water. Hence it is grown in bogs mainly in New Jersey, Massachusetts, and central Wisconsin. These bogs must be drained, but it is necessary that they be carefully leveled off as flooding is usually required to cover the berries and protect them from early frosts or injurious insects, and irrigation may be necessary in times of drought. The bogs may produce 100 or more barrels per acre.

Nuts.—Although playing but a small part in the channels of trade, nuts are very important locally. Even in the large areas where they are not important as sources of food they add to the diet a pleasing variety. Great quantities would doubtless be eaten if it were not for the high prices which make most kinds of nuts a luxury.   If waste slopes should be devoted to raising nuts in the way suggested by J. Russell Smith (page 167) this condition might be changed.

The tree which bears *Brazil nuts* forms extensive forests along the Amazon and Orinoco.   It often reaches a height of 150 feet and a diameter of 4 feet.   The fruit is round, sometimes 6 inches in diameter, and is covered with a woody shell within which are about a dozen or more seeds or Brazil nuts.   The Brazil nuts of commerce come largely from South America.   Owing to the difficulty of getting the nuts many go to waste and only a fraction of the crop is gathered for the market. The tree is also quite widely cultivated in southeastern Asia, especially in Ceylon and the Federated Malay States.

The *kola* nut is important locally and of some importance as an export.   It is extensively cultivated in West Africa, where it is consumed as a food and a stimulant. The tree has been introduced into other parts of the tropics but the production is not yet large.   The nut contains much starch and a higher percentage of caffein than coffee.   It has been used in some countries of Europe, but because of an unpleasant flavor it is consumed only when mixed with cacao or in certain drinks.

The *ivory nut* is the fruit of the tagu palm, native to the forests of western Ecuador and Colombia.   It is a seed found in a drupe, a soft fleshy mass about the size of a man's head, each drupe containing 20 to 40 seeds.   The nuts are hard, white, and resemble real ivory.   They are exported to the United States and Europe, where the ivory is used in preparation of buttons and ornamental wares.

Palm nuts and kernels are obtained for the most part from West Africa, but since their main use is for the production of oil they will be discussed later.   The *cashew* nut grows on a tree 30 or 40 feet high.   It is a native of the West Indies, but the fruit has a peculiar double arrangement, for it grows at the end of a sort of apple. The apple is used for preserves, while the nut is commonly roasted and salted, or used in confectionery.

The pistachio nut was found native in Syria, in the Canaries, and in Mexico.   It is now grown widely in dry areas on the borders of the tropics and in the subtropics in such places as India, California, Florida, and other southern states.   Some of the most extensive plantations are found in Afghanistan, Persia, Syria, and Palestine. There the nuts are boiled in salt water till they crack, and are then sold on the streets like peanuts.   In the United States they are utilized principally in making confectionery and ice cream.

Nuts, as well as fruits, assume their greatest importance in regions with the Mediterranean Type of climate.   The *chestnut* illustrates this.   It probably originated near the Black Sea in Asia Minor but has spread westward along the Mediterranean Sea and northward into the heart of Europe.   Chestnut groves cover astonishingly large areas on rough slopes in many parts of France, Spain, and Italy.   Many communities depend largely on the chestnut for food and for a cash crop which is exported to northwestern Europe and other parts of the world.   The Corsican mountaineer eats bread made from chestnut meal, much as the Kentucky mountaineer eats bread from corn meal.   Chestnut trees were native to the hilly and mountainous parts of the United States and at one time were very common, but the ravages of the chestnut blight have killed nearly all of them.

The *Persian walnut* (commonly called the English walnut) is the nut most commonly used for food in the United States.   A native of the eastern Mediterranean region, it is now grown to some extent in nearly all parts of the world where the climatic conditions approach the Mediterranean Type.   The Mediterranean countries and parts of eastern Asia and the western United States are the great centers of production. France, Italy, and China are large exporters of English walnuts. In the Levant they are eaten almost as freely as are chestnuts at the other end of the Mediterranean. Many a meal consists of bread and walnuts. So common are they that they are used to fatten turkeys, the whole nut being actually worked down the bird's throat from the outside if it cannot swallow it. While they are grown in parts of the eastern United States, California supplies most of our domestic production.

The *almond* is also a native of countries around the Mediterranean, perhaps Asia Minor near the Black Sea. Today the world's almond crop is almost exclusively confined to areas of Mediterranean climate such as California, Spain, Italy, Morocco, and Sicily, with lesser amounts in Chile, South Africa, and South Australia. California now produces most of the almonds consumed in the United States. The almond can stand very dry weather. In southern Spain, for example, it replaces the olive and grape on the driest, sunniest slopes exposed to the full glare of the sun.

Leaving now the Mediterranean types of nuts, we come to the *pecan*, a native of North America ranging from the central Mississippi basin into Mexico. The pecan industry had its beginning with the marketing of the wild product, and this is still an important phase. In recent years, however, experimentation and culture have developed a larger nut with a softer shell which is now being produced in large orchards in the lower Mississippi Valley with beginnings in other parts of the southeastern United States.

Filberts are the fruit of a small shrub which is extensively grown in western North America. Hazel nuts, as they are known here, grow wild over much of this continent but are somewhat smaller, owing, perhaps, to lack of cultivation. Though in considerable demand, especially at holiday times, filberts do not make important contributions to trade.

Although few people think of pine trees as a source of human food, the *pine* nut is widely eaten. No statistical record of its use exists, but the piñon is often grown where agriculture is difficult or impossible, as along our southwestern borders. The piñon nuts have long been a mainstay of the Indians and Mexicans, and after the coming of the railroad many were collected and shipped out. It is believed by exponents of tree crops that the nut-bearing pines will have a much greater importance in the future.

More temperate in their requirements are the hickory nut, black walnut, butternut, acorn, and beechnut. It is too bad that the *hickory tree*, so widely distributed in much of eastern North America, had to succumb to make place for agriculture or to be used for axe-handles, carriage wheels, and other implements for which it is so valuable. Hickory nuts, now scarcely known by many Americans, once furnished an important part of the luxury diet of the pioneer.

The *black walnut* and the *butternut* have gone the way of the hickory tree. The former was also in the path of the farmer and was a valuable wood for gunstocks and furniture. The latter was never abundant, and while the nuts are rich in oil they are difficult to gather and even harder to crack. The meats of both of these nuts are prized not only to eat fresh but as flavoring in confectionery and ice cream. The black walnut retains its flavor when cooked and so is in great demand. The tree has great possibilities as a producer of food and probably will become more numerous than it was before the axe entered the American forest. Many groves were first planted to produce lumber. With the increasing modern demand for nuts the planting should continue, as there are many unused areas that could grow this tasty and nutritious product.

To most of us the *acorn* is merely an interesting product of the oak tree, though a few think of it as food for pigs. But many peoples rely on acorns as a substantial part of their food supply. J. Russell Smith suggests that "It may be possible that the human race has eaten more of acorns than it has of wheat." In any event, many of the primitive peoples of America used acorns for food. Moreover, perhaps 20 per cent of the sustenance of the poorer classes of certain parts of Spain and Italy consists of acorns. In many places the acorns have been improved until they are almost as good as chestnuts.

The *beechnut's* sweet flavor is excellent, but its diminutive size and triangular shape have limited its use as human food, although it is important as food for the pig and the wild boar of the European forest. The beach tree is common throughout central Europe, in southern Canada, and in the northeastern United States, and along the slopes of the Appalachians farther south. There are several varieties of beeches, and experimental propagation may produce a larger and better beechnut in the same way that many of the nuts described above have been brought to their present standard of excellence.

EXERCISES

In the exercises of this chapter use the following sources of information: (a) the maps and text of this book; (b) your desk atlas; (c) a large commercial atlas; (d) *Yearbook of Agriculture*; (e) *International Yearbook of Agricultural Statistics*.

1. Make a table showing (a) the amount and value of the fruits (or fruit products) imported into and exported from the United States in a given year; (b) the main sources of each fruit; (c) its main destination; (d) its form, i.e., fresh, dried, canned, made into drinks, etc. On the basis of your table choose the five fruits which seem to be most important in the foreign trade of the United States, and determine the region where each is produced most abundantly.

2. For one of the fruits chosen in Exercise 1, prepare a typical local climograph of the region of greatest production. Discuss the relation of the fruit to topography, markets, and transportation, and to methods of distribution and sale.

3 and 4. Repeat Exercises 1 and 2, using nuts instead of fruits.

5. From the *Yearbook of Agriculture* make a table showing the vegetables raised for market in the United States, the states in which each is produced in largest quantities, and, in as many cases as possible, the states from which the largest amounts are shipped in each month of the year.

6. For one of these vegetables draw a diagram like A361.

7. Investigate any one of the vegetables for which data are available in the *Yearbook of Agriculture* and write a well-rounded statistical account of its economic geography.

8. For some crop like potatoes, cabbage, onions, or strawberries search out all the data in the *Yearbook of Agriculture* as to prices at different seasons, and in different areas, total value of production, value per acre, etc. Explain the geographical conditions which govern whatever variations you may find.

9. If you were interested in growing nut trees in the United States, where would you plant the following: black walnut, pecan, hickory, English walnut? Why in each case? Your answer should consider soil, climate, topography, and economic factors. Some of the areas you will choose were once covered with such trees as you propose to plant. Would you recommend planting all the original areas to nut trees at this time? Why?

CHAPTER XVIII

VEGETABLE OILS, STIMULANTS, AND INDUSTRIAL CROPS

Vegetable Oils.—Although vegetable oils have been used for ages, the commercial value of the oils contained in a vast number of plants has only recently been appreciated. Now, however, the increased demand for oil not only in salads and other foods, but also for soaps, varnishes, lubricants, and other purposes, has caused an enormous increase in the production of vegetable oils. Most of them are extracted from the fruits or seeds of plants of all sizes which grow in fairly warm regions. Near the equator the Regions of Wet Tropical Agriculture supply coconut oil and palm oil, which are among the most important, as appears in the following table:

VEGETABLE OILS IN INTERNATIONAL COMMERCE DURING AN ESPECIALLY ACTIVE YEAR (1929)

Approximate net exports from all countries where the product is originally produced

Source of oil	Short tons of nuts or seeds	Tons of oil
Soy bean	3,000,000	140,000
Linseed	2,200,000	100,000
Peanuts	1,800,000	130,000
Coconuts (copra)	1,500,000	400,000
Cottonseed	770,000	510,000
Palm nuts	620,000	290,000
Sesame	125,000	23,000
Rape seed	110,000	......
Olives	......	165,000

As a source of food, drink, thatch, and fiber the *coconut palm* has long been highly important to dwellers in the moist tropics, and now it enters into general commerce among civilized nations. The meat and oil of the coconut are both used for human food; the poorer oil is good for soap, and the residue left after its extraction is good cattle feed. In the United States the imports of coconut oil and of the ill-smelling copra, or sun-dried meat of the nuts, outrank those of any other vegetable oil, amounting to over 370,000,000 pounds in 1930. Commercial copra comes mainly from the Philippines, but the remaining East Indies, Ceylon, and the islands of the Pacific are large producers in proportion to their size.

The main source of true *palm oil* is the fruit of a palm found mainly in West Africa, especially Nigeria, but now cultivated also in the East Indies. The fruit suggests a peach with an outer pulp surrounding a nut, but grows in huge, drooping clusters. The oil comes mainly from the pulp, and is used for soap, candles, lubricants, and in making tin plate. Oil from the inner kernel, however, is also used in making the butter substitute known as margarine. Palm nuts are one of the few tropical products whose main production is in the hands of natives and not of foreign plantation owners. Palm oil is used in such increasing amounts that it almost equals coconut oil and copra as an import into the United States.

Among the subtropical sources of vegetable oil, the *peanut*, or ground nut, ranks high. When the early Spaniards found the Brazilian Indians using peanuts for oil, they soon imitated them. Today India and the African region from Senegal to Nigeria export so many peanuts that only soy beans and linseed play a greater part among the oil producers in foreign trade. Peanut oil is widely used in cooking and on the table instead of olive oil, as well as in lard substitutes, margarine, and the woolen industry. Although the southern United States produces about 800,000,000 pounds of peanuts per year, considerable amounts are imported from China and some from the Philippines and Chosen. British India is the greatest exporter of peanuts, and Germany and France lead both in importing peanuts and in exporting peanut oil.

Sesame is the seed of an herb which was grown for its oil by the ancient Babylonians and Egyptians and is now important in India and China. The two latter countries and the Sudan are important exporters to Japan, the Netherlands, Italy, Germany, and Egypt. *Rape* is a species of cabbage grown in most countries of Europe but especially in India and China. Formerly rapeseed oil was the chief source of light in northern and central Europe. The Chinese today use it for this purpose as well as for cooking and candles. In some areas, such as Anatolia, the oil of *poppy* seeds is eaten and also exported for use in salads, soaps, paints, and varnishes.

The raising of trees for *tung oil* has been an oriental industry for centuries, but the rest of the world has only recently discovered that it is worth while. Now China's monopoly of this useful product must meet the competition of Florida. Because tung oil dries so quickly in paints and varnishes, we still import large quantities, sometimes 15,000,000 pounds per year. Expansion of the industry in Florida, however, seems certain because American methods produce a cheaper and purer product. Although *castor oil* is best known for its medicinal qualities, it is more largely used in soap making and as a lubricant. India and Brazil are the most important exporters of castor beans, and western Europe and the United States the chief buyers.

The greatest source of vegetable oils in the United States is *cottonseed*. These seeds, which were once wasted, are now often worth $200,000,000 a year to the farmers even before they are crushed, and of course far more when the oil is separated from the residue, which forms a cake or meal very good for cattle feed. The oil can be substituted for animal fats, for olive oil, and even for petroleum. The United States formerly exported vast quantities, as much as 200,000 tons in 1912, but now we need so much that only a little goes abroad. Of course all countries which raise cotton (B508) also produce cottonseed. In India if the monsoon rains are favorable, so that grass and other cattle feed are plentiful, perhaps half the cottonseed may be exported. When the monsoon rains fail, however, the Indian farmers hold their cottonseed for winter feed for cattle. An interesting sidelight on how different nations profit from their own products is the fact that the United States, which is by far the largest producer of cottonseed, exports none whatever. Egypt, India, Suez, and Uganda, on the other hand, export a great deal. The greatest exporter of cottonseed *oil* is Great Britain, which gets its raw material from the warmer countries just named.

Olive oil ranks at the very top for table use and cooking, and the poorer grades are of use in spinning, weaving, and for soap. Yet the table on page 382 shows that in foreign trade fresh olives play no part, while the oil ranks only a little above soy-bean oil and peanut oil. The reason is that the oil must be extracted while the olives are still fresh, and the worthless stones and pulp are so bulky that it would be foolish to ship them any distance. Moreover, because the making of olive oil is such an old industry, little mills for this purpose are found wherever olives are raised in the Old World. On the other hand, the high quality of olive oil keeps it far below cottonseed, coconut, and palm oils in international trade because the price is correspondingly high, and only a little is used as a raw material in manufacturing. The United States gets about 70 per cent of its edible olive oil from Italy, whereas about 90 per cent of the pickled olives come from Spain. The olives grown in the United States are not so rich in oil as those of Mediterranean regions.

The word *linseed* means linen seed, which is the same as flax seed. Flax is grown both for the fiber (linen) and for oil from the seed, but not always for both purposes in the same place. The chief centers for linseed oil are Argentina, Russia, India, China, and to a less extent the United States, Canada, and the Netherlands. Argentina has of late risen rapidly to a position where it raises much more than Russia and the United States combined, and supplies four-fifths of all the linseed that enters into foreign commerce. Nevertheless it exports practically no oil, leaving the Netherlands to do four-fifths of all the exporting. The fact that flax resists droughts and does especially well on new land makes it a good crop for Argentina, but the climate is too warm and dry to produce good fiber. Our high tariff on linseed causes a "sore spot" in the minds of the Argentines. Linseed oil is used in great quantities for paints and to a less extent in soap, oilcloth, and patent leather.

Various other vegetable oils are used much like those already discussed. *Sunflower oil* is important in certain parts of Russia. In many tropical countries people smear large quantities of oil on their skins to keep them soft in the hot sun. This is especially the case in regions like Africa from the Sudan southward where few clothes are worn.

In addition to the more common oils certain expensive extracts known as *essential oils* are used in the manufacture of perfumes and flavoring extracts. The raw materials for such oils include lavender, bergamot, geranium, bitter orange, peppermint, bay, mint, sassafras, cloves, and a number of others.

Stimulants and Narcotics.—Many plants provide stimulants or narcotics, some of which are very important both in local and international trade. Two products of the *cacao bean*—cocoa and chocolate—are not only stimulating but also valuable as food. Although cacao was introduced into Europe early in the sixteenth century it was long a Spanish monopoly and far too expensive for general use. Even in the early nineteenth century the entire European consumption was probably less than 12,000 tons. In recent years, however, there has been an extraordinary increase in output accompanied by a shift in the areas of production from the Caribbean region and Ecuador to Brazil, and especially to the Gold Coast and Nigeria in Africa. In 1900 the world production of raw cacao was about 150,000 tons per year; now 600,000 is not uncommon.

The cacao tree bears well only in the warmer, lower parts of the Regions of Wet Tropical Agriculture, chiefly within 12° or 15° of the equator. The yield is best where there is little wind, for dry winds injure the growth of the heavy green, red, or brown pods which are attached directly to the main branches and trunks, and strong winds often break them. Hence cacao plantations are restricted to calm belts, protected valleys, and small clearings in the equatorial forest. Moreover, they are often protected by taller trees which furnish shade and diminish the dangers from both sun and wind. In Trinidad, for example, the pink blossoms of these trees present a superb aspect when seen above the cliffs that border the northern side of the island. The shift in production from American to African regions has been accompanied by a corresponding shift from large plantations owned mainly by foreigners to small holdings owned by natives. This means that in the production of cacao, as well as of palm oil, the natives of the Guinea Coast of Africa hold the unique position of being the main producers of an important crop which is raised almost entirely for export. Whether the natives are more competent than those of other tropical regions or whether they owe their success to the care of their British rulers is not certain. The Spaniards still drink more cocoa than most people, but the rapidly increasing demand for this delicious product comes largely from the use of chocolate in confectionery. Because of its population and wealth, the United States is the greatest consumer, taking over 50 per cent of the world supply, while western Europe takes most of the balance.

Coffee.—Coffee provides remarkable illustrations of a number of geographical principles. For example, it illustrates the way in which diseases alter the areas of production. Coffee was introduced to western Europe from Arabia in 1650. The name "Mocha coffee" is a reminiscence of that time. It was then introduced into Java and Ceylon, which for nearly two hundred years were the main coffee areas of the world. "Java coffee" is still famous, although it no longer comes from there. About 1875, however, a leaf blight ruined the plantations of Ceylon, and spread to India and Java, where it worked similar disaster. So these regions turned to tea and other plantation crops, or to hardier types of coffee, as in East Java. Meanwhile, coffee had been introduced in the Caribbean region and Brazil, which now produces most of the world's supply. It grows best in the Regions of Wet Tropical Agriculture with a rainfall of 50 to 100 inches.

Coffee also illustrates a principle which we meet repeatedly, namely that crops tend to do best near their cooler limits. The coffees of the finest flavor are largely produced at high altitudes and in places where the cost of transportation is great. Nevertheless, the delicate flavor makes the crops profitable. Again, southern Brazil is by far the greatest producer of coffee, and the production there is almost entirely upon the cool plateaus. Moreover, by far the greatest production is in the relatively southern province of São Paulo (A386), where frosts are not unknown at the higher levels. More significant than this, however, is the fact that in São Paulo the production per tree is greater than in any other Brazilian province except Bahia, where it is about the same, and Paraná, where the production is nearly three times that of

São Paulo. Paraná lies south of São Paulo and at the very coldward margin of coffee culture. Part of its huge yield per tree is doubtless due to the use of new and suitable lands, and to the fact that there are no old trees to bring down the average, but part is probably due to climatic conditions analogous to those which make the yield of potatoes in Canada so much higher than in the United States (Λ87). Another advantage of the cooler regions is that, since there is a distinct cool season, all the coffee berries ripen at about the same time. Hence there is need of only one picking, instead of several as in the tropical regions.

Coffee also furnishes a singularly good illustration of the effect of soils. We saw in an earlier chapter that the plantations are almost always placed on slopes because that is where the best soil is. We also saw that from Rio de Janeiro and São Paulo coffee production has moved inland, and tends to center upon certain volcanic soils which are particularly well adapted to it. It is said that rocky places, with pockets of rich soil, are the most suitable, which merely means that coffee thrives best in young, new soils which are also well drained.

A—Coffee Trees in Provinces of Brazil.

Coffee also illustrates the social effect of crops. Where it is raised in especially rugged regions such as the mountainous parts of Colombia, Guatemala, and other Caribbean countries, the plantations are likely to be small and are often owned by natives. Where the slopes are gentler and also where climatic conditions are most favorable, as in São Paulo, huge plantations are the rule, some of them extending twenty miles in each direction. Among the large plantations, a system of contract labor has become highly developed. When new lands are being planted, the owners make contracts with "colonists," who undertake to plant the trees and take care of them for five years. In return they receive a certain amount of pay and are allowed to plant crops in the broad lanes between the young coffee bushes. They also get whatever coffee is produced before the end of their contract. That may be a good deal the fifth year, but the trees do not come into full bearing until they are about seven years old. Other workers, who are considered lower in the social scale, make a contract to keep certain tracts free from weeds and to gather the crop each year. Another important social result of coffee raising is the so-called valorization scheme. For a while the coffee plantations in Brazil were so profitable that far too many trees were set out. Therefore, the supply of coffee became so great that prices dropped to ruinously low levels. Accordingly, at various times the Brazilian government has intervened, buying coffee from the planters and storing it in government warehouses in hope of selling it later at a profit. This profit, however, has often failed to materialize, and in some cases hundreds of thousands of sacks of coffee of the poorer qualities have been piled along the railroad tracks and burned, or else thrown into the sea. The Brazilian government has spent millions of dollars in this way without much success—another example of the danger of relying too much on one product.

Chicory is a more northern perennial plant that deserves mention with coffee. For a long time the parsnip-like roots of this plant were used as food in central Europe, but in modern times the roots are mainly dried, pulverized, and used for making beverages. When added to ground coffee the chicory powder acquires the flavor and aroma of coffee. Consequently it is often blended with cheap coffees. About 14,500,000 pounds were used for this purpose in the United States in a recent year. Of this amount 13,400,000 pounds were produced here, almost entirely in the southeastern part of Michigan. The imports come from Europe, where Belgium, France, Germany, Holland, and Czechoslovakia are important producers.

Tea illustrates still another important phase of the relation between social conditions and economic geography. This hardy bush is probably a native of the highlands of southern China. From there it has spread equatorward as far as Java, westward to Ceylon and Assam, and northward to southern Japan. Nevertheless the greatest production and local use of tea are still in southern China. Many Australians do indeed drink tea five or even seven times a day, but even to them tea is not quite so great a necessity as to the multitudes of Chinese and Japanese who drink practically nothing else. This results from the combined effect of the ease with which tea can be raised on slopes that are too steep for other crops and the danger of infection from unboiled water because of the density of population and the use of sewage in the fields. But the fact that tea is so universally grown in southern China has had a bad effect on the foreign tea trade. Fifty or a hundred years ago China was the great source of tea for all the western world. Then Assam became the world's greatest tea exporter. Moreover, in Ceylon and West Java tea replaced coffee, which suffered from disease. There the moist climate is better for tea than for coffee, which needs a dry season. New tea areas were also developed in Sumatra and Formosa, and Japan began to export its unfermented *green* tea, which is stronger than the fermented *black* tea. Thus China became a minor factor in the tea trade. This was not because the other regions could raise tea more cheaply or of better quality than could China, but simply because they were better organized, kept their tea cleaner, and graded it better. In China each owner of a little tea patch raised whatever kind he happened to have and picked it and cured it in his own way without much regard to the sticks and dust that it might contain. The big planters in the new tea regions raised large amounts of a single variety, cured it and cleaned it systematically, and made contracts to sell large quantities. In other words they drove the Chinese out of the market by substantially the same process as that by which large-scale manufacturing has driven out hand work. Another social aspect of the tea industry appears in the fact that it has never spread appreciably beyond southwestern Asia and the East Indies. The reason is found mainly in the fact that nowhere else is there any such supply of cheap yet industrious labor for the slow, painstaking work of picking the tea leaves. Climatically the demands of tea are like those of coffee except that the plant can stand lower temperatures and thus is found farther north in Japan and Assam and higher up the mountains. Few kinds of tea have a better flavor than that raised at a height of 6,000 feet on the south slope of the Himalayas near Darjeeling. Many tea patches are occasionally nipped by the frost.

Yerba maté, or *Paraguay tea*, belongs in the same group of stimulants as tea and coffee. Like tea it is a dried leaf. It grows on a bushy tree 12 to 25 feet high and looks like holly. Many people claim that it has all the stimulating qualties of tea with even less in the way of harmful reactions. Nevertheless, very little is yet used outside of the regions where it grows in far southern Brazil, Paraguay, and northern Argentina.

Several minor stimulants of a much more harmful kind are raised in tropical and subtropical countries. One of these is *coca*, a little shrub which grows on the lower eastern slopes of the Andes in the Yungas region of Bolivia and Peru. The tiny leaves, either fresh or dry, are chewed by the Indians, especially when unusual exertion is demanded. The effect is indeed to overcome fatigue and temporarily make people forget their weariness and trouble, but this is followed by a very depressing reaction. Some people think that the dullness and stupidity of the South American Indians have been much accentuated by this drug. Coca enters international commerce for use in certain tonics and as the source of cocaine, which physicians use as a local anaesthetic to deaden the nerves and prevent pain in minor operations. The *hemp* of northern India, Persia, Arabia, and Brazil is an even more powerful stimulant than coca. When smoked or chewed it throws people into a curious kind of trancelike dream. *Opium*, which is derived from the hardened juice of the green seed of a cultivated species of poppy, has a similar effect. In Persia, India, and China, great fields of these big poppies can still be seen. So great is the harm done by this drug, so completely does it enslave its victims, and so eager are they to get it at any price that great social evil has resulted from it. In 1840 and again in 1855 importation of opium into China by foreign traders contrary to the wishes of the

Chinese government led to war between Great Britain and China. Today one of the most important committees of the League of Nations is charged with the duty of suppressing all traffic in opium except for medicinal purposes in the form of morphine and laudanum. Yet even now millions of people, especially in the opium-producing countries, lose much of their ability because of this terrible habit-forming drug. Less harmful by far is the *kola* nut of tropical Africa which is eaten by the natives as food and chewed as a stimulant. A similar stimulation is produced by *betel* leaves which are chewed with the areca nut and lime. They are the favorite stimulant of a vast number of people in India and other parts of southeastern Asia.

Few crops are more widely cultivated than *tobacco* (A389). Although tobacco is generally smoked or chewed for the narcotic

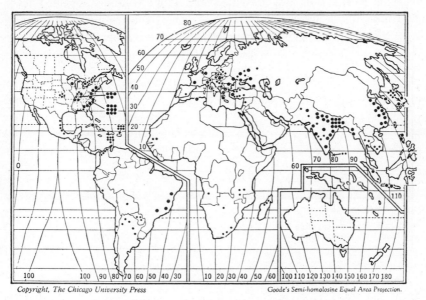

Goode's Semi-homolosine Equal Area Projection.

A—World Production of Tobacco. Each large dot indicates one per cent of the world production, each small dot one-tenth of one per cent.

effect of its nicotine, it is also valuable as a sheep wash, and for insecticides and medicines. Because tobacco produces a pleasant narcotic effect without any very noticeable reaction, it has been carried in all directions from its original home in subtropical or tropical America. It is raised at the equator and also as far north as Canada, Scotland, and northern Poland, although a hard frost may spoil the whole crop. Where the growing season is short the plants are usually started under glass, then transplanted after the danger of frost is over. Later they may be protected by cheese cloth, as in the Connecticut Valley, in order to give the plants greater warmth, humidity, and freedom from insects.   Although tobacco plants in general can endure a great diversity of climates, they make heavy demands upon the soil, and certain varieties do well only under special combinations of soil and climate.   This has led to considerable localization, and to the growth of "filler" and "wrapper" tobacco in different places. Because of such conditions approximately 90 per cent of the tobacco of the United States is produced in six states—Kentucky, North Carolina, Virginia, Tennessee, South Carolina, and Ohio.   Other small but important centers are found in southern Maryland, Lancaster County in Pennsylvania, the Connecticut Valley, and southern Wisconsin (A390).

This localization and specialization is not confined to the United States.   Cuba is noted for tobacco of fine aroma from the province of

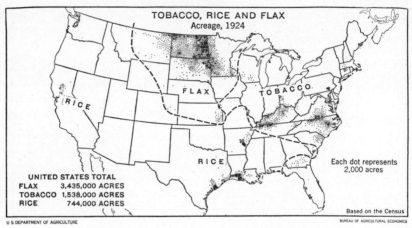

A—Tobacco, Rice and Flax in the United States.

Pinar del Río; Sumatra and Java produce a tobacco well adapted for use as wrappers; and Turkish tobacco is generally made into cigarettes. The leading producers of tobacco are the United States, India, China, Russia, and Japan, with large amounts also in the Philippines, Dutch East Indies, Brazil, and most of the countries of central and western Europe.   Tobacco is exceedingly important in international trade.   In the neighborhood of 700,000,000 pounds enter commercial channels yearly.   The leading exporters are generally the United States, Sumatra, Cuba, Brazil, Bulgaria, and Turkey.   Western Europe is the important importing section, especially Germany, the United Kingdom, and France.

Alcoholic Drinks.—Almost every main group of peoples uses one or more forms of fermented or distilled liquors.   No attempt is made here to describe all of these.

We shall merely show what large amounts of grains, fruits, and vegetables are used in making them and how much time and energy are taken up in the preparation, distribution, and consumption of both mild and strong liquors. Turning to the tropics we find wide use of *palm wine*, made by tapping the flower stalk of the palms and fermenting the juice. *Rum*, which is distilled from molasses and other juices of the sugar cane, is also a common product of many tropical and subtropical areas. The West Indies and East Indies are noted for the rum which they export to Europe and other temperate regions. The sap of certain agaves having fleshy leaves is the source of *pulque*, a favorite fermented beverage in much of Mexico. From the roots of this same plant is distilled a much stronger liquor known as *mescal*. *Chicha* is a name applied in Latin America to a fermented or distilled drink whose alcoholic content varies according to the process of production and the raw material. It may be made from corn and honey in Colombia, or potatoes in Peru, or from cane sugar or a poor quality of grape in Chile. *Saki*, a kind of wine made by the fermentation of rice, is important as an article of local trade in Japan. As an article of commerce, *wine*, the fermented juice of the grape, is far more important than fresh grape juice.

We have already seen that the great vine centers, especially those for wine production, are located in regions with a Mediterranean climate. Wine is used so commonly in many countries there that it may be considered the national drink in France, Spain, Portugal, Italy, Greece, and even Austria, Hungary, Switzerland, and the Rhine Valley. It is produced in large quantites in all important areas of grape cultivation except where some sort of prohibition prevails, as in California under the eighteenth amendment or in Turkey and North Africa under Mohammedanism. If "sweet" wine is desired the grapes are picked before they are fully ripe and fermentation is stopped after a limited period. In the manufacture of "dry" wines the grape juice is fully fermented. Conditions of soil and climate seem to have a noticeable effect on wines regardless of methods of manufacture. So we have distinct localization of types such as champagne from the dry chalk hills of the same name in France, sherry from the vicinity of Jerez in Spain, port from the Douro Valley, chianti from Tuscany, the tokay of Hungary, and many others. The production of grapes for wine is the outstanding industry in some regions, and in Italy the acreage given to their culture is next to that of wheat. France produces even more wine but on less acreage than Italy. In a recent year the value of French wine was about $460,000,000, the most valuable product of the country. Wine is also made extensively in the other areas with the Mediterranean Type of climate, namely portions of Australia, South Africa, Chile, and Argentina.

Of the liquors belonging principally to temperate and cyclonic areas the best known are whiskey, gin, brandy, and vodka. *Whiskey* is a distilled product made from various grains or potatoes. In the United States, before the days of prohibition, it was generally made from corn or sometimes rye. In Scotland much is made from barley. *Gin* is usually distilled from some grain to which juniper berries have been added. Because of the large production in Holland it is often known as Hollands or Holland gin. *Beer* is a fermented product and hence much lower in alcoholic content than either whiskey or gin. It is made chiefly from malted barley and is manufactured and consumed in all parts of Europe, especially Germany, and in many other countries in temperate latitudes. *Brandy* was formerly almost entirely a distillate of wine, but is now made in large amounts from the fermented juices of various fruits such as peaches, cherries, apples, etc., by distillation. *Vodka* is a Russian distilled liquor made more often from rye but sometimes from potatoes or barley.

From this enumeration of liquors it is evident that all parts of the world tend to use their local resources as a source of alcoholic drinks. Not only the taste but the strength and the effect of the liquors also vary from region to region. The grape wines of the Mediterranean region and the malted beers of central Europe seem to produce far less drunkenness than the palm wine, rum, mescal, and chicha of tropical regions, or the whiskey and vodka of the colder countries. Accordingly we find much inefficiency due to alcohol in the warmest regions, while in the comparatively cool countries we find a constant struggle as to how alcoholic liquors shall be regulated. Prohibition has been tried in Canada, the United States, Scandinavia, and Finland, but not in countries farther south except in the dry lands where Mohammedanism prevails.

Spices and Flavorings.—Trade in spices is as old as history. In the past, even more than now, poor cooking and a monotonous diet made spices highly desirable. Since most spices came from the East Indies and India, the difficulties of transportation made them very costly, but spices weigh little, and the demand was so great that the trade was profitable. Spices ranked with gold as an incentive to Ferdinand and Isabella in encouraging Columbus to search for a shorter route to the East Indies. In our day the East Indies and the neighboring shores of India are still the chief source of spices, although many kinds are also grown in the West Indies. *Nutmeg* and *mace*, for example, come from the same East Indian tree, nutmeg being the kernel of the fruit and mace the inner shell. In the fashion typical of many spices they have spread from their original home in the Molucca Islands to others of the East Indies, the West Indies, and Brazil. *Cloves* have followed the same course, and have also gone to the islands of Zanzibar and Pemba off the east coast of Africa, which are now the chief producers. They are dried flower buds, and are used not only in cooking, confectionery, and liquors, but also as a source of a flavoring oil. The tree whose bark furnishes *cinnamon* is so sensitive to soil and climate that it does not grow widely and is produced mainly in Ceylon. The twining and climbing plant that furnishes ordinary *pepper*, on the other hand, grows widely in Malaya, the East Indies, and India, and on a small scale in the West Indies. The berries of this plant are known as peppercorns. If ground whole they give black pepper; if ground after the removal of the outer skin, the resultant powder is white pepper. *Cayenne* or *red pepper* (Mexican chili, Spanish pepper, or Guiana pepper), on the contrary, is one of the spices which Columbus or his successors really found in tropical America. The ground pods of this capsicum plant are one of the hottest spices. Paprika is a milder form, and there are several other kinds of pepper. *Allspice* is another spice which the Spaniards found in the West Indies. Its name indicates the opinion of its discoverers that they thought they could detect in it the flavor of other or perhaps all spices. The best known area of production is Jamaica. The last of the tropical spices to claim attention is *curry*. This powder is much used in warm countries, especially India, to flavor rice, poultry, and other meats. It consists of sago, tamarind flour, or some similar base, mixed with curry leaves and other spices. *Sarsaparilla* and *vanilla* are two widely used tropical flavoring extracts which serve almost the same purpose as spices. Sarsaparilla is derived from the root of a plant found native in Central and South America. Vanilla is unique in being derived from the pods of an orchid, a parasitic plant which attaches itself to trees by means of aerial rootlets, although the roots also penetrate the ground. The main source of vanilla is an orchid native to southeastern Mexico, but now also cultivated in Java, Mauretania, and some of the smaller oceanic islands.

Outside the Regions of Wet Tropical Agriculture spices are rare, but a number of plants furnish flavoring extracts. Oil of *mustard* is derived from the seed of black mustard. *Soya* is a sauce or flavoring compound like chile sauce, which is much used in Japan to improve tasteless foods like rice. It is made in large quantities in little home factories from fermented beans, usually soy beans. *Licorice* is used not only in medicine and confectionery but for flavoring chewing tobacco. It is extracted from the root of a plant found in Europe. *Wintergreen*, or checkerberry, is one of the few sources of flavoring extracts that grows in the United States. The aromatic little leaves are picked wild in woods and pastures. *Mints* of various kinds are also familiar not only in gardens but also wild in the United States and Europe. Nevertheless, mint flavoring extracts are made mainly from plants found native in Central and South America.

Medicinal Plants.—The number of medicinal plants is so great that a mere list of them would fill many pages. The cinchona tree, however, from the bark of which *quinine* is extracted, is too important to be passed by. Quinine is probably the most important of all commodities that are used purely for medicinal purposes. It has long been the one great remedy for malaria, and is also useful in other ailments. The cinchona tree is a native of the eastern slopes of the Andes at elevations of three to ten thousand feet from Colombia to Bolivia. It grows in the same zone of rather young soil and abundant rains at all seasons which fosters the coca plant. This Yungas zone, as we have seen, may some day become a great plantation region when transportation becomes easy. Now, however, it is so inaccessible that in 1860 when attempts were first made to cultivate cinchona the seeds were taken to India and the East Indies, thus repeating the history of rubber. Today, after experiments in various islands the quinine plantations have become concentrated in Java, which produces more than nine-tenths of the world's supply. Quinine is now so cheap that it does not pay the South American natives to go to the forest and gather the wild bark. It is interesting that the histories of cinchona and of the coca plant from which we get the valuable medical product, cocaine, should be so different. The reason lies in the fact that the local demand for coca among the Indians far exceeds the foreign demand, whereas the demand for quinine comes chiefly from Europeans who wish to live in India, the East Indies, Africa, and other tropical regions that are under European influence. In both cases production is localized in places where fitness of climate and soil combine with accessibility to the main market.

Ginseng is another medicinal plant which enters considerably into commerce. The Chinese are the main users. They get their supplies mainly from Chosen and the United States. The root is usually dug in the forests, but is sometimes cultivated in small plots that are well shaded. There is also considerable international trade in *camphor*, which is extracted from a tree that grows in Japan, Taiwan (Formosa), China, and the Malay Peninsula. The Japanese government holds a monopoly on the Taiwan supply which furnishes about three-fourths of the world's camphor.

Floriculture.—This term is used to indicate the raising of flowers, shrubs, and other plants for ornamental purposes and also as sources of perfumes. Every modern city of sufficient size has greenhouses and nurseries for the purpose of supplying florists' shops or of selling not only cut flowers but potted plants and ornamental shrubs and trees to householders. So important has the use of living plants become that it forms the basis of a distinct and growing profession, landscape gardening. In Europe and even in many oriental cities the sale of flowers is called to one's attention more than in the United States because of the open flower markets. From Sicily to Finland, or from Bordeaux to Constantinople, such flower markets in open squares are one of the pleasantest features of European cities. Equally pleasant are the areas like the borders of the sand dunes in Holland or the gladiolus gardens in the northern United States where special kinds of flowers are grown in bulk. The Riviera in France is noted for the production of roses, sour oranges, lavender, and other flowers for perfumes. In the southern part of Bulgaria a part of the Maritza Valley some 80 miles long and 30 wide contains nearly 20,000 acres of roses upon which the people of about 150 villages depend largely for a living. Rose water, rose wax, and attar of roses are produced from these plants. It takes 3,000 to 5,000 ounces of rose petals to make a single ounce of attar of roses. Naturally the product is enormously expensive, but a single drop of this distillate gives lasting perfume to a large amount of other material. Easter lilies for the early market in the United States are shipped in large quantities from Bermuda. Many other examples of the localization of floriculture might be cited, but the greatest production of the florists is in the flower gardens, nurseries, and greenhouses near our cities where the product can readily be marketed. According to the census of 1930 the products of this kind grown in the United States in 1929 were worth $146,000,000.

Textiles and Fibers.—The importance of warm regions, and especially of the Regions of Wet Tropical Agriculture, is evident from a study of textile fibers as well as of spices and stimulants. Aside from flax all the important fibers come from regions at least as warm as the Cotton Belt of the United States and most from areas that belong to the wet tropics. Although *coir* is not one of the most important of these the British Conference which met at Ottawa in 1932 to arrange for preferential trade within the British Empire thought it worth including as one of the commodities for preference in trade between the United Kingdom and India. Coir fiber forms a sort of matting on the outside of coconut husks, and is exported from the same Malaysian regions which export copra. It is used for brushes, brooms, doormats, stair carpets, and other articles where a rough, tough cheap fiber is needed. *Kapok*, tree cotton, or vegetable down, as it is variously called, is obtained from the seed vessels of the so-called silk cotton tree. This is found wild in the tropical parts of both hemispheres, but is raised in groves commercially in Java. Some kapok is used for filling life preservers, but more for such purposes as filling mattresses.

Two other products of the Regions of Wet Tropical Agriculture, manila hemp and jute, are especially valuable because of the strength and length of their fiber. *Manila hemp* is also elastic and highly resistant to salt water. Naturally, then, it is fit not only for the higher grades of the binder twine used to bind sheaves in harvesting, but also for the superior grades of general cordage, and above all for marine cordage which must resist salt water. It is the fiber of the abaca, a banana-like plant whose production is practically limited to the Philippines. It seems to need a peculiar combination of warmth, moisture, and deep, loamy, fertile, loose-textured and well drained soil which is not yet too mature. Many of the best plantations grow on volcanic slopes, but even there the fiber often loses much of its value because it is so carelessly cleaned and dried. The United States imports about 60,000 tons of Manila hemp a year from the Philippines.

Jute is even more important than Manila hemp, the imports into the United States sometimes reaching 100,000 tons. In fact it comes next to cotton as the most widely used fiber. This is partly because it can be raised and spun so cheaply. For this reason, although it is the weakest and least durable of the main fibers, it has replaced hemp for many purposes, the most familiar of which are burlap, gunny sacks, and other bagging materials. It is also used in cheap comfits, rugs, linoleums, and tarpaulins, and is often mixed with other materials in sheetings, towels, and other articles. Jute can be grown in many countries, but no other region seems to combine so many advantages as eastern Bengal near Calcutta. Tropical heat, periodic floods of the Ganges, cheap labor, and a location close to a busy port all favor it. Jute matures so rapidly that three months after the seedlings have been transplanted like rice it is ready to harvest.

Henequen, often called sisal, is imported into the United States even more than hemp, the imports sometimes coming close to 150,000 tons. About three-fourths of this comes from Mexico, which supplied practically all up to 1910. Central America and the West Indies also supply some, but the dry coastal sections of the states of Yucatan and Campeche in Mexico remain the important centers of production. This is interesting because these regions belong to the Wet and Dry Low Latitudes. Henequen is one of the very few products of world importance supplied by such regions, and hence is of especial importance to them. The rainfall in the henequen areas of Mexico is only about 30 inches, which is low for so warm a region. Of course it is concentrated in the season when the sun is high, and there is a dry season in our winter. The soil is fairly young and consists of decomposed limestone, so that it is quite fertile. It is worth noting not only that this combination of environmental conditions on the coast of Yucatan appears to be unusually good for the Wet and Dry Low Latitudes, but moreover that it is associated with the later phase of the great ancient civilization of the Mayas and with a present degree of prosperity not common in this natural region. Mérida, the capital of Yucatan, is an unusually progressive city for its latitude. Nevertheless it suffers because the prosperity arising from henequen has led to overproduction and consequent low prices, just as has happened with rubber in Malaysia and coffee in Brazil. The interest of the United States in henequen centers largely in the fact that it is the great source of binder twine for our grain crops.

Ramie or China grass is like kapok in being a fiber long known in southwestern Asia and the East Indies but only lately used much in Europe and America. It has been woven into cloth since the earliest times in India, China, Japan, and the Malay Archipelago. Its strength and silky luster are making it popular for cloths of many kinds from stout sail cloth to dainty velvet.

Cotton is the most important of all fibers. Since it is used in every country and by almost every person in each country it is more widely employed and hence more widely bought and sold than any other material. Even iron cannot rival it, for hundreds of millions of people buy cotton clothing far more often than they buy anything made of iron. The reason for this popularity is found partly in the cheapness of cotton, partly in its adaptation to a wide variety of climates, and partly in its excellent qualities as a fiber. These qualities include tensile strength, elasticity, uniformity of texture, porosity, and durability. The characteristic kink or twist in the fibers is especially valuable in making them stick together when twisted and thus in giving strength and durability to cotton thread. Because of all this the uses of cotton have multiplied until they run into hundreds, yes thousands.

Although temperature conditions permit the growth of cotton from the equator as far as latitude 40° in Missouri and Asiatic Russia, conditions of soil, relief, and labor restrict it considerably. Hence, about 90 per cent of the world's cotton is produced in four countries, the United States, India, China, and Egypt. The remaining 10 per cent comes from fifty or more widely scattered countries. The fact that England, other European countries, and Japan cannot raise cotton has led to active attempts to produce it in areas where these countries can control the product without depending on the United States. This is one reason why England has built great dams on the main Nile at Assuan in Egypt and on the Blue Nile in Sudan. She has also encouraged cotton growing and the improvement of the crop in India, South Africa, and Uganda. For the same reason the Soviet Republic is making great efforts to increase production in Transcaucasia and the irrigated regions near Bukhara and Samarkand east of the Caspian Sea. In South America, cotton-growing land is abundant but labor is scarce.

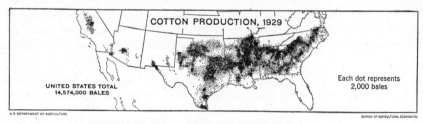

A—Cotton Production in the United States.

Ecuador makes cloth from wild cotton which grows near the seacoast and is spun and woven in little mills high in the Andes near Quito.

Cotton is a subtropical plant which grows best where numerous short summer showers alternate with longer periods of sunshine, and a warm growing season has a length of at least 200 days. Such conditions, as well as a good labor supply, are highly favorable to the growth of cotton in the southeastern United States (A396). The American crop maintains its position in spite of a number of pests such as the boll weevil, the pink boll worm, cotton boll worms, and cotton leaf worms. Cotton wilt, root-rot, root-knot and other diseases also take heavy toll, but all the others together do less harm than the boll weevil, which in newly infested areas may destroy half the crop. The methods designed by the Department of Agriculture for combating these evils are a great tribute to that section of the government.

There are three main kinds of cotton in addition to the wild cotton of tropical America. By far the most common in the United States is upland cotton. The other two kinds are more valuable because of their longer fiber. One is Egyptian cotton, which is raised in the hot, sunny irrigated sections of Arizona and southeastern California where the climate is much like that of Egypt. The third kind is called Sea Island cotton from the moist islands along the coast of the Carolinas and Georgia. It has the longest staple, or fiber, nearly 2 inches, in contrast to an inch and a half for Egyptian and 1 inch or less for upland. Hence it makes stronger thread and brings a higher price.

From the economic and social standpoints cotton suffers from two great disadvantages, namely great instability of price and the evils which result from one-crop production. During the present century the price has ranged from 5.5 to 43.75 cents per pound. The yield per acre also varies considerably, having been 183 pounds in 1926 versus 153 in 1928. Whenever the price rises the cotton growers are stimulated to plant a larger acreage. This automatically increases the crop and lowers the price. If the price happens to be high because the yield per acre has been unusually low by reason of drought, insects, or some other natural disaster, it sometimes happens that the next year sees not only an unusually large acreage but also an unusual yield per acre. Naturally, states like Texas and Mississippi, where 56 and 61 per cent respectively of all the cultivated land was in cotton at the last census and where cotton on an average supplies two-thirds or three-fourths of the total value of the crops, suffer terribly when prices collapse. Many attempts have been made to remedy this situation by mutual agreements among the farmers, and by persuading them to diversify their crops. The plans for restriction of area have met with little success, because when they are urged, multitudes of farmers say to themselves, "Now is my chance. Other people will cut down acreage; prices will be high. So I will say nothing and plant my full amount or more, and get the advantage of the high prices." Diversification of crops has made some progress. In this respect the boll weevil has been a godsend because it has forced many farmers to turn to other crops. Thus, in the Black Belt of Alabama with its rich black soil, large areas once in cotton are now given up to corn and to raising cattle.

More than half the cotton grown in the United States is exported. This has been true for some time in spite of increased consumption within the country and increased production outside. A noticeable feature of our cotton trade is a falling off in the percentage of our raw cotton sent to the United Kingdom and France, and an increase in the percentage sent to Germany, Italy, Japan, and certain minor European countries. We supply raw cotton to many countries which are newcomers in the cotton-manufacturing industry. Instead of manufacturing the cotton and selling them cotton cloth year after year, we manufacture cotton machinery, sell them that, and then send them raw cotton.

Hemp and flax are two plants of comparatively cool climates which have been largely superseded by cheaper products from warmer regions. *Hemp* was formerly the main source of rope and twine in Europe, and is still used for these purposes, especially wrapping twine, fishing lines, and the warp of carpets. But the production in the United States, mainly in Wisconsin, Ohio, and Kentucky, is unimportant, and that of western Europe is small. Eastern Europe, particularly Russia, is the main producer, but the best quality comes from Italy. Although *flax* is cultivated for both fiber and seeds, the two products, as we have seen, rarely come from the same plant. The fiber is generally raised in regions cooler than those where seed is the main product. Most of the world's flax fiber is raised in Europe—western Russia, Poland, and the Baltic States on the one hand, and Holland, Belgium, northern France, and northern Ireland on the other. Flax grows in a wide range of climates, and its production is mainly limited by the large amount of labor required in pulling up the plants by the roots, removing the seeds with a comb, and wetting the straw so that the soft parts decay and the fibers can be separated from them. Flax is used for twine, laces, canvas, and especially the various types of linen cloth. A surprising quantity of such linen is still made by hand in eastern Europe.

Miscellaneous.—Man makes use of many other plants which do not come under the classifications of this chapter. The most important of these is rubber, which was discussed in the first chapter. The sap of other plants supplies numerous *gums* and *resins*, which come mainly from trees which are tapped in the wild state. They are used for a great variety of purposes from incense to lacquers and varnishes. Dyestuffs of vegetable origin are also obtained from various trees and plants. By far the most important source of vegetable dyes is the shrub from which *indigo* is obtained. Until about 1900 indigo was an important export from India, but the competition of synthetic dyes has greatly curtailed its production.

Many other useful plants find a limited use in the tropics, but unless a demand for them arises elsewhere they are not likely to lead to important industries. It is quite possible, however, that some of them will spring into prominence as have abaca and rubber. Perhaps the most outstanding fact in this whole study of useful plants is the way in which the plants of temperate regions furnish the staple food products, and also the staple kinds of wood, as appears in the chapter on forests, while tropical regions, and particularly the Regions of Wet Tropical Agriculture, provide an enormous variety of products which are not essential but highly desirable.

EXERCISES

Note: Use the same reference books as in Chapter XVI.

1. From the *Oxford Economic Atlas*, or Goode's *School Atlas* make a map showing where coffee and tea are produced. Use this book and other sources to help you in summarizing the geographic and other factors which influence the production of each crop. Why is coffee produced so predominantly in the Western Hemisphere and tea almost entirely in the Eastern?

2. Make a map and summary like those of Exercise 1, but for Manila hemp, henequen (sisal), flax, hemp, and jute.

3. Study a map of cotton production. Where is the most important cotton-raising area? What five or six other areas come next? What other areas seem

to have good physical conditions for cotton production? Why do they produce so little?

4. Discuss the relative importance of vegetable oils, stimulants, and fibers. Consider each of the following factors: (a) area devoted to production in each case, (b) value per acre, (c) necessity to human welfare, (d) extent to which each enters into world trade, (e) recent growth in production and trade.

5. Study dot maps of the United States showing tobacco, corn, cotton, sugar beets, and vegetables. Use this book and the *Graphic Summary of American Agriculture*. How far do these maps explain the distribution of prosperity indicated by the maps of Kentucky (A162) (A176), North Carolina, (A165, B165), and Iowa (A207)?

6. Choose one vegetable oil and treat it according to the method of Exercises 1 and 2 in Chapter XVII.

7. Do the same for a stimulant.

8. Do the same for a fiber or other industrial product.

9. On a world map, indicate by different colors the areas where the chief vegetable oils are raised, and those where they are chiefly used, indicating regions where they are raised by lines and those where they are used by dots. What do you conclude as to the relation of the production and use to climate, soil, relief, and markets?

10. Write a general account of the geographic conditions which foster the raising of staple food products in contrast with industrial crops, stimulants, and food products which are more or less luxuries. Remember that a product like olive oil or dry beans is a staple food product in many regions, whereas lettuce and oranges fall in the luxury class for most of the world's people.

CHAPTER XIX

THE DISTRIBUTION OF USEFUL ANIMALS

Principles of Animal Distribution.—In the world as a whole, the annual return from domestic animals is approximately as valuable as from all cultivated vegetable products except food for animals; it is twice as valuable as that of all the minerals. The accompanying table lists the animals that furnish practically all of this vast value, according to their zoological families. The starred animals may be excluded from further consideration. Most of them represent attempts at domestication which have proved of little permanent value, or whose ultimate success is not yet known.

The Limitations of Domestication.—Several important features deserve notice in connection with the 30 unstarred animals. (1) All were domesticated so long ago that we have no certain knowledge of the event, in many cases not even a tradition. (2) The number of species that have proved permanently worthy of domestication is extremely small. Among approximately 3,500 known species of mammals, only 19 are unstarred in the table. Among 13,000 species of birds, only 9 fall among our 30 animals, and one of those, the ostrich, may drop out, if its feathers fail to find favor. Reptiles, 3,500 species; amphibia, 1,400; and fish, 13,000, have no domesticated representatives, except the doubtful goldfish. The case of insects is still more extreme, for silkworms and bees are the only domesticated species out of approximately 470,000. (3) The qualities which make an animal worth domesticating are concentrated in a few small groups. Among the 30 animals here discussed no less than 16 belong to a single group, the Ungulata, or hoofed mammals. Six of these are species of cattle, all from the genus *Bos*, which contains only 10 species in all. The cattle family, as distinguished from the genus, includes also the sheep and goat, so that one-fifth of all the domestic animals, and one-fourth of the important ones, come from this one family. In the same way, 4 out of 6 members of the camel family have been domesticated, and 2 out of the 7 members of the horse family. All the more important birds come from two orders, Galliformes, and Anseriformes.

THE WORLD'S DOMESTIC ANIMALS *

MAMMALS.
  A. Hoofed mammals. (*Ungulata.*)
      I. Order of odd-toed hoofed mammals. (*Perissodactyla.*)
          a. Horse family.
              1. Horse. (*Equus caballus.*) Central Asia.
              2. Ass. (*Equus africanus.*) North Africa.
      II. Order of even-toed hoofed mammals. (*Artiodactyla.*)
          a. Cattle family.
              3. Ordinary cattle. (*Bos primigenius.*) Europe.
              4. Humped zebu of India, and galla of Africa. (*Bos indicus.*) India.
              5. Gayal. (*Bos frontalis.*) India.
              6. Banteng or Javan cattle. (*Bos sondaicus.*) East Indies.
              7. Yak. (*Bos grunniens.*) Tibet and Himalayas.
              8. Water buffalo. (*Bos babulus.*) India.
              9. Sheep. (*Ovis aries.*) Probably Western Asia.
              10. Goat. (*Capra hircus.*) Western Asia.
          b. Pig family.
              11. Pig. (Perhaps several species.) Europe, Asia.
          c. Camel family.
              12. Arabian camel, one-humped. (*Camelus dromedarius.*) Arabia.
              13. Bactrian camel, two-humped. (*Camelus bactrianus.*) Central Asia.
              14. Llama. (*Llama glama.*) Peru.
              15. Alpaca. (*Llama pacos.*) Andes.
          d. Deer family.
              16. Reindeer. (*Rangifer tarandus.*) Arctic regions.
      III. Order of elephants. (*Proboscidea.*)
              *17. Elephant. (*Elephas indicus.*) India. Not bred in captivity.

  B. Clawed mammals. (*Unguiculata.*)
      I. Order of flesh-eating mammals. (*Carnivora.*)
          a. Dog family.
              18. Dog. (Descended from several species.) Place of origin unknown.
              *19. Silver fox. (*Vulpes fulvus.*) North America.
          b. Cat family.
              20. Cat. (*Felis libyca* and other species.) Probably North Africa.
              *21. Cheetah. (*Acinonyx jubatus.*) Subtropical Asia and Africa.
          c. Marten family.
              *22. Ferret. (*Putorius foetidus.*) Probably North Africa.
          d. Civet and mongoose family.
              *23. Mongoose. (*Herpestes mungo.*) India.
      II. Order of gnawing mammals. (*Rodentia.*)
          a. Rabbit family.
              24. Rabbit. (*Oryctolagus cuniculus.*) Western Mediterranean basin.
          b. Rat family.
              *25. White rat. Probably China, but first domesticated in England about 1850.
              *26. White mouse. Origin unknown.
          c. Guinea pig family.

              *27. Guinea pig. (*Cavia cutleri.*) Peruvian coast, originally kept for food.

BIRDS.
      I. Order of fowl-like birds. (*Galliformes.*)
              28. Hen. (*Gallus gallus.*) India.
              29. Turkey. (*Meleagris mexicana.*) Mexico.
              30. Guinea fowl. (Wild stock unknown.) Probably West Africa.
              31. Peafowl. (*Pavo cristatus.*) India.
      II. Order of goose-like birds. (*Anseriformes.*)
              32. Duck. (*Anas boschas.*) North America, temperate Europe and Asia.
              33. Goose. (*Anser anser.*) Northern Europe (?)
              34. Swan. (*Cygnus olor.*) Central Europe and Central Asia.
      III. Order of plover-like birds. (*Charadriiformes.*)
              35. Pigeon. (*Columba livia.*) Mediterranean region to China.
      IV. Order of ostriches. (*Struthioniformes.*)
              36. Ostrich. (*Struthio camelus.*) North Africa.
      V. Order of stork-like birds. (*Ciconiiformes.*)
              *37. Cormorant. (Several species.) Coast of Europe, Asia, America.
      VI. Order of falcon-like birds. (*Falconiformes.*)
              *38. Falcon. (Probably several species.) Southern and Eastern Asia.
      VII. Order of sparrow-like birds. (*Passeriformes.*)
              *39. Canary. (*Serinus canarius.*) Canary Islands and Madeira.

FISH.
      I. Order of the bony fishes. (*Teleostei.*)
              *40. Gold fish. (*Cyprinus auratus.*) China.

INSECTS.
      I. Order of butterflies and moths. (*Lepidoptera.*)
              41. Silkworm. (*Bombyx mori.*) China.
      II. Order of ants, bees, and wasps. (*Hymenoptera.*)
              42. Bee. (*Apis*, many species.) Mediterranean region. (?)

---

  * Nomenclature after Hegner. Arranged in the order of their importance to man so far as this is consistent with the zoological classification.

Uses of Domestic Animals.—Usefulness is the main quality which makes an animal worth domesticating. In a stage of culture like our own, the main uses of domestic animals are: (1) food, (2) transportation, (3) clothing, (4) raw materials other than for clothing, (5) protection, (6) hunting, (7) scavenging, (8) fertilizer. Food is put first because financially it occupies the main place. The main food products derived from animals are worth about one-third as much as all man's vegetable food. The world's annual production of animals for transportation has an estimated value of about two billion dollars, but the relative importance of animals in this respect is much greater, for animals live many years, whereas food is usually consumed the year it is raised. The wool, silk, and hides supplied by animals provide clothing materials worth another two billion dollars each year, although their importance is probably much less than that of the animals for transportation, as will appear below. The next four uses occupy such a minor rank that they are here excluded from further discussion; the importance of fertilizers has already been discussed.

Importance of Animals for Transportation.—Historically the use of animals for transportation and draft has probably been more important than for food. Without beasts of burden, human beings might never have progressed beyond the stage of carrying all loads with their own bodies, as among the highland Indians of Guatemala. Unless animals had been used to pull the plow, the main centers of agriculture and civilization might never have migrated into regions of forests and prairies where the climate is especially stimulating and the highest civilizations now center. In most such regions a cover of sod soon smothers a field that is not plowed. Such a field can be spaded by hand, but the excessive labor almost precludes a high standard of living. Without draft animals, mankind might never have realized the wonderful possibilities of the wheel, which led to modern machinery. The desire to utilize horses or other animals more fully for draft purposes presumably led primitive man to put wheels under his sledges, and later to gear wheels together so that his animals might grind grain, pump water, and the like. Thus in many ways beasts of burden and draft animals have been essential in the evolution of the highest types of civilization.

Motor transportation is sometimes supposed to have made the horse no longer a necessity. This is largely true in limited regions, but not in the world as a whole (A410). Motor traction in the farm is still far too expensive for most of mankind. The United States has three out of every four of the world's motor vehicles, and a still larger percentage of the tractors. Except for a few million people in Canada, Australia, New Zealand, and Argentina, the 2,000,000,000 inhabitants of the parts of the world outside the United States depend almost entirely upon horses, mules, cattle, and even camels for plowing and other farm work. In the United States, however, the number of horses, mules, and asses *in cities and villages* diminished from 3,470,000 in 1910 to 2,100,000 in 1920, and has now fallen much lower.   *On the farms* of the United States the horses and mules increased from 24,000,000 in 1910 to almost 26,000,-000 in 1920, the maximum being reached in 1919.   By 1925 the number had declined to 22,500,000 and by 1931 to 18,400,000 (A403 and A411). This represents a decrease of about 39 per cent from the maximum number of horses, but from 1910 to 1931 mules increased about 25 per cent.

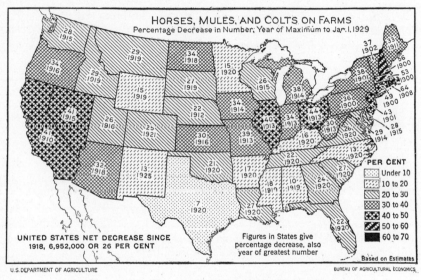

A—Decrease in Horses and Mules in the United States.

Mules are used mainly in the South, where tractors and trucks are still relatively scarce.   Further evidence of a diminished demand for horses is found in the decline in farm prices per head from $108 in 1910 to $64 in 1925 and to $60 in 1931.

Other factors may have helped in bringing about the decline in horses.   For example, it is estimated that from 1893 to 1897 the number of horses and mules in the United States declined $10\frac{1}{2}$ per cent and the price fell 49 per cent.   Thus a decline may take place without the automobile.   The two cases are not parallel, however, for in the present case the automobile and especially the truck and tractor are making steady inroads upon the work formerly done by horses.   Nevertheless, it is uncertain, how far the present decline in the number of horses and mules will go.   It depends partly on the degree of prosperity.   During the great depression of 1929–33 the use of horses in the United States increased, because farmers can raise grass and oats, but not gasoline and oil.   In almost no other country has motor traction yet caused any appreciable decline in the use of horses.

The geographical significance of all this lies in the fact that the environments in which horses and tractors are the most economical source of power for farms are different.   The tractor may some day do practically all the work where well-drained, level land is available, where the soil is rich enough so that the farmers have considerable capital, and

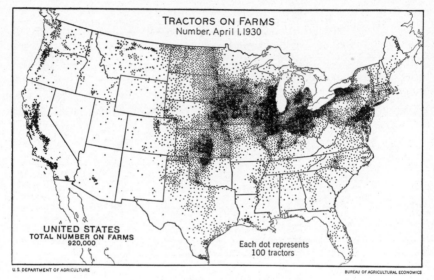

A—Tractors on Farms in the United States.

where the farms are large enough or the spirit of cooperation great enough so that there is work enough to keep the tractors busy much of the time.   One interesting result of the introduction of tractors is that the more prosperous and progressive farmers tend to buy land enough to fit the capacities of their machines.   Hence tractors are very numerous in regions like central Illionis where the soil is especially fertile; they are less numerous in such regions as southern Illinois with its poor gray soils; still less so in places like Mississippi; and almost unknown in backward regions like the Kentucky mountains (A404).

The horse and mule are of relatively greatest importance in regions where tractors are least important.   This case is like hundreds of others: each new invention produces its greatest effect in the most-favored centers; the old methods persist elsewhere. Thus, although horses and mules are fast being displaced by the tractor in the most-favored lowlands of the United States, Canada, Australia, and Argentina, their importance has as yet diminished very little on the farms of most parts of New England, the South, and Europe. Even in the best agricultural areas the demand for draft animals elsewhere may long make it profitable to keep horses for breeding purposes, and that in turn will make it worth while to use them for at least part of the farm work. Thus our net conclusion is not only that the horse and other draft animals have been and still are of almost incalculable importance in the evolution of civilization but that such animals will long continue to be of high value except in the most-favored areas.

The General Distribution of Domestic Animals.—Before discussing the distribution of the individual species of domestic animals, let us consider that of all species taken together. This obliges us to determine the relative importance of the different animals. How many hens or sheep, for example, are equivalent to a horse or cow? The United States Department of Agriculture uses a standard based on the amount of food consumed per animal, a horse, cow, or ox being counted as an animal unit equivalent to 5 swine, 7 sheep, or 100 hens. For our purpose, a standard based on values is advisable, for the price of an animal is the best available measure of its all-around usefulness. On the basis of recent United States censuses, together with data from other countries, the relative values are approximately as follows:

Poultry	0.1	Llamas	1.5
Goats	0.5	Asses	1.5
Reindeer	1.0	Cattle	5.0
Dogs (for work)	1.0	Horses	12.5
Sheep	1.0	Mules	17.5
Swine	1.5	Camels	20.0

These numbers may represent dollars, pounds sterling, francs, or any other unit of value. What we want is merely a measure of the relative value of one animal compared with another. As used here, an animal unit happens to correspond to the value of a sheep, work dog, or reindeer; we might equally well use a unit one-tenth as large and equivalent to a hen, or five times as large and equivalent to a cow. By adding together the relative values of all the animals in each country or state, we obtain the *total animal units*, and from this it is easy to determine the animal units *per capita* (A406) and per square mile (B406).

Relation of Density of Population to Numbers of Animals.—One of the outstanding features of the maps of animal units per square mile and per capita is that they are almost opposite in appearance. Where animals are numerous per capita (A406) they are generally scarce per square mile (B406), and vice versa. Often, to be sure, this generalization is obscured by other factors such as climate, stage of civilization,

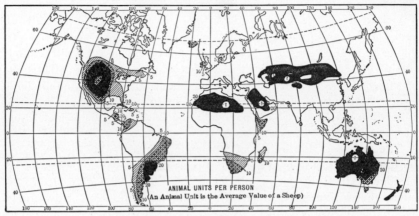

A—World Distribution of Animals per Person.

relief, diseases, and the location of markets. In large cities, animals are relatively inconspicuous because of the great numbers of people and automobiles. Nevertheless, in proportion to the area, the cities, outside the United States and a few other countries where automobiles are very

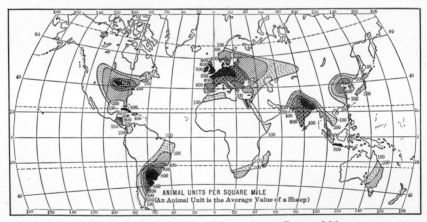

B—World Distribution of Animals per Square Mile.

abundant (A134), generally contain far more animals, especially horses, than do corresponding rural areas. In the United States there are many animals per capita, and this is a rough indication of the generally high standard of living arising from the newness of America, the energy of its people, and the great natural advantages. It is commonly believed that the dense populations of China and Japan leave little room for animals. However, China has about 250 animal units per square mile and Japan a little over 200. But because of the large human population the number of animal units per person is low, as might be expected, being 0.9 for China and 0.5 for Japan, but both of these are higher than Massachusetts, 0.4 (A406).

Value of Different Kinds of Animals for Transportation and Draft.— From the standpoint of transportation and farm work, the ideal animal possesses the following qualities: (1) Intelligence, so that it can be taught to start and stop at the word of command, and conduct itself quietly when ridden, harnessed, loaded, or driven. In this respect the dog, horse, donkey, and elephant rank especially high; cattle, reindeer, and camels are moderately good; and llamas, sheep, goats, and pigs are relatively poor. (2) Sufficient size and strength to carry one man long distances easily. The horse, ass, all six members of the cattle family, the reindeer, camel, llama, and elephant satisfy this requirement fairly well. That is one reason why they have been domesticated. The camel, however, is too large, for he can easily carry two or three people, and the elephant is still larger. Such large animals do not pay, for a man needs to ride alone far more often than with a companion. To feed and care for a big animal when a smaller one will suffice is like paying a man to do a boy's work. The donkey, reindeer, and llama, on the other hand, are too small. They can carry a man, to be sure, but not easily for long distances, especially if he has baggage. Horses and cattle are almost exactly the right size. (3) Fairly good speed day after day. Here the horse and camel are best. Cattle, donkeys, reindeer, and elephants are less speedy, or get tired more quickly. The elephant has little endurance and can work only a few hours per day. (4) An easy gait. In this respect the horse and the ass are much the best. (5) Ability to pull as well as carry. As a factor in human progress it is especially necessary to have animals that can pull wheeled vehicles, and draw the plow through grassy sod. Here again the horse is probably the best of all animals, but cattle are also excellent. The donkey would be almost equally good, but is not heavy enough. In some areas and for certain kinds of work the mule is best of all. The camel, llama, and elephant lack the hard hoofs which are essential for good draft animals. (6) Ease and cheapness with which the animals can be fed and cared for and the young brought to maturity.

According to these criteria, the horse stands much ahead of all other animals so far as transportation and farm work are concerned. Cattle, donkeys, and camels rank fairly well. Reindeer, elephants, and llamas are also useful. The dog, sheep, goat, pig, and alpaca are of practical use only when no other animal is available.

Relative Value of Animals as Producers of Food.—If all animals could be raised with equal ease, their value for food would depend on (1) the quality of the meat, (2) the extent to which they furnish other food products such as milk and eggs, and (3) the rapidity with which the young grow to maturity.

(1) All of the 17 Ungulata, or hoofed animals, in the table on page 401, furnish excellent meat, as do the unstarred birds and the rabbit. Among the unstarred animals only the carnivora and insects fail to furnish good meat. Differences in the quality of the meat, although important, are generally minor factors in determining where each species shall be raised, unless it be in the case of the rabbit and the pig.

(2) A far more important consideration is the extent to which an animal furnishes milk or eggs. All the ungulates in our list, except the pig and elephant, are milked in certain regions, and in all cases the milk is an admirable article of diet. Nevertheless, ordinary cattle, together with goats and sheep, far surpass other animals in this respect. That gives them great value, for milk appears to be the most valuable single product in the whole world. The world's annual production of eggs is worth about as much as that of oats or sheep. As a producer of eggs, no bird can compare with the hen. Thus as sources of food other than meat, the most desirable animals appear to rank as follows: cattle, hens, goats, sheep.

(3) As a rule, the more rapidly an animal reaches maturity, the less is the expense of producing a given weight of meat. Young horse-flesh is as good as the best beef, but the horse requires nearly four years to reach maturity, an ox little more than two. The sheep, goat, and pig, and the edible domestic birds are still better in this respect, for they attain almost their full size within a year. The pig and the birds have the further advantage of producing many young at one time, and more than one litter or brood per year. If we disregard the cost of their differing kinds of food, the best animals probably rank nearly as follows in respect to the amount of meat in proportion to their food; hens, pigs, sheep, goats, cattle.

Relative Value of Animals as Producers of Clothing.—As sources of materials for clothing, no animal, unless it be the alpaca, can compare with the sheep. Wool ranks second only to cotton as a material for clothing. It owes its value partly to the fact that, unlike fur, it can be sheared or plucked from the living animal, but chiefly to the ease with which it can be spun into thread, and also to the facility with which old wool that has already done duty in clothing or otherwise can be reworked. Nevertheless, the world's annual production of wool, reckoning again at American prices, is worth only about a tenth as much as the milk produced in the same time. The llama, camel, reindeer, and goat come next to the sheep and alpaca as sources of materials for cloth, for they yield hair which is soft and woolly and can be made into good clothing. Other domestic animals are of little use for clothing materials other than leather. But the world's annual production of leather is worth more than three-fourths as much as the wool. As the best leather comes from cattle and horses, that gives these animals another claim to high value.

The World's Most Valuable Animals.—Suppose that all domestic animals could live equally well in all environments. Which would be raised in greatest numbers? The horse would generally be the choice for transportation and draft purposes. Ordinary cattle would be raised practically everywhere because of their combined efficiency as producers of meat, milk, and hides, and because they are useful for transportation and farm work. There would be no use in raising the other species of the cattle family, for they yield less milk than European cattle, and at least the yak and water buffalo are less tractable. Sheep, likewise, would be wanted rather than goats, but the alpaca might be as popular as the sheep. Pigs would be raised in large numbers because they yield much meat in proportion to their food, and are easily fed. Hens would be still more in demand for the same reasons, and also because they are the best producers of eggs.

Silkworms and bees occupy unique though minor places in supplying human needs, and therefore would presumably be widely raised, even though artificial silk is now common. Accordingly, if each kind of animal could be raised as easily and profitably in one part of the world as in others, we should expect the following animals to be numerous wherever people are numerous and scarce wherever people are scarce: horses, ordinary cattle, sheep, hens, pigs, silkworms, and bees. Others would presumably be raised only as luxuries or for some special purpose.

As a matter of fact, the actual distribution of each of the domestic animals differs greatly from that of man. The causes of these differences are our next subject of investigation. They include climate, relief, soil, markets, stage of progress, density of population, social, religious, and political conditions, and certain other factors.

Distribution of Horses. *General.*—In one important respect, animals like the horse, that are used for transportation, resemble those like the dog and the cat, that are used for protection. They are of little use unless they live so close to their owners that they are available all the time. Wool, meat, eggs, and even milk may be shipped ten miles, or even ten thousand if rightly treated, and be almost as useful as if raised in the back yard, but a dog or cat living a quarter of a mile away is of little use, and if a farmer's horses were kept five miles away he might almost as well have none.   Therefore, if horses could thrive everywhere, their distribution over the earth's surface would presumably be almost identical with that of man, except that backward and unprogressive people would keep less than would the more progressive, but among the progressive regions the wealthy ones that can afford motor vehicles would not use so many as the others.   A comparison of A410 and A230 shows that in general the distribution of horses is like that of people in North America, Europe, and Australia, and there is a less marked resem-

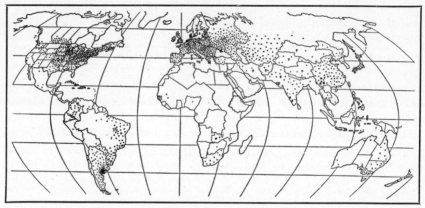

A—World Distribution of Horses.

blance in Asia and South America.   Only in Africa do the two maps become almost completely different, for horses are almost absent there except in the far north and south.

In spite of general resemblances, there are great differences in the distribution of horses and people.   For example, the number of horses per thousand people in the various continents varies from only 10 in southern Asia to nearly 300 in Australia, as appears in B411.   These great differences are partly climatic and partly cultural.   The only natural regions that are really good for horses are the Mediterranean, Temperate Grassland, the three Cyclonic, and the Cool Continental Regions.   The Arab horses that live in deserts are very few in number and have to be cared for almost like children.   The cultural condition most favorable to a great number of horses in comparison with the number of people is the nomadic form of life such as that of the Khirgiz in the steppes of Asia.   But the conditions that favor most horses per square mile are large farms where machinery is used but motor vehicles are not yet common among the farmers, and also areas of active manufacturing where motor transportation is not yet too highly developed. Countries like Denmark and northern France most nearly meet the

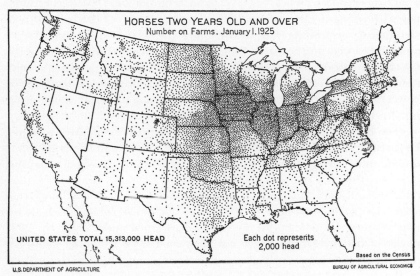

HORSES TWO YEARS OLD AND OVER
Number on Farms, January 1, 1925

UNITED STATES TOTAL 15,313,000 HEAD

Each dot represents
2,000 head

Based on the Census

U.S. DEPARTMENT OF AGRICULTURE

BUREAU OF AGRICULTURAL ECONOMICS

A—Horses in the United States.

ideal requirements for abundant horses when climate and cultural conditions are both considered. In very densely populated countries like China, horses would be scarce even if the climate were favorable, for the land must be used to feed people and not animals.

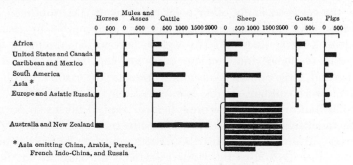

B—Animals per 1000 People.

*Asia omitting China, Arabia, Persia,
French Indo-China, and Russia

United States.—In order to appreciate more clearly the factors which determine the distribution of horses, a map showing all the land in harvested crops in the United States, may be compared with B000 showing the distribution of horses. The two are much alike in (1) the concentration of animals in the Corn Belt; (2) their sparsity in the dry regions of the West, the more rugged areas of the East, and Florida; (3) the local concentrations wherever level land, irrgation, and other conditions permit farming in the western half of the country; (4) the belts of relative density extending southward along the fertile Mississippi Valley and farther west in the strip of good soil from Kansas to eastern Texas; (5) the general decline southward where both climatic and social conditions are relatively unfavorable to the most productive agriculture. Nevertheless, the number of horses declines southward much more rapidly than the amount of land under cultivation.

The horse, like every other animal, has a distinct climatic optimum. Departures from this optimum inevitably cause the number of horses to decline until zero is reached at the extreme limits. It is worth noting, however, that the domestic horse and the wild horse presumably have different optima. Since man feeds and shelters the domestic horse, that animal's optimum is found in relatively cool, moist regions such as the northeastern United States and northwestern Europe, but the wild ponies of the British moors are not very good. On the other hand, the descendants of horses which escaped from man or were abandoned in the semi-arid regions of the southwestern United States and the pampa of South America at one time formed great herds of fairly good wild animals. This suggests that open grasslands that are not too hot probably have the best natural conditions for the development of the horse. The optimum for the ass is different from that for the horse. The ass can stand greater heat, greater drought, coarser food, and greater neglect. Mules inherit these qualities from their fathers, but inherit the size and many other good qualities of their mothers, which are horses. As climatic conditions become unfavorable by reason of warmth or aridity, asses tend to replace horses, but among people of progressive tendencies only enough asses are kept to serve as breeding animals, and large numbers of mules are raised. Mules become the dominant work animals as one goes southward in the United States. Their distribution follows the same laws as that of horses so far as the relation to cultivated land and cities is concerned.

Europe.—Europe illustrates the factors controlling the distribution of horses quite as well as the United States. Throughout all the central area horses are distributed almost in proportion to the cultivated land, with local concentrations in cities as at London, Paris, and Moscow, and in places especially favorable for horse-breeding. The northwestern corner of France has about three horses per capita, because the dampness favors wonderful grass but is not so favorable for crops. Northward and southward the horses diminish faster than the people. In the far north the reindeer replaces the horse; in the south, the ass, with a belt of mule-using country between the main areas of horses and asses.

The uses to which horses are put have tended to develop three types. The heavy draft animal originated in the good agricultural lands of western Europe. The thoroughbred race horse is the result of the Englishmen's love of sport. The driving horse is more the product of America and was developed to meet a demand for good carriage horses. This industry has met with quite a setback since the introduction of the automobile.

Africa.—In the other continents horses decline in number in response to lower human standards and unfavorable climate. In North Africa, after becoming scarce in a belt where asses are used, horses almost disappear and the camel becomes the dominant beast of burden. South of the Sahara, the plains of the Sudan and the central highlands afford fairly good food for horses, but the climate is not favorable, and in many places the tsetse fly almost exterminates them. The forests of equatorial Africa depart still farther from the equine optimum. There the climate, together with many pests in addition to the tsetse fly, causes vast areas to have no horses whatever. In fact, practically all domestic animals are so much at a disadvantage that this vast African area is the region, above all others, where men still carry loads hundreds or thousands of miles on their heads. Only where the climate ameliorates and the parasites decline in number toward the far south do horses again become numerous.

Asia.—In Asia similar but less extreme conditions prevail. Horses thrive fairly well on the steppes of southern Siberia and are very numerous per capita. Among the Khirgiz they are so prized that the word "animal" used alone, generally means "horse." A sheep may be called a "sheep animal." Nevertheless, the number of horses per square mile is small, for the dry climate with its great contrasts between summer and winter does not permit a large population either of men or horses. In northern China and Manchuria, horses again become fairly numerous, but are interspersed with asses, mules, and camels, as befits the climate. Japan likewise has a fair number of horses per square mile because of the dense population, but the climate and vegetation are so unfavorable that the number per capita is extremely small. Horse-breeding is largely confined to specially favored areas in the cooler and drier north.

Southward in Asia, horses decline as in tropical Africa. In India, camels and asses do much of the work of horses in the dry northwest, oxen do it in the moderately moist parts of the east and south, and water buffaloes wherever the climate and the opportunities for irrigation permit rice to be raised. In Indo-China and southern China, where the environment is especially unfit for horses, the water buffalo becomes almost the sole beast of burden. At Hongkong, for example, in spite of the large number of English people, there is only a handful of horses. Finally, in the most steadily warm, moist parts of Asia, where tropical forests provide a habitat peculiarly unfit for almost any domestic animals, man ekes out his own task of burden-bearing by using elephants. These animals, like dogs and reindeer in the far north, yaks in the Himalayas, sheep in the highest parts of Tibet, llamas in the Andes, and human coolies in central Africa, the Amazon basin, and parts of southeastern Asia, illustrate how man turns to less and less effective types of animals, as he finds himself in environments more and more unlike the optimum for the horse, the best of all animals for transportation.

Distribution of Cattle. *General.*—The distribution of other domestic animals follows the same laws as that of horses, but with important differences in details. In general the world map of cattle (A414), with its heavily shaded areas in India, Europe, the United States, and South America, seems more like that of population (A230) than does the map of horses (A410). This does not mean that ordinary cattle rival men in their ability to live in a wide variety of climates, although they are less sensitive than horses to certain pests and diseases of warm regions. The reason for the abundance of cattle in southern Asia is that several species are included in (A414). The cattle in Europe, the United States, South America, and Australia are generally of the European species (*Bos taurus*); those in southern Asia belong to the

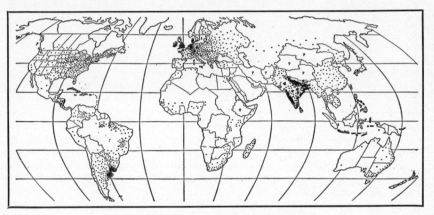

A—World Distribution of Cattle.

other five species shown on page 401. According to B411 Europe, in proportion to its population, has fewer cattle than any other continent, while South America and Australia have the most, but in B411 the lack of statistics makes it necessary to omit China, where cattle are very scarce.

The distribution of the European species of cattle is much like that of horses, although there is no such aggregation of animals in cities. Since modern transportation permits even so perishable a product as milk to be raised with profit a hundred or more miles from the cities where it is consumed, and since butter, cheese, and meat can stand almost any amount of transportation, the tendency in progressive countries is to keep numerous milch cows within a few hundred miles of all great cities, a smaller number within shorter distance of smaller communities, and a few upon practically every farm. But cows whose milk is used for butter, cheese, or condensed milk are kept where the climatic conditions and forage, and the demands of other crops, make them most profitable (B415). Beef cattle are raised still farther from the

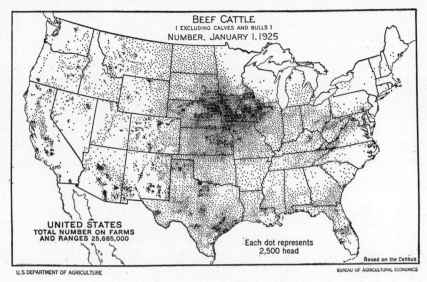

A—Beef Cattle in the United States.

main centers of population in regions where it pays to use the land for corn, or else where the climate is not favorable for agriculture (A415).

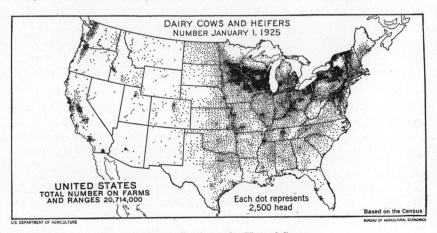

B—Dairy Cattle in the United States.

This, however, is true only of European cattle. In Asia, although a few cattle are kept for meat and milk, the vast majority are work ani-

mals, kept especially for plowing.   Hence their distribution corresponds
closely with that of the farmers, and there are also many in the cities.

Relation of Optimum to Uses of Cattle.—The optimum for European cattle is
fairly cool, moist summers, especially if milk rather than beef is the main object,
rain at all seasons, or else irrigation to supply fresh forage, and so little cold weather
and snow that the grass is green the year round.   This type of climate is illustrated by
Dublin in A416.   The cool summers discourage many kinds of agriculture, but foster
an abundance of tender, nutritious grass and other forage plants.   If good markets are
accessible, the farmers in such regions turn largely to dairy farming, as in the Irish
Free State, the Netherlands, and Denmark, where there are about 200 cattle per
square mile.

Such equable climates, with admirable conditions for cattle in both summer and
winter, are rare.   If the summers are cool and moist, but the winters cold, as in

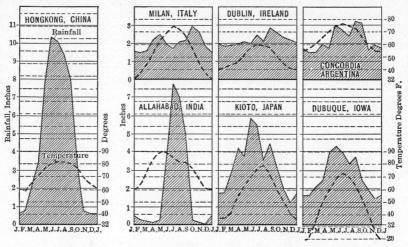

A—Rainfall and Temperature in Regions Especially Good or Poor for Cattle.

Vermont, northern New York, Wisconsin, and Minnesota, the dairy industry is
hampered only slightly, for low temperature does little harm if the cows are fed on
good hay and juicy silage.   If the summers are warm enough so that corn can be
raised, milk may still be of great importance, as in Iowa (Dubuque in A416), but the
fattening of beef cattle is also likely to be highly profitable.   For these reasons, and
also because it is farther from the great eastern centers of population, Iowa with 26
dairy cattle per square mile falls behind Wisconsin (39 per square mile), Vermont
(34 per square mile), New York (30), and Connecticut (30), and stands only a little
ahead of Ohio and Rhode Island (24), Minnesota (22), and Illinois, Indiana, and
Pennsylvania (20).   On the other hand, Iowa has 48 beef cattle per square mile,
whereas its nearest rivals have only 32 in Nebraska, 30 in Kansas, 26 in Missouri
and 22 in Illinois.

A region with summers as warm and rainy as those of Iowa, and with winters
sufficiently moist and warm to support good pasturage but not to make the grasses

tough, is excellent for beef cattle. That is why northeastern Argentina and Uruguay (Concordia in A416) are today the world's greatest beef-raising center.

Australia and New Zealand have also developed the beef industry by leaps and bounds. Here the cattle have increased rapidly on great pastures often unfenced. In Argentina they roamed the plains much as the buffalo (bison) roamed the Great Plains of North America. For years these cattle were hunted for their hides and tallow alone, and the carcasses were allowed to rot upon the pampa. Higher prices for meat, however, plus the cold-storage plant, the refrigerator car, and the refrigerator ship, have made it profitable for these areas to ship meat to the markets of northwestern Europe and the northeastern United States. With the increased desire for quantity there has come also a demand for a finer quality of meat. This has led to improved breeding and also to better pastures through the introduction of alfalfa. American and European firms have established packing plants in Argentina, thus contributing to the further expansion of the industry so important to the prosperity of these countries and to the diet of their northern neighbors.

The Po Valley in northern Italy is another cattle center, although much less important than the centers in the North Sea countries, the north central United States, and the Argentine region. One reason for its intermediate position is the climate (Milan in A416). The temperature is much like that of Iowa, though the summers are a trifle warmer than at Dubuque, and the winters considerably warmer. On the other hand, although northern Italy, like all the chief cattle centers, has a moderate rainfall of $1\frac{1}{2}$ to 2 inches per month in winter and more in spring and fall, its summer rainfall is too light. When the temperature averages 72 or 73° F. for three months, a region with only 2 inches of rain per month is likely to become so dry that irrigation is desirable although not essential, and the pasturage falls off in quality.

Physical Environment and Types of Cattle.—Different types of environment support different breeds or even species of cattle. This arises partly from the choice of the breeders, partly from the selective action of nature, and partly from other causes such as mutations. A well-known example is the contrast between Holsteins and Jerseys. The Holsteins originated on the northern coast of Holland, where the moist, cool summers combine with a heavy clay soil and very level land to make the grass luxuriant, but watery. Cows with large, bony frames and correspondingly large abdomens are apparently better able than others to support themselves and their calves on such vegetation. The watery food apparently tends to make the milk abundant, but relatively low in butter fat and other solids. The island of Jersey, on the contrary, although as rainy as Holland, averages about 4° F. warmer in summer, and has light loamy soil and many hills. Hence the herbage is shorter, finer, and less watery than in Holland, the Jersey cows do not need large stomachs or large frames, and the selection of nature and of the breeders has preserved a type less massive than the Holsteins, and notable for the production of milk which though moderate in quantity is very rich and creamy.

Non-European Species of Cattle.—The differences between species of cattle are like those between breeds, but more pronounced. Just as the environments of the Dutch coast and Jersey have led to the selection of special types by man and nature, so the environment of southern Asia has cooperated with other agencies in producing distinct species of cattle such as the Brahman or zebu type, the gayal, yak, water buffalo, and banteng. It is these which give southern Asia and the East Indies their heavy shading in A414. The Brahmans are the main type of cattle in India, especially in the north where the Indo-Gangetic Valley is almost black in A414.

The climate where they are most numerous is represented by Allahabad in A416. It is warm at all seasons and excessively hot in the spring before the summer rains begin.   The rainfall comes almost entirely in summer, the contrast between the seasons being enormous.   The native cattle of such a region must eat relatively coarse, watery forage during the rains and the same kind in its tough, dry state in winter. They must be able to resist droughts, which are often severe, and must not be sensitive to insect pests such as the ticks which cause Texas fever.

As long ago as 1849, the knowledge that the Brahman cattle possess such powers of resistance led to the introduction of a few into South Carolina.   During the present century a considerable number have been brought in and have been extensively crossed with European cattle on the Texas coast.   So well do the cross-bred animals endure drought, ticks, flies, and other pests that Brahman blood is being introduced all over the South.   In Brazil, huge prices are paid for high-grade Brahman bulls from India.

Even the Brahman cattle cannot stand all climates.   Neither a cool, moist climate, nor a steadily moist tropical climate is good for them.   Hence among the mountains north of the Indo-Gangetic plain in India, and also in other moist mountains of south India, the gayal replaces the Brahman.   In the lofty, snowy Himalayas the gayal in turn gives place to the yak.   Toward the south, likewise, the Brahmans decline in relative importance, and the water buffalo increases, until the two species are about equally numerous in the steadily warm, moist climate of Ceylon.   Farther east in the moist regions of Burma, Siam, Indo-China, and the East Indies, still another species, the banteng, largely replaces the Brahman type, but not the water buffalo.

The relation of the Brahman, gayal, banteng, water buffalo, and yak to European cattle is important because it illustrates one of the chief principles in respect to the distribution of domestic animals.   The same principle is illustrated by the relation of the ass, camel, ox, llama, reindeer, and dog to the horse.   Wherever man is able to raise the best type of animal for any purpose he does so, but where the more valuable type cannot thrive, others replace it.   Nevertheless man constantly strives to extend the range of the best species, partly by selecting certain types and thus establishing new breeds, partly by crosses with other species, and partly by providing special kinds of food and shelter.   In general, the number of breeds and their degree of diversity are a rough measure of the extent to which man values an animal.   Few people have seen more than one variety of peacock, although a pure white type is in existence; but almost everyone is familiar with Leghorns, Plymouth Rocks, Bantams, Rhode Island Reds, Wyandottes, Buff Cochins, and various other kinds of hens.

A Handicap of the Far East.—The region where there is most need of breeds of cattle with peculiar adaptations to climate and food is the southeastern coast of Asia.   There dwells by far the greatest population that suffers for lack of domestic animals.   Hongkong, with its heavy rains and high temperature throughout most of the year, represents the extreme of this type (A416).   Among the dairy cows kept there by the British, the yield of milk appears to decline systematically when the weather becomes excessively hot and damp.   The native grasses are so big, watery, and tough that horses, cattle, and sheep do not thrive on them.   Hence the few dairy cattle are fed on guinea grass, a species introduced from more tropical regions and raised as a cultivated crop.   Even this is so poor that the cows receive special rations, the composition of which is guarded as a trade secret.   Nevertheless, the cattle imported from Europe die at an alarming rate.   Because domestic animals thrive so poorly in South China, millions of acres of rugged land, such as form the finest pastures in Switzerland, are left unused. In Japan, although the conditions are not so bad as in southern China, attempt after attempt to introduce sheep has failed, and in the most populous parts of the islands neither horses, cattle, nor swine really thrive. The rainfall (Kyoto in A416) does not greatly exceed that of Iowa, but abundance of moisture throughout the year, and the absence of weather cold enough to check growth effectively, seem to cause the Japanese vegetation to be very poor as forage. Iowa, with its natural grasslands and restricted open forests, is almost ideal for cattle; Japan with its dense, damp forests and coarse reed-like grasses provides a peculiarly unfit environment. Hence Japan has only 12 cattle per square mile and 23 per thousand people, in contrast with 74 per square mile and 1,674 per thousand people in Iowa.

Distribution of Swine.—Domestic swine possess qualities which seem to favor an extremely wide distribution, like that of man himself.

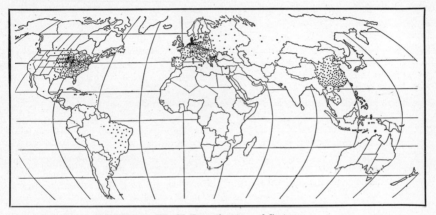

A—World Distribution of Swine.

In the first place, swine breed so freely and grow so rapidly that they furnish a great supply of meat and fat in proportion to their food. Second, they eat many kinds of food, such as acorns, potatoes, and garbage, which are of little use for most of the domestic animals. Third, although the exact facts are not known, domestic swine appear to be descended from several wild species, sufficiently alike to breed freely together, but diverse enough to include varieties adapted to almost every environment.

In spite of these advantages, swine are not nearly so widely distributed as horses, cattle, hens, or even sheep (A421). Even with more exact data for China, A419 would not look much like the map of population (A230). Even in the United States the swine show a marked concentration in the states from Ohio to Nebraska, while in Europe they abound in the Low Countries, Denmark, and western Germany. South America, especially Brazil, has a fair number distributed much as are the people; the Philippines nearly as many in proportion to the population; China, Australia, and South Africa about one-fourth as many proportionally as in the United States; and Japan a few—half as many as Norway, but only one-fiftieth as many per capita as Brazil. Vast areas in Asia and Africa are utterly blank in A419; in the United States such densely settled sections as the northeastern states have surprisingly few (A420).

The explanation of these conditions is found partly in the fact that although the pig eats nearly everything, it becomes commercially profitable chiefly in regions where one of the following types of food is cheap and abundant: corn, as in our Corn Belt and Brazil; potatoes, as

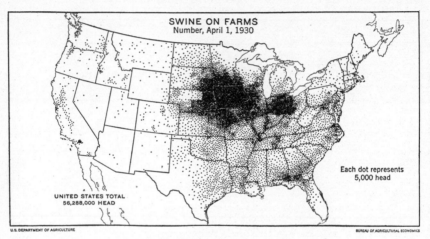

A—Swine in the United States.

in Belgium, the Netherlands, and Germany; and barley and skim milk, as in Denmark. Relatively high prices for these commodities, even where they are abundant, may reduce the production of swine. This happens near Chicago where corn is relatively more costly than farther from the great cities.

The disagreeableness of the pig is another reason why its distribution differs so much from that of man. In cities and towns all over the civilized world vast amounts of garbage which might profitably be employed for feeding swine are taken to rendering plants where the fats are extracted, or are disposed of as fertilizer or otherwise, because people object to the smell of pigpens. Although no exact information is available, the religious prejudice against swine may have arisen in part because the animal is disagreeable, and partly because it does not thrive in dry regions. The fact that swine are tabooed by Mohammedanism, Judaism, and Hinduism accounts largely for their absence throughout most of Asia and Africa.   (See page 211 and A419.)

In China there is no prejudice against swine, and they are kept in almost every village.   Nevertheless, the number is not so large as is often supposed.   Unlike draft animals which rely on grass, the swine, so to speak, competes with man for food.   A very dense and poverty-stricken population cannot afford to feed swine on anything that people can eat.   In China it would be almost criminal to use corn, barley, potatoes, and skim milk for such a purpose.   Hence swine must be content with the scanty materials which even the poorest Chinese cannot eat, or else with what they can grub up in fallow gardens and fields.

Distribution of Sheep and Goats.—If the world were limited to four domestic animals the choice would probably be horses, cattle, swine,

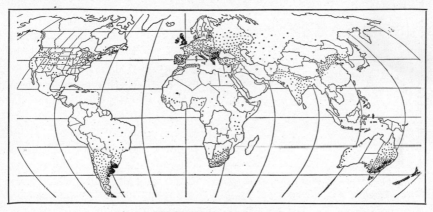

A—World Distribution of Sheep.

and sheep.   Nevertheless, sheep (A421) are generally crowded out of regions where population is numerous and intensive farming is practiced, whereas horses and cattle are most numerous in such regions. One reason is that sheep are better adapted than horses or cattle to dry and rugged regions.   They can thrive on grass so short that the other two animals cannot bite it off, and they can graze on slopes more comfortably than other domestic animals except the goat.   Another important reason is that although wool is highly valuable, it is not so essential as are animals for draft purposes, milk, and meat.   Again sheep can be raised and fattened on grass alone.   Moreover, wool is one of the easiest of animal products to raise and to transport.   Sheep require only a few people to care for them; their wool can be washed and clipped, and then transported vast distances without further treatment and without special precautions such as are needed for meat.   Since other

animals are almost everywhere available for meat, the sheep of Australia
and South America were long kept entirely for their wool. Their
extreme helplessness likewise causes the distribution of sheep to differ
from that of people. Such helplessness makes the animals need shepherds, but it is unduly expensive to provide shepherds unless large
numbers of sheep are kept. This in turn demands large open areas
such as exist chiefly in countries that are sparsely populated because of
newness, aridity, or ruggedness. In many parts of the United States
where settlement is dense and the enclosures relatively small, sheep
cannot be kept without a shepherd unless placed in enclosures so well
fenced that dogs cannot get in and kill the defenseless creatures.

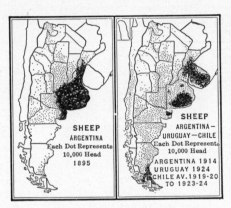

A—Sheep in South America.
(From *South America*, by C. F. Jones.)

For all these reasons sheep
tend to be animals of the marginal areas. That is why they
are especially numerous in four
southern areas—New Zealand,
Australia, South Africa, and the
Argentine-Uruguay section—and
in certain European centers,
namely Britain, the Balkans, and
southern Italy. The southern
areas are all newly settled
regions where land is still available for uses like sheep-raising,
even though this would not
pay if the farms or ranches were
small. When the population
becomes so dense that the holdings are small, and there is a market for
milk, vegetables, and other farm products, sheep give way to cattle and
general farming, provided such farming is feasible. In Australia and
South Africa, as a matter of fact, most of the sheep are raised on land so
dry that, if it were devoted to general agriculture, the farmers would be
in great danger of frequent and severe crop failures. The same is true
of considerable parts of Argentina. Even in those far-off countries
there has been a significant shift of the sheep-raising areas more and more
to the outer edges of civilization, as shown in Argentina (A422).
Because Australia has such vast marginal dry grasslands it has about
16 or 17 sheep for every inhabitant. Uruguay has nearly as many,
and New Zealand more (A411).

In the Balkans, southern Italy, Sicily, and other Mediterranean
lands, sheep are numerous because long experience has proved that it
does not pay to try to farm the dry hillsides, or to raise cattle on them.

The prolonged summer droughts put these regions near the limits so far as other modes of getting a living are concerned, and thus make it profitable to raise sheep.   In Britain a combination of climatic, economic, and social conditions produces a unique condition such that horses, cattle, and sheep are all numerous in almost the same regions.   But even there the sheep are abundant largely because the uplands of Britain are too cool and moist for profitable farming.   It does not pay to farm large portions of the country so long as food can be brought across the seas in exchange for manufactured goods.   Thus even Britain bears out the idea that sheep are relatively marginal animals.

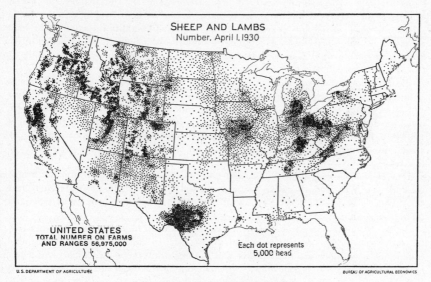

SHEEP AND LAMBS
Number, April 1, 1930

UNITED STATES
TOTAL NUMBER ON FARMS
AND RANGES 56,975,000

Each dot represents
5,000 head

U.S. DEPARTMENT OF AGRICULTURE   BUREAU OF AGRICULTURAL ECONOMICS

A—Sheep in the United States.

There are, however, considerable numbers of sheep in areas of rather intensive agriculture such as southern Michigan, the gently rolling or hilly areas of central and eastern Ohio, and other smaller centers in the Middle West (A423).   Most of these are of the dual purpose type and furnish both wool and mutton.

Goats.—Goats bear to sheep much the same relation as asses to horses, and Brahman to European cattle.   They supplant the more valuable type in regions that are especially dry or rugged.   In one important aspect the relation between goats and sheep is the reverse of that between Brahman and European cattle.   The goat is a much better producer of milk than is the sheep.   An average cow yields three or four thousand pounds of milk per year; the nanny-goat from five hundred to one thousand, and the average ewe less than one hundred.   Hence in relatively dry countries like South Africa, northern India, Mexico, and the Mediterranean lands, especially Greece and the Balkans, where goats reach their greatest density per square mile, they may replace the cow as a source of milk. In that case the distribution of goats becomes much like that of the people. In the eastern Mediterranean lands, both the goat and sheep are kept largely in the villages. This is possible because the dryness of the summers and the general ruggedness cause waste land to be abundant. The unfenced grain fields can be used for summer pasturage, for the harvest is usually finished by June. Moreover, the standards of living are so low that children do not go to school, and the village boys can be employed to herd the goats and sheep, thus making fences unnecessary.

Distribution of Some Other Useful Animals.—The *camel* has been used from earliest times. It is still the chief beast of burden in large areas of western Asia and northern Africa. Camels have many advantages as carriers in the desert. They store fat in their humps and water in compartments of their stomachs, and hence can travel several days, in some cases as many as ten, without food or water. Their soft, flat feet act as cushions to keep the animals from sinking into the sand. Furthermore, camels carry heavier loads than most animals—the single-humped camel often bears from 300 to 400 pounds and the double-humped from one and one-half to two times as much.

In the Andes, the little cousins of the camel, known as *llamas*, are used as beasts of burden and the closely related *alpaca* supplies wool. The llamas are sure footed and often forage for their food along the way, but they cannot carry much. Their usual burden is 40 to 100 pounds, but when loaded to the latter figure the animals are often ill-tempered, as is the camel under similar conditions. Llamas are of special importance in Peru and Bolivia, although used to some extent in other parts of the Andes.

The *elephant* is captured, tamed, and taught to carry freight and do other useful work in the Wet Tropical Regions, especially India and Siam. Although it can carry very heavy loads it soon grows tired. Since it is also a very great eater, its usefulness is limited.

In the mountainous parts of central Asia the *yak* is an important beast of burden, but only where the climate is too cold for cattle. In the far north under similar conditions of temperature the *reindeer* and the *dog* draw the sleds which furnish the best means of travel over the snow. Without one or the other of these animals, the areas that could be occupied by the Eskimos, Lapps, Samoyeds, and other people of the far north would have been greatly restricted, and the exploration of polar regions would have been impossible until very recent years. The reindeer has a great advantage over the dog, because it supplies meat and milk. On the other hand, the dog is a much more faithful helper and companion. In certain warmer areas, such as the lowlands of northwest Europe, the dog is also used as a beast of burden, but throughout most of the world he is a pet, a guardian, or an assistant either in herding sheep, cattle, and other animals or in the hunt and chase.

Widespread Distribution of Hens.—Hens possess most of the qualities that cause an animal to be widespread. The qualities include: (1) relative independence of climate, perhaps because hens were derived from several wild ancestors in different parts of the world; (2) a cosmopolitan attitude toward food, so that, like the pig, they can thrive almost anywhere on all sorts of food, including garbage; and (3) the power to furnish a very useful product which cannot easily be transported. Only in our own day has there been any extensive attempt to transport eggs long distances. China, which today supplies the greatest surplus of eggs for export, ships millions of dozens in the shell. In general, however, such transportation is wasteful, and dealers expect to lose 15 per cent by breakage. Hence a much larger share of the Chinese eggs, over a hundred million pounds, are dried or frozen for shipment. But freshness is a very important quality which is soon lost by transportation, and fresh eggs bring the highest price.

The net result is that the distribution of hens (A425) is much like that of farms all over the world, except in two respects. First, the lower the stage of civilization, the smaller the number of hens per capita and per square mile, as appears from their relative scarcity in tropical countries. Second, hens tend to be especially numerous in favorable localities near great markets, as in eastern Pennsylvania and New Jersey, and in regions with an especially good supply of food, as in the Corn Belt of the United States from Ohio to Iowa.

The following quotation from *The World's Food Resources* by J. Russell Smith shows the importance of eggs to the people of Denmark:

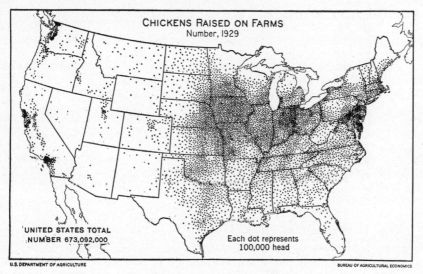

A—Chickens in the United States.

"A few years ago Mr. H. Rider Haggard, the English novelist, who is also a land owner, and much interested in rural betterment, went to Denmark to investigate the rural cooperation which has replaced poverty and despair with comfort and contentment in that cool and sandy little country. On his first morning in Copenhagen he called for boiled eggs. They came with printing on their shells. When he was examining the eggs, the printing, after the fashion of a rubber stamp, was transferred to his hand, and there was not enough soap in all Denmark to wash it off in the space of two days, during which time he went about numbered No. 174 and initialed D.A.A.G., N.P. Upon investigation, he found that the lettering signified literally that he was a good egg from the Danish Cooperative Association, Branch 174. He further found that this branch was located on the Island of Folster in the Baltic Sea, and that N. P. was Nils Poulsen, the Danish peasant who had turned in that particular egg. If the egg had been bad, the thrifty Nils would have been fined something like $1.40. If he had turned in another bad egg, the fine would have been

increased.   If he had turned in a third he would have been expelled from member-
ship in the egg society—three terrible calamities for a thrifty farmer.   That is the
kind of individual responsibility that has made Denmark great in the egg market as
in the realm of butter and bacon."

Other Kinds of Poultry.—*Turkeys* among fowls are like elephants among the
domestic mammals.   They are too large.   Because of its delicious flavor this bird
of purely American origin is raised on more than a tenth of all the farms in the
United States and on a great many in Europe.   Since even a small turkey weighs
about 10 pounds and a large one 36, families of the ordinary size cannot afford to
buy them except on special occasions like Thanksgiving and Christmas.   The decline
in the size of families in recent years is probably one reason why the turkeys of the
United States, which were 4 per cent as numerous as the chickens in 1890, are now
only 1 per cent as numerous.   Cold, wet weather is bad for turkeys; hence they are
most numerous in the South and in the drier states from the Dakotas to Texas and
westward.   *Guinea fowls* are kept on about half as many American farms as are
turkeys, and are most numerous in the Middle Atlantic and Southern States.
Pigeons are kept on far fewer farms, mainly in the North Atlantic area.   There are
many kinds.   Most are kept for food, but many for shooting, homing contests, and
prize exhibits.   In some countries like Egypt, huge pigeon cotes of dried mud form
the largest and most imposing buildings of many villages.

In most countries *ducks* and *geese* are insignificant compared with hens, but in
Europe, especially from the Low Countries eastward to Hungary, and in Japan and
China, they rise to real importance.   The regions where this happens have abundant
water in canals for irrigation or other purposes.   Where rice is raised, domestic
waterfowl are especially likely to be abundant, as in South China, where they are
often herded by small boys who drive them with long sticks as readily as the shepherd
boys of western Asia drive their sheep.   As soon as one leaves the ricelands of China
and reaches a section so cold that the water courses are frozen for some time in
winter, ducks and geese decline greatly in number.

The Limitations of the Silkworm.—The silkworm is peculiarly
interesting because it illustrates how the distribution of domestic
animals is expanded by man and limited by nature.   The silkworm
was first raised in China, but spread to India, Persia, and finally the
Mediterranean lands, where it reached its maximum profitable expansion.   Efforts were made to introduce it into England, Mexico, and
colonial Virginia.   As late as the American Revolution, Benjamin
Franklin was engaged in a silk enterprise in Philadelphia, and in 1866
California was offering bounties for the cultivation of silk.   All these
efforts proved abortive for reasons that we shall now discuss.

On the one hand, the silkworm is subject to very strict geographical
limitations.   On the other hand, the durability of raw silk and its high
value—averaging about six dollars a pound on the New York market,
1925 to 1929—make the cost of transportation negligible, so that there is
little incentive to overcome the geographical limitations.   The first
limitation is set by the mulberry tree.   No other easily raised tree provides leaves on which the silkworm can thrive.   The various species

of mulberry grow in the warmer parts of the temperate zone and in semi-tropical regions, but do not thrive in equatorial regions except on the mountains. With proper care they can be raised in climates as cool as those of Philadelphia and southern England, but thrive better somewhat farther south. Thus the mulberry tree limits silk cultivation to a zone lying roughly between latitudes 15° and 40° on either side of the equator, although in Europe and western America the limit rises to about 45°.

The next limit is set by standards of living and habits of industry. The rearing of silkworms is a very painstaking and laborious occupation requiring great concentration during a short season. Fresh leaves must be cut daily with absolute regularity; the trays on which the worms are kept must be cleaned; the air must not be allowed to become too close and hot, or too cool. The labor must be cheap or else the cost of production will be greater than the market can stand. Such labor is found only among people with low standards of living combined with established habits of great regularity and industry. In America no such labor has ever been available on a large scale, for the Indians, even in the rare cases where they work, do not display the steadiness which is so characteristic of the Chinese and Japanese, while European labor has always been expensive. The Negroes, to be sure, might supply the necessary labor, but many of them dislike work which binds them so rigidly to long steady hours. Moreover, the demand for their work in other lines, especially cotton-raising, is so great that their labor is more expensive than that of the regions where silk is actually raised. Only in such places as Japan, China, northern India, Persia, and the Mediterranean lands does one find such labor, and those are the regions whence comes our silk.

Another natural limitation is the degree of moisture during the season when the worms are growing. In regions with the Mediterranean Type of climate, unless irrigation is practiced, there is always danger that the rainy season will end too soon, so that fresh mulberry leaves will be scarce. In China and Japan, on the contrary, the rains come in summer, so that fresh leaves can be procured for many months instead of only a few weeks. In such places the dangers from the many diseases to which the silkworm is subject are indeed increased, but this does not offset the great advantage of China and Japan in their rainy summers, as well as in their labor supply.

Finally, the work of silk-raising is likely to be still more limited in the future by the fact that some varieties of silkworms produce only one generation per year, that is, the eggs laid one spring hatch the next, but other varieties are bivoltine, that is, the eggs laid in the spring hatch in a few weeks, and another set of worms is raised the same year. Still others are multivoltine, so that several generations are raised in a year. Already modern science appears to be able to produce varieties whose eggs can be hatched whenever desired, so that worms may be available at any season. Thus silk-raising is changing from an occupation requiring many unskilled people for a few weeks in the spring to one where high skill is required among the technical workers who use the microscope to examine the eggs, while the unskilled workers can be kept busy as long as fresh mulberry leaves are available. Hence a region like South China, so warm and moist that the mulberry tree sends forth leaves much of the year, has a great advantage over Mediterranean lands where the growth of the trees is limited both by low temperature in winter and drought in summer, or even over Japan with its cool, but not cold, winters. Naturally the silk industry is diminishing in the Mediterranean countries, and growing in Japan and China, especially South China. As methods of transportation and storage become still better, and as peace and international harmony become more fully assured, the distribution of all sorts of products, including plants as well as animals, tends to go through the same process as silk. First, the area where the product is raised tends to expand; then it contracts, and production becomes intensified in the most favorable areas.

Wide Distribution of Bees.—The common hive or honey-bee is found in nearly all parts of the world. It is native to the warmer portions of the Eastern Hemisphere but has been naturalized in the Western. Honey is used widely, and bees' wax is a commercial product from widely dispersed localities. In our own country California is the most important commercial bee-keeping state. Other important producers of honey are Texas, Michigan, Iowa, and Wisconsin. The bee industry in California has developed some interesting customs and problems. One of these is migratory agriculture. The Egyptians 4,000 years ago carried apiaries by boats on the Nile, and considerable numbers are moved from place to place in the eastern part of the United States; California, however, has developed a distinctive procedure in migratory bee-keeping. This practice is necessary and profitable in regions where climatic or other conditions cause abundant nectar-producing flowers to abound at one season and not at another. In California the flowers of various kinds of sage plants in the southern part of the state are the best source of honey. In order to use these, as well as the blossoms of the orange and prune, and of grass, alfalfa, and so forth, the apiaries are often moved 200 to 400 miles by automobile and have sometimes been carried 1,500 or 1,700 miles by railroad.

Another element is added to the situation by the fact that the honey-bee is very effective in pollinization and thus in improving the yield of fruit. But many fruit growers do not want to bother with colonies of bees throughout the year. Hence has arisen the industry of shipping package bees. Boxes containing three or more pounds of bees, something about which the insects may cluster, and food in the form of syrup, are shipped to the orchardists and distributed among the trees. Unfortunately other insects seriously damage the fruit. Insects and insectides designed to get rid of them kill the bees. Furthermore, it is believed that bees carry a disease known as fire blight. Hence the relationship of bee-keeping, pollinization, and fruit growing makes a perplexing problem for research.

The Distribution of Fisheries.—A great many types of undomesticated animals have long been of importance to man. Among these none has engaged the energies of so many men or supplied so much food as fish. The catching of fish rivals hunting as man's oldest industry. It still survives as an important commercial industry, whereas hunting is now little more than a pastime. Fish add not only proteids but vitamins to man's food, and furnish important substitutes for meat in some areas. The amounts used in different countries vary greatly. It has been estimated that in the world as a whole fish form less than 3 per

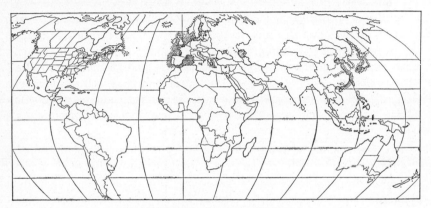

A—World Distribution of Fisheries.

cent of the animal food used by man, but in places like Iceland, Newfoundland, and parts of Norway and Japan they probably form 10 per cent of the whole food supply. The main factor in determining the consumption of fish is the ease with which fish can be obtained in comparison with other kinds of food, but local customs and religious beliefs also have an important influence.

Although an abundant local supply of fish is obtained from some rivers and lakes, this is of little importance compared with the supply from the ocean. The important fishing areas are found within a few hundred miles of the coast. They lie partly in the littoral, or shore, belt of shallow water which covers the continental shelf or submerged platform surrounding the continents. Others are located in the shallow water overlying banks, or elevated parts of the sea floor some distance from the shore. The shallowness of the water permits an abundant growth of small plant organisms which serve as food for many small animals. These in turn are eaten by fish large enough to be important sources of human food. Not all littoral belts, however, support commercial fisheries (A430). The four outstanding fishing areas are:

(1) The coasts of Japan, China, Chosen, eastern Siberia, and Taiwan.

(2) The coasts of northwest Europe from France to northern Norway, including the North Sea and its arms.

(3) The west Atlantic area from the Carolinas to Labrador but especially the coastal and offshore banks from New England to Newfoundland.

(4) The Pacific region along the coast of California, Oregon, Washington, British Columbia, and Alaska.

The first three areas have many types of fish in common. The haddock and herring are taken in large numbers, and the cod is especially important in the two Atlantic fishing grounds. On the west coast of North America the outstanding commercial fish is the salmon; of lesser importance are the sardines and tuna of southern California. The statistics of fisheries include not only these fish, but various other marine animals. Of these the best known are oysters, lobsters, and clams.

Although fishing is an important industry in a few restricted localities it does not rank high among the important occupations of modern nations. Among the people of the world who are actively engaged in primary production, only a very small proportion are fishermen—about one man out of every 600 in the entire United States. Furthermore, the total annual value of the world's fish products is probably less than a billion dollars, which is less than the value of the poultry and eggs of the United States alone. The fishing industry, however, has had great importance in the rise of maritime nations. The merchant marine of many countries has depended on the fishing grounds as a training school for seamen. The same has been true of the navies of the world in many cases, especially in the past. The fast sailing vessels for which New England was noted were an outgrowth of the fishing industry. Drake's seadogs had their training in the mackerel fleets of the North Sea. The charm and romance of the ocean as well as the picturesqueness of fishing and the dangers that often go with it catch our fancy. All these tend to cause us to overemphasize the true economic importance of fisheries in the world as a whole. On the other hand, along few lines of production is there greater opportunity for future expansion.

EXERCISES

1. On a map of the world, indicate the general areas where horses, mules, asses, oxen, camels, llamas, elephants, reindeer, and dogs are used as draft animals or beasts of burden. What do you note as to the general latitudinal distribution of these various animals? Why is this so? What are the most important agricultural products in the areas where each of the above animals is important?

2. From this book and your atlas determine which of the animals mentioned in Exercise 1 is most widely distributed over the earth. Why is this? Name some of the largest areas with few or none of these animals; why are animals so scarce there?

3. What domestic animal (including all in the table on page 401) is most numerous in your region? What one is most important? In what respects are both conditions the result of physical as compared with economic factors?

4. Study B406 and A136 in order to determine whether an abundance of animals per square mile is any indication of high civilization? How about a large number per capita?

5. In A411 pick out the areas which have the most and the least horses per capita, and explain the geographic and economic conditions which lead to this. Do the same for each of the animals in B411.

6. Let several members of the class cooperate in a study of domestic animals in relation to natural regions. On the basis of this book and your atlas, supplemented by the *Geography of the World's Agriculture*, the encylopedia, and other books, prepare a table in which the names of the natural regions are followed by a space for each of the main domestic animals. Indicate the abundance of each animal in each region by such terms as none, scarce, some, many, very many. Then write a discussion of the world-wide distribution of domestic animals in relation to natural regions, explaining the great differences.

7. On the basis of the statistics of fisheries in the *Statistical Yearbook of the League of Nations* prepare a world map showing the approximate amount or value of fishery products in different countries. Explain what your map indicates as to the conditions that stimulate fisheries.

CHAPTER XX

FORESTS AND THE LUMBER INDUSTRY

Distribution.—Forests cover slightly less than one-fourth of the lands of the earth. This ratio has constantly declined, for man, with his cropland and meadows, now occupies vast areas once covered with trees. With their present extent of $7\frac{1}{2}$ billion acres, however, forests still occupy three times as much space as crops; and lumber ranks with iron in economic significance.

The map of vegetation (A433) shows the main types of forests. The tundra belt in the north, with its ever-frozen subsoils, and monotonous surface of swampy moss and lichens, borders the great coniferous zone which extends around the world roughly between 50° and 70° N. An around-the-world airplane trip through Alaska, Canada, northern Europe, and Siberia would show the same continental picture everywhere—an immense forest of spruce, fir, and pine with a slight mingling of birch and ash. This great Taiga zone, to use the Russian name, is practically identical with the Cool Forest Region of Chapter XVI. In the western United States it extends southward on both sides of the Great Basin, covering the slopes of the Coast Ranges, Cascades, Sierra Nevada, and Rockies. Because of the milder climate the forest here reaches its optimum in beautiful stands of Douglas fir, white pine, and redwood. Except for this extension, a zone of temperate hard woods, often mixed with conifers, adjoins the Taiga toward the south. Among these deciduous trees which drop their broad, flat leaves each winter, beech and oak, together with maple and chestnut, are the most typical, but some conifers like hemlock are mixed with them. On its southern margin this type of forest becomes drier on the west side of the continents, and the so-called Mediterranean type of vegetation, of which the live-oak is a good example, becomes dominant. The rainy east side shows a tropical influence, as in Japan and China, where the transition between temperate and tropical is very gradual.

The tropical hard woods, with their enormous variety of species, form another world belt on both sides of the equator. On the east side of the continents and of certain mountain ranges this belt usually extends to the north and south as far as the trade winds carry moisture

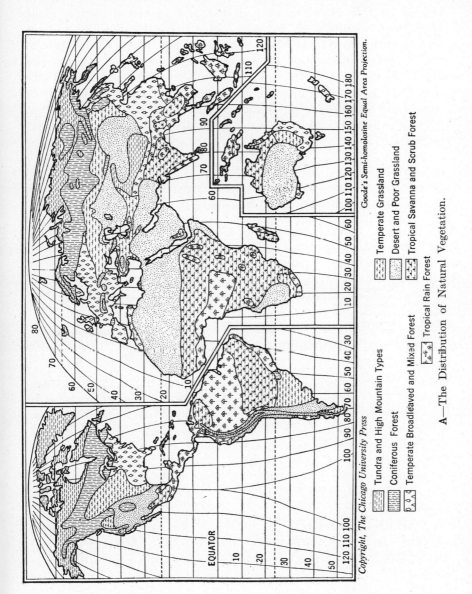

Copyright, The Chicago University Press

Goode's Semi-homolosine Equal Area Projection.

Tundra and High Mountain Types

Coniferous Forest

Temperate Broadleaved and Mixed Forest

Temperate Grassland

Desert and Poor Grassland

Tropical Savanna and Scrub Forest

Tropical Rain Forest

A—The Distribution of Natural Vegetation.

during the dry season. In spite of local differences, the hard wood
tropical forest in its central part, where it is a product of rain the whole
year round, resembles the Taiga in that it is largely unbroken and has
withstood the invasion of man. On both sides, however, this tropical
rainforest belt is accompanied by open dry forests and savannas, or
grasslands dotted with trees. These show an adjustment to dry winters. The uplands of Brazil and vast highland areas in Africa from
Angola and Rhodesia on the south through Tanganyika to French West
Africa illustrate this type of forest. So do the Deccan Plateau in India,
the inner basins of southeastern Asia, and the west slopes of the eastern
Australian mountains. South of 30° S. the temperate hard woods and
mixed forest appear once more. The tapering shape of the continents,
however, limits their area and causes the Taiga to be absent entirely.

The influence of man on the distribution of forests has, with a few
exceptions like India, Java, and the east coast of Brazil. been mainly

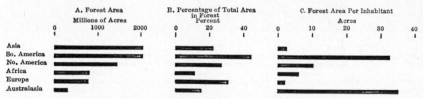

A—Distribution of Forests by Continents.

limited to the temperate zone of hard wood and mixed forests. Here,
however, the forest has often been so completely destroyed that it is
now restricted to the mountains or to less productive soils. The Appalachian system in the United States, the many ranges of west and central Europe, the mountainous backbone of southern China, and the
rough topography of Japan are still covered with forests. The coniferous belts of the southeastern United States and of the sandy moraine
region of Germany, Poland, and Russia are examples of the influence
of poor soils.

Total Area of Forests.—The division of the world's 7½ billion acres
of forest among the continents is shown in A434. Although Asia has
about 2,100 million acres, its enormous deserts and the density of population in India and China cause it to have only about 22 per cent of
its area in forests, as appears in B of A434, while North America has
27 per cent, Europe 31, and South America 44. On the other hand,
Australia and Africa have such huge deserts that their forest areas comprise respectively only 15 and 11 per cent of their total area. A more
important consideration, so far as industry and commerce are con-

cerned, is seen in A434, which shows that Australia has about 35 acres of forest per inhabitant, South America 32, North America 10, and Africa less than 6, while Asia has only 2.4 and Europe 1.7.

The area of forests in individual countries is illustrated in A435. Russia stands first, as is generally the case where mere area is con-

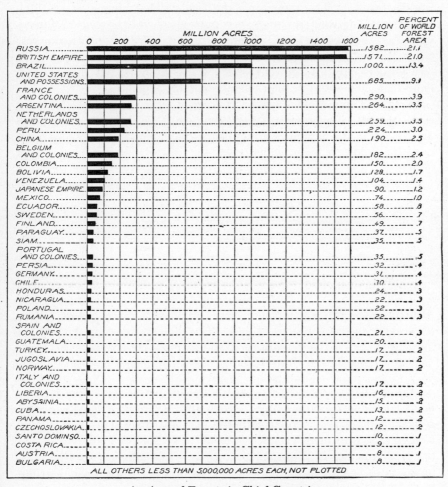

A—Area of Forests in Chief Countries.

cerned. The British Empire comes second, for although 95 per cent of the original forest has been removed in Great Britain itself, Canada has nearly 600 million acres of forest, British Africa 350, Australia 90, and even populous India 40. Brazil, with approximately a billion acres of forest, considerably outranks the United States with 550 million acres at home, 95 million in Alaska, and 38 million in the Philippines. Originally, the two were nearly equal, but Brazil has as yet removed only a small percentage of its forests, whereas the United States has permanently cleared about 40 per cent. These four political units—Russian, British, Brazilian, and American—possess nearly two-thirds of the world's forests. The remaining third is divided among about fifty countries. The most progressive countries control the world's forests much as they control its minerals, manufacturing, and commerce. Great Britain, France, Belgium, and the Netherlands have within their own borders only 0.4 per cent of the world's forests, but they control more than 30 per cent in their colonies and dependencies.

Area of Three Main Types.—The general distribution of the three types, namely, coniferous soft wood, temperate hard wood, and tropical hard wood, in the various continents may be judged from A433 and also from the following table, which gives the area of each type in millions of acres:

	Conifers	Temperate hard woods	Tropical hard woods
Europe	579	195	0
Asia	889	572	635
Africa	7	17	773
Australasia	15	15	253
North America	1,046	290	108
South America	109	115	1,869
World	2,645 (35%)	1,204 (16%)	3,638 (49)%

Europe has mainly conifers with some temperate hard woods; Asia has a large acreage of all three; Africa and Australia have little except tropical hard woods; North America has all three kinds, but chiefly conifers; South America likewise has all three, but with an overwhelming predominance of tropical hard woods. The different uses and different rates of growth of the three types of wood cause their distribution in individual countries to be extremely important.

For most purposes mankind prefers soft wood. The conifers can be felled, trimmed, sawed, and worked so much more easily than either the temperate or tropical hard woods, that they are the first choice for an overwhelming majority of uses. About 95 per cent of the coniferous forests are located between latitudes 30° and 60° N. and hence in the regions where human progress is most active. It is not surprising, then, that they have been exploited on an enormous scale. One-half of all the world's wood and three-fourths of all the saw timber, or logs that are fit for the sawmill, are today cut from coniferous forests. The temperate hard woods are cut to a much smaller extent. In the United States, for example, the cut of soft woods since 1921 has averaged about four times as great as that of hard woods. In the world as a whole, the temperate hard woods may furnish 40 per cent of the total cut, for Europe uses much hard wood for fuel, but they probably do not supply much more than 20 per cent of the saw timber.

The tropical hard woods are only beginning to be used. At present they supply perhaps 9 per cent of the total that is cut for all purposes, and 3 per cent of the saw timber. Their great disadvantage is that while the temperate forests are rather uniform and open, the tropical forests show a great variety of trees amid an amazing growth of vegetation. When no permanent path or trail is available, as is nearly always the case, the crossing of such a forest is a tremendous task. In order to get out a single valuable tree many others of other kinds have to be felled to obtain space for action. The use of timber from tropical rainforests is limited to a few very valuable kinds like mahogany and ebony wood, and the present main value of such forests lies in the gathering of resins (and, until rather recently, rubber) by the native inhabitants. The dry, tropical forests of the Wet and Dry Low Latitudes have the advantage of being open and of having a more uniform structure, which means that trees of a single species are more likely to grow together. This greatly enhances their value. The teak of Burma, Siam, and Java, the sal of the lower slopes of the Himalayas, and the quebracho of Paraguay are examples of this kind. Nevertheless, the world timber trade shows its main concentration in the southeastern and northwestern United States and in northern and eastern Europe.

The Optimum for Conifers.—Each species of tree, and likewise each of the three great types of forest, has its own optimum of climate, soil, and relief. The conifers are most widespread in cold, snowy regions like Siberia and Canada. The largest and most rapidly growing species, however, are found in lower latitudes where the altitude or the position in respect to the ocean gives them cool, moist summers and snowy winters. The slopes of the Himalayas at altitudes of 5,000 to 7,000 feet around Kashmir, certain remote mountains in the far west of China near the Tibetan border, the Andean slopes of southern Chile, and the ocean-girt mountains of southern New Zealand illustrate the type. The most familiar example is the western parts of the states of Oregon and Washington. There grow the Oregon pine, or Douglas fir as it really is, which today rivals the southern pine as a wood available in large quantities for general purposes, and the Washington spruce, the best kind of wood for airplanes, where lightness, strength, and freedom from knots must be combined.   Not far away in similar climates grow the great redwoods of the California coast; and at higher levels the giant sequoias, 300 feet high and 20 or even 30 feet in diameter at the base, and often 2,000 or even 3,000 years old.   In general, the regions where soft conifers grow most rapidly and hence yield most per acre have a summer temperature averaging not over 60° F. and a winter temperature varying from about 15° to 32°.   In summer they are so moist, as well as cool, that they are not good for the majority of crops.   In winter the main requisite appears to be that they be either so cold that snow lies on the ground many months or else so rainy that the ground is soaked with water practically all the time.

The Optimum for Hard Woods.—The temperate hard woods find their optimum in such places as the deep-soiled, well-watered lowlands of central Europe and the southeastern quarter of the United States. Much of this area, however, has been cleared for agriculture, and now the large deciduous forests lie chiefly among mountains.   Almost nowhere do great oaks, beeches, maples, chestnuts, tulip trees, ashes, and other such trees make a finer growth than in North Carolina at the eastern base of the southern Appalachians.   There the trunks of the trees often rise straight up 50 or 75 feet before branching, and sometimes continue another 50 above that.   In summer the climate is warmer and rainier than that of the Oregon region most favorable to conifers.   This is the chief reason why deciduous trees rather than conifers prevail. Here, as in Oregon, the presence of the mountains, causing abundant rain, helps in producing excellent stands of timber.

A still better region for the broadleaved trees is that where the optimum for the tropical hard woods is found.   The ideal combination appears to be temperatures above 70° at all seasons, but not often above 90°, abundant rain at all seasons, plenty of sun, deep young soil, and good drainage.   Such conditions prevail, for example, at the eastern base of the Andes in the Amazon basin.   At what would otherwise be a dry season, the great height of the Andes forces the easterly trade winds to rise, thus producing abundant moisture where the soil is deep and the temperature high.   Moreover, in such tropical regions, even in the rainiest seasons, there is generally bright sunshine during the morning.   Not till the plants have had a good amount of sunshine do the clouds gather for the afternoon showers.   As yet the demand for lumber is not strong enough to cause the hard woods of the moist tropical regions to be cut extensively even in the plains, but as time goes on the lower parts of the moist, rugged tropical regions will presumably rank among the world's greatest timber regions. Students of forestry have found that a given area near the eastern foot of the Andes in Brazil, where the drainage is good, where showers are frequent, and where the sun shines warmly, produces two to six times as much wood each year as the best deciduous areas in the Appalachians.

The Growing Demand for Wood.—Each advance in material civilization seems to create a greater demand for wood. Coal, to be sure, has now been substituted for wood as fuel by hundreds of millions of people, and iron, brick, concrete, and stucco often take its place as structural materials. In carriages, railway cars, ships, and other means of transportation, a similar curtailment has occurred. Nevertheless, not only the total demand but the demand per capita keeps on increasing. This is partly due to the great number of new uses for wood. To take a single example, here is the per capita consumption of pulp wood cut from the trees of the forest and used in the United States:

Year	Per capita consumption of wood for paper	Year	Per capita consumption of wood for paper
1879	18 cu. ft.	1909	93 cu. ft.
1889	36	1919	124
1899	57	1923	169
		1930	220

The half century from 1879 to 1929 witnessed a twelve-fold increase in the use of paper and almost a thirty-fold increase in the use of pulp wood until we now use nearly eight million cords per year.

The consumption of wood varies enormously. In Egypt, practically no wood is available, but almost none is needed for heating or industries, and only a little for cooking. So the consumption is estimated at only 2 cubic feet per capita each year. In cooler and more advanced countries like England and the Netherlands, where the supply of wood has for centuries been insufficient, the widespread use of coal for fuel, and of brick and tile for buildings, keeps consumption below 20 cubic feet per year. In the United States, on the contrary, although the per capita consumption of coal is larger than almost anywhere else, the abundance of wood, the demand for it in manufacturing and in the construction of new buildings, and its widespread use as fuel among farmers raise the consumption to about 230 cubic feet. In Finland, where the supply is more accessible than in the United States and also more abundant in proportion to the population, and where the very severe winters and the scarcity of coal lead to a large demand for wood as fuel, the annual consumption attains the extreme figure of about 300 cubic feet per capita.

The Uses of Timber.—A general idea of the uses of timber and the kinds of trees used for different purposes can be obtained by studying the data for the United States. Seventy-one per cent of the timber removed from the forest is classified as *lumber*. This includes sawed timber used for different purposes, such as the boards turned out by planing mills, structural timber, boxes and crating, and also lumber for export. Nearly five times as much soft wood as hard wood is used. Of the soft woods the yellow pine of the Southeast and the Douglas fir stand out as the main trees, contributing nearly three-fourths of the total. Among the hard woods the oak and red gum contribute about half.

Fuel wood probably forms 9 per cent of the timber production, but this is only a rough estimate, for much fire wood is used on the farms where it is cut. Hard wood here leads soft wood in the ratio of three to one, partly because of the denser population of the hard wood region and also because it burns longer, more evenly (because of less resin), and with less smoke. Hard maple is the highest priced fire wood on the market. In general the type of fire wood depends on the local type of trees.

The production of *pulp wood*, which comprises $4\frac{1}{2}$ per cent of the total wood cut in the United States, has increased constantly. Soft wood dominates here, with spruce and yellow pine the leading trees. Both spruce and hemlock are also imported from Canada for this purpose. Wood pulp is produced out of pulp wood partly by the mechanical process of grinding (20 per cent), but mainly by chemical processes, that is, by cooking with bisulphite, sulphate of soda, or caustic soda. A442 shows the main concentration in the northern forest belt from Maine to Wisconsin. The United States produces about one-fourth of the world's pulp wood, but the great paper consumption here causes a large import of wood pulp (40 per cent of the consumption) from Canada and the Scandinavian countries. Europe and North America each take nearly half of the world's wood pulp, with only Japan as a relatively important outsider. The importance of international trade comes strongly to the foreground when we realize that the *New York Times* is printed entirely on the produce of the Canadian forest, while the correspondingly important Northcliffe concern of Great Britain has its main pulp mills in Newfoundland.

Hewed Ties.—Although sawed ties belong under lumber, hewed ties, consuming 4 per cent of the timber supply, come under a special heading. They are made from small logs which are smoothed on two sides with an adze and then sawed into tie lengths. This is done at the place where the tree is felled. Hard woods, especially oak, provide 80 per cent of the hewed ties. The southern pine is the main soft wood used.

Cooperage, or the making of barrels, hogsheads, and firkins, uses 3 per cent of the timber consumed in the United States. Pine and gum are the leading trees for this, and the production of staves, headings, and hoops is correspondingly concentrated in the southern belt from Virginia to Louisiana and Arkansas.

Shingles.—Nearly 2 per cent of our timber is cut up into six to nine million shingles each year. This is done mainly in the state of Washington from the western red cedar. The increased importance of non-inflammable artificial shingles has decreased the shingle production to one-half of what it was twenty years ago.

Mine timber, fence posts, and poles use nearly 4 per cent of the timber supply, all kinds of timber being used accordingly to the local supply. The amount of timber used as props to hold up the roofs of coal mines is astonishing, even though concrete is beginning to be used. The removal or decay of the props often permits old mines to cave in, with damage to overlying houses.

Veneer logs (1 per cent) were, until recently, made predominantly from hard woods with the red gum of the Mississippi Valley the basic tree. Recent years show an increased importance of the Douglas fir (tripled since 1925), and yellow pine (doubled since 1923). Maple, yellow poplar, cottonwood, walnut, and oak are also used a great deal. Fancy hard woods for veneer purposes are imported from the tropics, New York being the main import harbor. Mexican cedar from Mexico and Central America, mahogany from the West Indies and Central America, the Circassian walnut from the Mediterranean region, ebony wood from Africa and Java, light balsa wood and extremely hard lignum vitae from the Caribbean, satin wood from Ceylon, rose wood from Brazil, and teak from the forests of Siam and Burma are examples. They are used to veneer many products ranging from musical instruments and cigar boxes to Pullman car interiors and motor boats.

Distillation.—Another use of timber is for distillation. Hard woods, especially maple, birch, and beech, are mainly used for this, although in the South turpentine, pine oil, tar, and pitch are obtained from the distillation of pines. The chief products are acetate of lime, used in the acetic acid industry, and wood alcohol used as a solvent in many chemical industries.

Charcoal production has decreased greatly in the United States, but is still of importance in Europe. In Sweden, charcoal is still used in melting iron ore for certain kinds of especially fine steel. Great charcoal pits are still a familiar sight in the European forests.

Naval Stores.—Although tree crops and the production of rubber are discussed in other chapters, some special forest products should be mentioned here. In the United States the production of naval stores, which means chiefly turpentine for paint and rosin for use with tow in calking seams, is limited to the pine forests of the sandy strips of the Atlantic coastal plain, with Georgia and Florida the leading states. Because of the great loss of trees under the old method of cutting the bark, a new method was introduced from Les Landes in France. In that section, 2,000,000 acres, which were once a swampy wasteland, are now planted with maritime pine and have been yielding an increasing amount. While the United States is the main world producer, with Europe second, various resins are exported from the tropical forests. These include benzoe, damar, and copal. Still another resinous product, gum Arabic, is gathered from small trees on the borders between the Wet and Dry Low Latitudes and the Deserts in regions like the Anglo-Egyptian Sudan.

Although *tannin* exists in all plants, it is obtained only from certain trees in sufficient quantity to be of commercial use for tanning. Oak bark is the main source of tannin in the United States. A South American tree, the quebracho, growing in the Gran Chaco region of southern Brazil, Paraguay, Bolivia, and northern Argentina, is another important tannin producer. The imports into the United States amount to one-fourth of the consumption. The Sicilian sumach tree, the Valonian oak (the acorn of which contains up to 45 per cent tannin), and the tropical gambier, a product of the Malay Archipelago, are other tannin producers.

Dyestuffs are also extracted from timber. Logwood from Central America and Brazilwood are the most important sources.

Finally, the bark of an evergreen oak has attained commercial importance in the form of *cork.* An area of 4 to 5 million acres in the Mediterranean region is covered with this kind of oak, mainly in southern Spain and Portugal. The cork oak, as J. Russell Smith points out, could probably be grown here. Its acorns are so valuable that the Spaniards herd their pigs under the trees in order to fatten them. Yet the United States imports 10 million dollars' worth of cork per year, mainly from Portugal and Spain.

The Future Supply of Timber.—The map of timber distribution in the United States (A442) shows two marked regions of concentration, one in the Northwest and one in the South. In the last half century a

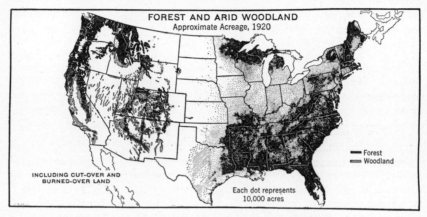

FOREST AND ARID WOODLAND
Approximate Acreage, 1920

INCLUDING CUT-OVER AND
BURNED-OVER LAND

Forest
Woodland

Each dot represents
10,000 acres

A—Forests and Woodland in the United States.

remarkable shift has taken place. This is indicated in the following table showing the percentage of the total timber cut in various regions at each census.

PERCENTAGE OF DISTRIBUTION

Regions	1889	1899	1909	1919	1929
Northeastern	19.8	16.3	11.7	4.4	3.3
Lake	34.6	24.9	12.3	6.4	4.8
Central	13.1	16.1	12.3	5.5	6.4
North Carolina pine	4.7	7.7	11.6	7.1	8.1
Southern	15.6	24.0	33.3	37.6	33.8
Rocky Mountain	1.1	1.6	2.9	5.0	5.0
Pacific	8.5	8.3	15.5	34.7	38.4
All others	2.6	1.1	0.4	0.2	0.2

The year of maximum percentage in each region is italicized. Notice the steady decline in the percentages for the northeastern and lake regions. The central region passed its maximum in 1899, and the North Carolina pine region in 1909. Now the South seems to have passed its maximum, and the Northwest, in spite of its distance from the main market, has gained the leadership.

The alarming feature of all this is that in many parts of the world the consumption of timber decidedly exceeds the growth. For example, in the United States it is estimated that the amount cut each year is nearly six times as great as the growth during the same period. Moreover, the yearly destruction by fire, in spite of government fire prevention, often amounts to a value of a hundred million dollars per year. Even more important than fire is destruction by insects and diseases, which are partly responsible for the low economic value of the tropical forest. Even in the United States certain types of trees have been almost eliminated in this way, as happened to the chestnut after the chestnut blight. In fact, reliable foresters estimate that in North America more wood is destroyed each year by fire, insects, and disease than is used by man. How new diseases can become of sudden importance was shown in 1930 when the northeastern white pine region was threatened by the white pine blister rust. This spread rapidly and necessitated the eradication of wild currants and gooseberries, the hosts of the insect, over the whole area. The control of the bark beetle epidemics is one of the main problems of American forestry. It is estimated that the bark beetle in the western pine and spruce annually destroys 5 billion board feet, which is about one and one-half times the amount cut. Similar conditions in countries like Germany necessitate the greatest care if new production is to exceed consumption.

Such conditions add weight to the question: from where will the future timber supply of the world come? With the growth of population, the area of forests has greatly diminished and will doubtless continue to diminish. The diminution will presumably be slow in well settled countries, but elsewhere it is likely to be rapid. Even now in Australia one can see thousands of acres where the trees, after being girdled by cutting the bark near the base, are left standing to rot in order to clear the land for pasturage. In large parts, although by no means all, of northern Canada, Alaska, northern Russia and Siberia, the timber is merely a small growth fit for little except pulp wood. It grows so slowly that after an area has been cut over, new trees do not attain even the small size needed for pulpwood in much less than half a century. Nevertheless, Siberia, with over a billion acres of forest, could probably export 6 billion cubic feet of timber, and yet not deplete its resources, if they were properly managed. On the other hand, in the tropical parts of South America, Africa, southeastern Asia and the East Indies, the forests grow with great rapidity, and almost no timber is cut. This is natural, for the climate not only stimulates growth and makes fire wood almost unnecessary, but also retards civilization and thus restricts the use of fuel in transportation and manufacturing. The trees often grow to a height of 100 feet or more in less time than it takes for the northern trees to attain a height of 20 or 30. The tropical rainforests of Africa with 350 million acres, of Asia and the East Indies with 500 million, and of South America with 1,000 million, if fully developed and fairly well handled, could produce each year from 200 to 250 billion cubic feet of wood, or perhaps four times the present consumption of the entire world.

To put the matter in another way, there are still 4.4 acres of forest for each person. Such an area is capable of producing many times the present consumption of wood, which amounts to about 32 cubic feet per capita each year. This is approximately $7\frac{1}{2}$ cubic feet per acre of forest, but the average growth in well managed coniferous forests amounts to 60 or 80 cubic feet. In Finland, for example, the average for poorly managed as well as carefully managed forests is 33, in France 38, in Germany 50, in lower Austria 51, and in Belgium 57. A very careful survey of a strip in Värmland County, Sweden, showed that from 1911 to 1929 the stand, or number of trees, increased 37 per cent. In tropical countries this figure is of course capable of being increased several-fold, although nothing of the kind has yet been done. Thus the prospects for an ample supply of lumber in the future are good, so far as the amount of timber is concerned. The main question is whether we can get the right kinds at a cost that is reasonable.

Transportation, Labor, and Nature of Trees as Factors in Use of Forests.—Excellent transportation facilities are one of the chief reasons why Washington and Oregon supply enormous quantities of lumber not only to the northeastern United States, but to China with its depleted forests, and even to forested Japan when a great calamity like the earthquake of 1923 causes an unusual demand. In the same way, good transportation facilities make it possible for Europe, with its favorable climate and progressive forestry system, to supply timber to South Africa where the climate is unfavorable. But transportation facilities are very poor in most of the regions where there is a great surplus of timber. Not only are the forests of Siberia and much of Canada remote and without railroads, but the rivers mostly run north, and are of little use in floating lumber to places where it is needed. In the tropical forests the difficulties of transportation, though different, are equally great. Torrential rains make it difficult to construct roads and railways, and insects and parasitic diseases are a still greater handicap. Moreover, the labor for such hard work as cutting trees is especially inefficient, and it would be difficult to introduce the proper kind of labor from other countries.

Another difficulty lies in the character of the trees. First, as we have seen, the tropical forests do not contain large stands of a single kind of tree as do the coniferous forests. Few buyers want to purchase mixed lots of timber containing many species. Therefore in cutting the virgin tropical forests it is necessary to work on one species at a time, or else to take a great deal of pains to keep the kinds separate. Both methods are expensive. Again, the hardness of the wood of the tropical forests not only adds to the expense of cutting and preparing the lumber, but makes the wood far less useful than that of the soft conifers. The net result is that the development of tropical forests is likely to be slow so long as conifers are available.

The consumption of wood, like that of practically every other commodity, tends more and more to be concentrated in a few highly active industrial areas. For the present the needs of such regions can apparently best be met by a more rational forestry practice in the $2\frac{1}{2}$ billion acres of coniferous forests. In other words, although improved transportation facilities and the development of tropical forests are undoubtedly great factors in determining where the future timber supply shall come from, good forestry methods in the coniferous areas may be a still greater factor. The distribution of timber production in the future appears to depend largely upon whether timber is looked upon as a resource like the minerals, which are mined once for all, or as a crop to be conserved, cultivated, and harvested year by year.

The Conservation of Forests.—The basis of any rational policy of forest conservation is selective cutting, which is used in good forest practice everywhere. In Europe it is very widespread; in the United States it is beginning. Except for thinning purposes, only mature trees are cut; young trees and seed trees are allowed to grow. In the long run this is profitable. It means that a steady supply of good trees is available year after year and the growth of the local forest can be properly balanced against the cutting. The removal of all the merchantable trees at one cutting means not only that the forest needs a great many years to become productive again, especially if the seed trees are destroyed, but also that the trees which spring up are likely to be of species less valuable than those that were cut. For example, a forest of white pine, which is one of the most valuable trees, has some admixture of hard woods such as maple, beech, hemlock, and yellow birch. When it is cut, the new forest is likely to contain comparatively little white pine and much hard wood, because hard wood seedlings, being relatively tolerant, as the botanists say, are more numerous in the shady places of a well established forest than pine seedlings. If the hard wood forest is cut off and burned over, as often happens, the next growth will contain a large percentage of such relatively poor species as birch and aspen, because these can thrive in an impoverished soil better than can the hard woods. Another cutting and another fire will increase the percentage of birch and aspen. Thus as a general rule the second growth is not so good as the first, and the third and fourth are still less valuable.

But with proper forest conservation, there is nothing but growth of the desired type. Often where no conservation is practiced and big companies have swept away the most valuable trees of the virgin growth, small companies have to be content with the second growth, and the third is cut only for pulp wood for paper. In tropical countries the reckless cutting of forests works havoc with the future in still another way. In Sumatra, for example, the authors have seen considerable areas where, after the forest had been destroyed, tough alang-alang grass came up and stopped reforestation. The problem of balanced cutting and reforestation is not yet urgent in such tropical regions, but it is in the United States. If the natural reforestation of New England after the retreat of the farmer could be properly guided, and if the forests now being cut in the Southeast could be properly controlled, the future of the timber supply even in the eastern United States would be far from hopeless.

Why Lumbering Communities Are Relatively Backward.—It is well to examine the effect of forests in controlling the geographical distribution not only of the lumber industry, but of certain well-defined social and economic conditions. We have seen that permanence of residence is a potent factor in the evolution of civilization. Almost no type of civilized community is more transitory than many lumbering communities, and the standards of living are correspondingly low. This is because lumbering has hitherto been, in most cases, not only an *extractive* but an *exhaustive* industry. Like hunting, fishing, farming, and mining, the lumbering industry extracts from nature a primary product. Except under modern methods of forestry, it also exhausts the supply of nature's gifts without making much effort to replace them. Thus for centuries the world has been growing poorer in forests almost as rapidly as in minerals, and far more rapidly than in animals, fish, or soil.

The rapidity with which lumbering exhausts the supply of trees causes the industry to be highly transitory. As soon as the merchantable timber has been cut within easy reach of a camp, the lumbermen must move on or be idle. The work of cutting the timber proceeds so rapidly that it is not worth while to build good houses, and the lumbermen live in rough shacks or log cabins. In many cases the men are housed in long bunk-houses, which are not much more than closed sheds containing bunks along the sides where a score or more men can sleep in one room. The same thing is true of the lumber camps in the equatorial forests. For a time the forests resound with the noises of modern enterprise. In Siam and Burma, white supervisors with the help of native labor and huge elephants bring the teak to a branch line of the railroad system. But finally, when the supply is exhausted, everything is left, and the great forest recovers the area which it for a moment lost. Only when the policy of forest exhaustion gives place to conservation and slow steady use of the timber can the lumber industry become permanent and thus maintain high standards of living.

How Sweden Maintains High Standards in the Lumber Industry.—Sweden gives the best example of a balanced forest industry. There lumbering is the most important industry aside from agriculture. Sawmills and planing-mills alone employ about as many men as all the iron mines, machinery factories, and other metal work for which Sweden is famous. Most of the lumbering is done in winter, making it possible for the inhabitants to combine farming and lumbering. In many cases, however, the Swedish lumber crews are considered permanent labor, and some sawmill companies furnish houses and gardens for their men. In the summer the trees to be cut the following winter are marked. Real work starts when the first snow falls. The marked trees are felled, the branches cut, the bark peeled off, and the trunks sawed into lengths. The branches and bark may be used near where they are cut for extracting tar or for making charcoal to be shipped to the iron industry. The timber is transported to the nearest river and piled on the ice to wait for the spring thaw. Transportation is a very important factor in lumbering, for the product is bulky and heavy in proportion to its value. Moreover, it comes largely from rugged regions where the population in scanty and the roads poor, while it finds a market chiefly in the lowlands and the cities. In Sweden, as in Finland, Russia, New England, and Wisconsin, snow facilitates transportation immensely. Sledges pulled by horses, and sometimes by reindeer, or driven by motor power, bring the timber over the smooth snow surface to the nearest river. When the snow is icy, enormous loads can be hauled with ease. The fact that Sweden has many short parallel rivers is a great advantage, for most of the lumber has to be hauled only 2 or 3 miles to a river. When it is piled up on the river ice the main labor is done, and the spring thaw carries the lumber down the river to the seashore. Timber drivers, with long poles, direct the floating timber around the river bends or to tugboats which gather it into rafts. The only remaining labor is to tow the chained timber rafts across the lakes which interrupt the rivers. Finally the timber reaches the mill or pulp factory located at the river outlet. In Sweden these are often combined into one. The northern part of the seacoast is lined with such mills (A448 and B448). From here the final product is shipped to the market. The direction of the rivers, their continuous fall, and rather steady water supply are of the greatest importance. The fact that Sweden's rivers run from northwest to southeast gives them the advantage of thawing first at their mouths in spring and then having high water when the snow melts higher up. The northward-flowing rivers of Russia, Siberia, and Canada, it will be remembered, thaw upstream first, causing floods, which spread very widely when the water is unable to escape to the sea because the lower parts of the rivers are icebound. Moreover, ice in the ocean to which these rivers finally run permits shipping for only a few months in summer.

Effect of Transportation on the Lumber Industry.—Transportation is in many respects the key to the lumber industry. We have already seen that snow, ice, and an abundance of rapid rivers whose mouths thaw before their upper portions, are an immense advantage in lumbering. In the south and west of the United States, where there is little snow and where the trees are often of great size, transportation is more expensive than in New England, Minnesota, or Sweden. Frequently the logs are fastened beneath the axles of huge pairs of wheels. Sometimes two pairs are

employed, but often one end of the log is allowed to drag behind.   In the bigger
camps such methods of hauling with animals have almost wholly given way to steam
power or tractors.   Donkey engines snake the logs through the forest and then by
means of a skidder, which is something like an electric crane, dump them onto flat
cars or into chutes or flumes.   Skyline cables drag great logs over long distances,
leaving a wake of débris and broken timber, the opposite of sound forest policy.

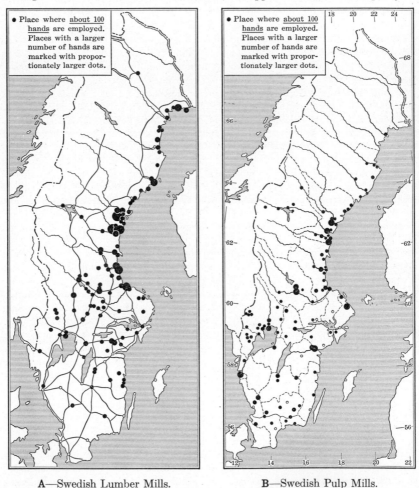

A—Swedish Lumber Mills.   B—Swedish Pulp Mills.

In places where rivers are not available, it is necessary to construct logging railroads.   These are generally of flimsy construction, for the owners do not expect to
use them long.   As forest conservation becomes more general, the roads and railways
in the forested areas improve.   In fact, the greatest hope of making lumbering a
permanent occupation, and hence desirable from the social standpoint, seems to lie in
having such transportation facilities that logs from any part of a forest can easily
be transported to the sawmills and to market, while the lumbermen can get to any

desired region so quickly that they can live at home and devote part of their time to farming. The old-time isolated lumber camp, with its abuses, is disappearing. Its place is being taken by a much more permanent and useful type of community.

Transportation also has an effect on the ownership of the lumber industry. The lumber operator who wants to use a river must control not only the rugged region where his trees grow, but also an area beside the river as far down as possible in order to set up his sawmill. This gives the big company with much capital a great advantage over the small one. The big company has a similar advantage in respect to railroads, for the initial investment in these is so high that much land must be owned in order to make them pay. If the investment in railroads is heavy, it does not pay to move the tracks oftener than once in about twenty years. Hence, large companies seek to protect their railroad investments by buying up the timber for many miles around their mills. This is one reason why much of the timber of the United States is in large holdings. In fact, about 11 per cent of all the privately owned trees in the country belong to three such companies. Small lumber firms who bargain every two or three years for a supply of standing timber can rarely cut cheaply enough to compete with large companies. Often the best they can do is to invest in portable sawmills, buy the cut-over lands at low prices, and make their profits from the second and third growths. The worst feature of the lumber industry, so far as ownership is concerned, is that vast holdings have been acquired by private interests which have paid little or even nothing for them, and are chiefly desirous of making fortunes regardless of whether the forests are ruined. In the United States, the government forest reserves, established to counteract this difficulty and prevent its continuance, include over 260,000 square miles, or nearly 9 per cent of the United States proper, and another 33,000 square miles in Alaska. In tropical countries and likewise in the far northern coniferous areas most of the forests are still owned by the governments.

EXERCISES

1. Investigate the amount, kind, and source of your local supply of lumber and firewood. In the *Yearbook of Agriculture* look up the supply and consumption of both hard woods and soft woods in your state. Compare your state with some others like Pennsylvania, Michigan, Oklahoma, or Oregon as to both the total and the per capita production and consumption. What geographic conditions have most effect in causing your state's supply and demand for lumber to be either large or small?

2. Use the following figures to make a graph illustrating the changes in the production of lumber in eighty years. Explain the relation of these changes to relief, location, climate, transportation, and cost of lumber in regions where it is most used.

PERCENTAGE OF UNITED STATES TIMBER SUPPLY CUT IN VARIOUS REGIONS

	1850	1860	1870	1880	1890	1900	1910	1920	1930
Northeastern states	*54.5*	36.2	36.8	24.8	18.4	16.0	9.9	6.5	3.8
Lake states	6.4	13.6	24.4	33.4	*36.3*	27.4	12.6	7.1	5.1
Southern states	13.8	16.5	9.4	11.9	15.9	25.2	*44.0*	42.6	31.3
Pacific states	3.9	6.2	3.6	3.5	7.3	9.6	18.6	29.7	41.0

3. Assign to each of the natural regions of Chapters XII to XV an approximate rank of one, two, or three according to each of the following criteria: (*a*) quality of lumber, i.e., size of trees; (*b*) degree to which the land was originally covered with forests; (*c*) degree to which original forest still remains uncut; (*d*) extent to which the present forest supplies the needs of the inhabitants. (See Zon and Sparhawk: *Forest Resources of the World.*) Judging by the ranks thus assigned, which natural regions are now most favored in their supply of timber? Which are least favored? Where does the demand most exceed the supply?

4. In A442 point out features of the present distribution of forests in the United States which are due to (*a*) aridity, (*b*) abundant rainfall, (*c*) low temperature, (*d*) relief, (*f*) unfitness for agriculture. Study the map as a whole and compare it with A443 showing the natural vegetation before man interfered with it. To what factors, both physical and human, is the present distribution of our forests mainly due?

5. Compare maps of natural vegetation, and of present-day forests. In what areas have the forests been removed? Why? Where have they been retained? Why? In which of the areas now marked as forest has lumbering been carried on as a business? Explain why this has not been the case in some of the deforested areas.

6. Name the important areas which still have large amounts of each of the three kinds of forests shown in A433. After each name put down the following facts: (*a*) temperature in July and January, (*b*) annual rainfall, (*c*) seasonal distribution of rain, (*d*) topography, and (*e*) density of population. To what conclusions are you led?

CHAPTER XXI

MINERAL PRODUCTS

Relative Value of Minerals.—Although the total value of all the minerals produced each year, including metals, non-metallic minerals and fuels, is far inferior to that of animals and plants, the ultimate significance of the minerals may be equally great. This is because the mineral products, with the exception of fuels, last a long time and can be used again and again. Food and fuel, on the contrary, serve their purpose once—that is all. Clothing and rubber goods last longer than food and fuel, but rarely more than a few years. Wood stands almost alone as a highly durable and yet important organic product, but it does not rival brick, cement, copper, or steel. In order to judge fairly as to the relative importance of mineral versus organic products, it would be necessary to take account of the world's entire supply as well as of the annual production. Nevertheless, for practical reasons we shall limit this chapter to the geographic distribution of current production and consumption.

Geographical Distribution.—Maps A452 and A453 give a clear picture of what the production of minerals means to various parts of the world. A452 shows the annual value of mineral production per square mile. Europe and North America stand out very strongly in contrast to the other continents. Elsewhere only a few regions like northern Chile, with its nitrate and copper, South Africa (gold and diamonds), the copper region of Katanga, Japan, the southeastern fringe of Asia, southeastern Australia, and New Zealand stand out because of an appreciable output. In Europe the great mining region includes Great Britain, Belgium, northern France, Germany, and Czechoslovakia. It is surrounded by a zone of considerable mining, as may be seen in Holland, the rest of France, Austria, and western Poland. The distribution in North America is more complex. California and Oklahoma rank very high because of oil, as do the eastern states from Illinois to Pennsylvania and West Virginia because of coal. The mountain states of Utah and Arizona rank high because of copper, while Minnesota and northern Michigan with iron and copper, Missouri with lead and zinc, and Texas with its oil wells, also stand well up. Unimportant, except for sand,

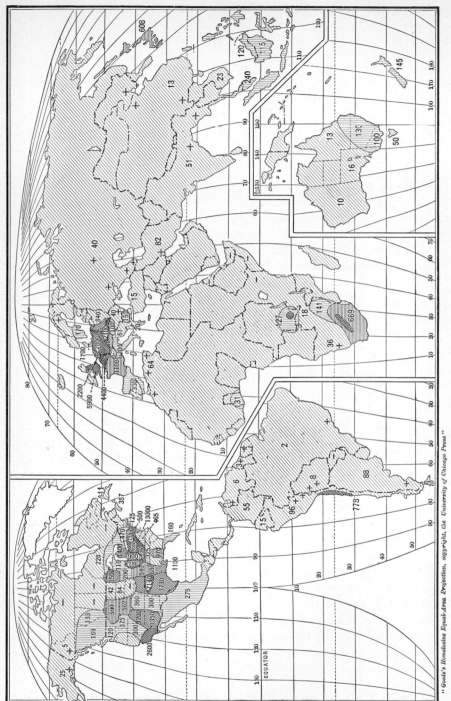

A—World Map of Mineral Production per Square Mile.

"Goode's Homolosine Equal-Area Projection, copyright, the University of Chicago Press"

452

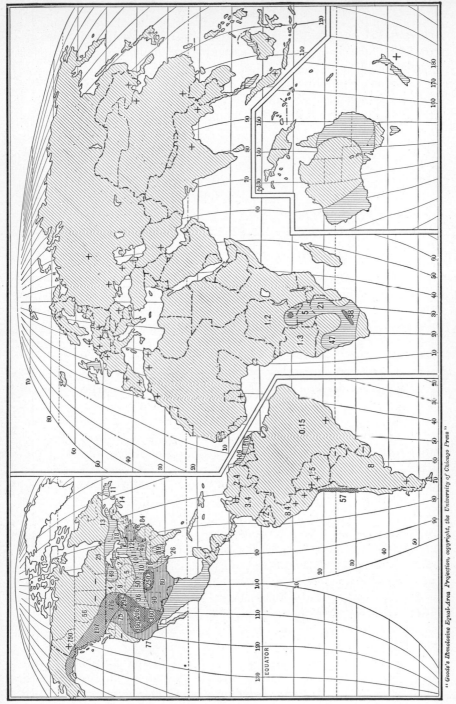

A—World Map of Mineral Production per Capita.

"Goode's Homolosine Equal-Area Projection, copyright, the University of Chicago Press"

453

clay, and stone, are the northwestern states (Oregon and Washington), the Southeast, with the exception of Alabama, and the New England States.

Now compare this map with A453, which shows the value of the mineral production per capita. Because of the density of population, the concentration in Europe has disappeared entirely, except that England's coal gives that country a slight excess per capita above its neighbors. Japan has likewise lost its advantage. The other continents outside of North America show about the same distribution as on map A452, generally a low output, but with a few exceptions which combine a high output per square mile and a high output per capita. In North America, A453 is entirely different from A452. Only Pennsylvania and West Virginia still indicate the great eastern concentration; elsewhere it has disappeared because of the rather dense population. Oklahoma keeps its high rank, while in the West four mountain states come to the fore, namely Nevada, Arizona, Utah, and Wyoming. There the density of population is very low, varying from 6.2 in Utah to 1.8 in Nevada, so that a low output of minerals per square miles means a high output per capita. The Alaska coast, being nearly unihabited, and having a number of mines, shows still another high output per capita. The much lower figure for California in A453 than in A452 indicates a greater concentration of population there than in the states east of the Sierra.

Relation of Mineral Deposits to Relief.—A more detailed study of the location of mineral products would show that mining is primarily an industry of rugged regions. In the United States the two main centers of production are decidedly rugged. One is the coal-mining center among the rough Appalachians and the much-dissected Allegheny Plateau. There the percentage of miners among men engaged in gainful occupations rises to about 25 in West Virginia, 11 in Pennsylvania, and 9 in Kentucky. The second mining region, the one from which most of our metals other than iron and zinc are obtained, centers in the Rocky Mountains. There the percentage of miners ranges from 6 in Colorado and 10 in Wyoming, to 13 in Arizona and 16 among the basins and ranges of Nevada. The iron and copper region of Minnesota and Michigan and the zinc region of Oklahoma are likewise somewhat rugged. Contrast this with states of gentle relief like Nebraska, Delaware, South Carolina, and Mississippi. There scarcely one man in a thousand is engaged in extracting minerals, even when we include not only coal, metals, petroleum and stone, but also gravel and sand.

In Europe the relation between relief and mining is much the same as in the United States. The greatest mining area comprises the coal districts of Wales, England, Belgium, western Germany, and northern

France.   Less important is the eastward continuation of this region, first where Germany, Poland, and Czechoslovakia come together, and then in the Donets region of southern Russia.   These regions range from rough mountains in Wales to hilly uplands in England, Belgium, and Germany, and still gentler hills in Russia.   None of them is flat.   Metallic ores show the same tendency toward abundance in rugged regions. The rolling plateau of northern Sweden, the upland of central England and eastern France, the Erz Gebirge (Ore Mountains) between Germany and Czechoslovakia, and the Mediterranean ranges of Spain, Italy, and the Balkans are all rugged regions which contain metallic ores sometimes in great variety.   Famous mining regions are also located in the mountains or plateaus of Alaska, Mexico, Colombia, Peru, Bolivia, Chile, South Africa, and Australia, and valuable ores are known to exist in the rugged parts of the Caucasus, Turkey, Persia, central Asia, and China.   In contrast to these are the lowlands of all the continents where even stone is often scarce, and metallic ores and coal cannot usually be easily discovered or profitably worked even if they exist.   The tendency for rugged relief and mining activity to go together, however, is by no means universal.   Many mountain ranges like the Cascades, the California Coast Range, the Alps, and the Himalayas, as well as plateaus like that of New England, are of little or no value from the mining point of view, whereas some rather flat plains like that of Louisiana produce abundant oil and gas.   Nevertheless the relation between mining and relief is strong enough to require an explanation.   This explanation will be helped by a discussion of how ores are formed.

Formation of Ore.—Most of the igneous rocks which constitute the main mass of the earth's crust contain very small quantities of many metals, mainly in oxidized form.   How minute these quantities are may be judged from the fact that whereas aluminum is estimated to constitute between 7 and 8 per cent of the earth's crust and iron over 4 per cent, copper probably forms only one part in 10,000.   Except for iron and aluminum, the quantities found originally in the igneous rocks are seldom great enough to be profitably extracted unless the metals have been concentrated by some process of nature.   Even with iron and aluminum a process of segregation is usually needed whereby the metallic compounds scattered through a great mass of rock are brought together into ore bodies of appreciable size.

The process of segregation is extremely important, for without it the metals could scarcely be used by man.   It may also be extremely slow—a matter of millions of years.   It takes place partly through the action of water.   As water percolates through the rocks far down under ground, it dissolves the widely scattered oxides, sulphides, or other compounds of the metals, and later deposits them after the solution has become concentrated by the addition of material from a wide area.   Water-formed ores are of two classes.   One is formed at considerable depths by hot water given off from the igneous rocks themselves.   This magmatic water, as it is usually called, generally carries the metals upward, and this process has given rise to much of the world's metallic wealth, including practically all the copper of the United States, the gold veins of California, the silver deposits of Cobalt in Ontario, and the lead of Germany. When the water reaches a certain level, the dissolved metals are partially deposited, thus giving rise to a zone of deposition. This is commonly located where the superheated lower water becomes cool enough so that it cannot hold all the material that it has dissolved. At higher levels where the magmatic water comes in contact with the cooler water from the surface, or where it is otherwise cooled or evaporated, a zone of especially rich deposition may occur. Since the level of permanent ground water in dry regions is much lower than in moist, and also much more variable in position, the zone in which this kind of enrichment of ores may occur is much more extensive in arid than in humid regions. This is one reason why rich metallic ores are more abundant in dry regions than in moist.

Ores of a less important type are sometimes formed by water that percolates downward from the surface, dissolving particles of metal as it goes and depositing them at lower levels. Again opportunities for the formation of such deposits are greater in dry regions than in moist. The large lead and zinc deposits of the Mississippi Valley in Wisconsin, Illinois, and Missouri were formed in this way.

Another chief way in which ores are segregated occurs when masses of molten rock push up through the earth's crust. Often, although not always, they reach the surface in volcanoes. Occasionally, during the vast periods while such a mass is slowly cooling below the surface, certain metallic minerals which form crystals at high temperatures solidify before the others. They collect near the relatively cool margins of the molten mass and finally come to rest as bodies of ore. The magnetic form of iron—magnetite—which occurs abundantly in Sweden, is the commonest mineral of this type. In other cases the gases which accompany a rising mass of molten rock contain metallic vapors. If the surrounding rock is of the right kind, especially limestone, the vapors may be deposited to form a zone of ore bordering the igneous intrusion. Iron and copper ores are the commonest minerals formed in this way, but lead, zinc, and gold may also occur.

Surface water may cause the local enrichment of ores formed in any of the preceding ways. By trickling down through the ores it may dissolve metals from the upper parts and deposit them lower down. Such secondary enrichment is especially likely to occur in dry regions. It produces relatively small bodies of extremely rich ore like the upper parts of the Arizona copper deposits and the famous Comstock silver lode in Nevada. It also produces great bodies of low-grade ore whose aggregate value is enormous. The great iron deposits of Lake Superior are supposed to be due to the action of water in a relatively dry and much-folded mountain region of pre-Cambrian times.

Advantages of Mountains above Plains.—The geologic structure of mountains causes ore segregation, both by magmatic water and by upward movements of molten rock, to be more active in mountain regions than in plains. Mountains are regions where the earth's rocky crust has been bent, folded, cracked, broken, and shoved upward or downward along what are called fault lines. This produces endless cracks and fissures along which water can move and deposit ores. Here, too, molten rock is pushed upward, thus forming dykes, sheets, or iregular masses. Where these come in contact with cooler rocks there is opportunity for ores to be formed. As a result of these advantages, the upper layer of the earth's crust contains metallic ore more abundantly in mountainous regions than in parts where the earth's crust has suffered little disturbance. Nevertheless, it seems that young mountains, like the Cascades and the Alps, with their very complex structure, are at a disadvantage when compared with block faulted regions like the Great Basin or geologically older mountainous regions where the process of segregation has continued for much longer periods.

Mountains have still another advantage. Many conditions make it easy to discover ores in them. The most obvious is that on steep slopes the soil is usually shallow and bare rock is often exposed. In regions of low relief, on the contrary, the soil is often so deep that no rock is visible for miles. Another advantageous condition is that mountains, as a result of their elevation, are full of valleys which expose rock of different geologic periods for a vertical distance of hundreds or thousands of feet, while similar rocks underneath the alluvial deposits of the lowland plains are entirely out of economic reach. This is also the case with coal, the most important non-metallic mineral. In the Cumberland Plateau, for example, the many river canyons expose the undisturbed horizontal coal layers and make mining easy, whereas similar valuable coal layers are out of reach under the deep alluvial deposits of the Mississippi. In recent years new methods of measuring the density of the rocks below the surface have given us some insight into the geologic substructure beneath alluvial plains. Thus salt domes, for instance, where oil might be obtained by boring, have been successfully located. Nevertheless, a flat state like Louisiana with its level strata, deep soil, vast river deposits, moist climate, and consequently abundant vegetation, is at a great disadvantage compared with New Mexico, where mountains, deep erosion, scanty soil, and a dry climate make it easy to examine the rocks at many geological levels.

Historic Importance of Mining.—The use of minerals is nearly as old as mankind itself. Buildings of clay, stones, and bricks were one of the first steps in the cultural development of Egypt and Mesopotamia. The first use of clay for pottery thousands of years before Christ was one of the most epochal events in history. The use of metals is even more important—so much so that historians consider it the beginning of two new historical eras, the Bronze Age, and later the Iron Age. In the ancient civilization of the Mediterranean and Near East the output of mines was a basic factor in political power. The silver mines of Laurium near Athens supplied parts of the revenues of that city. The famous gold mines of Ophir, mentioned in the days of King Solomon, were probably located in South Africa where great ruins show foreign influences. Spain provided metals to the Phœnician cities and later to Carthage and Rome. The present Rio Tinto mines there are a continuation of ancient activity. Even in pre-Roman times, Britain was known for its tin. In China, coal was used for smelting ore long before Europe commenced to be a part of the ancient civilized world. The use of charcoal for smelting iron ore was the base of important home industries in Great Britain, Sweden, and elsewhere centuries ago. In England and in some sections of continental Europe it caused such depletion of forests that laws were passed to prevent it.

Social Aspects.—The possession of metals has long been a vital sociological factor. The predominance of Spain in the sixteenth century was based to no small degree on her valuable mineral resources, especially gold and silver, partly in Spain itself, but mainly in America. The thirst for gold was responsible for many explorations and discoveries, and hence for political domination in many parts of the New World. All this, however, is overshadowed by the tremendous increase of mineral output during the nineteenth century. Today the use of power and an ever-increasing demand for minerals have created a totally new situation. Old mines have been reopened, new mines started, geologists have explored the world for more mineral resources, and newly discovered metals and minerals have found a place in the world market. Regions that were unproductive have been brought into the sphere of economic activity. Mining centers have been built in the dry Great Basin of the United States, on the high South American Andes, in the Chilean and Australian deserts, in the equatorial forests, and on the bleak, cold plateaus of northern Sweden and southern Patagonia. Gold rushes have brought adventurers from all over the world to California, Alaska, Australia, and South Africa, and in some cases have been precursors of permanent colonization.

In spite of all this, the social character of the mining settlements has remained almost unchanged. Mining is still an exhaustive industry, and the towns to which it gives rise are generally short lived. In fact, mining cities are generally doomed to die unless other economic factors justify their existence. The population does not have the same stability as in more balanced industries. Women and children are scarce in mining towns. So are schools, churches, and other means of improvement. Few of the miners own their homes, for even if they could afford homes they rarely expect to stay long. Dust, unsightly dump heaps, and the disagreeable smoke of smelters add to the unpleasant characteristics. Moreover, lawless people and those of radical tendencies gravitate toward mining centers so that strikes and outbreaks of lawlessness are frequent.

A good example of the rise and decline of modern mining centers was seen by the authors in Australia. The city of Broken Hill, with its 20,000 inhabitants, its broad streets, stores, theaters, and good hotels seems paradoxical in the midst of a treeless dreary desert. Already it is on the wane. Based as it is on valuable silver, lead, and zinc deposits, it is sure to be deserted when these are exhausted. Three hundred miles west of Broken Hill on the sheep grazing grassland, the former city of Cobar, once famous for its copper mines, has already dwindled almost to the vanishing point. The closing of the mines brought the complete downfall of the city. Grass-covered streets, cracked houses with broken windows, and deserted, partly demolished mining plants tell the story of how once for a short time smoke and noise interfered with the quiet monotony of the desert landscape.

Many of the social difficulties connected with mining arise from the irregularity of the work. Most metals are used mainly in new construction. Iron is consumed chiefly in new railroads, new ships, new skyscrapers, new machines, new automobiles, and all sorts of other new articles which will in most cases be used for a long time. As soon as hard times arrive and business becomes depressed, people stop new construction. They buy about as much food and gasoline as ever; they cut down only a little on clothing and coal; but they do not construct new railways and apartment houses, or install new machinery, or buy new automobiles at the same rate as formerly. Thus the demand for iron drops off far more than the demand for flour. Copper suffers similarly because most of it is used in installing new lines for telephones and power, and in equipping new buildings and machines, and all these things promptly fall to low proportions in hard times. Lead and zinc, too, are used mainly in constructing buildings, so that they also suffer. The result is that in a civilization like ours, which has not yet learned how to prevent the alternation of periods of inflation and depression, the demand for the metals varies enormously from year to year. From the boom year of 1929 to the depressed year of 1932 the production of iron ore in the United States fell from 73,000,000 tons to 9,600,000; that of copper fell from 999,000 tons to 344,000; lead, 775,000 to 287,000; and zinc, 625,000 to 207,000. This means a diminution of about 87 per cent in the use of iron, and 63 to 67 per cent in the use of the other main metals. Bituminous coal did not decline so much, about 43 per cent, because trains must run, and houses must be lighted and heated, even in a depression. The use of cotton also fell off about 40 per cent. On the other hand, since houses must be heated every winter, the production of anthracite coal fell off only 27 per cent from 1929 to 1932, and much of this was because of exceptionally warm winters. And finally, people eat about as much in bad times as in good, so that the consumption of wheat changed scarcely at all. Such conditions cause even the most stable mining towns to fluctuate violently from intense activity to painful stagnation and unemployment. Thousands of miners are thrown out of work, and thousands of others have only a few hours' work each week. Moreover, many of the smaller mines close entirely.

In all kinds of mining there is a growing tendency to work the biggest mines as fully and steadily as possible. They can often make a profit even when production and prices are low. The smaller mines cannot do this. Accordingly they run when prices are high and the demand great. But as soon as unfavorable conditions ensue they close down and employ only a few caretakers to watch the property and keep the pumps running so that the mines will not be filled with water. This of course creates great hardship, for the miners have to move away. They are apt to flock to the bigger mining centers, crowding them with men who want jobs, and thereby lowering the wages. All this makes mining an undesirable occupation. It leads the more competent and reliable men to choose something else; it increases the tendency toward strikes, radicalism, and violence; and it prevents desirable people from living in mining towns unless their work compels them to stay there.

In recent years the organization of mining activity by large companies has led to some improvement in these respects. Better communications, attractive houses, and a deeper insight into the need for social aids such as sports and libraries have brought a higher level of life. Nevertheless the temporary character of mining still remains as a tremendous obstacle.

Major Metallic Minerals. *Iron.**—Although iron ore is found all over the world, more than 60 per cent of the mining is concentrated in two spots, namely the Upper Lake region in the United States around Duluth, and the Minette region in French Lorraine and Luxemburg (A461).† Of these two, the American region is still the leader. From the lake harbors of Minnesota and upper Michigan and Wisconsin some 75 million tons of ore are shipped in good years to the blast furnaces in Illinois, Indiana, Ohio, New York, and most of all Pennsylvania. The Minette region, which, before the World War belonged mostly to Germany, but now to France, smelts two-thirds of its ore locally, importing coal for this purpose. Other regions which combine ore mining and iron

---

* The production and use of iron in the United States are treated fully in Chapter XXVI.

† The explanation given below this map as to the meaning of solid dots and open circles applies to all the maps of minerals in this chapter and the next.

plants include Great Britain, where the Cleveland fields are the most important, Germany where ore is mined in several sections, and Russia where the iron mines west of Dniepropetrovsk and the coal of the Donets Basin are relatively near to one another. Alabama is still another of this group, and is particularly fortunate in having iron, coal, and limestone—the three requisites of steel making—almost within a stone's throw of one another. Another group of regions export iron ore. These include Sweden, Newfoundland, and Chile. A typical example of the way in which coal and iron from different countries come together

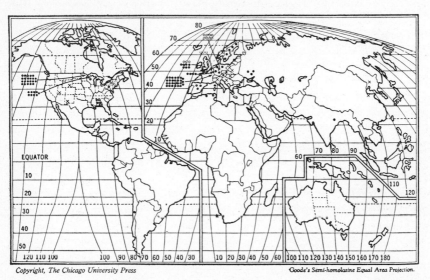

Goode's Semi-homolosine Equal Area Projection.

A—World Production of Iron. Each solid dot indicates the mining of ore yielding 1 per cent of the world's annual production of iron. Crosses indicate minor production. Each open circle indicates importation of ore which after smelting yields 1 per cent of the world's production.

is found in the great iron works at Sparrows Point, Maryland, where cheap ocean transportation makes it possible to use imported ore from Chile, Cuba, Algeria, Australia, France, Morocco, Newfoundland, Norway, Sweden, and Spain. Aside from times of world depression the production of iron has long increased steadily, the increase in some exporting countries like Sweden and northern Africa being especially noteworthy. Of much greater importance seems to be the increasing production of Russia. Such places as Magnitogorsk in the Urals, and the iron works of western Siberia, as well as many others of later construction, illustrate the Russian activity. Yet in spite of this activity at home Russia still exports iron ore in considerable quantities.

Copper.—The United States mines about half of the world's copper and imports another 7 per cent in the form of copper concentrates and refined copper (A462). Arizona, Utah, and Montana, together with Michigan and Nevada, are the main domestic ore producers; the region from Connecticut to Baltimore is the great consumer and importer. In Chile, the second largest producer, the copper mines are controlled by American capital and function almost as part of the American copper industry. Copper production is unimportant in Europe except for Spain, and in Asia except for Japan. In central Africa, however, the so-called Katanga region in the southern Congo and northern Rho-

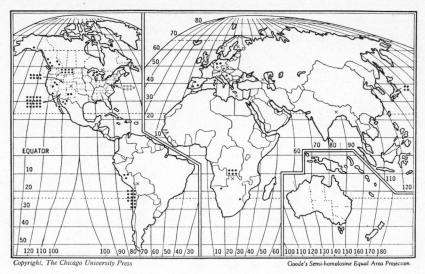

Copyright, The Chicago University Press   Goode's Semi-homolosine Equal Area Projection.

A—World Production of Copper.

desia is very rich in high-yielding copper ore, and its production has increased regularly and rapidly. Elizabethville, its center, is a prosperous town with the largest white population between North Africa and the Transvaal. The new railroad to Lobito in Angola provides a considerably shorter outlet than the old route to Mozambique. The chief difficulties in Katanga are the small supply and poor quality of the native labor.

Lead.—A little more than one-third of the world's lead is mined in the United States (A463). Missouri still produces the most, but Idaho, Utah, Colorado, and Oklahoma are also of importance. The large output of British Columbia and Mexico also finds its main market in the United States, partly in the form of ore and partly as unrefined lead. In Europe, Spain is the main producer. The great Baldwin silver-lead mine in Burma is located in the densely wooded Shan Plateau, a center of action in an almost uninhabited region. Most of the Australian production also comes from a largely uninhabited area, that is, from the silver-lead-zinc mines of Broken Hill in the desert. A new and very modern plant at Mount Ida in Queensland promises to be an important factor in world production.

Zinc.—The general distribution of zinc ore production is similar to that of lead, except that Europe produces relatively more (A464). It furnishes one-fourth of the output, with Silesia as the main zinc mining district. The share of the United States in world production is 40 per

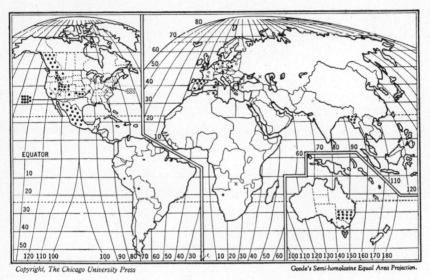

Goode's Semi-homolosine Equal Area Projection.

A—World Production of Lead.

cent. The leading centers are Missouri, Oklahoma, New Jersey, and some of the Rocky Mountain States. The amount of foreign ore smelted in the United States is relatively unimportant. British Columbia and Mexico export most of their zinc in the form of ore or of spelter, which means merely unrefined metal. Western Europe, especially Belgium, is an interesting example of an ore importer. Although without zinc mines, Belgium is the world's second largest zinc producer, its production being based entirely on imported ore. The zinc of Burma and Australia comes from the same mines as the lead, for the two kinds of ore are often found together.

Tin.—The area around Singapore, including the southern part of the Malay Peninsula and the islands Banka and Billiton of the Dutch

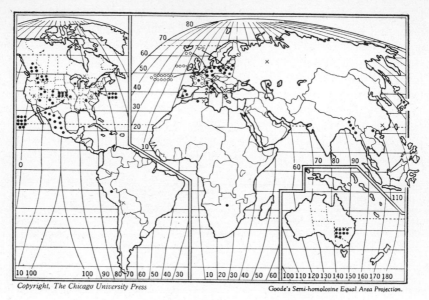

A—World Production of Zinc.

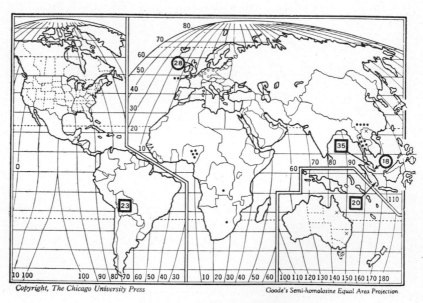

B—World Production of Tin.

Squares indicate ore mined; circles, ore smelted.

East Indies, produces about 55 per cent of the world's tin (B464). If Siam and southern Burma are also included the production rises above 60 per cent. Only three tin regions of importance lie outside this section of southeastern Asia: Nigeria, Yunan in southwestern China, and Bolivia where mines at very high elevations on the central plateau of the Andes produce nearly a quarter of the world total. The ores of the Malay region are smelted locally, but those of the other regions are carried to Europe, especially Great Britain. That country once boasted of important tin mines, and Cornwall still produces 2 per cent of the world's supply.

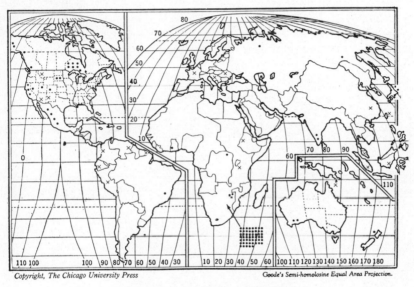

Goode's Semi-homolosine Equal Area Projection.

A—World Production of Gold.

Gold and Silver.—Gold, the most-desired and most-sought-after mineral, is found in small quantities in most parts of the world, but more than half is mined at one spot, the Witwatersrand at Johannesburg in the Transvaal (A465). Elsewhere the output of gold is not of much importance in world affairs, although Mexico, California, Alaska, and Australia are famous as places whose gold once attracted thousands of adventurers. Ontario, with its gold mines in the Laurentian Upland, is the world's second largest producer. The rate at which gold is produced is particularly important. If it increases and gold becomes abundant, the prices of other commodities rise because gold becomes relatively cheap. If the supply of gold diminishes, there is a tendency for prices to fall because there is not enough gold and therefore people give more goods for a given amount of metal. Hence changes in the amount of gold supplied by a region like South Africa influence people all over the world.

The production of silver is still increasing in spite of the low prices. With the exception of the Inca region in the Peruvian Andes, and the mines already mentioned in Burma and Broken Hill, the production of silver is almost entirely concentrated in North America (A466). Mexico produces about 40 per cent of the total output, the United States nearly a quarter, with Utah, Montana, and Arizona the leading states, while British Columbia and Ontario enable Canada to supply nearly a tenth of the world's production.

Bauxite.—The last of the major metals is aluminum, which is derived

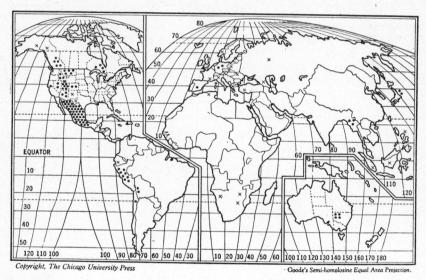

Goode's Semi-homolosine Equal Area Projection.

A—World Production of Silver.

almost entirely from bauxite. Since its production has recently increased with extraordinary speed this metal deserves a place among the major metals. France, with a fourth to a third of the world's output, is the main producer of bauxite, the United States comes second with about one-sixth, nearly all of which comes from Arkansas. British and Dutch Guiana (Surinam) account together for another fifth, and the rest comes mainly from Hungary, Italy, and Yugoslavia. Bauxite ores travel around a great deal. Since electric power is the main factor in recovering aluminum from the ore, Canada, Norway, and Switzerland with their abundant water power, and Germany with its coal, rival

France as producers of aluminum, although they produce little or no bauxite.

Minor Metallic Minerals.—*Arsenic* is used for quite diverse purposes, such as killing insects, making special kinds of glass, and preserving wood. It is recovered mainly from copper ores. The United States is the main producer, and is still more important as a consumer, importing from Mexico and Canada.

Chromium is derived from chromite, a chromic iron ore used for such purposes as chromite steel and refractory bricks. More than half of the chromite comes from Rhodesia and the Union of South Africa, but some is also obtained on the island of New Caledonia, and in Cuba and India. The output of the United States is insignificant.

Manganese ore is used for the hardening of iron and steel. Russia has regained its pre-war leadership, but is nearly equaled by India. The rest (40 per cent) comes from different places, with Brazil and the Gold Coast of special importance.

When Austria lost her Idria *mercury* mine, Italy gained first position as a mercury producer; but with its Almaden mine, Spain is a close rival. In the United States, the third producer, California provides most of the output, which is not sufficient for the consumption in this country.

Molybdenum is used for a special kind of iron and steel. The United States is the main world producer, with the chief mine in Colorado.

Nickel is important in art and some industries, especially because of its non-rusting qualities and for the hardening of steel. About 90 per cent comes from Sudbury, Ontario, the home of the International Nickel Company.

Platinum is so scarce and expensive that the 200,000 ounces used each year go mainly to jewelry and dental work. Although no figures are available, Russia is still probably the main producer with about 50 per cent. South Africa, a new producer since 1926, gained second rank in 1930, and Colombia and Canada are next.

Radium is derived from uranium. It is still a very rare metal. The world production comes from the Congo, which has an output of 60 ounces a year. Associated with uranium is *vanadium*, which is used as an alloy in steels. It comes from Peru and southwestern Africa.

Titanium has a rather wide chemical use. It comes mainly from India, Norway, and Brazil. The production in the United States is slight.

Zirconium is sometimes called a scavenger because when mixed with steel it takes up all the oxygen and nitrogen, thus strengthening the steel. Its ore is imported from Brazil. China, Burma, and the Malay States produce more than three-fourths of the *tungsten* ores. The output in the United States, although protected by tariff, is only 4 per cent of the world production. There are still other minor metals like *antimony*, *bismuth*, *cadmium*, and *cobalt*, but they play a very small part in world trade and industry.

Major Non-Metallic Stony or Earthy Minerals.—Aside from *coal* and *petroleum*, which will be treated in the chapter on power, and the *fertilizers*, which have already been discussed, the number of major non-metallic minerals is rather limited. Nevertheless, they give rise to important industries like the making of glass, pottery, cement, and bricks which are discussed in a later chapter.

Building Stone.—In many rugged regions, building stones of various sorts are an important source of income, and the great quarries are an impressive feature of the landscape. Granites of three different compositions, gneisses, limestones, together with marbles, sandstones, and slates for roofing and walks are the chief kinds. Because of their weight their main use is in local construction, but the finer kinds are transported long distances. Famous buildings are often real exhibits of what building stone can produce in the way of beauty. In some sections of England, the value of stone overshadows that of all other mining enterprises. In New England, granite and marble are practically the only mineral products aside from gravel, sand, and clay. The limestone of Indiana is one of that state's great assets.

Clay.—Clays may be the product of ocean, lake, or river; they may be brought by glaciers or winds, or derived from the decay of local rocks. From the pure kaolin of the southeastern Atlantic states, down to the more common fire and brick clays, all have their value and add to the natural resources. Pottery and stoneware, bricks and tiles, and also fine porcelain are made from clay. Useful clays, like building stone, are found in each state, and only the finer kinds enter world trade.

Cement.—Portland cement is a manufactured product, being a finely powdered, burned mixture of lime, silica, aluminum, and some iron oxides. Natural rock cements with a similar mixture of materials exist in nature and can be used by burning only. The great cement belt in the United States is in eastern Pennsylvania between the Lehigh and the Delaware Rivers.

Salt.—Common salt, sodium chloride, can be mined as rock salt, tapped from natural brine by way of springs or wells, or evaporated from sea-water. The last method can be used only in warm countries, whereas rock salt and brine are utilized mostly in temperate regions. Michigan, New York, and Ohio are the main salt-producing states in America. Few people realize that rock salt mines actually extend under Detroit. The total production of salt in the United States is about one-third of that of the world. Europe produces one-half of the world output, Germany and France, the leading countries, getting their supplies mainly from mines. Chile saltpetre and potash are also kinds of "salt," but they have been discussed before. The only other salt product worth mentioning is *borax*. The United States and Chile are the main producers, with the United States far in the lead. Borax beds are mostly found on the bottom of dried-up lakes like Death Valley, Searles Lake in California, and the dry Chilean lake beds of the Atacama.

Gypsum.—Gypsum, like salt, is found in layers laid down long ago in geological times when the salt water of seas or lakes evaporated. It is found mainly in the form of anhydrite gypsum without water content. New York, the main American producer, gets its gypsum from ancient rock formations between Buffalo and Utica. France, the European leader, uses deposits found in the Paris basin.

The last mineral that can be considered important is *sulphur*. This is mined either in the pure state or as pyrite, a chemical combination with iron or copper. Louisiana and especially Texas furnish nearly 90 cent cent of the world's pure sulphur. Sicily, now second in rank, and Japan, third, get their sulphur from volcanic deposits. The greater part of the pyrites, mainly used for sulphuric acid, comes from Spain, Norway, and Italy.

Minor Stony and Earthy Minerals.—Of the different kinds of *abrasives* two stand out—*corundum* and *emery*. *Corundum*, next to diamonds in hardness, comes mainly from South Africa, and its main consumption is in the United States for grinding wheels, lenses, and optical grinding.

Emery, a mixture of corundum and magnetite, is mined in New York State, but the main output comes from the Greek island Naxos in the Ægean Sea and from near Smyrna in Turkish Asia Minor.

Grindstones, pulpstones, millstones, sharpening stones, and volcanic pumice complete the group of abrasives.

Asbestos, the only mineral which is used mainly as a fiber, comes from a kind of rock known as serpentine. The main source of supply is southern Quebec (Asbestos City), but the production of Rhodesia has been coming up rapidly and has broken the hold of Canada on the world asbestos market. South Africa, Cyprus, and Russia are other producers.

Barium minerals, mainly in the form of the barium sulphate known as barite, are used for compounds like lithopone, a substitute for white lead.

Strontium, often named with barium, is used in the form of strontium salts and comes from England and Germany.

Diatomite, a powdery substance composed of microscopically small siliceous shells of diatoms, is used chiefly as an insulator and filter. Half of the world's production comes from the United States, with the main source the diatom beds along the California coast in Santa Barbara County. Denmark and Germany are other large producers.

Feldspar, which is ground up for pottery, is a rock that is dug from quarries especially in New England and North Carolina.

Fluorspar, of importance in the steel industry, is found in veins and is mined in the United States mainly in Kentucky and Illinois. Outside of the United States, Germany and France are the chief producers, both exporting to the United States.

Fuller's Earth is a clay of great absorbing qualities which is used for the decolorizing, bleaching, and filtering of oils and fats. It is found especially in Georgia, Florida, and Texas. England and Germany are foreign producers.

Graphite occurs in two varieties, the crystalline and the amorphous. It is much used for lead pencils. Although it is found all over the world, the main producing regions are Czechoslovakia, Austria, Bavaria, Chosen, and Madagascar. Bavaria is famous for its pencils.

Mica comes in thin sheets which are used as insulating material for electrical purposes. Although widely distributed in crystalline rocks, it generally occurs in fragments too small to be of commercial value. New Hampshire and North Carolina provide most of the American output. India and South Africa are the main world producers and exporters.

Precious stones owe their value partly to their hardness and luster and partly to their rarity, but their economic value is also greatly influenced by fashion. Green emeralds, golden topazes, red rubies, blue sapphires, and many-colored opals are important in the world gem market. Pearl fishing is a valuable source of income in northern Australia, Ceylon, and the Bahrein Islands in the Persian Gulf. But by far the most important precious stone is the diamond, a very hard mineral of pure carbon, of which Africa is the main producer. Found in the blue ground of volcanic necks, as well as in alluvial deposits, they equal gold in their attractiveness for mineral hunters. Kimberley is the world's greatest diamond center, but other deposits are found in South Africa, as well as along the southwestern African coast in the Congo-Angola region, the Gold Coast, and Brazil and British Guiana in South America.

Talc and *soapstone* are closely related and are nearly always recorded together. Talc is mined chiefly in New York and Vermont; soapstone almost entirely in Virginia. Talc has many uses, but soapstone, because of its softness and the ease with which it can be sawed, is used principally for the making of tubs, tanks, switchboards, mantels, and so forth. The production of the rest of the world is insignificant when compared with that of the United States.

Glass sand, gravel, mineral paints like ocher, mineral waters with their worldwide distribution and medical uses, and some very minor minerals like cyanite and zircon complete this review of mineral resources.

EXERCISES

1. In the *Statistical Abstract of the United States*, or elsewhere, find a list of the value of mineral production by states. Arrange the states in the order of this value, and then use *Business Geography*, or statements and maps in this book or elsewhere, as a guide in writing after the name of each state the kind of mineral wealth for which it is important.

2. On the basis of A452 and A453 make a list of six regions which fall in each of the following categories: (*a*) relatively large producers of mineral wealth per square mile and per capita, (*b*) large producers per square mile but not per capita, (*c*) large producers per capita but not per square mile. Use the maps in this chapter and the next in order to list the minerals which give each of your eighteen regions their importance.

3. Watch the papers for evidence as to the importance of changes in the gold supply. Try to find evidence as to what happened to the prices of commodities in general after the discovery of new supplies of gold in California, Alaska, South Africa, and elsewhere.

4. From the world maps of metals in this chapter prepare a list showing in the order of their importance the three countries that are the most important producers of at least eight metals.

5. Many of the maps in this chapter show open circles indicating the smelting of ores from other regions. Make a list of the countries and metals for which this is true. What reasons for such conditions can you give?

6. For each of the important minerals make a list of three types of countries: (*a*) those that have abundant supplies, (*b*) those that have enough for their own needs, (*c*) those that have little or none. What do your lists indicate as to the relative advantages of the various nations for the carrying on of industry? What nations depend on their colonies to supply strategic minerals?

7. Name and locate three parts of the world that have all four of the following advantages: sufficient coal, sufficient iron, good transportation, and a dense population. What types of product would you expect to be made there? Why?

CHAPTER XXII

FUELS AND OTHER SOURCES OF POWER

Relative Importance of Sources of Power.—The relative importance of coal, oil, and water, the three great sources of power, has changed considerably. Reckoned on the basis of their caloric value, that is, of the amount of heat or energy that they supply, the percentage of the world's total power derived from each source showed the following changes from 1913 to 1925: coal fell from 88.5 per cent to 75.5; oil rose from 7.2 to 16.1; and water power from 4.3 to 8.4. Since 1925 the importance of coal has still further declined. A survey made by the Dresden Bank shows that the available resources and the comparative use of the three principal sources of energy in the main regions of the world, so far as they can be estimated, are as follows:

Place	Power production in an active year, expressed as the equivalent of millions of tons of coal				Resources available, in millions of tons			
	Coal	Oil	Water power	Total	Coal	Oil	Water power *	Total
Germany	188	....	6	194	250,000	....	27	
Great Britain	242	....	1	243	190,000	....	3	
France	51	....	8	60	30,000	....	22	
Russia (European)	32	20	1	52	60,000	1,570	86	
Rest of Europe	135	10	38	182	260,000	260	150	
EUROPE	647	29	55	731	800,000	1,800	288	
United States	515	203	47	764	2,700,000	1,620	140	
Canada	13	....	18	32	700,000	220	73	
Mexico	....	11	1	13	....	1,050	24	
Rest of America	3	35	3	41	30,000	2,180	244	
AMERICA	531	249	70	849	3,400,000	5,050	481	
China	16	....	....	16	1,000,000	310	80	
Japan	32	....	7	39	8,000	280	18	
India	22	3	0.7	25	80,000	} 930	108	
Dutch Indies	....	6	....	6			16	
Siberia	4	....	0.4	4	110,000	....	164	
Rest of Asia	14	10	0.1	24	20,000	1,310	23	
ASIA	87	19	8.4	115	1,200,000	2,830	408	
AFRICA	13	0.5	0.1	14	60,000	....	744	
AUSTRALIA	18	....	0.8	18	149,000	210	67	
WORLD TOTALS	1,296	298	134	1,727	5,600,000	9,940	1,988	

* The figures in this column mean *annual* production of power expressed as the equivalent of tons of coal, and hence are different from the *totals* in the two columns to the left.

Coal.—The world production of coal has in late years risen sometimes to about 1.4 billion metric tons. This includes the three different kinds of coal, semi-bituminous, bituminous, and anthracite, as well as lignite expressed in terms of coal. It does not take into consideration the output of peat, which has merely a local value, although in some countries like Ireland and Holland it is still of importance as a fuel. Coal, of course, is used not only as fuel, but for a great many other purposes as well, such as chemical dyes, explosives, antiseptics, fertilizers, and even perfumes; but from a quantitative point of view,

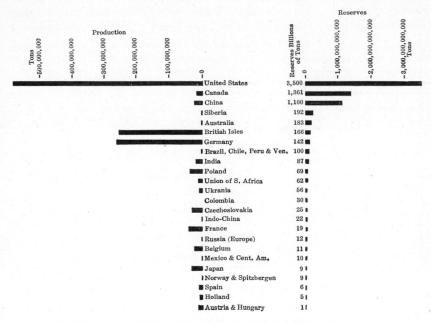

A—Normal Production of Coal Compared with Known Reserves.

these are negligible compared with its use as fuel. Much coal is also turned into coke by heating it to drive off the gaseous portions. The coke and much of the gas are used as fuel, but part of the gas becomes solid or liquid when cool and is the source of paraffin, dyes, and a certain amount of gasoline.

A comparison between the distribution of coal fields and of coal production (A472) shows that a great many fields produce very little. This is due partly to political instability, as in China where immense coal fields are still nearly untouched (see table), but mainly to distance from the centers of consumption as in Utah and Siberia, or to the poor quality of the coal, which has much to do with the low value of coal fields in the Dakotas and Alberta (B473).

The production of the United States, which comprises a little less than 40 per cent of that of the world, is almost entirely concentrated in the central eastern states, especially Pennsylvania, West Virginia, Kentucky, and Illinois. While Pennsylvania and West Virginia rank nearly the same as producers of bituminous coal, Pennsylvania ranks first in total coal production because of its monopoly of anthracite. Canadian mines in Nova Scotia and New Brunswick attempt to compete with

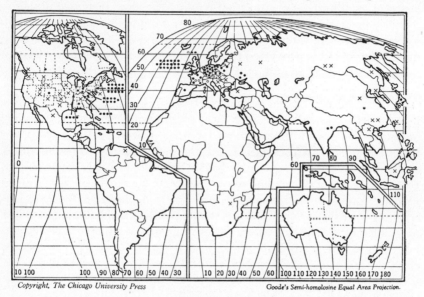

Goode's Semi-homolosine Equal Area Projection.

A—World Production of Coal. Each solid dot indicates 1 per cent of world production. Crosses indicate minor amounts. Each open circle indicates an import of 1 per cent.

American coal in Montreal, which is one of the chief Canadian centers of consumption, but are too remote to compete in the other Canadian center, that is, Toronto and the other cities of Ontario. Europe produces one-half of the world's coal, with Great Britain first and Germany second. Together these two countries produce nearly as much as the United States.

The production of coal per miner is much less in Europe than in the United States. It has recently averaged 708 metric tons per year in the United States, 268 in Germany, 224 in Great Britain, and as low as 151 in France and 136 in Belgium. The lower European production is due to less advanced technical methods, production in many small, decentralized units, or, as is often the case, difficult mining conditions. Although the export of coal is still an important factor in British trade, the expensive British production has great difficulty in holding its own in comparison with the rest of the world. Because of their age many British mines are very deep, a fourth of them having a depth of at least 1,500 feet. Moreover many of the seams are thin, only a third being 4 feet or over. Nevertheless very short hauls to centers of trade and transportation still enable Great Britain to hold her place as the world's chief seller of coal. Germany, on the other hand, in spite of great losses of coal territory after the World War, has increased its production regularly since that time. The production of lignite is of special importance there. It is dug cheaply out of open mines, or vast quarry holes, and is converted into electric power at the mines. Transportation is still a great factor in the coal trade. English coal competes with German coal in Germany's North Sea harbors because of the fact that shipment by sea is so very cheap. Holland, which has mines in its southeastern section, sells most of its output to the neighboring industrial centers of Belgium and Germany, and buys approximately the same quantity from Great Britain or Germany. The imported coal comes by water across the North Sea or down the Rhine River. France, in spite of her extensive coal mines in the north, buys coal from England and Germany, especially for her iron plants in the Lorraine region. Outside of North America and Europe, coal mining remains insignificant. China and Siberia are still great potential coal producers, but the southern continents are singularly devoid of coal. Two exceptions, the mines of Natal and New South Wales, are of special significance because they replace the coal of Great Britain in supplying two of the most active parts of the southern hemisphere.

Petroleum.—The production of oil has been increasing rapidly most of the time for many years. It doubled between 1921 and 1929. Old fields have been used up and new fields have been brought into production; but, with a few exceptions, such as Mexico and Venezuela, the general world distribution of production has not changed (A475). Although conservation of oil resources would everywhere be wise, there seems now to be little fear of lack of oil in the near future. During a recent World Power Conference the following statement was made: "The total amount of crude oil in the earth's crust is unknown and unestimated, but it is certainly an astonishing volume. Geologists state that oil discovery is a possibility in 1,100,000,000 acres in the United States alone, or 56 per cent of its total land area. The contrast of this huge territory with the 2,000,000 acres producing oil at the present time, makes it certain that new fields will be continually discovered and that the oil of that country will prove ample for many years to come. What is true regarding the potential oil production of the United States, probably is true in even greater measure for many of the other countries of the world where oil exploration has been even less thorough than in the United States."

Two-thirds of the oil output comes from the United States (A475). California, which for some years was the leader and is still a large producer, is now overshadowed by the mid-continental oil fields of Texas, Oklahoma, and Kansas. A complex system of pipelines brings the oil from the places of production to the centers of consumption or to the

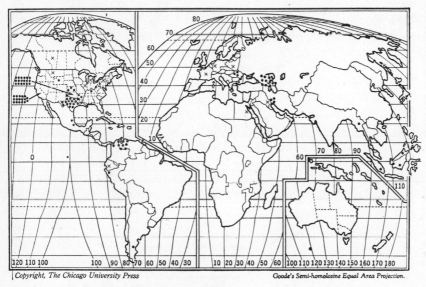

Goode's Semi-homolosine Equal Area Projection.

A—World Production of Petroleum. Each dot indicates 1 per cent of the world production. Crosses indicate minor amounts.

harbors for export. More than 100,000 miles of pipeline transport a load of one billion barrels a year, some of it as far as 1,700 miles.

Russia takes second place. Its two main fields, Baku and Grozny, on opposite sides of the Caucasus, are connected by pipelines with the Black Sea. The third great oil center is around the Gulf of Maracaibo in Venezuela, where the oil fields extend into Colombia. Mexico, once the only rival of the United States in production, has dropped to seventh place. Other important oil fields include the foothills of the Rumanian Carpathians in Europe, Persia in eastern Mesopotamia, the Dutch East Indies (Sumatra, Borneo), the coastal plain of Peru, southern Patagonia, and Trinidad.

Natural Gas.—Connected with petroleum is the output of natural gas and of gasoline made from natural gas. Although natural gas is

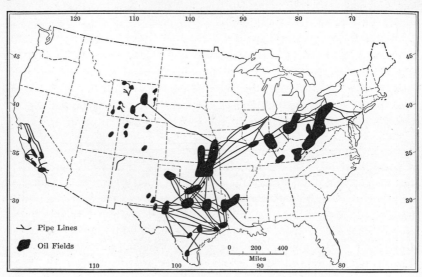

A—Oil Fields and Pipe Lines in the United States.
(Courtesy of Economic Geography and J. K. Rose.)

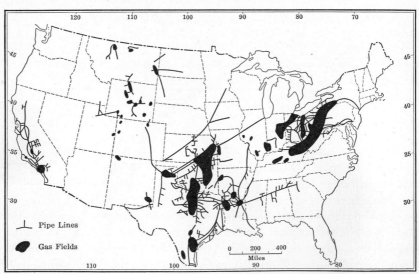

B—Natural Gas Fields and Pipe Lines in the United States.

abundant in other regions its use is almost confined to the United States. Its center of production corresponds with the oil fields (B476), and

65,000 miles of trunk pipe lines carry gas to many districts, sometimes as far as from Texas to Chicago. Artificial gas is produced by heating coal and is of special importance in western Europe, although very widely used in the United States.

Water Power.—A comparison of the distribution of developed and potential water power (A478 and B478) shows that the present development is almost entirely in regions of high economic standing and has little relation to the amount that might be developed. Two great centers, the eastern United States with adjacent parts of Canada, and western and central Europe, stand out clearly. So do two smaller areas of high relative development, namely the Pacific Coast of the United States and Japan. Southern Russia, with the newly built power plant of Dniepropetrovsk, and southern Brazil where the water falls over the steep edge of the plateau, are minor centers worth mentioning. In some portions of the regions of high relative development a very large share of the available water power is used. The New England States have developed 100 per cent of their potential water power available 90 per cent of the time. The highest development outside the United States is in Switzerland with 86 per cent, followed by Italy with 80 per cent. None of these highly developed sections has coal or oil of its own. The number of horse power utilized per capita gives another good measure of the relative importance of water power. If we call the rank of the United States 100, the other countries would rank as follows:

Norway	652	France	46
Newfoundland	500 (?)	New Zealand	40
Canada	442	Japan	26
Switzerland	433	Chile	26
Sweden	200	Germany	16
Italy	54	Brazil	12
		Great Britain	5

A478 indicates that in the United States the use of water power is very unevenly distributed. The following regions are conspicuous:

1. The Pacific slope of the western mountains (Cascades and Sierra Nevada).
2. The Piedmont from New York to Alabama, and the Fall line between the Atlantic Coastal Plain and the Piedmont.
3. The glaciated area of New England, northern Michigan, Wisconsin, and Minnesota.
4. Niagara Falls.
5. The glaciated northern Rockies, in Montana and Idaho.

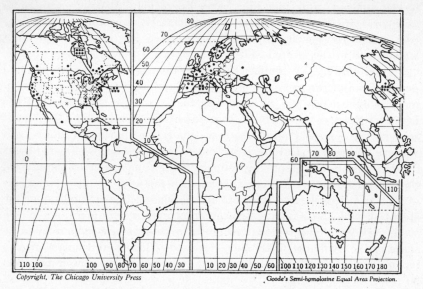

A—World Map of Developed Water Power. Each dot indicates 1 per cent, each cross a minor amount.

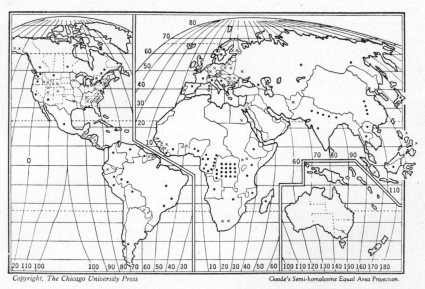

B—Potential Water Power Available 90 Per Cent of the Time. Crosses indicate minor amounts. Note that the unit here is 10 times as great as in A478.

To these we may add a section of Canada, namely the southern edge of the Laurentian Upland in Quebec.

The 2 per cent of the world's developed power in Brazil is located on the southeastern slope of the plateau facing the southeast trades around Rio de Janeiro and São Paulo.   In some cases, notably near São Paulo, water which would normally flow 1,500 miles to the La Plata is dammed and turned back so that it drops down a steep slope of about 2,000 feet into the ocean only 10 or 20 miles away.   Japan, with its mountainous relief and heavy summer rains, is well suited to develop water power.   In Europe the centers of water power are the Alps, supplying France, Italy, Switzerland, and Austria, and the Scandinavian glaciated plateaus with their many waterfalls.

The greatest of all concentrations of potential power is along the mountain ranges of Africa and South America, but especially in Central Africa (B478).   There the great rivers of the Congo system descend into the Congo Basin, and then, having joined to form the mighty Congo, break once more through the mountain wall to reach the sea.

Electricity.—Coal and water power are the two important sources of electricity, their relative share depending on the local natural resources. In the United Kingdom and Holland, for example, electricity is derived mainly from steam engines which burn coal; in Germany the ratio is 7 horsepower from coal to 1 from water; in the United States it is 2 to 1; and Switzerland and Canada get their electric power almost wholly from water.   Of the world total the United States produces 42 per cent, of the electric power, Germany 11, Great Britain 6, and France 5.   The highest production per capita is in Canada, twice as high as the United States, with Switzerland second.   Canada and Switzerland export electricity to neighboring countries.

Coal, Iron, and the Distribution of Manufacturing.—There is widespread misapprehension as to the part played by coal and water power in determining the location of manufacturing.   Many books give the impression that the presence of coal, or of coal and iron together, is the main reason why manufacturing has developed so remarkably in the northeastern United States and the North Sea region.   They seem to imply that if Italy, Rumania, Egypt, Peru, or Borneo had been equally well supplied, they too would have become great centers of manufacturing.   Such is by no means the case.   Coal—and the same thing may be said of iron or of both coal and iron together—is a *great help* in manufacturing, but it is not a *cause* of manufacturing.   It does not determine in which of the natural regions manufacturing shall be most active. Nevertheless, it greatly increases the efficiency of the regions which would otherwise stand highest, and it determines what kinds of industries shall be dominant in special sections of those regions.

We shall discuss this matter more fully in the chapter on manufacturing, but the general principle involved will be set forth here. The general relation between coal and manufacturing is illustrated in A480. The left-hand bars show the percentage of the occupied men engaged in industry; the middle bars show the *use* of coal per capita of the entire population; the third the corresponding *production* of coal; and the fourth the production of iron ore; if coal were a primary cause of industrialization the bars in the first three columns ought to vary in essentially the same way. Yet among the sixteen countries where industry

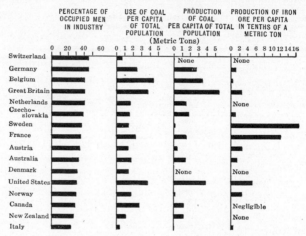

A—Industrial Development of Countries Compared with Their Use of Coal and Production of Coal and Iron.

is most highly developed, Switzerland, which has no coal, has the largest percentage of its men engaged in industry. It imports a small amount of coal; it also uses water power. But its chief method of making up for lack of coal is to manufacture goods that need only a little power. Similar reasoning applies to iron, but A480 shows no tendency whatever for a large production of iron ore to be associated with a high percentage of men engaged in industry. The fact is that if a nation is progressive it will develop its iron ores, as well as its coal, if it has any. But even if it lacks one or both it will devise some method of making progress industrially. In the United States the cost of fuel and power for every thousand dollars' worth of products amounts to only about $5 for jewelry and shoes; $6 for automobiles; $8 for watches, clocks, and printing; $10 for knit goods and flour; $12 to $13 for electrical machinery, furniture, silk and rubber goods; and $16 to $21 for machine tools, agricultural implements, cutlery, foundry products, woolen goods, and the more expensive kinds of cotton goods. On the other hand, it rises to $40 for cheap cotton goods; $65 for paper and the products of steel works and rolling mills; $75 to $80 for chemicals and pottery; over $100 for glass-making; $160 for brick; $200 for cement; and $280 for blast furnaces. The Swiss, being wise people, make watches, clocks,

jewelry, silk goods, knit goods, and other products that require relatively little power. Sweden, Denmark, Austria, Norway, and Italy, all of which have very limited supplies of coal, behave similarly, although their choice of products is somewhat different. On the other hand, Germany, Great Britain, and Belgium, with plenty of coal, go in for the heavy industries in which iron plays the chief part and coal is highly necessary. If they have iron ore, as in Great Britain, they use it; if they are not well supplied, as in Belgium, they import it.

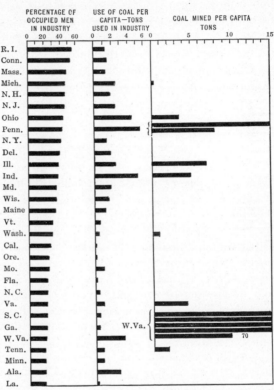

A—Relation of Industrial Development to the Use and Production of Coal.

A481 shows a similar condition among the 30 states of the United States where industry is most highly developed. States that mine a great deal of coal generally use a great deal also, but they are far from being the states where manufacturing is most active. Tennessee, Alabama, West Virginia, and Virginia all fall among the lowest 8 states on the left of A481 but are among the highest on the right. On the other hand, among the 30 states that are most highly industrialized 21 mine no appreciable amount of coal per capita. Some of these can indeed get coal easily from neighboring states, but others like California and Florida are so remote that coal is extremely expensive. If iron ore were added to A481, the only states with a large production per capita would be Minnesota, Michigan, Alabama, and Wyoming. A similar condition exists in Canada. Most of that country's coal is mined in Nova Scotia or Alberta, but neither of those provinces is highly developed industrially. On the other hand, Ontario with the city of Toronto, and Quebec with Montreal mine no coal at all but lead in industry. Ontario can bring coal cheaply from the United States, but Montreal is put to considerable expense in this respect. Yet Ontario and Quebec are far more active industrially than are Nova Scotia or Alberta and their near neighbors. Newfoundland mines a huge amount of iron ore per capita and might get coal very cheaply by water from Nova Scotia, but its industrial development is very simple.

Looking at the matter historically we find conditions similar. Ever since the dawn of civilization the regions of greatest industrial activity have always been those where civilization in general has stood highest. Of course, all industries were primitive in ancient times, but even then the work of all sorts of artisans reached its highest level and its greatest degree of activity in the most highly civilized regions like Egypt, Babylonia, and later Greece and southern Italy. In the Middle Ages, northern Italy and Spain took the lead. Then, as the world's culture and power migrated farther north with man's increasing control over nature, the center moved to France, Germany, Great Britain, the Low Countries, and Scandinavia. Before people learned how to use coal the forests of certain parts of Great Britain became exhausted because of their use in smelting iron ore. Laws were passed to prevent further cutting. Before the invention of the steam engine, Paris was famous as a center of artistic manufactures, the Swiss were the best clock-makers, the Flemings of Belgium were noted for their linen fabrics, British cutlery was sold all over the world, and the woolen industry had reached a higher stage of development in Great Britain than anywhere else. This made it possible for England to take the lead in cotton manufacturing as soon as the cotton gin and power loom were invented. The essential point is that before either coal or the steam engine was used the highest development of industry was found in the same general section of Europe as at present, that is, in the Marine Cyclonic Region where the climate is especially healthful and stimulating. The fact that wonderful supplies of coal happen to be present in this same region greatly intensified this development after the steam engine was invented, but did not materially alter its *general* location.

Nevertheless, coal did cause a shift in the *local* distribution of manufacturing, as shown by the shading in A483.   In 1700, industrial occupations were almost as common in the sparsely settled, agricultural eastern section of England as in the more densely settled southwestern section centering around Bristol or in the similar northwestern section centering around Liverpool.   In 1900, manufacturing was relatively insignificant in the eastern and southwestern sections, which are now primarily agricultural and commercial.   It had greatly expanded in the northwestern section, however, and had developed in two new centers, namely, southern Wales in the south and Durham in the north.   Thus the great-

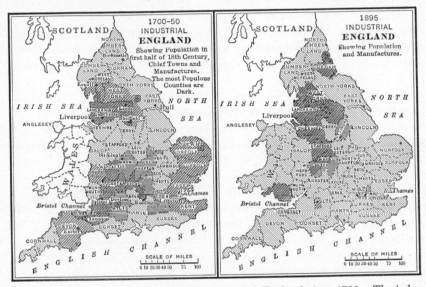

A—Changes in the Location of the Industries of England since 1700.   The industrial areas in both maps are those having lines that slope from the right above to the left below.   (From *Industry in England*, by H. de Gibbins.)

est concentration of manufacturing is now close to the coal mines. But bear in mind that practically every part of England is highly industrialized compared with most parts of the world, or with what it was in 1700.   Moreover, although London is not shown as a modern industrial region in A483, the goods produced by the ten million people within a radius of 20 miles of that place are worth about one-fifth as much as all the manufactured goods produced in England, and more than those of the whole of Spain or Poland.   These goods, however, like those of Switzerland, Massachusetts, New York, or any place a little removed from the coal fields, are mainly of the kinds which need only moderate amounts of coal.

Water Power and Manufacturing.—The case of water power is like that of coal. The general distribution of manufacturing in the world as a whole has little to do with the amount of water power. Here are the 17 countries with the greatest possibilities of water power development, together with the millions of horse power that they are capable of developing during nine-tenths of the time: Belgian Congo 90, French Equatorial Africa 35, the United States 35, India 27, China 20, Canada 20, Russia 16, French Cameroon 13, British West Africa 12, British East Africa 7, French West Africa 6, Japan 6, Mexico 6, Norway 5.5, New Guinea 5, Argentina 5, Madagascar 5. Among all these countries only the United States, Norway, and Canada appear in A480 among the 16 countries that are most highly industrialized. Nevertheless, in the natural regions which are best fitted for manufacturing, the presence of water power is a great help. New England illustrates the matter. Manufacturing began there without any help from water power. Almost as soon as Europeans settled in the United States they began to set up little industries of the primitive type. They made furniture, saddles, harness, and carts; they wove cloth, prepared candles, smelted the local iron ore, and forged tools. England tried to hinder this, because her merchants and artisans wanted a monopoly on colonial trade. In the South the climate made tobacco a highly profitable export crop, although cotton was not yet important. It also discouraged white labor and rendered slave labor profitable. All this discouraged manufacturing still more, so that it increased very little. In the North the absence of any such crop, and a climate which made the settlers extremely active, encouraged manufacturing and commerce and made the people feel disposed to resist England. Long before the invention of the steam engine, New England, New York, and Pennsylvania had already developed the art of manufacturing more than had any other parts of the New World. As yet there were no real factories, although there were local forges, and flour mills run by water power. Thus when power looms were invented New England was ready to seize upon them and set up factories run by water power. This illustrates what almost always happens. The regions which are most advanced are the ones that seize upon new inventions and thereby are enabled to utilize resources which were formerly wasted. The use of these resources in turn stimulates further development.

A metaphor will perhaps clarify the relation between manufacturing and both coal and water power. Manufacturing is like a plant. The seeds sprout in many places, but cannot thrive unless the climate is favorable. If the soil is favorable, so much the better, but proper fertilization can make almost any soil productive if only the climate is right.

Coal and water power are like fertilizers. If they are present along with
the right climate, a region is highly blessed, as is the case in Pennsylvania
and Belgium. If they are absent they can be brought from a distance,
as in Wisconsin and Sweden. But no amount of such fertilizers will
cause manufacturing to flourish unless the seeds are there in the form
of human energy and initiative, and these qualities are highly developed
only in a few natural regions with cyclonic climates at least part of the
year. When an industry is well established and has become relatively
easy to manage, it may be transplanted to other natural regions with a
less favorable environment, but in such cases it needs careful attention
by people from the more favored regions.

EXERCISES

1. On the basis of A472, B478, and the table on page 471, what parts of the
earth appear most likely to have an abundance of cheap power a hundred years
hence? A thousand years hence? On what do you base your conclusions? In
what regions do you anticipate the greatest development of water power? Of
coal? Of oil? Why?

2. What apparent inconsistency do you find between the table on page 471
and the quotation from the World Power Conference on a later page? Can you
reconcile the two?

3. Discuss the relation between the use of water power and the conditions
of relief, rainfall, and cultural progress in several of the countries that stand
either high or low in the table on page 471.

4. Find places where glaciation is mentioned in this chapter. What is its
significance in respect to power? Cite examples.

5. Investigate the power resources of your own city or state. How much
electrical power is used, and for what purposes? How much water power?
Where does the coal come from? Judging by pp. 480–1, how does the cost of
the power used in making the kinds of goods most widely manufactured in your
city or state compare with the final value of the goods? Does your city or
state confirm or confute the conclusions of this chapter? How?

6. In addition to coal, oil, and water, name other sources of power that are
ed locally. For what purposes? Where and under what geographic condi-
ns? Why are they generally unfitted for wide use in modern industry?

7. Why does New England get a larger percentage of its electrical power
water than does Pennsylvania? Why is electricity carried greater dis-
s in some areas than in others? Cite examples.

PART IV

INDUSTRY AND COMMERCE

CHAPTER XXIII

THE DISTRIBUTION OF FOUR GREAT TYPES OF INDUSTRY

The Measurement of Industrial Activity.—It is much more difficult to measure industry than agriculture. In measuring agriculture the main features are indicated by the yield of a relatively small number of products like wheat, corn, oats, cotton, flax, and rubber. For most of these, fairly accurate statistics are available for all countries except China, Persia, Turkey, Ethiopia, and a few minor areas. Moreover, although the quality varies from country to country, the difference between the best and the worst countries is not excessive. Only an expert can tell, for example, whether cocoa comes from Ecuador or San Thomé off the west coast of Africa. With manufactures, on the other hand, the number of articles to be considered is enormous, running into thousands or tens of thousands. Then, too, such industrial pursuits as house building, painting, printing, smelting, and all sorts of work done by carpenters, masons, plumbers, electricians, blacksmiths, engravers, and so forth are usually classified with manufacturing. Moreover, the same materials are used over and over in different kinds of manufacturing. Thus iron ore is smelted in blast furnaces; then rolled into sheets or drawn into bars in steel works and rolling mills; next it may be made into special shapes in an iron foundry; after that another manufacturing plant may convert it into some kind of machine. Thus the same iron is reckoned as part of the ouput of four different factories. Again each special kind of manufactured article usually varies more than do the products of agriculture. The different kinds of watches, typewriters, pens, books, desks, and electric light fixtures vary ever so much more than do the different kinds of rice, barley, jute, oranges, or grapes.

In addition to all this, statistics of manufacturing are not so accurate and complete as those of agriculture, mining, or even lumbering. Many countries publish no data at all as to the kind and value of their manu-

factures.   Among the countries that do publish such data there is so
much diversity of method that it is very difficult to make accurate comparisons.   Within the limits of the United States, however, we can make
accurate comparisons in several different ways, for example, by means
of the total value of manufactured goods, the value added to the raw
materials by manufacturing, or the percentage of goods belonging to
different classes.

For the world as a whole, the best way of comparing industrial
activity is by means of the number of people engaged in industry.   For
this there are fairly good statistics in most countries, although for some,
like China, Afghanistan, Mexico, and other tropical regions, we are
obliged to use estimates.   In their ordinary form, however, the statistics
are not always a safe guide.   For example, according to the ordinary
tables Mexico appears to be a more industrial country than Bulgaria,
having 11.4 per cent of its occupied population engaged in industrial
pursuits as against 7.9 in Bulgaria.   This, however, is misleading,
because these percentages are based on totals which include agriculture.
In Bulgaria practically all the women on the farms are recorded as agricultural workers, whereas in Mexico only a few are thus recorded.   Yet
actually the Mexican women help a great deal in the fields.   Even if they
did not, we should get a better comparison by using only the men, for
the best available measure of the degree to which a country depends on
industrial pursuits is the percentage of families which depend on these
for a living.   Reckoned in this way, Bulgaria's percentage is 12.3, while
that of Mexico is 9.1.   Even this gives only an approximation to the
truth, for in Bulgaria many men who are reckoned as farmers spend
much of their spare time in making knives, cloth, wooden articles, and
other small manufactured goods, while in Mexico this is comparatively
rare.   Nevertheless, the percentage of the occupied men who are
engaged in industrial pursuits is the best available measure of the degree
to which a country depends upon industry.   Therefore it is used in
A489.

The World-wide Distribution of Industry.—The central features of
A489 are two areas where more than 40 per cent of the men are engaged
in industrial pursuits.   One of these centers around the North Sea
and includes much of western Europe.   Switzerland and Germany,
with 45 per cent of their men in industry, are the most highly industrialized of all nations.   Scotland with 43 per cent and England, Belgium, and the Netherlands with 40 follow closely.   The United States
as a whole falls far behind, having 31 per cent of its men in industry.
Czechoslovakia, Sweden, France, Australia, and Denmark all surpass
it, and Austria with 30 per cent almost rivals it.   Nevertheless, indi-

vidual states like Rhode Island with 56 per cent, Connecticut 53, and Massachusetts 49, are even more highly industrialized than either Switzerland or Belgium.   These southern New England States form the eastern end of a second main industrial area in which more than 40 per cent of the men are engaged in industry.   This extends westward to Chicago and includes Toronto in Canada.   In size it almost equals the North Sea area of high industrialization, although its population is far less.   From both of these areas the percentage of men employed in industry decreases gradually outward, but the decline toward the south in the United States is broken not only by the cotton factories of the South, but by the fact that even Florida and Louisiana, which have few

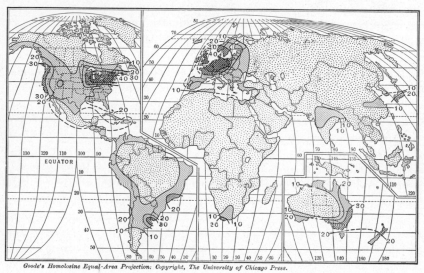

Goode's Homolosine Equal-Area Projection: Copyright, The University of Chicago Press.

A—Percentage of Occupied Men Engaged in Industrial Pursuits.

cotton factories, have more than 20 per cent of their men engaged in industry.

A489 shows six other minor areas where the percentage of men engaged in industry rises to 20 or in most cases 30 per cent.   Notice how symmetrically the entire eight industrial areas are located.   They lie on the east and west sides of the continents in middle latitudes, and have only two little outliers, in Utah and Brazil, respectively. The coast of the three Pacific States and southern British Columbia displays many features which indicate that as time goes on it will become more and more like the two main manufacturing regions. Washington as a whole already has 30 per cent of its men engaged in industry, and the coastal parts of the other three rise to that level.

Australia is even more industrialized than our Pacific Coast. In Victoria no less than 35 per cent of the men are engaged in industry, chiefly around Melbourne, while in both New South Wales (around Sydney) and South Australia (around Adelaide) the percentage rises above 30. Melbourne, Sydney, Adelaide, and even Brisbane in Queensland are fairly well industrialized. The same is true around Auckland and Wellington in New Zealand. There, too, the north island has about 30 per cent of its men engaged in industry. Immediately around Buenos Aires and Montevideo in Argentina and Uruguay there is still another area where the percentage engaged in industry rises above 30. Farther north the growth of industry on the relatively cool plateau at São Paulo joins with a number of factories at Rio de Janeiro in producing a minor outlier of this eastern South American industrial area.

In many ways the Australian and South American industrial areas resemble one another, just as do those of the eastern United States and western Europe. A similar resemblance is apparent between the minor industrial area of Western Australia centering around Perth and that of Chile around Santiago and Valparaiso. Finally in Japan on the eastern side of Asia at a similar distance from the equator there is a rather important industrial area which is beginning to spread into China. As yet, however, the really industrial area comprises only a narrow coastal section from Tokyo and Yokohama through Nagoya to Osaka and Kobe. A little manufacturing is carried on here and there in other regions such as India and South Africa, but it is of slight importance.

The overwhelming bulk of the world's manufacturing is carried on in these eight areas, and especially in the first two. One way of judging the amount of manufacturing is by means of the power employed. This is mainly derived from coal, but water power must also be considered. We can express the water power in terms of the amount of coal needed to produce the same amount of power. On this basis the approximate industrial activity in the various areas where at least 20 per cent of the men are engaged in industry is shown in A491. The importance of the North Sea region and the United States is so overwhelming as to need no comment. When we analyze industries according to their complexity and the degree of skill required in them, the outstanding importance of these advanced areas becomes even greater.

The Four Types of Manufacturing. 1. *The Primitive Type.*— Industrial activities fall into four great types, primitive, simple, community, and complex. Primitive industries are those which are carried on by hand with little use of power other than man's own strength or that of animals. They are generally confined to people's homes, and may also be called home industries. Here are some illustrations; the making of bows and arrows by Indians; the grinding of grain in hand mills as is still done by hundreds of millions of people in China, India, Persia, Turkey, and among the Indians of South America; the making of toys from wood in Swiss homes; the making of lace by women as they watch the flocks and herds in central France; the weaving of linen at home in Poland; the making of Turkish rugs; the canning of peaches or blueberries in our own kitchens; the ordinary cooking of food; dressmaking, sewing, and knitting; the making of paper dolls, kites, or whistles by children. Such industries in one form or another are found everywhere from the lowest savages upward. As one rises in the scale of civilization their importance steadily diminishes. Among primitive people they supply the only kinds of manufactured goods; among highly advanced urban people who live in apartment houses and take their

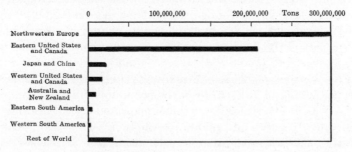

A—Approximate Use of Power in Manufacturing Expressed as the Equivalent of Tons of Coal.

meals in restaurants they have dwindled to mere pastimes. Some people believe that the growth of community kitchens, laundries, mending establishments, and similar services will cause them to disappear completely for all practical purposes among civilized people. Nevertheless, in our day they are still highly important in the form of cooking, sewing, and washing, but their products rarely go outside the home.

2. *The Simple Type.*—Simple industries are those which are designed to reduce the weight or bulk of raw materials, or to make it possible to preserve or transport them easily. Generally they prepare products for use in other industries which in turn put them into shape for final consumption. The grinding of wheat into flour, for example, not only takes out the oily germ, or little plant, which tends to become rancid, but also removes the bran. Thus the keeping qualities are improved, the weight to be transported is reduced, and the product is made ready for the next manufacturing process, namely baking. Other examples of simple industries are the sawing of wood into lumber,

or its conversion into paper pulp; the smelting of ores; the grinding and heating of lime and cement; the canning of fruits, vegetables, and fish in factories; the work of slaughtering and meat packing; the tanning of hides; the ginning of cotton and the extraction of cottonseed oil. As a rule these occupations are carried on close to the place where the original products are produced. The main exceptions are ores that arc sometimes carried to supplies of coal as in the case of iron, petroleum which goes to refineries in pipes or ships, and materials like hides that can be kept a long time in their original state and lose little weight in the process of manufacture. Another noteworthy feature of simple industries is that as a rule little or nothing in the way of other raw materials is needed in order to prepare them. Thus a flour mill needs no raw material except wheat; a cotton ginnery needs only cotton; and a sawmill only logs. Even when other raw materials are required they are usually either flavorings or preservatives like the salt used in meat packing, chemicals such as are employed in tanning, or fluxes which do not form part of the finished product, as in the case of the lime used in smelting iron.

3. *The Community Type.*—Community industries are those which are needed locally in order to keep the community functioning. Every civilized community wants its own newspapers and local printing plant. It also wants bakeries, and plants to supply it with ice, ice cream, gas, electricity, and telephone service. It needs iron foundries, railroad repair shops, and garages within easy reach. Then, too, it must have carpenters, plumbers, masons, electricians, and all the other kinds of workers who are needed to build new structures and repair old ones. Not all of these are required in every small town, but no civilized community can get along without having practically all of them within easy reach. Nobody in Panama wants to depend on New York for daily newspapers, bread, ice cream, railroad repairs, or the setting of new panes of glass. Even though a community makes nothing at all in the way of goods to be sent away for sale, it must have a considerable number of people engaged in community industries.

4. *The Complex Type.*—The remaining industries belong to the complex type. They are complex in their methods not only of manufacture, but also of distribution. Their outstanding qualities are that in general they are made with the help of complex machinery; they usually combine two or more kinds of raw material, for even a steel machine has parts like brass cups, wooden handles, and glass dials; the purpose in manufacturing them is not to preserve the materials or make them easy for transportation, but to fit them for some special use; in most cases they are adapted to the use of the final consumer, that is, of the

person who finally uses them up; and they are not designed for purely local use, but for sale in many places. After leather has gone through the simple manufacturing process of tanning, some of it may be sold to cobblers who will use it in the community industry of resoling the shoes of the people who live nearby. A larger part will go to complex industries to be made into belts, suitcases, straps, and especially boots and shoes. There it is combined with metal, cloth, wood, oil, rubber, and other raw materials to produce finished products ready for the ultimate consumer. Some of these products may of course be sold locally, but the greater part are sold in widely scattered markets. Iron, after the simple process of smelting in a blast furnace, usually goes through an intermediate or semi-simple process of being rolled into sheets, bars, plates, and rods in steel works and rolling mills. These semi-final products may go to iron foundries, railroad repair shops, blacksmith shops, and garages to be used in community industries. Or they may go to factories where machinery, screws, automobiles, locomotives, or stoves are made. There they enter into the complex industries and are prepared for the factory, house, or transportation system where the final product is ultimately consumed in the sense of being worn out.

The Distribution of the Four Types of Manufacturing. 1. *Distribution of Primitive Industries.*—Each of the four types of industries has its own distinctive geographical distribution. A map of primitive industries is almost the opposite of A489 which shows the distribution of the other three types combined. In Central Asia, for example, there is very little manufacturing of the three higher types. In the villages and among the nomads many people still make their own clothing, bedding, and even tents out of the wool of their sheep, goats, camels, or yaks. They make their own saddles out of wood and leather, which they themselves have tanned, while their saddles, bags, and containers for milk are made of the skins of their own animals. Even in the towns a multitude of people spin wool in their spare moments, make rugs, felts, and even cloth at home, slaughter animals in the streets for meat, and build their own houses out of dried mud with a little rough wood. The relative importance of primitive industries as a factor in the life of the people is at a maximum among primitive people like the Australian aborigines who still make arrow heads out of glass from old bottles. It falls to a minimum among the dwellers in the great cities of the United States and western Europe. Nevertheless, primitive and barbarous people usually do so little work that the actual production by means of primitive industries is perhaps greatest in fairly active but poor and rather backward civilized countries like Bulgaria.

2. *Distribution of Simple Industries.*—In studying the remaining types of manufacturing, we are fortunate in being able to use maps based on the exact statistics of the United States, even though no accurate world maps are possible. A494 shows that among its non-agricultural workers southern New England has a very small percentage who are engaged in simple manufacturing. A few sawmills, some brick yards, and some works where marble and granite are shaped into blocks, or where concrete, cement, and paving materials are prepared, almost complete the list. New York, too, stands low in spite of some flour milling, canning, brick-making, slaughtering, tanning, and work in

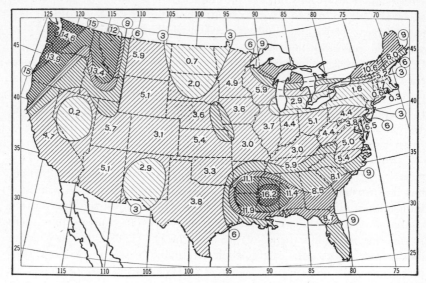

A—Percentage of the Non-agricultural Workers of the United States Engaged in Simple Industries.

stone, cement, lumber, and pulp wood. Pennsylvania rises somewhat higher on account of its blast furnaces, cement works, brick yards, coke ovens, slaughtering, tanning, and stone work. Ohio, Indiana, Illinois, Missouri, and Iowa rank about like Pennsylvania with three to five out of every hundred non-agricultural workers engaged in simple industries. As one goes westward, however, agricultural products like butter, cheese, corn syrup, canned vegetables, slaughter-house products, and flour gradually replace lumber and products of stone, clay, and iron. Nevertheless, from southern New England to Chicago we have a fairly persistent belt where the simple industries are relatively unimportant. Farther north in northern New England, Michigan, and Wisconsin, the presence of lumber, together with canning and the making of butter and cheese, raise the percentage engaged in such industries a little but not much.   Over the line in Canada there is a great increase, however. To the south there is also a rapid increase until 8.7 per cent is reached in Florida and 16.2 in Mississippi.   This is due partly to canning, the making of cottonseed oil and cake, and the preparation of peanuts, pecans, and sugar.   In some states, especially Louisiana, Oklahoma, and Texas, it is also due partly to petroleum refining.   But the greatest factor almost everywhere is lumbering and the preparation of turpentine and rosin.

In the western half of the United States, aside from a very low dip in the Dakotas, there is also an increase in the percentage of men engaged in simple manufacturing.   In the Rocky Mountain and Plateau States this is due largely to the smelting of ores.   On the Pacific Coast the canning industry accounts in part for a still greater rise, but petroleum refining is important in California.   Lumbering plays a great part everywhere, and causes Washington, with 14.6 per cent, to surpass all other states except Mississippi in the percentage of its non-agricultural population engaged in simple industries.

This picture of the distribution of simple industries will give a wrong impression unless we correct it by considering the amount of simple manufacturing per square mile as well as in proportion to the population.   The fact that Massachusetts has the lightest shading in A494 does not mean that that state fails to exploit its resources, but merely that it has a very dense population.   A496 shows that in proportion to its *area* it ranks second only to New Jersey.   The shaping of stone, brick-making, planing-mills and the like employ a good many men in proportion to the area.   New Jersey far outranks all other states because it imports so much crude petroleum, hides, and ore, but even if it were limited to simple industries based on its own products, it would still stand close to the top.   The neighboring states and those directly west as far as Illinois, by reason of their coal, clay, and agricultural products, have at least one man in simple industries for every square mile of area.   Elsewhere the percentages decline in fairly close harmony with the density of the population except in the lumbering areas of the Southeast and Northwest.   From all this we infer that all parts of the country are fairly active in exploiting their natural resources and in basing simple industries upon them.   Wherever there are many people all the available resources are being drawn upon so far as they are needed.   In regions like the Dakotas there are very few people and only scanty or remote supplies of good stone, cement, clay, lumber, and fish for canning.   Naturally the simple industries are not well developed.

In regions like southern New England and New York the resources are
not large and many of them have been more or less exhausted, but the
population is so dense that they are very fully exploited.   Nevertheless,
this exploitation needs only a very small percentage of the workers.   In
the South and West the resources of lumber, agriculture, petroleum, and
other products are so abundant and the people in some cases so few that
a large percentage of the workers is needed in simple industries, even
though the natural resources are not so completely utilized as in the East.

In the world as a whole the same general situation prevails.   Because
of their coal, iron, fish, and intensive agriculture, a fairly high percentage

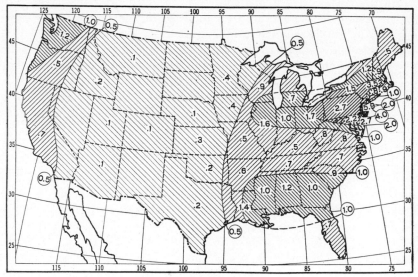

A—Number of Men Engaged in Simple Industries per Square Mile in the United
States.

of the workers in England, Belgium, and Germany is engaged in simple
manufacturing.   The same is true in Norway and Sweden because of
their lumbering, fishing, and dairying.   On the other hand, France,
Holland, Scotland, northern Italy, and especially Switzerland, although
ranking high as industrial nations, have only a small percentage of their
men in simple industries.   They have so few natural resources that they
devote most of their attention to manufacturing goods of the community and complex types.   From all this it is evident that, although the
location of natural resources has a decided effect upon manufacturing,
it is only a minor factor in determining where the chief manufacturing
regions shall be located.

As one goes away from the main centers of manufacturing, the relative importance of simple manufacturing increases, even though the actual amount of such manufacturing per square mile may decrease. Thus in India almost the only large-scale complex manufacturing is the weaving of coarse cotton cloth, and even that is one of the simplest in this group.   A similar condition prevails in China where the cotton industry has established itself around Shanghai.   Up the Yangtze River at Hankow there are iron works which are often heralded as the beginning of a great industrial development.   Such may be the case, but thus far, even more than the iron works in Alabama, these factories have been mainly blast furnaces with relatively little in the way of rolling mills,

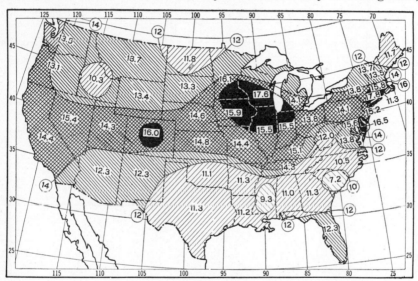

A—Percentage of Non-agricultural Workers in the United States Engaged in Community Industries.

and practically nothing in the really complex iron industries.   Even in Japan, aside from the great cotton and silk mills, which after all are relatively simple, most of the manufacturing consists of simple operations like preparing raw silk, cotton yarn, oil, and crude copper.   In tropical countries like Brazil, Venezuela, Java, and most parts of Africa the greater part of what little modern manufacturing there is consists of the simplest kinds like extracting oil from palm nuts or coconuts, making raw sugar, shelling peanuts, and curing coffee, cacao, and rubber.

3. *Distribution of Community Industries.*—A497, showing the percentage of the non-agricultural workers engaged in community industries, is quite different from A494, showing simple industries.   Here we

find a considerable degree of uniformity all over the country.   There is, to be sure, a strip of rather high appearance extending across the country from southern New England and New Jersey to California, but the highest percentage, 17.8 in Connecticut, is only two and a half times as great as the smallest, 7.2 in South Carolina.   Moreover, all except 4 states have percentages of 10 to 16.   This is quite different from the map of simple industries (A494) where the largest percentage (Mississippi) is 81 times the smallest (Nevada).   It seems to show that in a civilized country like the United States all parts employ about the same proportion of their non-agricultural workers to keep up the ordinary

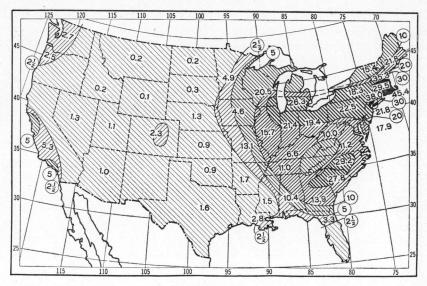

A—Percentage of Non-agricultural Workers in the United States Engaged in Complex Industries.

activities of bakeries, printing plants, planing mills, repair shops, and the like.

4. *Distribution of Complex Industries.*—In A498 the general distribution of complex industries presents somewhat the same aspect as the maps of health (B122), education (A136), yield of milk per cow (A102), yield of eggs per hen (A96), and number of persons per automobile (A135).   The contrasts, however, between the East and the West, and even between the North and the South, are greatly accentuated.   This means that an astonishingly large part of the United States takes practically no share in making the complex kinds of goods which are the main element in modern manufacturing.   The Pacific

Coast does a little such manufacturing; the mountain states and those of the plains as far east as Iowa do only a negligible amount, even when we make allowance for their scanty population. The South likewise does relatively little except for the cotton manufacturing. It is interesting, however, to note that among all the types of complex manufacturing the spinning of thread and the weaving of cloth are almost the simplest. When the spindles and looms have once been set up, they run a long time with practically no alteration and with no care aside from ordinary upkeep. Moreover, the cloth when finished is not yet ready for the final consumer. It must first be dyed, bleached, cut into shape, and sewed to make clothing, bedding, awnings, and a host of other products. Thus the cotton industry of the South, like the steel works and rolling mills of both North and South, is a semi-simple industry. This merely accentuates the fact which stands out most clearly in A494, namely, that the complex industries are mainly developed in the northeastern quarter of the United States. There a state like Connecticut has 38 per cent of all its non-agricultural men engaged in such industries. Even as far west as Illinois this number still stands at 15.7.

Outside of the United States a similar condition prevails. Practically all the complex manufactured goods are made within the limits of the area where at least 40 per cent of the men are engaged in industrial pursuits as shown in A489. Even in the southern half of France and in Italy outside the region of Milan and Turin the manufacturing is mainly of the simple and community types. Australia does a little complex manufacturing, and there are the beginnings of this kind in the five great southern cities of Santiago, Buenos Aires, Montevideo, São Paulo, and Rio de Janeiro. All this, however, is on so small a scale that these countries by no means supply their own needs for machinery, tools, motor vehicles, clocks, chemicals, and even shoes and clothing. Moreover, in many cases what factories there are for this sort of work are branches of those within the two main areas of complex manufacturing, or else are run by people from those areas. Thus it appears that complex manufacturing, more than almost any other occupation, is very largely limited to a few areas where the combined conditions of temperature, humidity, and storminess give the greatest climatic energy, the best health, and the greatest degree of surplus energy and initiative. Later we shall see how strictly certain types of manufacturing are limited to these areas. We shall also see that, as a type of manufacturing becomes simplified into a mere matter of routine, it tends to spread from the areas of highest energy into those which are not quite so stimulating. This is notably the case with cotton, not only in the southern United States, but in Japan, and even in India, Mexico, and Brazil.

Markets, Labor, and Capital in Relation to the Geography of Manu-facturing.—Manufacturing industries can thrive only if they have good markets, a good labor supply, and enough capital. These three things generally go together, for where people are numerous and prosperous they are likely to be good buyers and good workers, and to have money to invest. This combination of good workers, good savers, and good spenders is found mainly in the cyclonic regions and the immediately neighboring areas. This tends to concentrate manufacturing in the same general areas where climatic energy also concentrates it. It is like coal and water power in having a very marked effect upon the local distribution of industries. Thus in the Continental Cyclonic Region of North America, which is superlatively good for manufacturing, a location near the large cities of the eastern coast was long especially favorable. It insured the presence of a good market close at hand, and also of a constantly replenished supply of cheap labor among the immigrants who were constantly arriving from Europe. It also insured capital, for the wealth of the country was centered there and people are generally more ready to invest in local enterprises than in those at a distance. As time went on, the cities farther west, especially those on the Great Lakes, the Upper Mississippi and its branches, and the Pacific Coast, began to enjoy almost equal advantages in this respect.

In some cases, however, the high wages which are a regular concomitant of very high industrial activity have joined with the location of raw materials and markets in driving industries away from the natural regions where manufacturing is generally most favored. This has been especially the case with the cotton industry, which in recent decades has spread not only to our own southern states, but to Japan, India, China, Brazil, and even Mexico. Nevertheless, the rest of the world, outside of the United States, Canada, and Europe west of Moscow, has only about one-seventh of all the cotton spindles and makes an even smaller fraction of the cloth. It is true that in the United States cheap labor, plus the advantages of unused water power and of being able to sell cloth without transporting it to the North and back again, have favored the growth of a great southern cotton industry. But it must be remembered that from the standpoint of the efficiency of labor and even of the degree of healthfulness of the climate a region like Georgia comes much nearer to Philadelphia than to Shanghai. Even in this simplest of complex industries the cheap labor and large markets of tropical and oriental countries have had only a relatively small effect in drawing the factories away from the cyclonic regions. The same is true of the iron industries. In spite of large supplies of coal in China, Siberia, India, and elsewhere, only about 4 per cent of the world's steel is made outside of Europe, Canada, and the United States, and half of that comes from Japan.

Within the natural regions which are favorable to manufacturing, the presence of a given industry and hence of a labor supply trained in that special work is often a determining factor in the location of factories. Thus makers of gloves tend to establish new factories near Johnstown and Gloversville in the Mohawk Valley; factories for motor cars tend to be established near Detroit; those for shoes in eastern Massachusetts; for silk between New York and Philadelphia; and for small brass goods in Connecticut. The presence of a market and the absence of local factories led to the establishment of shoe factories in St. Louis, but these did not succeed at first because of the absence of a trained labor supply. Success was assured only when workers were brought from the East by the companies which supplied the shoe machinery.

The Stage and Type of Civilization in Respect to Manufacturing.— It is not to be expected that a new country will have as much manufacturing or the same kind as an old country. We have already seen that simple industries tend to be dominant so long as a region has a relatively sparse population and large resources. Such is preeminently the case in California, Oregon, Washington, and British Columbia. In due time this region, especially its northern part, will probably resemble New England, Switzerland, and central Sweden in being highly industrialized, and in having a large part of its population engaged in the lighter types of complex industry. New Zealand and southeastern Australia show strong tendencies in this same direction, as do Buenos Aires, Montevideo, and São Paulo to a much milder extent. Eastern Canada, on the contrary, is farther along, but by no means fully developed. South central Chile also gives similar promise, but as a home of the white race it is still too new to have developed greatly. Industrially such countries as India, China, and Japan are also relatively new. In view of the natural regions in which they lie and of the achievements of their people thus far, it is scarcely to be expected that they will rival the regions where manufacturing is already highly developed. Nevertheless, we may confidently expect a very considerable growth in manufacturing, if only to supply their own needs. As various types of manufacturing become highly standardized and therefore easy, we may expect them to spread to regions that are less advanced industrially. In later chapters we shall see more evidence along this line, but we have already seen it in the cotton mills of India and the steel works of China.

Another interesting possibility as to the future of manufacturing is presented by Russia. One of the greatest handicaps to the progress of industry is that mass production enables us to make such vast quantities of goods very cheaply. Having made hundreds of thousands of automobiles, millions of pairs of shoes, and hundreds of millions of yards of cloth we often find ourselves unable to sell them. Moreover, when we invent a new machine which enables one man to do the work formerly done by a dozen, we do not know what to do with the eleven who are thus thrown out of employment. Hence the manufacturing regions are more and more puzzled by the problem of technological unemployment. Moreover, these advanced regions are fast teaching the less advanced regions to make at least the less elaborate kinds of goods for themselves. This diminishes their own market at the very time when their new inventions make them need larger markets. From all these conditions, together with others that cannot here be discussed, arise our crises, financial panics, and hard times. These, be it noted, are most acute in the countries where manufacturing has made the greatest progress. This raises the question whether our present type of economic and social organization is any more sound and permanent than was the old type which prevailed in the days of the feudal system or of slavery. The Russians say that they have found a new type which will in due time overcome these evils, making mass production a blessing to everyone and eliminating technological unemployment, financial crises, and hard times. In pursuance of this idea they are striving to introduce complex manufacturing in natural regions which have not hitherto seemed adapted to it. This raises the problem of whether the right kind of organization of society will be able to overcome the handicaps imposed by geography. The Russians claim that it will. How true this may be will be known only to future generations.

EXERCISES

For Chapters XXIII–XXVI the following sources of information are especially valuable:

(a) The volumes of the U. S. Census dealing with Manufactures and Occupations.
(b) The *Abstract of the U. S. Census.*
(c) The *Statistical Abstract of the United States*
(d) The *Commerce Yearbook.*

1. Describe some primitive industry with which you are familiar and analyze the conditions of its geographical distribution.
2. Do the same for some simple industry, and make a map showing its distribution in the United States. As a model in drawing your map use either A520, in which each dot represents 1 per cent of the country's total workers in the industry there shown, or A494, in which isopleths are drawn on the basis of the percentage of occupied persons in the industries under discussion.

3. Let the whole class join in a study of the geographic relationships of the industries of your city, county, or state. Divide the study into the following parts: (a) classification of the industries into primitive, simple, community, and complex types; (b) statistics derived from the census and other sources; (c) map study and field work in which the different types of industries are located in reference to relief, waterways, routes of transportation, etc.; (d) sources of raw materials, fuel, and power; (e) markets; (f) social conditions connected with the industries; and (g) general interpretation of geographic relationships.

4. Study A489 to see whether you find any regions where manufacturing is either more or less highly developed than you would expect from the geographic environment. Discuss and explain any such exceptional conditions.

5. List the geographic and other conditions under which each of the four great types of industry tend to be important or predominate. Illustrate each by some country or part of a country.

6. What type of manufacture would you expect to find in the following places (give reasons in each case): central isolated New Guinea; the banana plantations of Honduras; average small city of Texas; Belgium?

7. What changes would take place in the world map of the distribution of industry (A489) if all the simple and community industries were eliminated?

8. Look up the industries, imports, and exports, of the following regions and thereby determine the relative importance of the four great types of industry in each region: Denmark, Switzerland, Cuba, Japan, Latvia, Egypt.

CHAPTER XXIV

THE CLOTHING AND LEATHER INDUSTRIES

Great Divisons of Industries.—Manufactures may be divided into
five major divisions pertaining to (1) food, (2) clothing, (3) shelter,
(4) tools, and (5) "progressals." The *food industries* are the most basic.
They not only support life, but in the world as a whole they excel the
others in value of products and number of people employed. Ordinary statistics do not show their full importance because they omit
a vast amount of primitive manufacturing in the shape of activities
like threshing, cutting silage, making butter on the farm, and above
all cooking. Thus in the United States census they appear to employ
less than 900,000 people. Here, however, the food industries are relatively much less important than in more backward countries like Persia
and Nigeria where the women spend much of their time grinding grain
by hand.

The *clothing industries* include not only the textiles, but leather products, for by far the chief leather work is shoemaking. The textile industries, as classified in the census, include every process from spinning the
thread through weaving to dressmaking and hat-trimming. They
employ about 2,000,000 people in the United States, while the leather
industries employ almost 400,000 more. This leaves out the enormous
number of women whose work in making and mending clothes at home
is just as truly manufacturing as is the work of the cobbler, or of the
man in a railroad repair shop. In backward countries, spinning and
weaving are a common way of spending spare time among men as
well as women.

The *shelter industries* include 1,200,000 workers in what the census
of manufacturers calls "forest products" and "stone, clay, and glass
products." These serve mainly to supply wood, stone, bricks, cement,
and glass for buildings. About 2,600,000 carpenters, masons, electricians, laborers, and others engaged in the "building industries"
also belong in this group. In their primitive form the industries connected with shelter occupy part of the time of most of the men among
far more than half of the world's people. The log houses of northern
Russia, the adobe houses of the zone from Morocco and Spain to

northern India and China, and the crude thatched huts of the tropics are usually constructed by their owners.

Our next major division, the *tool-making industries,* includes iron and steel products, machinery, transportation equipment, railroad repair shops, garages, and non-ferrous metals and their products. All of these are based on metals, and are primarily engaged in producing or repairing tools in the broadest sense of the word, that is, devices for doing work which we should otherwise have to do with our own bodies. These devices include not only ordinary tools and implements like knives, saws, spades, pens, and augers, but also motors, microscopes, adding machines, locomotives, printing presses, derricks, looms, machine tools, telephones, and innumerable other articles which help in our work, or in getting ourselves, our goods, and our ideas from place to place. Of course some tools in this broad sense are made of wood, stone, or cloth, but the percentage is insignificant compared with metal. Altogether, the tool-making, metal-using industries in the United States employ about 4,600,000 persons and thus surpass any of our other major divisons of manufactures. On the other hand, outside the United States and western Europe they employ relatively few people. Such industries are now very rarely carried on in primitive forms such as are still widely prevalent in the industries supplying food, clothing, and shelter.

The products of the remaining industries are here called *progressals* because most of them supply needs which are felt, or at least gratified, only among the most highly progressive people, or where such people are introducing a new and alien mode of life among more primitive people. The use of paper in books and other forms; the use of paint, fertilizers, medicines, explosives, soap, and other chemical preparations; the luxury of riding on rubber tires and keeping dry with raincoats; and dependence on gasoline, coke, gas, and other products of petroleum and coal are still in their infancy except in the advanced countries. With these, we may put the group called "miscellaneous" in the census, including such things as dental goods, mattresses, motion pictures, pianos, phonographs, sporting goods, tobacco products, toys, writing and drafting materials, and a host of others which in most parts of the world are luxuries or else unknown. All these progressals together employ about 3,700,000 people. Only to a very slight degree do they enter into primitive industry, and only rarely are most of them produced outside of the regions of most intensive manufacturing.

The geographical distribution of these five major divisions of manufacturing becomes more restricted and their methods more complex as we go from those that are most essential to those that can easily be dispensed with. Thus the preparation of food is universal, and the primitive forms are far more important than the complex. The preparation of clothing is almost equally universal, but some savages dispense with it. Primitive methods of work still persist almost everywhere, but are being displaced by complex methods among the advanced nations. Shelter is also needed universally, but in advanced nations the primitive methods of preparing it have largely disappeared, although they still dominate the lands occupied by far more than half the earth's inhabitants. Tools are also needed everywhere, but in our day even the backward nations rely mainly on the complex industries of Europe, the United States, and Japan for the vast majority of their simple tools, as well as for their machines. And finally the use, as well as the manufacture, of the great group of progressals sinks to astonishingly low proportions outside the quarter of the earth's population which can really be counted as progressive. On the other hand, in the United States the percentage of all industrial workers engaged in the various divisions of industry increases as we go from the lower to the higher needs, as appears in the following table:

Food industries............................. 6 per cent
Clothing industries......................... 15 per cent
Shelter industries.......................... 25 per cent
Tool-making industries...................... 30 per cent
Progressals................................. 24 per cent

In the future we may confidently expect the progressals to surpass all the others. On the other hand, in backward countries, if we include the primitive industries, exactly the reverse order prevails.

The Textile Industries.—We shall begin our study of individual industries with the textiles because they afford such good illustrations of important principles. A comparison of A507*, showing where cotton is used in manufacturing, with B507, showing where cotton is raised, discloses two types of cotton-manufacturing areas. One consists of areas where cotton is shipped in and manufactured. It is indicated by a great many dots in places like New England, Old England, and by a few dots in Japan. The other consists of areas where cotton is raised and also manufactured. It is indicated by many dots in the Carolinas, Georgia, and their neighbors, and by smaller numbers in India, Brazil, and China. Sixty years ago a similar map would have shown practically no dots in these areas and a far greater concen-

---

* In most of the numerous dot maps in the following pages each dot indicates 1 per cent of the production in the area under discussion. Where the production amounts to more than half of 1 per cent a dot is shown and for this reason the total number of dots may range above 100 as well as below. Minor production of from one-tenth to one-half of 1 per cent is indicated by crosses.

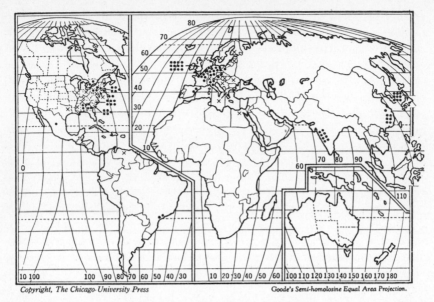

Goode's Semi-homolosine Equal Area Projection.

A—World Map of the Distribution of Cotton Manufacturing. Each dot indicates the use of 1 per cent of the world's cotton crop in manufacturing. Crosses indicate minor amounts.

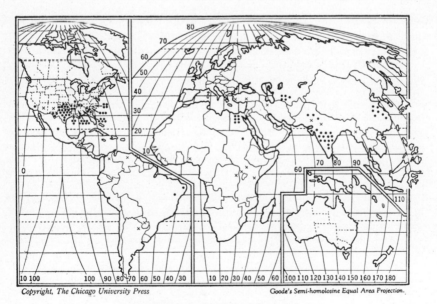

Goode's Semi-homolosine Equal Area Projection.

B—World Production of Cotton.

tration in England and New England. Our problem is to ascertain first why such a concentration occurred in the two " Englands," and then why the cotton industry is moving back to the cotton-raising areas where it first arose in its primitive form. The matter can best be understood by examining the historical development of the whole textile industry, for cotton became important only after the use of linen, silk, and wool had brought the industry to the brink of the modern factory system.

The Changing Geographic Location of the Early Textile Industries.—In ancient times the earliest good cloth was probably the silk of China. Northern India wove cotton, and Babylonia and Egypt wove linen in very early days. At a later date Persian silks, and the fine woolen goods of Anatolia, Greece, and Phoenicia, were widely sought articles of commerce. In the Middle Ages, northern Italy with its fine silks, as well as linens, became the chief textile center of Europe and of western Asia. At the end of the Middle Ages, however, the supremacy in textiles, as in many other elements of civilization, passed first to France and then to the other regions surrounding the North Sea. The Flemings, in the Belgian province of Flanders, were noted as weavers of both wool and linen. The English, too, especially in the eastern lowland, were becoming skillful in weaving woolens, in which they were fast establishing an important foreign trade. During the Thirty Years' War (1618–48), continental Europe was in constant turmoil, while England, being an island, remained in comparative peace. The mild English Civil War under Cromwell had no discernible effect in raising prices or otherwise producing commercial distress. This is very different from the wars which devastated the continent not only at this time, but long before and after. The Low Countries, in strong contrast to free England, were long held in cruel bondage by Spain, and this continued in Belgium until after the War of the Spanish Succession (1701–14). These prolonged commotions had practically annihilated Flemish competition with the British woolen trade by the end of the sixteenth century. They also caused "a constant stream of emigrants" to pass from Flanders to England. Some Germans and Dutch came in the same way. These newcomers greatly improved the British manufactures. As a result England gradually gave up exporting raw wool, and exported more and more woolen cloth until this formed two-thirds of the country's exports at the close of the seventeenth century. About this time (1685), Louis XIV of France revoked the Edict of Nantes, which had guaranteed certain rights to Protestants. Thereupon renewed persecutions arose, and many Hugenots sought refuge in England. According to Gibbin in *Industry in England*, the Huguenot immigrants are said to have numbered 50,000 with a capital of £3,000,000 sterling. They must have been very competent. Otherwise they never could have saved and carried away an average of $1,500 per *family*, which probably meant more than $10,000 would mean today. Many of them were skilled artisans and manufacturers who greatly improved the silk, glass, and paper trades in England, and aided considerably in the general development of manufactures.

As a factor in the growth of industries such migrations are highly important. Ancient conquerors in Egypt, Palestine, Mesopotamia, Greece, and Rome were especially eager to bring home skilled artisans as slaves. All through history we find such items as these: In A.D. 1147 Roger of Sicily made a successful raid on the shores of Greece and carried off a number of weavers whom he established at Palermo in a silk factory. This gave rise to new and rich fabrics which combined Byzantine and Saracen influences, and later spread to northern Italy. Or again, in any account of the weavers who made cloths and velvets of silk in Paris, Rouen, Lyon, Nîmes, and Avignon during the fourteenth and fifteenth centuries, "it must be remembered that they were almost solely Italian immigrants who had fled from Lucca and Florence in times of trouble." William the Conqueror in the eleventh century, Edward III in the fourteenth, and Henry VII in the fifteenth all brought artisans from Flanders to England to improve the woolen industry. These few examples show how relatively small but select migrations carried textile skill from Greece to Italy, and thence to France, whence the Hugenots carried it to England, and later migrants took it across the sea to America. The direction of migration is generally from the older countries to those that are newer, freer, and less densely populated.

By 1660, manufacturing had become so important that England systematically framed its laws so as to cause the home country to do all the manufacturing for the colonies, which were to be developed as sources of raw material for British manufactures. In other words, more than a century before the steam engine and other inventions brought the Industrial Revolution, England already occupied the same sort of industrial position as now in comparison with the rest of the world. This had come to pass merely as part of the general march of civilization from southeast to northwest. At all stages of history the greatest activity and skill in manufacturing and commerce appear to have been closely associated with the highest development in literature, political organization, and other elements of culture. As each type of activity moves from region to region, it generally tends to rise to higher levels, especially in the case of arts like manufacturing where the skill of one age or country can be passed on to another in the forms of tools, machines, or the technique by which something is produced.

This increasing technical skill was applied to different materials according to the products or trade of the various countries. In China, silk has always been the main textile because the mulberry tree and silkworm grow so well there. In India, cotton early became important. Even as late as the days of the East India Company which brought India under British rule two or three hundred years ago, fine cotton goods were still made in that country, and such materials as calicoes which get their name from Calicut or Calcutta and chintzes which are so called from an Indian word meaning spotted were exported to Europe. In the early Mediterranean countries, where neither silk nor cotton became common until a late date, wool was the main material for the robes and togas of the Greeks and Romans, although linen was also used. In the Middle Ages northern Italy had learned to raise silk as well as flax, and therefore expressed its textile supremacy by making the world's best silks. In the North Sea countries, wool was far more important than any other fiber because the climate demanded warm clothing and favored the raising of sheep. It was in this phase of the textile industry that England had become supreme.

The Localization of the Textile Industry in England.—Even after England had become the leader in making cloth for sale abroad, the migration of the center of activity had not ceased. Between 1700 and 1750, industries increased in Lancashire, where lie Manchester and Liverpool, and in the neighboring counties, far faster than in eastern and southern England. In *England on the Eve of the Industrial Revolution*, L. W. Moffit points out that in these 50 years the population of England as a whole increased only 18 per cent, while that of Lancashire increased 79 per cent. The other counties which increased most rapidly were all in western or northern

England in what are now the most active parts industrially. Still more significant is the fact that from 1685 to 1760 the increase in population in the northwestern commercial and manufacturing towns was as follows: Liverpool tenfold, Manchester about sixfold, Birmingham seven, Sheffield six, and Nottingham two. On the other hand, among the southern towns, aside from London, Bristol alone had shown a good growth (to $3\frac{1}{2}$ times its former size), while Norwich nearly doubled, and the increase in all the other provincial towns was negligible. This, as Moffit says, "represents a very considerable advance in industry and trade" in the northwest "although there were no notable improvements in the producing power of industry."

Coal, iron, and water power had little or nothing to do with this increase in industry in western England, although the increase happened to occur where coal and iron later became highly important. Wood, not coal, was then the chief fuel of England. Iron was still smelted with wood or charcoal, the use of coal being still in the experimental stage. Such coal as was mined was chiefly for domestic consumption, or for glass and salt works. Neither coal nor water power had anything whatever to do with the weaving industry, for such a thing as a power loom was unknown, and the weavers threw their shuttles back and forth by hand. Iron also played little part in the growth of industry in northwestern England before the Industrial Revolution. Farm implements were merely shod with iron. Plows were often made entirely of wood. So far as possible, wood was employed for tools and machines. In the looms of the textile industry only a few small parts were iron. Yet in 1774 when the Industrial Revolution was just beginning, about 4,500,000 pounds of wool from perhaps 20,000,000 sheep were manufactured into cloth valued at £13,000,000 sterling. This means about $50 worth for every family in England, and is a very large amount for those days.

The conclusion to be drawn from all this is that the textile industry of England occupied essentially its present location and had almost its present importance in comparison with other countries before coal, iron, or water power had an opportunity to exert any determining influence. The same is true of other industries. As Moffit puts it, "The new conditions arising out of the mechanical and chemical discoveries of the later nineteenth century did not create new forces so much as intensify and give greater play to those already in being."

Reasons for Localization in Northwestern England.—Here are the chief reasons why the textile industry was more highly developed in northwestern England than anywhere else even before the Industrial Revolution. (1) The first is the slow *coldward march of civilization*, as described in previous chapters. As man became better able to protect himself from the cold and wet, as he acquired better tools wherewith to cut the forests and till the soil, and as he selected varieties of animals and plants better adapted to a cool, moist climate, he was able to dwell in greater and greater numbers and in more and more comfort in the climates that are most healthful and stimulating. In the North Sea region he found the part of the Old World where health and energy are near their best. Here, therefore, man has a great inclination to work hard and accumulate a surplus which can be used as capital for manufacturing. Here, too, the conditions of health and energy give him the greatest inner urge to use his mind in making inventions and developing new ideas. Hence, even if other conditions were everywhere identical, the principles of geography suggest that the manufacturing industries, as well as other phases of civilization, would rise to very high levels not far from the North Sea.

(2) Although climate thus determines the general area where we should expect the most active manufacturing, other factors determine the local distribution of activity within the broad North Sea area. One such factor is *selective migration*, that is, migrations containing an unusually large proportion of particular kinds of people such as weavers, farmers, or criminals. During the turmoil of the Middle Ages the people most likely to migrate were not ignorant peasants, who were tied to the soil, but the more alert, intelligent, and prosperous townspeople of the artisan and mercantile classes. Among these the migratory tendency was strongest in those who protested against what they believed to be the wrongs of politics and religion. Switzerland owes much of her preeminence in science, political organization, and industry to the fact that the freedom fostered by her mountains made her a haven for thousands of such people. Likewise the Dutch Republic attracted Flemings from Spanish possessions which now form Belgium, Huguenots from France, and Jews from Portugal.

(3) The *insularity* of England made that country a great haven for immigrants of this sort. By protecting Great Britain from continental wars and invasions, the sea made that island a refuge for numerous able people who improved the British stock biologically and stimulated British industries. They brought not only their own skill, but likewise a knowledge of the methods employed in other countries. The insularity of England also stimulated commerce by obliging the people to go to sea in order to get anywhere. Having learned the art of seamanship in fishing boats and coastal trading vessels, the British sailors had no fear of the broad ocean. Having once loaded their ships, they found it almost as easy to cross the ocean as to cross the North Sea. Thus their markets and profits were greatly increased, while the people at home were stimulated to manufacture not only more goods, but also new kinds adapted to distant markets.

(4) *Maritime discoveries* increased the value of England's insularity by offering new and rich rewards to people who freely crossed the sea. This, of course, furnished an additional incentive to manufacturing. It also had an important effect upon the local distribution of manufacturing within the limits of Great Britain itself. Before the discovery of America and of the South African route to Asia, such cities as Bristol, Liverpool, and Glasgow had been merely back doors facing away from the main avenues of trade with continental Europe. Now, they became

front doors. Woolen cloth made at Leeds could be shipped to the American colonies via Liverpool more easily than cloth made at Norwich could be shipped via London.

(5) As the demand for woolen cloth expanded with the growth of the colonies, the presence of *land too cool, wet, or rough for agriculture* became a real asset. So long as England was mainly agricultural the southeastern lowlands possessed distinct advantages in climate, relief, and soil. As woolen manufacturing increased, however, the less-favored northwest and southern Scotland began to surpass the southeast in two respects. First, the people were especially desirous of entering some form of industry. Their poor farms afforded such small incomes that they were eager to get wool from a master-weaver and make it into yarn or cloth at home. Moreover, they were relatively free to give up farm work if they chose, because many owned little farms, and were not like the humble peasants who were tenants on the big estates of the better land to the southeast. Thus in northwestern England and southern Scotland there grew up a large body of agricultural village people who were also skilled spinners and weavers. As yet they knew only a little about cotton, although it was occasionally mixed with their wool, but the fundamental processes of the cotton and woolen industries are the same.

The other advantage of the poorer lands was that they made it possible to meet the increasing demand for woolen cloth by raising more sheep. The southeastern farmers could not do this so fully, nor did they want to, for most of their land was in crops, which sold at profitable prices because of the growth in population. In the northwest, however, there were large tracts, especially on the high, cool, grassy uplands of the Pennine Hills and southern Scotland, where the number of sheep could be greatly increased. As a result the sheep at the beginning of the Industrial Revolution, that is, at the time of the American Revolution, were almost as numerous as now, although the population was only one-fifth its present size. This concentration of sheep naturally made the woolen industry grow especially fast in the north, at the base of the hills near towns like Leeds.

(6) The last, but not least, factor in the concentration of the textile industry in northwestern England previous to the Industrial Revolution was the *character of the people*. For complex causes into which we cannot here enter the French are generally agreed to have an artistic temperament; the Germans are more philosophical and phlegmatic; the English are adventurous and inventive. In spite of violent discussions as to the nature and cause of racial differences, most people feel sure that a Scotchman is somehow innately different from a Greek, and

that a Spaniard will react differently from a Finn.   Selective migration, climate, training, and occupations all play a part in this.   For our present purpose the main thing is that the inventive faculties and the spirit of innovation were at this time very active in England and Scotland.   This resulted in the spinning-jenny, the power loom, the blast furnace, the steam engine, and all that has sprung from them.   Other results were the factory system, and a great expansion of commerce. But these innovations did not occur until after the textile industry had become firmly established in its present location.

Fuel, Iron, Cotton, and the Industrial Revolution.—In the preceding discussion, coal, iron, cotton, and factories have played little part. Their day had not yet come.   But during the eighteenth century, and especially from 1750 to 1800, the same human qualities which caused British commerce and hand industry to expand also caused many inventions.   Although resources never *compel* people to do anything, they often stimulate man's activity and decide which of his attempts shall be successful.   If inventors like Watt, Stephenson, Hargreaves and Arkwright had not been of high ability and had not grown up where manufacturing was already active, no amount of coal and iron would have led them to develop the arts of smelting iron with coal, turning wheels with steam, and making thread and cloth by means of power derived from steam engines or water-wheels.   The fact that excellent coal and iron happened to be located in the same region where industry had already made the greatest progress was merely a geographical accident, but it vastly increased the importance of the inventions. It turned the British to developing other resources in addition to the agricultural land, the sea, and the sheep which they had previously exploited so skillfully.   It caused the iron industry to expand enormously, and enabled towns like Birmingham, which lie close to both coal and iron, to grow with amazing rapidity.   It stimulated the demand for coal not only in Great Britain, but also in other regions to which British ships were traveling.   This in turn made it easy and cheap to bring wheat and other food as well as raw materials from across the sea.   Thus food and clothing became cheaper in England, and more people could live there.   The new use of coal to produce steam also led directly to the development of the modern factory. Previously there had indeed been buildings where a hundred or more people worked together, but each person operated just as if he were at home.   The main thing that distinguishes the modern factory from everything that preceded it is that its tools are run by power.   Thus one person can manage five hundred spindles, or anywhere from 24 to 72 looms instead of only one, and each spindle and loom works many times as fast as if run by hand. The use of iron and coal and the development of textiles factories also interested the British in an American invention of this time, namely Eli Whitney's cotton gin, by which the seeds of cotton are combed out by power instead of being laboriously picked out by hand. Previously the day's work of one man had sufficed to prepare only 1 to 3 pounds of cotton fiber, if the work was done wholly by hand, and only 5 or 10 with the crude machines then available. The gin at once raised this to 100 and soon to 500. Today one man's work, where many gins are run together, cleans 4000 to 6000 pounds in an eight-hour day. Cotton thus became the cheapest of fibers, instead of one of the most expensive. Since it is the best for many purposes, the British began to use it in large quantities sooner than any other people. This illustrates the geographic principle that inventions and discoveries, no matter where they are made, generally benefit the most advanced people more than any others. Thus England in a few decades after Whitney's invention in 1792 had built up an enormous cotton industry.

Still another geographic factor has a bearing on the location of factories. Cotton thread breaks very easily when dry. This occurs especially in weaving, where the thread has to be pulled rapidly back and forth by the shuttle. The early power looms were improved so rapidly that soon the main work of the weaver was merely to watch for broken threads, and, as soon as he saw one, stop the loom and tie it up. The less the threads break, the greater the number of looms that one weaver can run. When the cotton industry arose in England it was at first merely a branch of the woolen industry. Therefore it was located mainly on the two sides of the Pennine Hills in northern England. But the manufacturers soon discovered that the prevailing west winds from the sea make the west side of the Hills moister than the east side. Therefore there arose a strong tendency to build new cotton mills on the west side around Manchester. That side is also better than the east side because of its excellent harbors and because it is more accessible not only to overseas supplies of raw cotton but also to great foreign markets. The freedom of its water from lime was also a help. Thus, during the nineteenth century an extraordinary combination of circumstances culminated by giving a small section of England a preeminent position in the textile industry. Man's growing power to withstand cold and wet, selective migrations, insularity, unused land fit for sheep but not for crops, highly inventive and ingenious people who were able to develop both industry and commerce, good harbors, some of the world's best supplies of coal and iron, a mild, humid climate good for both men and cotton thread, and a location easily accessible to America, all cooperated.   Had any one of these been different, the results would have been different.   Yet the fact that Switzerland, Norway, Denmark, and Iceland now stand so high in civilization, even though lacking many of the British advantages, seems to indicate that racial character and climate stand first in importance.

The Early Localization of the Cotton Industry in New England.—New England's textile history is similar in many ways to that of Old England. In early colonial times, in spite of British laws to the contrary, the colonials tried to make iron tools, guns, ammunition, cloth, carts, harness, furniture, and other manufactured goods. The North, however, gradually forged ahead. One reason was the people. They came more largely than the southerners from groups which were used to hard work. They also included fewer Negroes and indentured servants of a kind who had little initiative. Another reason was the climate, which not only caused manual labor to be easier in the North than in the South, but made slavery profitable in the South, thus making labor seem degrading. Again, so long as linen and especially wool were the main fibers, the raw materials of the textile industry could be produced more easily north of Philadelphia than south of it, although nowhere were they sufficiently abundant. Then, too, during colonial days tobacco was so profitable in the South that people tended to rely on it for ready money. All this does not apply to the Piedmont section between the Appalachians and the coastal plain so much as to the coastal plain itself. In the Piedmont the land was rougher and the soil poorer than on the plain. Accordingly, the Scotch-Irish and others who settled there did not own many slaves or raise much tobacco. They therefore devoted more time to home industries, including not only textiles but also iron work.

On the poorer farms farther north, where no crop yielded any profit like that of the southern tobacco, the need of ready money made people turn to household manufacturing, especially weaving. These same conditions, together with the many good northern harbors and the abundance of fish along the coast and on the shallow "banks" farther out, led the northerners, and especially the New Englanders, to engage in extensive commerce. Hence the shipowners were on the lookout for goods to carry to other countries, and textiles were in great demand. As a result of all these conditions the textile industry of America at the end of the eighteenth century was most highly developed in southern New England and southeastern Pennsylvania, but there was also considerable activity in the Piedmont region of the Carolinas and Virginia. In other words, before any form of power was used in the textile industry and while it was still a purely hand industry carried on at home, its main centers were the same as now (A520). Philadelphia was the center of fine weaving, which corresponds to the fact that it is now the center of the knitting industry. Southern New England was the greatest region for woolen goods, and made some cloth from cotton imported from the West Indies. The southern section where the cotton industry has now again become active probably made more cotton cloth than the north. Its activity in this respect, however, declined during the fifty years before the Civil War because the raising of cotton became much more profitable than its manufacture.

The Growth of the Cotton Industry in New England.—The industrial Revolution of the eighteenth century had the same effect in New England as in Old England.   England did its best to prevent the use of its new machines and methods elsewhere, but emigrants soon carried the new knowledge to America. New England was the place where it was received and used most readily. In 1789 an emigrant named Slater, who thoroughly understood the new British looms, tried vainly in Philadelphia and New York to get someone to supply the capital with which to set up a factory. In Providence, however, he succeeded and soon started the first real factories in the United States.

1. *Early Progress.*—The textile industry in southern New England was already in an advanced state before the introduction of power and factories. This is the first of the main reasons why a little area near the coast of southeastern New England from Portsmouth to New London soon became second only to Lancashire as a textile center.

2. *Character of Manufacturers.*—The founders of the early cotton factories were men of energy and vision who had made New England ports known in every corner where trade promised generous gain. As Miss Caroline F. Ware puts it in *The Early New England Cotton Manufacture*, they had made money "by taking risks, looking ahead, and using enough imagination to carry ice to both the East and West Indies and to develop a taste for ice cream among the Brazilians." Being used to taking risks and doing new things, they did not hesitate to experiment with new machines, with factories, and with corporations where many men invested their money in place of having the whole business owned by one man. These things seem commonplace to us, but were great innovations in those days. The activity of New England at this time shows itself in the fact that 48 new turnpike companies were incorporated in Massachusetts from 1796 to 1804. Old turnpikes were extended, and toll roads and toll bridges were constructed. In 1808 the opening of the Middlesex Canal afforded a direct water route from northeastern Massachusetts and southern New Hampshire to Boston. Similar activity occurred in neighboring states.

The New Englanders who organized the new factories form an interesting contrast to the leaders of the textile industry in Philadelphia. The latter were mainly master-weavers rather than merchants. They were interested in good workmanship, and were not in the habit of trying new ventures. The skill of their hands prevented them from seeing the advantages of machines. Some of this skill went to New England in the form of weavers who were hired to serve as teachers in the new factories. The contrast between New England and Philadelphia was much like that between Old England and France. In Philadelphia and France the cotton industry is still organized with special reference to small shops which make especially fine goods and carry on the most difficult parts of the industry; in the two Englands the big factory surrounded by the houses of hundreds of factory workers is the rule.

(3) *Water Power*.—Natural advantages in respect to water also encouraged the rapid development of manufacturing in New England. It is sometimes said that New England owes its textile industry to water power, but this is not quite correct. After deciding to replace their already active hand industries by factories, the New Englanders looked around for sources of power. Some tried horses, but since small water power sites for grinding grain were already widely in use, they were promptly utilized. This might have been done in Pennsylvania and the South, also, but the water power in New England is more widely distributed, nearer the sea, and more regular in volume at all seasons than farther south. It is by no means better, however, than farther to the northeast in Maine and Canada, where no textile industry has grown up. The New England water is also unusually free from mud and hence better for bleaching. Moreover, the nearness of the water power sites to the sea makes it easy to import raw cotton and export finished cloth.

4. *Climate*.—The climate at New Bedford and Fall River, the greatest American cotton cities, is like the Manchester climate of England in being humid because of winds from the sea. In the South the summer heat and dryness are so unfavorable that until the artificial humidification of cotton mills was perfected, it was difficult to spin fine yarn there by machinery. In the interior of both the North and South the low temperatures of winter have a similar effect, for the air becomes extremely dry when warmed. And if the air is artificially humidified it usually feels much too warm, which is bad for the workers. The climate of the southeastern corner of New England also approaches closely to being the most healthful and stimulating in all North America. This is one reason why Newport continues to be so famous and wealthy a resort.

5. *Labor*.—Some authorities lay great stress upon the abundance of labor available to start the cotton mills in New England. We have already seen that the combination of poor farms and energetic farmers made the early New Englanders carry on hand industries. The same conditions made them ready to work in factories. Moreover, immigrant labor has long been easily available in southern New England, but the cotton industry had already become well established before this became important.

6. *Capital*.—Financial resources were probably more important than labor in starting the New England cotton industry. Personal

wealth in early America was mainly in two forms, that of the planter and that of the merchant prince. The southern planter held riches in the form of land and slaves, but rarely had ready money beyond the limits of what came each year from the crops. In other words he had little readily available capital. The northern merchant made his money by taking risks, putting a large sum of capital into a single venture, and waiting a long time for profits. His capital was liquid at frequent intervals. Thus it was not at all revolutionary for the merchant to buy stock in a corporation or even to start a factory, whereas it required a complete change of habits for the planter to do so. Moreover, the War of 1812 made foreign commerce unprofitable in New England at the very time when money was needed for cotton factories which were proving highly profitable. Hence, in the early nineteenth century, almost every merchant in Boston owned shares in cotton mills.

South versus North in the Present Cotton Industry.—A519 shows that in the spinning of cotton thread, or yarn as the factory people say, New England is still important, but the Carolinas, Georgia, and Alabama are far more so. This looks as if most of the cotton industry had migrated to the South. A520, however, which shows the total value of all kinds of cotton goods, suggests that the migration is not so complete as might appear from A519. The two maps differ partly because northern mills often buy southern yarn, but mainly because the northern mills make more expensive goods than do those of the South. This is evident in B520, which shows the distribution of the finer kinds of cotton yarn, those above 40 counts, which are used in better sorts of cloth. In this respect New England still does more than half of the country's work, although here, too, the South is catching up. One of the most highly specialized forms of cotton manufacturing is knit goods. A521 indicates that these still hold their own in Philadelphia where we found them well established a century and a half ago. They are spreading to the South, and even to the West. The fact that more than half the knit goods are still manufactured within a hundred miles or so of Philadelphia shows how prone an industry is to stay in its original location.

These cotton maps form a series of increasing complexity in which the product is farther and farther removed from the original raw material, and more and more skill is required. They culminate in B521, which shows where the major part of our cotton cloth passes through its final manufacturing process and is made into wearing apparel. B521 does indeed include some goods made of wool, silk, and linen, but if these were eliminated the appearance of the map would not be altered. It indicates that dresses, suits, and other articles of wearing apparel are made mainly in the Northeast, and overwhelmingly in New York City. It is interesting to note, however, that the central and western states are represented here more than in any of the preceding maps. St. Louis, St. Paul and Minneapolis, Kansas City, Denver, Seattle, Portland, San Francisco, and Los Angeles all appear as centers where clothing is made, although their importance as makers of cloth is negligible. On the other hand, the South, which produces all the cotton, has only the most fragmentary representation in B521. The obvious conclusion from all these maps is that, although the South is the main user of raw cotton, the more skilled processes and the more

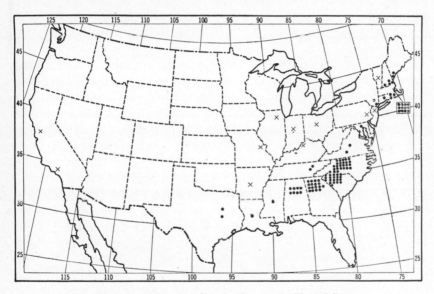

A—The Manufacture of Cotton Yarn in the United States.

technical types of manufacturing are carried on in the North. This is illustrated in another way in A522. The shading there indicates the percentage by which the final value of the cloth sent out from factories, after it has been bleached, dyed, or embroidered, if such is the case, exceeds the value of the original raw material. In the South, values as low as 40 per cent are registered. In the North from New England westward they rise above 50 or even 60 per cent. The South uses much material; the North uses much skill.

World Distribution of Cotton Industry.—In the world as a whole the relation between the production and manufacture of cotton is much the same as in the United States. B507 shows that most of the world's

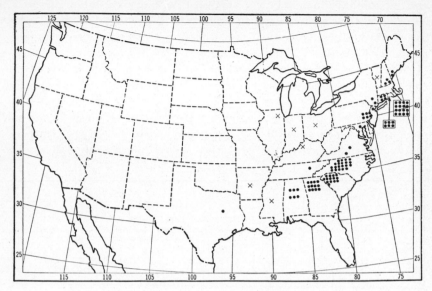

A—The Manufacture of Cotton Goods in the United States.

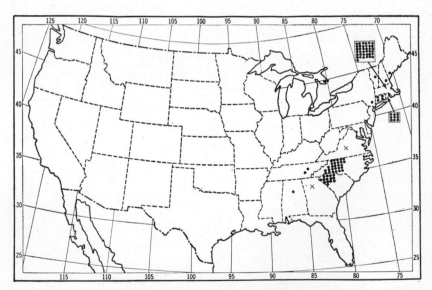

B—The Manufacture of Fine Cotton Yarn in the United States (above forty counts).

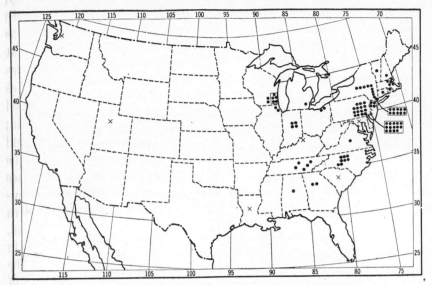

A—The Manufacture of Knit Goods in the United States.

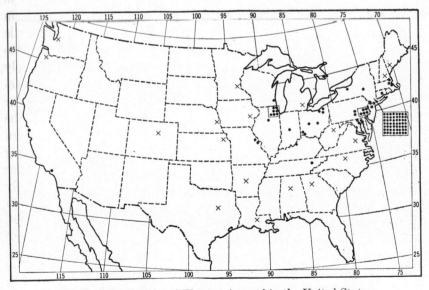

B—The Manufacture of Wearing Apparel in the United States.

cotton is raised in latitudes lower than 35°, while A507 indicates that half is manufactured in regions north of 40°. The greatest non-producing manufacturers are (1) the North Sea countries and central Europe, including Great Britain, Germany, France, northern Italy, and some minor countries; (2) the coastal part of the northeastern United States; (3) Japan; and (4) the Ukraine and Russia in the regions of Kiev and Moscow. The United States and Russia are so large that they use their own cotton grown in areas much warmer than the relatively cool manufacturing districts. Western Europe gets its supplies

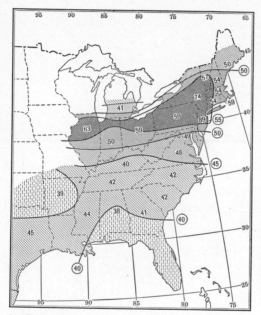

mainly from the United States, Egypt, and India; Japan draws on India and the United States. The main areas which produce cotton and also manufacture it are our southern states, China, India, Brazil, and Mexico. Yet even in the southern states the mills use a good deal of cotton that has moved northward, coming from Texas and Mississippi to the Carolinas, while in Brazil, although a little cotton grows near São Paulo, the main supply which is there manufactured comes from near Recife, 1,400 miles to the northeast. The southern states and China, being

A—Percentage Added to Value of Raw Material by Manufacturing in Cotton Group of Industries. Dyeing, finishing, and embroidering are included.

in the Warm Temperate Humid Region, show a distinct resemblance so far as cotton is concerned. In China, however, the land is so fully needed for food that some cotton is actually imported. India, on the contrary, sends the major part of its cotton to Japan, England, and other European countries. Its cotton for home consumption goes mainly to the seacoast near Bombay, where the climate, though constantly warm, is at least moist rather than very dry as it is farther north. Egypt is the only important producer which is not also an important manufacturer. There is plenty of labor there and its quality is probably better than that of India, and coal might be imported cheaply by sea from England. The extreme dryness of the climate, however, puts a great handicap upon cotton manufacturing.

The Equatorward Migration of Cotton Manufacturing.—Most of the dots in A507 within 40° of the equator represent a development since 1880. Before that date our South, Japan, China, Brazil, and Mexico bought practically all their cotton cloth from higher latitudes. There has been much discussion as to why the center of the American cotton industry has moved from New England to the Carolinas and Georgia. Most of the discussion has overlooked the fact that this movement is merely an example of a widespread general tendency which is apparent all over the world. The main reasons for it are abundant and cheap supplies of labor in lower latitudes, low costs of living there, local supplies of raw material, large local markets, low taxes or other political help, and the fact that the cotton industry is more nearly

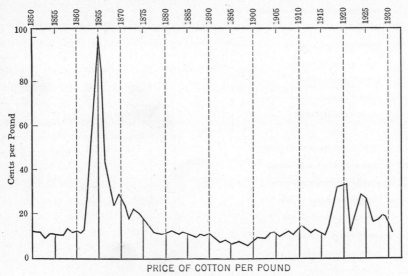

A—Fluctuations in the Price of Cotton since 1850.

automatic than any other type of complex industry. This last reason is commonly neglected, but without it the others would lose much of their force.

After the Civil War, when the price of cotton again fell to a low level (A523), many southerners saw that cotton factories might be very profitable and at the same time help the suffering farmers. With the price of cotton so low, the cost of transporting the raw material to New England and bringing the cloth back again formed an unduly large percentage of the cost of clothing in the Cotton Belt. The population there was growing, the standards of living were rising, and the demand for cloth was constantly increasing. Labor could be hired cheaply not only because the farmers were in distress but also because wages always decline as one goes from more active to less active sections. This is partly because less work is accomplished in the less active areas, as appears from the fact that under similar conditions the number of spindles tended by one person is three or four hundred in Japan and only half as many in Bombay. The low cost of living in warm climates also helps to keep down wages. Because of the warm winters, no cellars, furnaces, or double windows are required and only a little fuel and woolen clothing. Home gardens also supply food during a long season, and expensive products like meat are not in great demand. Then, too, the workers are not so well organized in unions as in the North. For all these reasons the average wages in the South are still much lower than in the North (A524). In the New York cotton factories the men on an average get 75 per cent more per hour than do those of Alabama; for women this difference rises above 80 per cent. In Japan the women's wages are about 6 cents an hour, or a quarter as much as in South Carolina. In India the men spinners get about 3 cents an hour. In our southern mills, however, the hours are longer than farther north. This means not only that the daily wages are relatively not quite so low as the above figures would indicate, but also that overhead costs for the manufacturers are reduced, and the same office force can take care of more business. Many mills in the South and Japan do a great deal of night work in order to save in this way. Then, too, many children work in the southern mills. This increases the income per family and reduces the cost to the factory, for children work about as well as adults and are paid less. In addition to this, it is even more common in the South than in the North for the mills to supply houses for their workers. These houses are often much better than those in which the surrounding farmers live, and are usually supplied with electric light, running water, toilet facilities, and in later times bathrooms, all of which have till recently been rare on farms. Each house usually has its own yard with space for a garden, and a shed for a cow and chickens. The cow can often be pastured free on a tract owned by the company. The rent is comparatively low, so that the employees feel that they are getting a good deal. In India and China the labor supply is so huge and people are so poor that there is no need of building villages to accommodate the factory workers. In Japan a different scheme is employed. Women outnumber men in the textile mills. Most of them are young girls from the farm villages. Their people are not willing to let them come to the city unless they are taken care of. Accordingly, instead of neat little houses like those of our South, the Japanese build great dormitories, some very wretched but others with pretty gardens, and huge stone-paved baths where hundreds of girls are abundantly supplied with hot water when they come from the hot, steamy factories where they perspire profusely. When all these addi-

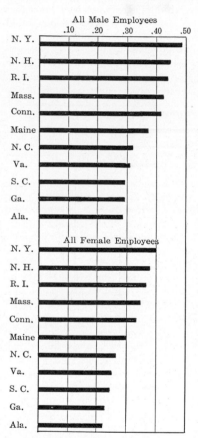

A—Average Earnings per Hour in the Cotton Goods Industry in 1930.

tions are considered there is still much debate as to whether labor in the southern and newer regions really costs more or less than in the old manufacturing regions farther north.   The advantages enjoyed by the mills in the cotton-producing areas in using local cotton and selling the cloth locally are obvious.   They are especially great in regions like our South, China, and India, where the cotton is raised in the midst of a dense population whose aggregate buying power is huge even though the individuals are as poor as in India.   The astonishing thing is not that mills have grown up in the cotton sections, but that the greater efficiency of places like Britain and Japan still enables them to compete in the markets of India and China.

In the textile industry, as in most problems of economic geography, we must take account not only of geographic and economic factors, but also of those that are political.   In Japan the government assisted the factories in starting.   The United States has a high protective tariff on cotton goods.   In our South many mills have been helped by tax reductions.   Often this is combined with an economic factor in the form of cheap sites.   The southern factories are rarely located in large cities.   Even when they are close to cities there is a strong tendency to locate them on land beyond the city limits.   In some cases cities have deliberately changed the city limits in order to put the cotton mills outside and thus permit them to enjoy lower rates of taxation.

The importance of the automatic quality of the cotton industry in determining its geographic location is great.   Unless the thread breaks, a spindle or loom may run all day without being touched by the operator.   Modern looms and spindles stop automatically when the thread breaks.   Because of this it is the custom in many mills to leave the looms in operation during the noon hour.   In very few other kinds of industry is the major part of the work so automatic.   Moreover, when once the textile machinery has been adjusted it needs very little attention for years aside from keeping it well oiled.   Thus the coarser grades of cotton are extremely well adapted to sluggish and inefficient workers like those of Bombay who would make a complete failure in more complicated manufacturing.   This helps to explain why cotton manufacturing has spread into low latitudes and backward countries far more than any other complex industry.   Yet in all industries, as the processes become simplified and automatic, there is a decided tendency to carry on the easier processes, or those in which transportation is difficult, in outlying regions of less efficiency but with large markets.   Thus, in Brazil and other regions, American manufacturers of electric appliances have factories for the simple kinds of fixtures that are merely stamped and punched by machines, and also for breakable glass bulbs, but the more complex motors are generally made in our North.   In the same way, A526 shows that rayon, which involves complex technical processes, is made only in western Europe and in the United States from Tennessee northward.

It must not be supposed that the growth of cotton manufacturing and other industries in lower latitudes and less stimulating climates means that the old homes of manufacturing are going backward.   Malcolm Keir in his book entitled *Manufacturing* sums up the matter very clearly: New England's "fisheries have lost place, her overseas commerce has become negligible, her farms were abandoned in competition with the rich soils of the Middle West, and her lumber cut long ago passed its zenith.   When each of these mortalities occurred New England's doom was announced.   Yet as compared with 1850 the fisheries are twice as valuable, the income from investments in transportation several times as much as the amount garnered from commerce, the farm products valued at three times their former total, and the lumber cut almost three times as great in dollars received.   At present

New England mourns the departure of the shoe manufacturing to St. Louis, machine production to Detroit, and cotton manufacture to Spartanburg. The truth is that once New England enjoyed a lonely position at the pinnacle of industry, whereas now she has plenty of company; first rank has been snatched from her, but her absolute production and income have suffered no casualty" (page 359). With proper changes this applies to Old England also. One evidence of its truth is that some of the largest New England cotton factories have been converted to other purposes where greater technical skill is required. Still stronger evidence is the admiration of travelers when they see the fine roads, neatly painted houses, and well-kept lawns which are preeminently characteristic of New England. The greatest evidence is that according to general opinion New England weathered the depression of 1929–33 better than any other part of the country, while many people claim that England came through the depression less scathed than any other part of Europe.

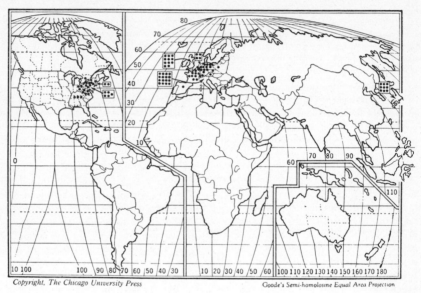

Goode's Semi-homolosine Equal Area Projection

A—World Production of Rayon.

The Woolen Industry.—Many of the main facts about the woolen industry have already been stated in our general discussion of textiles. A comparison of A527 and B527 brings out a curious contrast between wool and cotton. The primitive cotton-spinning industry has practically come to an end. The majority of the dots and crosses in the Asiatic and tropical parts of A527, however, and many of those in the Mediterranean lands, represent wool which is used locally in primitive household industries for the making of clothing, rugs, bags, felts, and even thick tent-cloth. Again, a part of the cotton industry has left the old areas of manufacture and gone to those where the raw material is raised, but the woolen industry shows little of this. The western

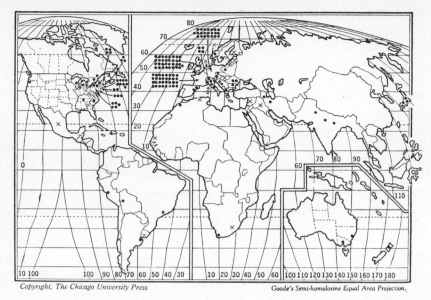

Goode's Semi-homolosine Equal Area Projection.

A—Wool Consumed in Manufacturing. Each dot represents one-half of 1 per cent of world total, omitting China and Russia. The latter should probably have 14 dots.

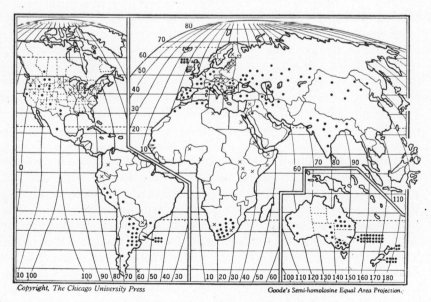

Goode's Semi-homolosine Equal Area Projection.

B—World Production of Wool. Each dot indicates one-half of 1 per cent of world total. Crosses indicate minor production.

United States, Argentina, South Africa, Australia, and New Zealand, with their enormous numbers of sheep, show only a slight development of manufacturing. England, France, the Low Countries, Germany, and the northeastern United States are great centers of the woolen industry even though some of them have few sheep. So far as climate and labor are concerned, all these main wool-raising areas are at least as favorable to manufacturing as is our South, and far more favorable than India and China. Southeastern Australia and New Zealand rank very high in these respects. If their people wanted to carry on woolen manufacturing they certainly could get all manner of governmental help. Both places are well supplied with power from coal or water, as are our western sheep states. But fuel enters into the matter only slightly, for the woolen industry requires only a little power. The high development of woolen manufacturing in New England where there is no coal, in parts of France where there is very little, and in England before coal was used, shows that it plays only a minor rôle. So far as governmental help is concerned, there are few if any industries in favor of which so many laws have been made, but on the whole they have been ineffective just as was England's prolonged and vigorous attempt to prevent woolen manufacturing in the American colonies. On the other hand, the skill required in the woolen industry appears to be an important factor in determining where it shall be carried on. Woolen manufacturing requires more skill than cotton manufacturing. This is evident from the fact that in 1919, when both industries were working under pressure, the average wage earner in Massachusetts received $895 in the cotton industry and $1,045 in the woolen industry. Before the depression of 1929–32, but after the New England cotton industry had suffered its post-war setback, a similar ratio prevailed, $970 per year for cotton workers and $1,220 for woolen workers. Thus wool provides another example of the fact that the greater the skill required in an industry, the more likely that industry is to be located where the conditions of health and activity are best. Another factor in keeping the woolen industry in the northeastern United States and western Europe is the price of wool compared with the cost of transportation. A pound of washed wool may cost two or three times as much as a pound of cotton. The more expensive product can of course stand transportation much better than the less expensive. Still a third factor is the supply of labor. The five regions where much wool is raised abundantly but not manufactured to any great extent (A527 and B527) are all newly settled sections with only a sparse population. Hence the labor supply is not large, new enterprises connected with the development of the country demand much labor, and wages are high. Therefore, although the labor is skillful, there is little to tempt the woolen manufacturer to use it. Finally, the regions where most of the world's wool is raised do not afford a large market. In our western states the population is small and scattered, and there are few centers from which goods can be cheaply shipped to large numbers of people. In Argentina, Australia, South Africa, and New Zealand also the population is small, all four regions having fewer people than a single province of China or India. Of course their buying power is high per person, but their climates are comparatively warm so that they need much less wool than do the people of the northern United States and Europe.

The Silk Industry.—In the silk industry some of the principles which we have just seen are carried still further. Production is mainly limited to Japan and China, with minor areas in north Italy, other Mediterranean lands, and southern Russia (A530). In practically all these places the primitive type of silk manufacturing attained a fairly high development, thus illustrating how the presence of a resource stimulates people to use it. In our day the primitive industry still continues on a small scale in regions like Persia and on a larger scale in China and Japan. On the other hand the silk industry in its complex form has developed mainly in France, Japan, Germany, and above all the United States, with a little in Italy, Switzerland, and England. In Japan, France, and Italy this represents a response to a native product. In France the response has gone so far that large imports are needed, and the mills around Lyon use the most modern methods. The outstanding fact in B530 is that the United States consumes nearly three-fifths of all the world's silk. The single city of Paterson, New Jersey, manufactures close to one-twelfth of the entire world production, while nearly half is utilized within not much more than a hundred miles of that city. In few other lines of manufacturing is there so remarkable a concentration. The reason for the choice of Paterson rather than some neighboring city is pure accident. The city has water power, and someone happened to use it for silk mills rather than some other kind. But the concentration near New York and Philadelphia is by no means accidental. It is the ultimate expression of (1) the energy of the northeastern United States which we discussed in connection with cotton manufacturing, (2) the great natural resources of the country, and the consequent opportunities for acquiring wealth, (3) the newness of the country and consequently its relatively sparse population and ample opportunities, and (4) the fact that New York and to a less extent Philadelphia, by virtue of their location in a highly favorable climate and on good harbors with easy access to the interior, have become the country's main foci of both population and

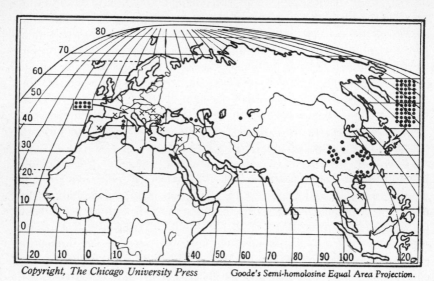

Goode's Semi-homolosine Equal Area Projection.

A—World Production of Silk.

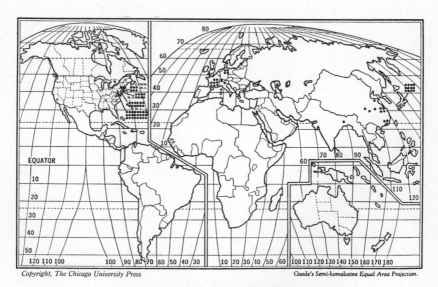

Goode's Semi-homolosine Equal Area Projection.

B—World Map of Silk Manufacture.

wealth. Raw silk is worth about thirty times as much as raw cotton. Therefore the cost of transportation is of little importance in the final cost of the goods. The cost of the power used in silk manufacturing is also of minor importance. Hence the final product is manufactured where people of high skill and great energy, like the old Philadelphia weavers, are available, and close to the main center for the manufacture of dresses and other garments to be bought by women who are able to afford such expensive materials.

Leather and Shoes.—Leather shoes are a necessity to us, but a luxury to fully half the world's people. In the cyclonic regions and in the cool temperate interior, practically everyone wears them, although they are still displaced to a small extent by wooden shoes in parts of Holland and elsewhere. In Mediterranean regions almost everyone owns leather shoes. Nevertheless, in countries like Turkey they are such a luxury that people often walk barefooted, but carry their shoes and put them on for looks when they reach their destination. In the rest of the world, substitutes for leather are used in the more progressive countries, but bare feet become more and more predominant as one goes toward the equator. Even in our own South barefooted Negroes are numerous. In Japan, cloth shoes and wooden sandals are common, and in China they are worn by the more prosperous people, but in both countries the vast majority of people go barefooted while at work in the house or in the fields. This is still more true in India, the East Indies, and the tropical parts of Africa and America. Such a situation is unfortunate from the standpoint of health. Shoes become least common in the very regions where the hookworm and other parasites are most abundant and where the bruises and cuts on people's feet are most likely to form persistent sores. If everyone wore shoes the hookworm disease would be greatly reduced and the efficiency of the vast area within 35° of the equator would be much increased.

This distribution of the use of shoes arises partly from the temperature, for in warm weather bare feet are comfortable; partly from the scarcity of good leather outside the Cool Continental, Cyclonic, Mediterranean, and Desert climates; and partly from the distribution of energy and skill which is so important in all phases of industry. In A414, India appears to have an enormous number of cattle, and so it has—far more than any other country in the world, and almost as many as the United States per capita. But four animals for every ten people may not provide one-tenth as much leather per capita as we get from five animals per ten people. Our animals are twice as heavy as those of India, and of course have larger hides. Half of them are killed when two or three years old, and few live beyond ten years. In India, on the contrary, the cattle are used mainly for plowing and hauling, and to a very slight degree, for milk. They are never killed for meat, however. Hence the number per capita that die each year is probably not a quarter as great as with us. The hides of such old animals are usually poor because full of holes where the animals have been galled by the yoke, wounded in fights, or stung by insects which have produced sores. Moreover, the hides are not well collected or tanned. The poor peasants may skin the animals where they die, but many hides are not collected at all, and others are cut in skinning. Furthermore, the tanning is poorly done, and in some cases the hides are used with only the most meager preparation. This illustrates the way in which the quality as well as the quantity of goods generally improves from equatorial to cyclonic regions. Yet even though its hides are poor and relatively scanty, India has to export a great many of them. Against this, however, must be set the facts that in breeding cattle for tender beef and abundant milk we have also bred thin hides, and that we kill great numbers of animals before their hides have attained their full strength. Nevertheless, the hides of our own cattle and the great number that we import provide us with stout shoes, whereas most of India goes barefooted and suffers from ankylostomiasis (hookworm disease) even though cattle are abundant.

Tanning and Shoemaking in the United States.—The distribution of the tanning industry in the United States (A533) shows little relation to that of either cattle (A414) or slaughtering (A542). The abundant hides from the slaughter houses of Chicago, St. Louis, Kansas City, Iowa, Minnesota, and Nebraska go in large numbers to eastern cities, where they join imported hides and are tanned in the vicinity of Wilmington, Philadelphia, New York, and Boston. Something evidently draws the raw hides eastward. At first thought one might suppose that shoe manufacturing is the reason, but B533 does not bear this out. It does indeed show a tremendous concentration of shoe manufacturing in eastern Massachusetts in places like Lynn for women's shoes and Brockton for men's shoes, and a lesser concentration in New York City, together with scattered production in Maine, New Hampshire, New York State, and eastern Pennsylvania. The maps show that this eastern region makes about 60 per cent of the country's shoes, but tans about 65 per cent of the leather. A second shoe manufacturing district, centering in Chicago and Milwaukee, makes nearly 15 per cent of the shoes, and tans nearly the same proportion of leather. A third area centering in St. Louis makes another 15 per cent of the shoes, but tans only 1 or 2 per cent of the leather. Yet A542 indicates that St. Louis does about 7 per cent of the country's slaughtering, while

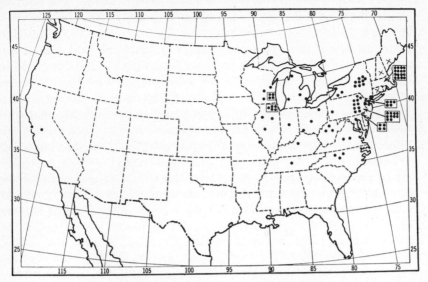

A—The Tanning Industry in the United States.

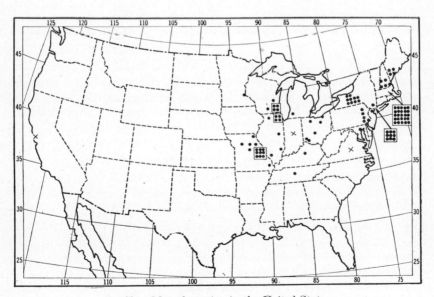

B—Shoe Manufacturing in the United States.

Kansas City and neighboring regions that are nearer to St. Louis than to any other shoe center carry on another 20 per cent of the slaughtering. Why then does St. Louis draw on regions far to the east for its leather? The maps suggest that hides which are carried through St. Louis to the states near the Atlantic Coast must be brought back again as dressed leather. Apparently we have here a case analogous to that of cotton before the revival of the cotton industry in the South. Raw hides and dressed leather differ so little in weight that it does not make much difference which one is shipped. Therefore we should normally expect the tanning industry to show a fairly close relation to the shoe industry. St. Louis, however, still allows the advantages of an earlier start farther east to prevent her from tanning even the hides of her own slaughter houses. This vividly illustrates the conservatism of industry. When a certain type of factory and a certain way of supplying it with raw materials are once established, they tend to persist even though not economical.

EXERCISES

1. In the order of their relative importance make a list of the factors which influence the location of the textile industries. Explain the reasons for this order. In what way do the factors differ in their effect upon the manufacture of cotton, wool, and silk?

2. In parallel columns tabulate the advantages and disadvantages of the South and of New England for cotton manufacturing. Will all these conditions probably be permanent? Explain.

3. Discuss the statement that the type of clothing worn by man often reflects his physical environment. Do you think there has been much change in the weight and quality of the clothing worn in the eastern United States since colonial times? Why? What has this to do with economic geography?

4. Compare the distribution of the industries based on cotton (A507), rayon (A526), wool (A527), and silk (A530). What countries or states stand high in all of these? What is your explanation of this? What countries or states stand high in only one? Explain.

5. A535 illustrates the number of people engaged in all textile industries in Europe, whereas A519, B520, A521, and B521 are based on the amount of material consumed in the textile industries. Which is the better method of representing the intensity of manufacturing? Why does neither method give a result so good as would the use of value added by manufacturing? What do you suppose to be the reason why this last method is not used? How would A535 probably differ if it were used?

6. Study the maps in this chapter to see how much manufacturing there is in the western half of the United States. Explain the reasons for what you observe.

7. The maps in this chapter fall naturally into four groups. What are they? Which group seems to you to afford the most impressive illustration of the

diverse influence of geographic environment upon the distribution of (a) the production of a given product, (b) the manufacture of that product, and (c) the use of the manufactured article? Explain.

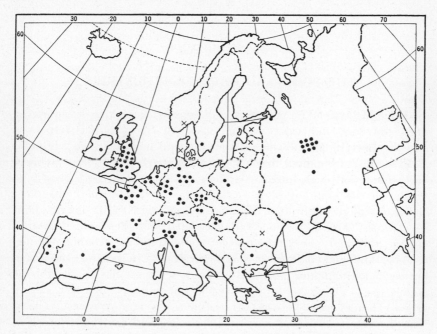

A—Workers in Textile Industries in Europe. Each dot indicates 1 per cent of European total.

8. On the basis of the U. S. Census make a map of the distribution of some special form of clothing industry. Use any method you like. Discuss the geographic principles illustrated by your map. Compare your results with those in this book.

CHAPTER XXV

THE FOOD AND SHELTER INDUSTRIES

Flour Milling.—The preparation of cereals for cooking is one of the most universal industrial occupations. All over southeastern Asia and the East Indies millions of women spend hours each day lifting a small log and dropping it into a big bowl of rough rice in order to break and loosen the tough husks. Millions of others from northern China to Morocco are grinding wheat or barley by hand with small millstones. In Latin America still other millions are grinding corn in similar primitive ways. And in the more advanced parts of the world thousands of large mills and tens of thousands of smaller ones are grinding, bolting, grading, and sacking flour of many varieties. In general, the distribution of flour milling and kindred processes is similar to that of the population. The higher forms of this simple industry, however, show a growing tendency to be concentrated in a few large centers. This is true in Europe, where Budapest, Marseille, and Le Havre are conspicuous milling centers. It is even more pronounced in the United States.

B538 includes all kinds of flour mills, no matter whether they grind wheat, corn, or other grains, but wheat is overwhelmingly predominant. A comparison of B538 with A538 shows that each main wheat-growing section has its local centers of flour milling, and one or more outlying centers located nearer the main centers of population. Thus much of the spring wheat of the Dakotas and Minnesota is milled in Minneapolis. The winter wheat section of Kansas and the neighboring states grinds more grain at Kansas City than anywhere else, although Wichita and Omaha are also important, and many smaller places in Kansas and Missouri grind much wheat. Outside the main wheat regions there is a good deal of local milling from Illinois and southern Wisconsin to Pennsylvania and also in the northern tier of southern states. In these sections, and especially in the South, small local mills and the grinding of corn or of other feed for cattle assume an increasing importance.

Buffalo, far to the east of the main wheat areas, rivals Minneapolis as a flour-milling center. This eastern concentration of flour milling is a response to the very easy transportation which brings part of the huge production of the spring wheat area over the Great Lakes from Duluth. So important is the lake traffic that special steamers have been designed for the grain trade alone, while the elevators and the arrangements for loading and unloading at Duluth and Buffalo are marvelous. A steamer holding 300,000 bushels can be loaded in 3 hours by simply letting the grain run out of the elevators; it can be unloaded in 6 hours. At Buffalo the grain must be removed from the big grain boats. It may then be shipped to New York by rail, or by the New York State Barge Canal, for export to Europe, or it may be ground into flour for distribution in the eastern states. Here, as at Minneapolis and elsewhere, huge mills which turn out flour by thousands of barrels per day are so arranged that the grain is deposited high in their upper stories and comes out at the bottom as sacks of bran and flour ready for shipment. In few other industries does machinery do so much and man so little.

In the western United States the same features are repeated on a small scale. No one large city, to be sure, stands out conspicuously as a milling center in the wheat section of eastern Washington and Oregon, but the ports of Seattle and Portland correspond closely to Buffalo and Toledo.

In Europe, in spite of places like Budapest, a large part of the flour is still ground in small local mills. Tropical and oriental countries import a little flour for the use of foreigners and the rich, but rely mainly on small water mills, or on their own primitive industry in the homes.

The Baking Industry.—After the wheat has become flour a great deal is baked in homes, but a growing percentage goes to public bakeries— enough to give the United States nearly a billion dollars' worth of bread in addition to cake and crackers (A539). In most of our cities, practically no families bake bread regularly at home. Even in the villages and on the farms of the North and West, baker's bread is fast becoming the rule. Nevertheless, the use of baker's bread is still preeminently a city custom. Yet the great amounts baked in New York, Chicago, Philadelphia, Pittsburgh, Detroit, and other cities are used partly to supply surrounding rural areas whose radius amounts to a hundred miles or more in some cases. Not all the large cities are shown separately in A539, partly to avoid crowding, partly because they do not bake so much bread as might be expected, and partly because in some cases the census does not give the necessary data for fear of disclosing the operations of individual companies. This applies to all the maps of this kind in this book. The bakery map, with its dots or crosses in all states except Nevada, Wyoming, and New Mexico, shows how widely such a universal community industry as baking is distributed.

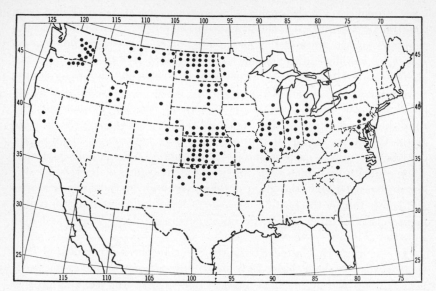

A—Annual Production of Wheat in the United States.. Dots equal one-half of 1 per cent.

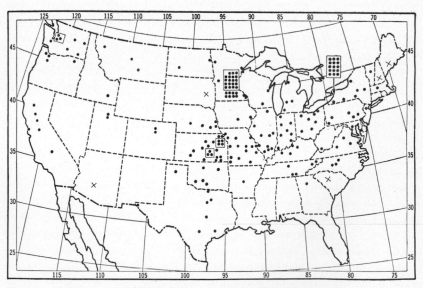

B—Flour Milling in the United States.. Each dot indicates one-half of 1 per cent of the value of the flour and other grain-mill products.

These three states do not get even a cross because their population is so small that they do not make even one-tenth of 1 per cent of the country's bread and cake. The use of baker's bread has long been far more common in Europe than in the United States. In many homes as well as hotels there one cannot get an early breakfast because the rolls from the baker have not yet arrived. Americans who are used to seeing bread wrapped in oiled paper are sometimes shocked to see loaves of enormous length laid down unwrapped on doorsteps. Reliance on public bakeries is common in Europe partly because people there live in villages and have never developed the individualistic habits which are

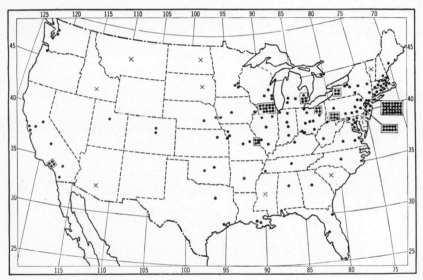

A—The Baking Industry in the United States. Each dot indicates one-half of 1 per cent of the annual value of all bakery products.

so strongly characteristic of our independent and isolated farmers. In oriental and tropical countries the more prosperous townspeople buy a great deal of bread from bakeries, either because fuel is scarce or because the heat makes fires unpleasant.

A540 indicates that in the United States—and the same is true in the world as a whole—the prosperous people who live in towns use the most baker's bread per capita. A540 is almost like a whole series of other maps showing such conditions as climatic energy, health, wages, and the percentages of the population engaged in complex manufacturing, living in cities, or getting a higher education. It confirms our earlier conclusion that climate sets a certain general pattern to which all sorts of other conditions conform more or less closely although modified materially in detail.   For example, in A540 the effect of great cities is obvious in the fact that Louisiana and Colorado, by reason of New Orleans and Denver, rise well above their neighbors.   Connecticut and Rhode Island, on the other hand, fall below their neighbors, probably because they are located so close to New York and Boston that they are partly supplied with bread and cake from those cities.   Again, climate alone would never cause the Dakotas, Wyoming, and Montana to use less than a third as much baker's bread as do the states from southern New England to Chicago, but climate, relief, and continental location

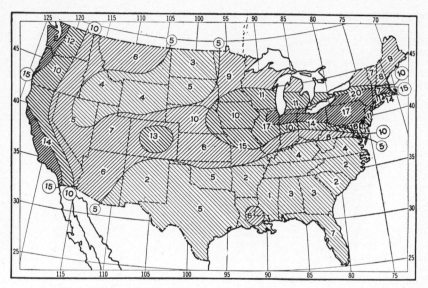

A—Annual Value of Bakery Products per Capita in the United States.

combine to give these northwestern states a sparse population, largely agricultural, and without many cities.   Note that, in A540, as in many other maps, the migration of northerners has raised the level of Florida, while migration from Mexico has lowered that of New Mexico.

The Canning of Fruits and Vegetables.—The canning industry has evolved in much the same way as the baking industry.   Formerly anyone who wanted either fruit or vegetables aside from potatoes, at all seasons, had to can them at home.   Now the canning of both fruits and vegetables has become a large business.   War has been one of its chief stimulants.   More than a century ago Napoleon offered a reward of 12,000 francs for an improved method of preserving food for his armies.   The American Civil War greatly stimulated the industry by proving that canned goods are both safe and cheap. Canning, unlike baking, is a simple rather than a community industry, and shows the extreme localization which is characteristic of simple industries (A541). Markets, labor supply, fuel, and almost all other factors fade into insignificance as reasons for the geographical location of this industry. The thing that counts overwhelmingly is an abundance of good fruit and vegetables. This causes a small area in California to put up nearly one-third of the country's canned goods, while a similar area near the Atlantic Coast from Baltimore to New York puts up another quarter. Most of the remaining canning factories are located in three

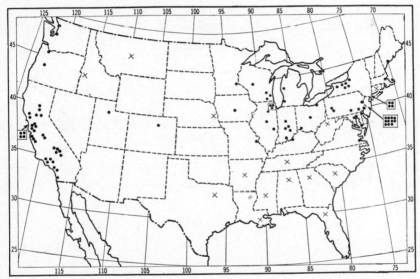

A—The Canning and Preserving of Fruits and Vegetables in the United States.

types of areas. One comprises especially fertile sections of the states from New England to Illinois, another includes the irrigated oases of the Rocky Mountain and Great Basin regions, and a third is the Willamette-Puget Sound Valley of the Northwest. In all these regions, as well as in the two main regions, the problem of a highly seasonal supply of labor has to be met. This favors the establishment of canning factories near cities where women and children are available in summer to work both in truck gardens and canning factories.

Food Industries Based on Animal Products.—The most important industry based on animal products is slaughtering and meat packing. The dominance of Chicago, with its famous stock yards and packing plants and its superb location for transportation, is conspicuous in

A542.   Kansas City, Omaha, South St. Paul, and St. Louis also stand
out because they too are easily accessible centers of transportation.
A542 shows that numerous smaller packing centers have their share of
the business.   Thus Iowa and the adjacent states contain well over
half the dots in A542.   The concentration in the regions surrounding
Iowa is due largely to corn and its value as animal feed.   How important this is may be judged from A543, which shows the value of the
cattle, calves, hogs, sheep, and lambs sold from the farms, or killed for
home use on the farms each year.   Iowa and the states that touch it
furnish 56 per cent of this value, which is only slightly more than their

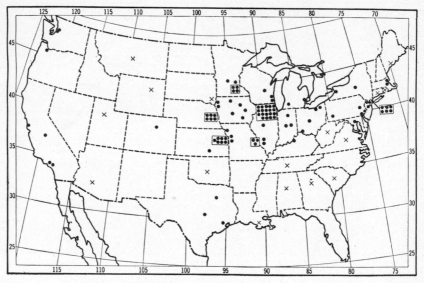

A—Slaughtering and Meat Packing in the United States.

percentage of the slaughtering and meat packing.   The minor concentration of slaughtering and meat packing in New York, which rivals
Kansas City and Omaha, is in part a relic of earlier days before meat
could be shipped from the West, but it is also a response to the eastern
supply of beef cattle.   The Pacific States carry on the occupations of
slaughtering and meat packing almost in proportion to their populations.
The South, on the other hand, because of its warmer climate, smaller
and more expensive supply of corn, and smaller type of animals, slaugh-
ters and packs less than its share of meat either on the basis of population or of production of animals.

   The Milk Products Industries.—The distribution of butter, cheese
and condensed or evaporated milk factories (A544) affords an interesting

contrast to that of animals sold from the farms (A543).   In each of
the northern tier of states from Vermont to North Dakota the map
of milk-using factories shows more dots than the animal map.   In New
York and Wisconsin the milk products map gets five times as many dots
as the other.   On the other hand, in the Corn Belt every state west of
Ohio has a smaller percentage of milk products than of live animals or
slaughtering.   Thus the industries as well as the farms of the cool dairy
states differ decidedly from those of the warmer, corn-raising, meat-
producing states.   Similar conditions are evident on the Pacific Coast,
where each state shows a higher percentage of the milk industries than

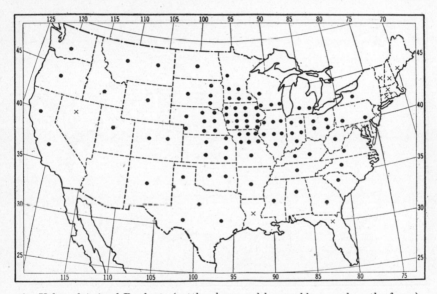

A—Value of Animal Products (cattle, sheep and hogs sold or used on the farm.)

of the meat industries.   Evidently the manufacturing side of dairying
is most highly developed where cool summers not only favor good cattle
feed, but also induce the physiological conditions which cause cows to
give much milk and a large percentage of butter fat.   Minnesota and
Iowa make the most butter; Wisconsin makes the most cheese and condensed milk as well as an enormous quantity of butter.   These products,
unlike fresh milk, can be shipped any distance and thus reach all densely
settled parts of the country.   The North Sea region and Switzerland in
their milk industries closely repeat the conditions of our cooler states.

The fact that a state like Wisconsin, with many cattle, sends so few
to the slaughter houses, as indicated in A543, may seem surprising, but
it is natural.   The dairymen there want to send as much milk as pos-

sible to the factories, as well as to Chicago. Therefore they raise few
hogs and sheep, and sell the male calves while they are still young.
The northeastern seacoast, on the other hand, although it has a good
many dairy cattle, makes very little butter and cheese because its dense
population uses most of the milk in the fresh form. The South makes
little because the warm climate not only reduces the amount of butter
and fat per cow and cuts down the total number of cattle, but also makes
it difficult to transport and keep the milk without souring. In contrast
with the map of slaughtering A542, the map of the industries that manufacture milk products, such as butter, cheese and condensed milk, is

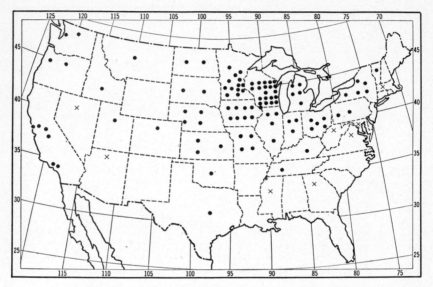

A—The Manufacture of Milk Products in the United States.

conspicuous for the absence of dots near large cities, or where population is dense. In such places, practically all the fresh milk is needed for
families. Moreover, the manufactured milk products do not lend themselves to production in large units. The factories are usually small and
well scattered, so that they may be within reach of all the farmers.

The Fish-canning Industries.—In many respects these are the opposite of the milk industries. They are located on the seacoast, and to a
slight extent on the coasts of the Great Lakes (A545). By reason of
the salmon in the north, the sardines south of San Francisco and the
tuna fish from Santa Barbara southward, the Pacific Coast cans more
than half the country's fish. Where harbors are scarce the simple
industry of fish canning is obliged to locate itself at the main ports, as

is evident at Los Angeles (San Pedro) and San Diego. Where good harbors are numerous, as along the drowned coasts of Maine and Washington, the canneries are more scattered.

Outside the United States the canning of fish is actively carried on in the North Sea regions, especially England and Norway, where herring are packed in large quantities, in Spain where the true sardine and the tuna are the main products, and in Japan. Wherever it is found, fish canning is a highly seasonal and rather disagreeable occupation. It is also very irregular from year to year. The salmon in the Maritime Provinces of Canada have a regular cycle of a little less than ten years.

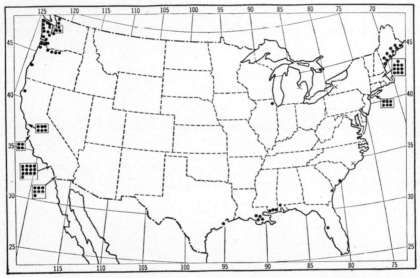

A—The Canning and Preservation of Fish in the United States.

Their number goes up and down enormously. On the Pacific Coast a similar cycle is said to have a length of four years. Other fish vary similarly, but the nature of these cycles is not yet well understood, and their dates cannot be accurately predicted.

Some Luxury Food Industries.—A-B546 and A547 are maps of three types of food products which are widely used in the United States, less widely used in other advanced countries, and used by only a very small number of the wealthier people among three-quarters of the world's population. They differ greatly in the degree to which their manufacture is concentrated. The making of chocolate and cocoa (A546) affords an example of a complex and very highly localized industry. Except for a little activity near Chicago, practically the whole industry is located near Boston, New York, Philadelphia, and San Francisco. Most of the ships that bring cacao and sugar come to these seaports. The country's main sugar refineries, aside from those near New Orleans, are located near them. So is the main market, no matter whether we consider the number of people or their wealth and buying power.

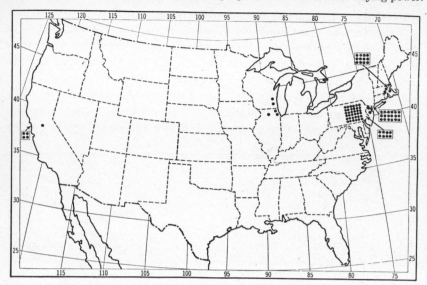

A—The Manufacture of Chocolate and Cocoa in the United States.

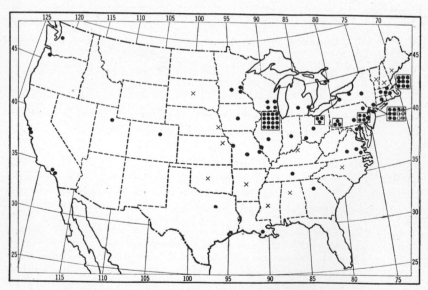

B—The Manufacture of Confectionery in the United States.

Such a business profits greatly by being run in large units. The excellent transportation of the big cities and of suburban cities like Lancaster near Philadelphia makes it easy to get raw materials, labor, and fuel, and to get in touch with buyers over a wide area. Luxury food products of this kind are like the progressals in being manufactured almost entirely in regions of intensive manufacturing. The famous chocolates of Switzerland and Holland illustrate this point.

The cities on the North Atlantic Coast that make chocolate also make more than their share of candy (B546). But candy-making is still to some extent a community industry. So Pittsburgh, Cleveland, Chicago, and many other cities become centers of manufacture.

Ice cream (A547) is still more decidedly the product of a community industry. Therefore its distribution conforms more closely to that of population than does that of any other product that we have yet studied. A map of the use of ice cream per capita is almost a duplicate of A540 showing the use of bakery products. The

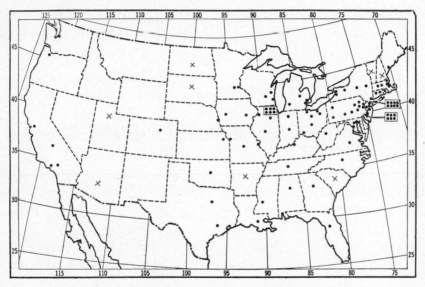

A—The Manufacture of Ice Cream in the United States.

chief peculiar feature of the manufacture of ice cream is the very large amount made in Pennsylvania and in neighboring cities such as Springfield, Syracuse, Utica, Columbus, and Washington that do not get the cooling influence of the ocean in summer. The whole area bounded by these cities consumes between three and four gallons of ice cream per capita each year, and the cities consume still more. This means the astonishing figure of $40 or more per family of five persons for this one luxury. This is a third as much as is spent for bread.

The Shelter Industries. *Forest Products.*—Wood, like many other products, furnishes the material for a simple industry, a community industry, and one main complex industry, as well as several minor ones such as the making of matches and lasts. The simple industry is that which is carried on in sawmills. It begins with dragging the logs out of the water in which they are usually floating, and skidding them onto rollers which carry them to circular saws.   There slabs are sliced off to

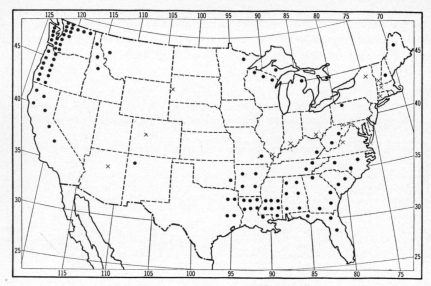

A—Lumber Sawed in the United States.

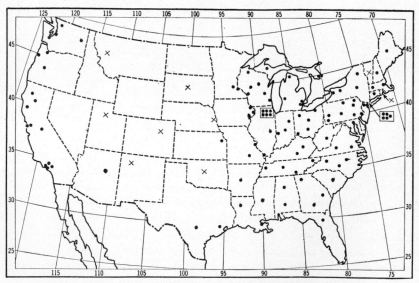

B—The Manufacture of Planing Mill Products in the United States.

get rid of the bark, and the logs are sawed into rough beams and boards, or sometimes into shingles, lathes, staves, mine props, ties, or other forms.

The distribution of this industry (A548) is practically identical with that of the cutting of lumber in the forests. A large share of the mills get their power by burning the waste wood cut from the logs, but in recent years electric power has increased in importance. Some sawmills have steam-heated drying kilns, but others let the lumber dry in the open air. The size of the mills varies geographically. Large mills with modern equipment are most common on the Pacific Coast. The great size of the logs there requires mechanical handling. The fact that large tracts are owned by single interests also favors large mills. In that region three great companies own 11 per cent of all privately owned tim-

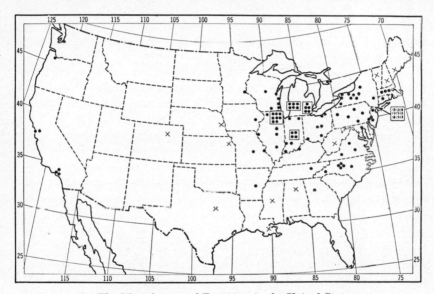

A—The Manufacture of Furniture in the United States.

ber in the United States. Accordingly, about a third of the mills on the Pacific Coast are really large. In the South, where neither the trees nor the lumber tracts are so huge, about a quarter of the mills are large. In the Appalachian and Great Lakes regions the preponderance of small holdings reduces the large mills to about a tenth. In New England the only really large tracts under a single ownership are held by a few paper companies which control about half the pulp wood of New England. Accordingly, very few sawmills there are really large, and small mills that are moved every year or two are common.

The community industry based on lumber is carried on in planing-mills and by contractors and carpenters. Planing-mills are often attached to sawmills, but they are also needed in every community of any appreciable size.   The census, to be sure, reports only 4,500 planing-mills against nearly 14,000 sawmills, but this does not include the thousands of planing-mills which are attached to sawmills, nor the still larger number of carpenters' shops which are in reality small planing-mills.   The work of such mills and shops is to take the rough lumber as it comes from the sawmills, and plane, bevel, saw, and chisel it to the exact shape and size desired by the contractors who are engaged in building operations.   Naturally the map of planing-mills (B548) is very different from that of sawmills.   Cities like New York, Detroit, Chicago, and Los Angeles become conspicuous in it because many buildings are being erected there.   States like Massachusetts, Pennsylvania, Ohio, Indiana, and Iowa, although not important as lumber producers, need many planing-mills to build their comfortable houses, offices, and factories.   On the other hand, states like Mississippi, Louisiana, Arkansas, and Orgeon drop to relatively minor importance. They have enough planing-mills to take care of their local work, and even to ship out some planed lumber, but the size of their populations and the large proportion of their interests centered in agriculture do not demand so much lumber as do the more populous industrial states.

A house or office is not complete until it is furnished.   Therefore the complex industry of furniture making is needed to complete the contribution of wood to the buildings that shelter us.   Furniture is so bulky that it cannot easily be transported.   It is much cheaper to carry the wood to some place near the market, where the furniture is to be sold, and there make it into chairs, tables, desks, bedsteads, and bookcases. Nevertheless it is also convenient to make furniture close to the forests where the wood is cut.   A549 displays the result of these two conflicting tendencies.   The three Pacific States have about 6 per cent of the country's population.   A549 shows that they make about 7 per cent of the furniture.   Thus in this respect, as in many others, they just about take care of themselves, with a little left over to sell to the drier states behind them.   New England and Ohio likewise take care of their own needs for furniture.   So do the three Middle Atlantic States when taken together, although the state and city of New York do more than their share.   This is in strong contrast to products like silk and chocolate, which are highly concentrated in a few localities because their weight and bulk are insignificant in proportion to the value.   The furniture industry affords a very clear example of the fact that the distribution of the industries which make heavy or bulky products is greatly influenced by transportation.   New York City and Philadelphia are good places for the furniture industry because lumber reaches them by water, while the finished furniture finds a market close by among a vast number of people who are very active in building and furnishing new structures. Skill, however, is as important as transportation, as appears from the fact that the average wage earner of Massachusetts earns about $1,400 in the furniture factories in contrast to only $970 in the cotton industry. Certain towns where numerous skilled men work in large furniture factories with good machinery are able to maintain their business in competition with factories nearer the markets by transporting their products in the "knock-down" condition. Thus the products of Grand Rapids, Michigan; Sheboygan, Wisconsin; Gardner, Massachusetts; and several towns in Indiana, Tennessee, and North Carolina, have

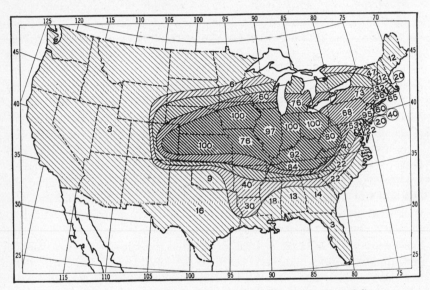

A—Percentage of Hard Wood in the Lumber Cut of the United States.

been able to hold and expand their markets at the expense of the older local industry far away. A gigantic chair at the railroad station proclaims that Gardner boasts of being "Chair Town," just as its neighbor, Winchendon, is "Toy Town" because it excels in a minor branch of the wood industry.

The quality of the wood joins with transportation and human skill in determining where the furniture industry is located. A549 displays a concentration in North Carolina, and in the East North Central States where Chicago, Detroit, and Grand Rapids are conspicuous. Ease of transportation of course has much to do with the dominance of Chicago and Detroit, but the general concentration of furniture making in all these states is due to the character of their forests. Most furniture is made of hard wood. Oak, curly maple, chestnut, and walnut are not only more durable but much more beautiful than pine or spruce, because of their irregular grain and their capacity for taking a high polish. A551 shows that in the part of the East North Central States where the furniture industry is best developed, more than 80 per cent of the timber is hard wood. In the southern Appalachians a similar condition prevails. Thus the furniture factories in the Carolinas and Virginia as well as in Indiana, Illinois, Michigan, and Wisconsin were originally located close to their raw materials, as well as in thickly populated regions where there is a large market for the product.

The Stone and Earth Industries.—Although in some regions most of the houses are built without stone, brick, cement, or glass, the vast majority of mankind uses at least two of these in every building. Millions of tropical huts are indeed made wholly of untrimmed sticks and palm leaves; the Sudanis live in huts of grass; many Negro cabins are made entirely of boards; a temporary Eskimo igloo consists of snow and ice; millions of Asiatic nomads spend their lives in tents of wool, goat's hair, or camel's hair supported on a few sticks; and even the log cabins in which dwell many Siberians, northern Russians, and frontier Canadians may contain no stony or earthy products except a few panes of glass. But a good house in almost any latitude usually has a cellar or basement with a cement floor and walls of brick or stone; it also has chimneys of brick or stone, and windows made of glass. In cities the walls also are made of brick, stone, or stucco, which is closely allied to cement. In most parts of the world, as we have seen, even the rural houses are made of stone or brick with tiled roofs in the more advanced and moister regions like much of Europe, and of dry mud with either thatched roofs or flat roofs made also of dry mud in the less advanced and drier regions like Egypt, India, and China. In the remote Hadhramaut Valley of southern Arabia and in the similarly dry depressions of Turfan and Seistan, buildings of astonishing height are constructed of pure adobe. In Hadhramaut a tower of this sort is 175 feet high.

In the world as a whole the industries that deal with brick, stone, cement, and glass are of first-rate importance. In the United States the products of these four kinds are worth well over a billion dollars per year, or more than all the flour and as much as all the bread, cake, and crackers made in bakeries.

Cement Mills.—Few industries have grown faster than that of cement. The chief uses of cement are for city and farm buildings and roads. The latter use is growing faster than the other because of the demand for good automobile roads. Portland cement, the kind now mainly used, consists of lime, silica, and alumina, which are found respectively in limestone, quartz, and shales or clays. These raw materials are common in most parts of the United States, although generally mixed with impurities. So far as raw materials are concerned, cement plants might be located in practically all states. The demand for cement is also universal wherever civilization is at all high, but naturally it is strongest where manufacturing is most active, wealth greatest, and the construction of new buildings and roads most rapid. This means that in the United States the demand follows the general lines of our maps of wages, consumption of baker's bread, health, and climatic energy. But cement is cheap and heavy, so that transportation by rail for 300 miles doubles its cost. Therefore it cannot be used in large quantities far from the mills, unless it travels by water. Moreover, the making of cement requires very large, heavy machinery, and hence needs large capital and also a large market for each mill. Moreover, each ton of cement needs half a ton of coal in finely powdered form, or a corresponding amount of natural gas or oil. The powdered cement has to be subjected to heat even greater than that used in making steel.

Because of all this the United States has only about 150 cement plants, which are grouped around the great cities in fairly close proportion to their population. The greatest single producing area, however, is the Lehigh Valley in eastern Pennsylvania and northern New Jersey. There the following conditions combine to give great advantages: unusually good limestone and cement rock in the same pits; cheap bituminous coal, the price of which is kept down by competition with the powdery refuse of the anthracite mines; good railroad facilities; and proximity to New York, Philadelphia, and Baltimore. The limestone and coal of Birmingham make Alabama the largest southern producer of cement. Abundant oil, great wealth which creates a demand for cement roads, and dryness which gives concrete a distinct advantage over wood for houses, cause California to produce more than twice as much cement as would be expected on the basis of population.

From the standpoint of competition, cement is peculiar. All the manufacturers have agreed to produce cement of only one quality, making it according to a strict formula. Thus competition does not depend upon quality, but upon price. The cost of production and hence the price that is worth taking depend mainly on geographical conditions, the chief of which are the location and quality of stone, the location of fuel and markets, and transportation facilities.

Clay-using Industries.—Clay is used as a raw material in two main industries, the making of pottery and of bricks. The pottery is more interesting and widely known than the bricks, but the bricks are four times as valuable. The leading pottery states are New Jersey, with Trenton as its chief representative, and Ohio, with East Liverpool as its chief place of manufacture. This industry, like others which require much fuel, shows two concentrations. One is in New Jersey where the population is most dense and the import of raw materials or export of finished products is easy. Another and greater concentration is in Ohio near coal fields where fuel costs scarcely half as much as in New Jersey. Cincinnati is famous for its Rockwood pottery, which is one of the few artistic products in which America has attained a degree of beauty rivaling the best works of Europe. Trenton also makes china which is entitled to high praise for its great beauty. England, France, and other European countries have long been famous for such products as Wedgwood china and French porcelain, but the Chinese and Japanese are in many respects the world's most famous potters.

Bricks and tile are the forms in which clay is used in providing shelter (A554). In the United States, to be sure, the main kind of tiling is for drainage, and is made chiefly in Ohio. In Europe, Asia, and Latin America, however, vast quantities of

tiles are used for roofing purposes. Bricks are like cement in three main ways:
(1) their raw material is very widely distributed, so that the industry is possible
almost everywhere; (2) they require a great deal of fuel, since they have to be fired
from six days to two weeks; (3) they are so heavy and bulky that they cannot stand
much transportation; (4) the chief demand for them is in regions where wood is
scarce, or where its use in buildings brings great danger of fire. Sun-dried bricks, or
adobe, as we have seen, give rise to an important though simple industry in all dry
regions; burned bricks give rise to a more complicated but still simple industry
where cities are large and abundant, and also where coal is abundant but lumber
expensive. The use of wood for houses in cities has brought disaster again and again.
The fact that London was a city of wood in 1666 permitted a great fire to destroy
much of it. It was reconstructed of brick. Chicago had large tracts of wooden

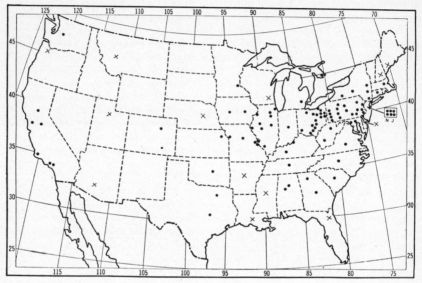

A—Annual Value of Bricks and other Clay Products in the United States.

houses until its disastrous fire of 1876; now Cook County, which is almost identical
with Chicago, makes more brick than any other county in the United States. The
region around New York is a second great brick-making area. Barge loads of
bricks come to the city down the Hudson, from the flats of northern New Jersey, and
even from Connecticut. Philadelphia, Pittsburgh, Cleveland, and Cincinnati are
cities of brick. Pennsylvania and Ohio, with their abundant coal, large supplies of
natural gas, and relative scarcity of lumber, make more than a third of the country's
bricks. Philadelphia still boasts of preserving the first brick house built in America,
but the bricks were imported from Holland. One reason why Philadelphia is the
"City of Homes" is probably the cheapness of bricks. This has permitted the construction of mile after mile of two-story brick houses like those which dominate most
of the industrial districts of England. In Pennsylvania and Ohio even the villages
and farm houses are often built of brick. A similar condition prevails in California
and the dry Southwest, and in Belgium, Holland, and parts of Germany, where fuel
is abundant. In Pennsylvania brick roads were formerly common.

In one respect brick-making is quite different from the manufacture of cement. It requires only very simple machinery, and hence can be carried on profitably in small units. Accordingly the average brick plant in the United States employs about 50 wage earners, while the average cement plant employs 225. The small investment in machinery and buildings makes it feasible to run many of the brick plants only in summer when the clay can easily be dug and less fuel is needed. The cement plants have to run more steadily in order to earn the interest on their large investment.

Building Stone Industries.—Stone and brick supply almost the same needs. Stone, however, is generally more expensive than brick, except for rough construction like cellar walls. But stone is also more durable and beautiful. Accordingly it is used abundantly where brick is costly for lack of clay or fuel, and where great wealth

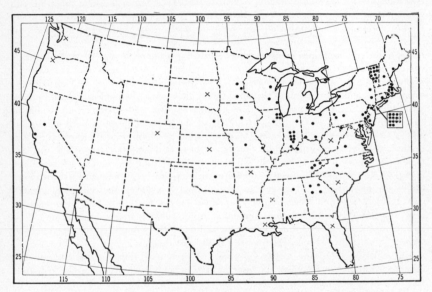

A—Production of Marble, Granite, Slate, and other Stone Products in the United States.

permits stone to be used in spite of its cost. A comparison of A554 and A555 brings out this contrast. New England, having no coal and being a rocky place where the icesheet scraped away most of the clay as well as the other soil, produces only 2 per cent of the country's bricks. On the other hand its produces close to one-fifth of the marble, granite, slate, and other building stones. Michigan, Wisconsin, and Minnesota, although extremely active states with 18 per cent of the country's population, are so much like New England that they make only about 2 per cent of the bricks, but quarry and dress 8 per cent of all the stone. In Georgia and Indiana a different situation appears. Both states make a fair amount of brick, but have so much good stone that they rank among the large producers. Indiana, in fact, comes next to New York and Vermont. It has a kind of limestone so soft that it can easily be sawed, although later it hardens on exposure to the air. At the quarries this limestone is cut into blocks exactly the size and shape needed in the building of which they are to form a part. The blocks are numbered according to a plan so that they can be fitted together easily and quickly hundreds of miles away.

Glass-Making.—The history of glass-making illustrates the same principles as the textile industry. The oldest known glass comes from ancient Thebes in upper Egypt. Carvings on ancient monuments there show glass-makers at work in essentially the modern fashion in 3500 B.C. At the time of Christ, glass was a well known but costly commodity in the eastern Mediterranean lands. When Augustus Caesar conquered Egypt, a good deal of glass was included in the tribute which he carried back to Rome. This excited so much interest that the Egyptian industry was stimulated by orders from Rome, and the Romans soon brought Egyptian glass-makers to their own city. The Romans learned so well that in many ways they surpassed Egypt. They, in turn, carried the art to the conquered provinces that later became France and Bohemia. During the Dark Ages, however, glass-making stagnated in central Europe, but continued at a fairly high level in Syria and the Byzantine Empire. Stimulated by contact with these countries the Venetians became the master glass-makers of the Middle Ages. Venice did its best to keep its glass-makers at home, making them almost prisoners on the island of Murano where the industry was segregated for fear of fire. Nevertheless, like the weavers, many glass-makers wandered north. Thus, Bohemia learned so well that in the seventeenth century it became the most noted glass center, while France and Belgium stood high. England learned the glass-making art still later, largely from Italian or French immigrants. In its turn, it added to the old art, introducing lead into the glass and thus making "cut" glass a possibility. Holland was another late comer in the art of glass-making, while Sweden, which now stands close to the top as a maker of beautiful glass, learned much of its skill from Bohemians. Thus glass-making, like the textile industry and many others, gradually moved northwestward, improving as it went. In every age the detailed location of the centers of greatest advancement within a given country depended on raw materials, fuel, or transportation, but their general location depended upon the advancing civilization of the people, and the degree to which ideas and skilled workers migrated from regions that already stood high to those which were rapidly advancing.

In America the same history is seen. Dutch and Polish glass-workers were brought to Jamestown almost as soon as it was founded, and began work in 1609. Early records say that glass was the first article of American manufacture to be exported. When Jamestown revived after the early Indian attacks Venetian glass-blowers were sent over to make glass beads for barter with the Indians. Their factory has been called America's first mint, but it was destroyed in the massacre of 1622 and not started again. Massachusetts was the next state to start glass-making, in 1641; then the Dutch began it in New York in 1645, Pennsylvania in 1683, and New Jersey, Connecticut, and New Hampshire during the following century. In the parts of Pennsylvania and New Jersey near Philadelphia, the colonial glass industry reached its greatest development. A plant at Glassboro, New Jersey, built in 1775, was until recently the oldest continuously operated factory in America. Throughout the colonial period, however, glass was a rarity except in the towns. Many frontier houses had no glass in their windows, and had to close the wooden shutters in cold weather and rain. For our present purpose, the important point is that even in colonial times the glass industry had reached its greatest development in precisely the latitude where it is now dominant.

During the nineteenth century, American glass-making moved westward, partly because the people moved west, and partly because coal and especially gas furnish cheaper fuel than wood. Today the old glass industry still holds its place in western New Jersey, but most of the industry is located on the gas and coal fields from Pennsylvania and West Virginia to Illinois (A557). The New Jersey factories used charcoal from the surrounding pine forests originally, but now must bring coal from farther west. A few of them, such as those at Vineland, still make the most expensive kinds of glass, and thus resemble the cotton factories of New England. The importance of fuel, however, has increased enormously in the glass industry during the present century. This is due to the invention of automatic machines for making bottles and window glass, which are the two main products of the industry. These machines are very large and expensive, and some of them require only one man to do what was formerly done by 54. In the old hand method, wages formed 50 to 75 per cent of the cost of making bottles, and fuel was responsible for a third to a

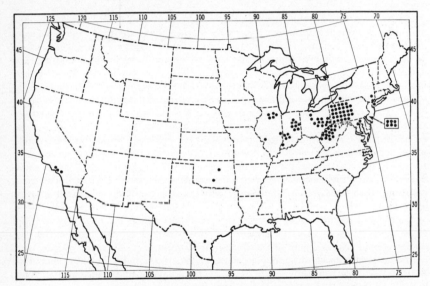

A—The Manufacture of Glass in the United States.

half of the remaining cost. In the new method, interest charges and depreciation of machinery replace a good share of the old labor charges, but the cost of fuel is relatively higher than before. Thus glass is one of the outstanding examples of the effect of fuel upon the location of industries.

The glass-making industry also illustrates how the social conditions of a region may change with inventions. The old glass-blowers were highly skilled and very well paid. They had to be active, alert men, able to move spryly and work hard under high temperatures. They needed good judgment, an artistic temperament, and a sense of proportion, as well as long training. Only a few men can meet these conditions. Accordingly the old glass-blowers were able to form very strong unions, and to raise their wages to 12 and in some cases 20 times those of common unskilled labor. They also gained an 8-hour day and a two months' vacation in hot weather, while most industries still had a 10-hour day. The automatic machines have changed all this. The best men, to be sure, must still be as skillful as ever, but the machine

tenders need not be skilled at all. The lessened demand for skilled men has caused
their wages to drop, so that glass-blowing communities no longer stand at their
former high economic and social level.

EXERCISES

1. Use the maps of flour milling (B538), baking (A539), and canning (A541)
as the basis for a discussion of the relative effects of the location of raw materials, the location of markets, and climate upon the distribution of industries.

2. On the basis of maps in this chapter discuss the effect of bulk and weight
upon the location of manufacturing industries.

3. Give a similar discussion of the effect of keeping qualities, with examples
from the maps.

4. Make a tabular summary of all the factors mentioned in this chapter as
playing a part in determining where industries are located. Cite examples, naming the product, the map, and the state or city where the given factor is evident.

5. In this chapter we have dealt with cereal products, canned goods, vegetables and fruits, dairy products, canned fish, products made of wood, and
products made of stone or earth. Make a table naming for each product (a) the
simple industries which belong to it, (b) the community industries, and (c) the
complex industries. Add notes as to the chief factors determining the distribution of each industry.

6. Baltimore is one of the greatest canning centers. Find out what products are canned in this city. Make a list of the geographic, economic, and other
factors that make the city so prominent in this industry. What other products
are made there in direct response to the canning industry? Find statistical evidence as to the importance of Baltimore's canning industry compared with its
other industries.

7. Minnesota has been called the bread and butter state. Why? Find
maps which demonstrate the truth of your answer. Give reasons for the predominance of Minneapolis in the flour-milling industry. How far do the same
reasons account for the importance of Budapest in this industry? Of Marseille?

8. Summarize the geographic, economic, and political conditions that have
helped to cause the following places to be meat-packing centers: Chicago;
Kansas City; Rosario; Buenos Aires.

9. Tabulate and discuss the social effects of industries mentioned in this
chapter. Add examples from your own knowledge, and show how the effects
differ from place to place according to the geographic environment.

CHAPTER XXVI

THE METAL AND PROGRESSAL INDUSTRIES

The Historic Location of Iron Manufacture.—The history of iron manufacturing repeats that of textiles, glass, and many other products. Beginning in North Africa or western Asia, the center of activity has moved more or less regularly northwestward during the historic period. The Damascus sword of Saladin that could cut a silk scarf laid on its edge, the Toledo blades of Spain, and the cutlery of Sheffield in England represent successive stages of this movement. At all stages the center of activity has been as near as possible to the places where civilization has been highest. Iron deposits are so widely spread that practically every part of the world contains them, although they may be small, or of low grade. Wood, too, which was the universal fuel for smelting the ore until two centuries ago, is found at least among the mountains in most of the regions that have become civilized. In all ages two of the main factors in fostering the smelting and manufacture of iron have been the activity of the people and the productivity of the land. High activity means the ability and energy to find and develop iron deposits; it also means relatively great wealth and hence ability to buy iron tools. Productivity of the land means a dense population, or at least a rapid growth in population as soon as settlement sets in. Combined with activity it means a large market. Since iron is heavy and both iron ore and fuel are widely distributed, markets and skill have always been main factors in determining the general location of the iron industry.

Before coal came into use for smelting iron ore the location of the iron industry was practically the same as now, except that it had not spread to the interior of the United States because there were no civilized people there. Belgium, England, and Sweden already possessed highly developed iron industries. In what is now the United States all the early colonies except Georgia had iron forges or bloomeries, which were the predecessors of blast furnaces. From 1650 to 1750 Massachusetts was the chief producer "by a generous margin," as Malcolm Keir says in his book on *Manufacturing*. Iron was needed there not only for nails, tools, guns, and kettles, as in the other colonies, but also for ship-building, for anchors, and for export. The metal was so rare that when old

559

cabins were abandoned it was not uncommon to burn them and rake over the ashes in order to get out the nails. The iron industry was located chiefly in the southeastern part of Massachusetts at the inner end of Cape Cod. There as everywhere, wood was abundant, oyster shells could be scraped up for lime far more cheaply than limestone could be quarried elsewhere, and the many shallow depressions left by the glaciers were filled with ponds and swamps in which bog iron ore accumulated.

As population increased and spread westward the supply of this iron became scarce while new markets were developing farther west. So the ore of inland places like Salisbury in Connecticut, and Lancaster in Pennsylvania, was exploited, but wood in the form of charcoal was still the only fuel. When settlers became numerous beyond the Appalachians, iron was needed, but it cost about 50 cents to transport a ton one mile by land. Hence new sources of iron had to be sought, and it was very desirable that they be located near rivers so as to take advantage of water transportation. So the ores of Ironton in Ohio were smelted locally, and the product was shipped to Cincinnati where it was made into the tools and utensils needed by the settlers.

In the same way Pittsburgh manufactured iron made from ore in the upper Monongahela Valley. The ore was smelted with charcoal, even though part of it came from Connellsville. That place was later noted as the source of the best coke for blast furnaces, but the art of making coke was not yet understood, and ordinary bituminous coal became so crushed and caked under the weight of ore in the blast furnaces that it could not be used profitably. Iron from charcoal furnaces also came to Pittsburgh from the Juniata region east of the Allegheny Front. At first it was carried across the mountains on the backs of horses, each animal carrying a horseshoe-shaped piece weighing 200 pounds, but later, after the Pennsylvania Canal was built, it came all the way by water. Pittsburgh, because of its location where the Allegheny and Monongahela Rivers unite to form the Ohio, became a great center of iron work, although not of smelting, long before its coal was used.

While Cincinnati and Pittsburgh, by reason of their location on rivers, were becoming centers for supplying the demand for iron goods west of the Alleghenies, the growth of railroads farther east created such a demand for iron that the local supplies of charcoal began to be inadequate. This led to experiments with anthracite coal, and from about 1840 to 1870 the valleys of the Schuylkill, Susquehanna, Juniata, and Lehigh Rivers in eastern Pennsylvania from Scranton to Reading and Harrisburg became the country's greatest center of blast furnaces. Places like Steelton and South Bethlehem in this region became famous for their steel works, although later overshadowed by other places as sources of pig iron. Only after the Civil War did the art of using coke in blast furnaces develop to such an extent that the bituminous coal of western Pennsylvania became important. At that same time the demand for iron to make railroads and for other purposes in the Middle West was swelling to great proportions. Moreover, the world's finest source of iron ore near Lake Superior in the states of Minnesota and Michigan had begun to be exploited. The little 20-ton boats which first brought the ore soon gave way to great steamships which evolved into "whalebacks" and are now replaced by huge craft like enormous canal barges. They carry 10,000 to 14,000 tons of ore, but can be loaded in half an hour and unloaded in three to five hours. At first the ore was mined by means of shafts and tunnels, but in the early nineties it was found cheaper to strip off the "overburden," and then quarry the ore instead of mining it. Horse scrapers did the work at first, and the ore was loaded into horse-drawn carts to be carried to the lake. But soon steam shovels were introduced and now there are also electric shovels. These giants weigh 300 tons and can scoop up 16 tons of ore at a mouthful. The carts have given place to trains of huge size which run down a gentle slope all the way to Duluth. The engines are needed only to control the train, and haul the empty cars back again. The cars can be automatically dumped from a high trestle, and the ore flows into bins from which it again flows by gravity into the ships. In busy times about 30 trains a day of 96 cars each bring ore to Duluth. Of course, all this development did not come at once, but it came fast enough to make the Pittsburgh region rival those of central England, Belgium, and the lower Rhine as one of the world's greatest iron-making sections.

Present Distribution of Iron Industries.—A564 shows where the iron ore of the United States now comes from, while B564 shows where it is smelted. By far the larger part of the ore comes from the Lake Superior region, but it is interesting to note that a fair amount, about one-tenth of the total, still comes from the Appalachians. The Birmingham region in Alabama produces most of this, but five other states have an appreciable share. The only other sources of iron ore worth mentioning in this country are the Rocky Mountain region, Utah, and Missouri. B564 shows that the western ores come to the coal of Colorado to be smelted; the Lake Superior ores meet eastern coal along the south shores of the Great Lakes; and the Appalachian ores find coal for smelting near their source. In Colorado the ore map (A564) shows only one cross, and the iron map (B564) three because ores are transported to the nearest good supply of coal (A473). It should be noted that the ore map is based on values while the iron map is based on tons of metal. In Alabama and still more in Colorado the cost of mining the ore is much greater than in the open pits of the Lake Superior region. In both cases, however, the iron in the ore has a high value because it is so far from other sources of supply and the transportation of iron is expensive. The value of the Birmingham ore is enhanced by the fact that ore, coal, and limestone for flux are found close together, thus making it easy and cheap to extract the metal when once the ore is mined.

The most notable feature of B564 is the concentration of dots along the southern shores of Lakes Michigan and Erie from Chicago and Gary through Toledo, Cleveland, and Erie to Buffalo, with a southward projection to Pittsburgh. This represents the combined effect of three factors. One is bituminous coal in western Pennsylvania, Ohio, and Illinois, with less in Indiana. The second is the Lake Superior ore, and the third is the people who are going to use the iron. Finished iron goods, because of their varied shapes and sizes, are more expensive to transport than is pig iron, and pig iron similarly costs more per ton-mile than iron ore because it cannot be so easily handled. But the weight of the lime and coal used in smelting iron ore is considerably greater than that of the ore. The states that border Lakes Michigan and Erie, and that can therefore be very easily supplied with iron made near the shores of those lakes, contain more than 45,000,000 people, or over 37 per cent of the country's entire population. Moreover, they comprise the main part of the belt where the conditions of human activity cause manufacturing to be most highly developed. Their normal demands for iron in the way of railroads, machinery, automobiles, builders' supplies, ship-building, and structural steel represent far more than half the demand of the whole country. Accordingly the location of the blast furnaces near the shores of the lakes between the iron mines and the coal mines represents the present solution of the problem of reducing transportation to a minimum. Most of the iron has to come to the manufacturing belt to be used. At Duluth it pays to smelt only a very little for local use. If the population in the surrounding region were as dense and industrially active as in Ohio we may be sure that both coal and limestone would be brought to Duluth in large amounts. But as things now are it is cheaper to carry the ore not only to the coal, but even *to the people*, that is, to the market. The ore, together with the wheat which is also shipped from Duluth and from Canadian ports, especially Port William, gives the Sault Ste. Marie Canal between Lakes Superior and Huron a tonnage of through traffic greater than that of any other waterway.

Some Iron and Steel Industries.—After it comes from the blast furnaces in the form of pigs, iron usually goes to steel works and rolling mills. There it is remelted, purified, and combined with carbon and minor metallic ingredients to make steel. The steel may be sold in pigs, but more often it is at once rolled into sheets and bars, or drawn into rods, or shaped in other ways so that it is more nearly ready to use. The production of steel is generally reported as about a quarter greater than that of pig iron in the United States, because it includes steel made not only from fresh iron, but from scrap iron, which is usually steel. In this country, railroads turn in about 5,000,000 tons of scrap each year. About a million automobiles are also junked each year, and most of them go to the steel plants. The Ford Company often melts up 50,000 old cars in a year. In Europe the steel production is generally only about one-eighth more than that of pig iron instead of one-quarter, as with us. This difference affords a rough measure of the way in which we scrap machines while they are still useful, whereas in Europe they are more likely to be used till they wear out. Although blast furnaces and steel mills are generally run separately, their distribution over the country as a whole is almost identical. Thus Pennsylvania makes about 33 per cent of the pig iron, and 36 per cent of the steel-mill products.

From the steel and rolling mills the steel goes to many different kinds of industries which show a distribution quite different from that of the blast furnaces. A565, for example, shows foundries and machine shops. Foundries are defined by the census as establishments in which metal is cast into various shapes; machine shops are establishments in which work is done by means of power-driven machine tools used in cutting and shaping metals. Some do odd jobs of many varieties, while others make only a few products. The ones that do odd jobs are needed everywhere, and may almost be classed with community industries. For this reason A565 shows a distribution a good deal like that of population. The Pacific Coast gets its normal 6 per cent; the Rocky Mountain States do not even get crosses, but nevertheless they have foundries and machine shops in proportion to their population and their type of industries. The South also gets a good representation, while the manufacturing section from Illinois and Wisconsin eastward gets the most dots because of both its dense population and its industrial activity.

Another fraction of the product of steel mills is used for making machinery, most of which is installed in other factories (B565). Most of this business, as might be expected, is carried on in the Northeast; Chicago, Cleveland, Detroit, and Milwaukee are the leading cities, but

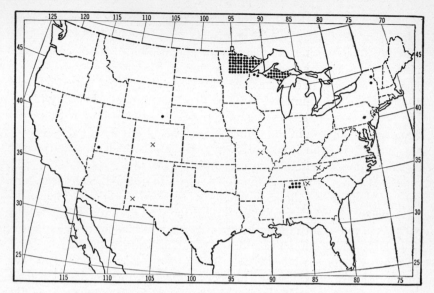

A—Annual Value of Iron Ore Produced in the United States.

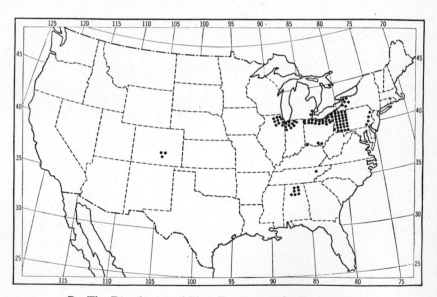

B—The Distribution of Blast Furnaces in the United States.

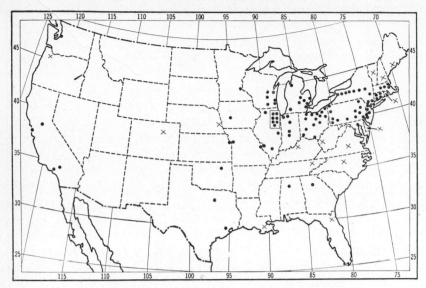

A—Foundry and Machine Shop Products in the United States.

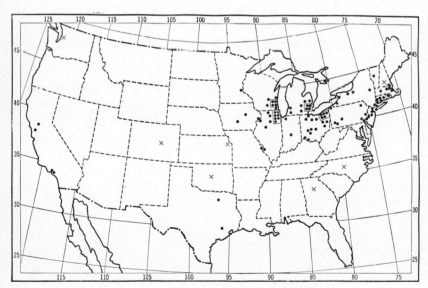

B—The Making of Machinery in the United States (omitting machinery for agriculture and transportation, and electrical machinery.)

Ohio and the Atlantic Coast from Boston to Philadelphia are also active. The Pacific Coast holds its own, but south of the Ohio and west of the Mississippi there is very little. The next map (A568) indicates that with electrical machinery, which is more difficult to make than most kinds, the northeastern concentration goes still further. The proportion of the industry carried on in California is less than with the more general type of machinery. The region west of the Mississippi and south of the Ohio falls out entirely except for St. Louis, St. Paul, and Louisville, which lie directly on the rivers. The most northern states also drop to a new low level as compared with other kinds of machinery, for northern New England gets no dots or crosses, while Michigan and Wisconsin get less than half as many as in B565. On the other hand, southern New England, New York, New Jersey, and eastern Pennsylvania rank relatively higher than in machinery in general. This is because electrical machinery is light, but requires much skill. Thus here, just as in the cotton industry, we find that the sections of the manufacturing belt which lack coal turn to industries which demand little fuel and raw material, but much skill.

Agricultural machinery (B568) displays quite a different pattern. California and the states from Michigan and Ohio eastward make about enough to supply their own needs. The southern states use more agricultural machinery than they make, bringing it from Chicago, but they use little in proportion to their acreage of crops. The outstanding feature of B568 is the extreme concentration around Chicago which spills over to Milwaukee and northern Indiana. The reason for this is that Chicago and its neighbors represent the center from which the major part of the Corn Belt can most easily be supplied. The iron and wood needed in the agricultural implements come to the ports at the southern end of Lake Michigan by water. The coal comes in the same way, or from the mines in Illinois. Transportation lines radiate in every direction, and the machines can in many cases be shipped in knocked-down condition. The Corn Belt, by reason of its wealth and of the fact that practically all the land can be cultivated, uses far more agricultural machinery than any other section. Thus B568, like the map of blast furnaces, represents a distribution based primarily on the market, and secondarily on the natural features which make it easy to collect the raw mateiials and fuel and ship the finished product. But the *activity* of the people has even more to do with the size of the market than has the *number* of people. Iowa farmers who cultivate 160 acres single handed, or with one hired man, work far harder than colored men in Mississippi who cultivate 30 acres. But the hard work of the Iowans gives them a surplus with which to buy machinery, so that a hundred Iowa farmers buy more machinery than a thousand southern Negroes.

Motor vehicles represent still another kind of machinery which uses a large amount of iron—about one-eighth of our whole supply. Their map (A569) is very much like that of agricultural machinery except that Detroit takes the place of Chicago. Moreover, the industry as a whole shifts toward the east and north, as appears from the fact that the automobile map has less dots than the agricultural machinery map in the West as well as the South, and more in New York, New Jersey, and Massachusetts. This eastward shift is like the shift which we see between machinery in general and electrical machinery. It is due partly to the fact that the market for automobiles is enormous in the densely populated eastern states as well as in the agricultural middle western states. It is also due in part to the fact that the making of automobiles requires more skill in proportion to raw material than does that of agricultural machinery and therefore is better fitted for the eastern states that have no coal and are far from the sources of iron. It should be noted in this connection that the eastern work in the automobile trade includes a relatively high proportion of parts such as electrical appliances. The automobile industry is to a high degree an "assembly industry." The final product is rarely made entirely in one factory, as are cloth, steel rails, and shoes. Even the Ford cars use tires bought from other manufacturers. Some less-known cars are made entirely from parts made by a great number of outside factories. Some writers emphasize the fact that this tends to cause many kinds of factories to concentrate near Detroit, but A569 seems to show that it also permits some phases of the industry to spread more widely than in the agricultural implement industry.

A569 also makes it clear that, while Detroit cannot rival Chicago in its location as to agriculture, it is ideally situated in respect to coal, iron, a dense and wealthy population, and other industries which can help in furnishing accessories like upholstery, tires, and the other one or two hundred parts which make up an automobile. For tractors, however, Chicago might be a better center except that the motor car industry is now firmly intrenched in Detroit. Chicago's advantage in this respect is its location near the Corn Belt farms which are the main users of tractors. Among the 920,000 tractors on farms in 1930 no less than 568,000, or 62 per cent, were owned in the 12 North Central States, and only 86,000 or 9 per cent in the 9 North Atlantic States. On the other hand out of the 26,000,000 automobiles only 38 per cent were owned in the North Central States and 25 per cent in the North Atlantic States. The tractor, as Malcolm Keir puts it, "may plow,

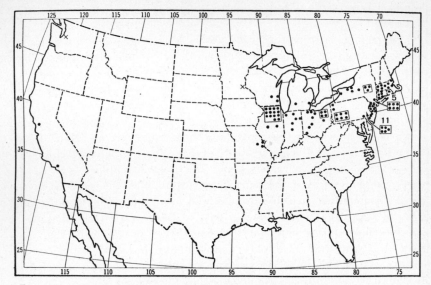

A—Electrical Machinery in the United States.

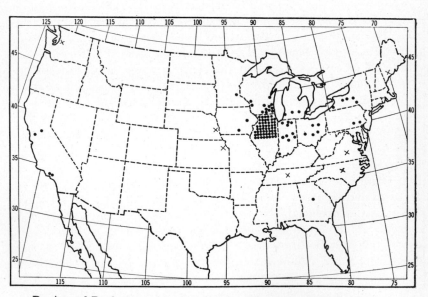

B—Annual Production of Agricultural Implements in the United States.

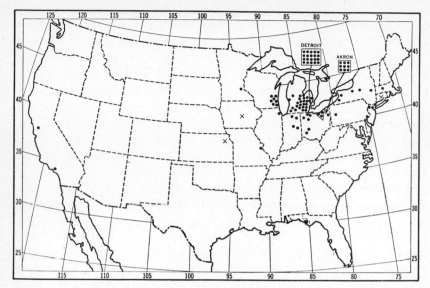

A—Annual Value of Motor Vehicle Production in the United States.

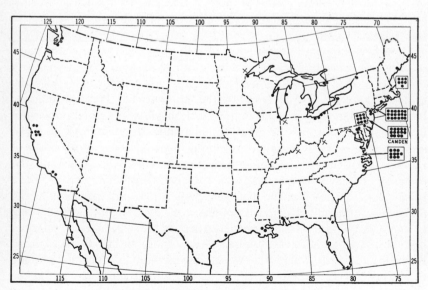

B—Ship and Boat Building in the United States.

reap, pull stumps, haul rocks, draw wagons filled with anything a farm needs or produces, run a sawmill, grist mill, or electric lighting plant, fill a reservoir with water, or milk a cow. But the tractor is equally valuable to men engaged in forest enterprises or mining operations. Public highway departments have found it valuable for road-making or repairing, while country clubs have rolled greens and tennis courts and cut grass with tractors. Indeed the tractor is more marvelous than the automobile, whose child it is." Nevertheless the farm is still the main market for tractors. During the next ten or twenty years it will be interesting to see whether the farm market draws the tractor industry westward away from the regular automobile industry.

One more great type of iron industry is illustrated in B569, where the location of ship-building is shown. Here the great preponderance of Boston, New York, Philadelphia with Camden, and Hampton Roads with Newport News needs no explanation. Active commerce, good harbors, and the presence of manufacturing industries to supply accessories like engines and furnishings, make this the natural location for ship-building. It is interesting to note how the growth of the great manufacturing cities, together with the traffic in iron ore and grain, keeps an active ship-building industry at work around the Great Lakes. But the most notable feature of B569 is that the Pacific Coast in proportion to its population and that of its hinterland goes well ahead of the Atlantic Coast.

Another map of the use of iron (A571) shows the value of the work done in railroad repair shops, including not only steam but also electric railroads. This map comes nearer than any other of our industry maps to being directly proportional to the population. Pennsylvania, to be sure, has much more than its fair share of dots, presumably because it is the home state of the great Pennsylvania Railroad System. The same is true of West Virginia, Wyoming, and Nevada, which boast of railroad yards much exceeding their local needs. Oklahoma, on the contrary, by mere chance happens to have very small yards. B571 brings out this relationship between population and railroad repairs, for it shows the value per capita of the work done in the railroad yards of each state. Its most curious feature is that aside from Virginia and Montana no state that touches the outer border of the country has railroad yards where the work amounts to as much as $10 per capita, and even in these states the main railroad yards are not on the coast or on the Canadian boundary. Pennsylvania, be it noted, does not touch the Atlantic Ocean, and the three-mile offshore limit is found far down Delaware Bay. On the other hand, a solid block of states from Pennsylvania and Virginia to Nevada shows from $10 to nearly

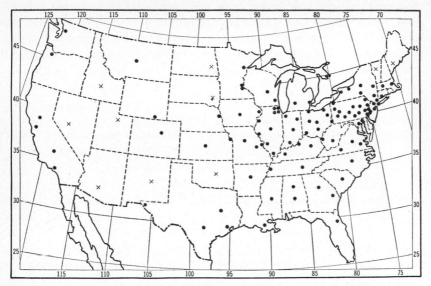

A—Value of the Work Done in Railroad Repair Shops in the United States.

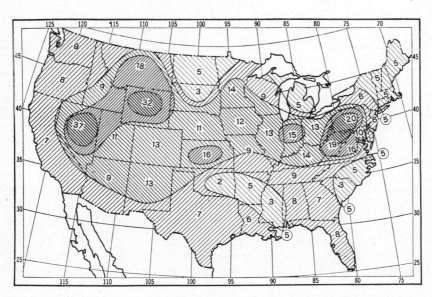

B—Annual Expenses in Railroad Repair Shops per Capita of the Entire Population of the United States.

$40 worth of railroad repair work per capita. If this were in Europe it would suggest that the repair shops were kept away from the borders of the country for safety in time of war. In this country it merely means that railroads locate their repair yards toward the central parts of their lines rather than at the ends.

Non-ferrous Metals and Alloys.—The minor metals included in this group bring out very clearly the importance of transportation in determining where goods are manufactured. The metals here included are copper, lead, zinc, and nickel, together with alloys or mixtures like brass, bronze, solder, babbitt, and type metal. The work here considered is merely the making of these into blocks, sheets, bars, rods, tubes,

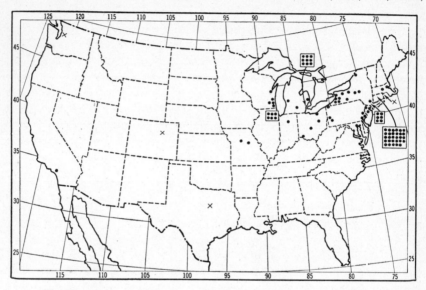

A—The Manufacture of Non-ferrous Metallic Products in the United States.

and castings, together with non-ferrous wire aside from that made in regular wire factories. It corresponds to what is done with iron in steel works and rolling mills. Its purpose is to prepare materials for use in industries like the making of clocks, electrical machinery, microscopes, cameras, and electric light fixtures, as well as for the small metal parts used in making furniture, plumbing appliances, and machinery. The noteworthy fact is that the industry is most highly developed in western Connecticut, especially in the Naugatuck Valley where Waterbury is the chief city (A572). This is largely the result of what may be called tradition or an early start. The industry was established here long ago in colonial times, and grew with the country. It has expanded westward with the growth of population, as appears from the dots around New York City, in the Mohawk Valley, and around Detroit and Chicago. Yet it still holds its own in Connecticut partly because copper, which is the chief raw material, comes from the West mainly by sea to New York, partly because not only factories but likewise skilled laborers and agencies for buying and selling are firmly intrenched here, and partly because not far away at places like

Bridgeport, New Haven, and Hartford there are many factories for clocks, sporting goods, door knobs, and innumerable other types of small hardware which supply a market for the sheets, bars, and tubes of metal made in the kind of factories here under discussion. It is curious to note that this kind of manufacturing has made very little progress outside of the strip from southern New England to Chicago. The main reason is that when industries like the making of clocks, small hardware, brass tacks, and the like are once well established they create for themselves conditions of cheap manufacture which cannot easily be duplicated elsewhere. Moreover, the products being relatively light in weight, needing only a small amount of heat and power for manufacture, and depending on raw materials located mainly in sparsely populated regions like Arizona or Montana, there is little except the market to drag the industries away from their old moorings.

The Distribution of Progressal Manufacturing. 1. *Paper.*—The number and variety of the products which are here called progressals are so great that we can discuss only a few of them. Among these products which are the peculiar property of the most progressive parts of the world, we shall begin with paper. In the world as a whole this is among the most widely used of the progressals. Yet in South and Central America the production of paper is estimated as only about two-thirds of 1 per cent of that of the United States and Canada, and the consumption is not much greater. Africa and Asia outside of Japan produce even less than Latin America, and their consumption is almost negligible. Even Japan, which is by far the greatest nation of readers outside those of European stock, uses only about one-twentieth as much paper as the United States.

The first stage in the manufacture of paper is the making of wood pulp. A574 indicates that in the United States a vast amount is made from local wood in Maine, New Hampshire, and Wisconsin, while northern New York and Pennsylvania also manufacture a good deal from wood which comes up the St. Lawrence River or across the lakes from Canada. The importance of Canada in this respect can scarcely be overestimated. Although Canada tries to have her pulp wood made into pulp inside the country, a great deal still comes to the United States, while the amount of wood pulp and paper made there and imported to the United States exceeds our own supply. A574 shows that Virginia and neighboring Appalachian regions, together with Louisiana, make pulp for the South, while the Pacific Coast with its 6 per cent of the country's pulp production from its coniferous forests is just about self-sufficing. In a general way it is clear that the wood pulp industry is primarily located near the forests which are best situated to supply the needs of the parts of the country that use most paper. The main users are newspapers, although books, magazines, writing paper, and products like cardboard and cartons are important. In the general

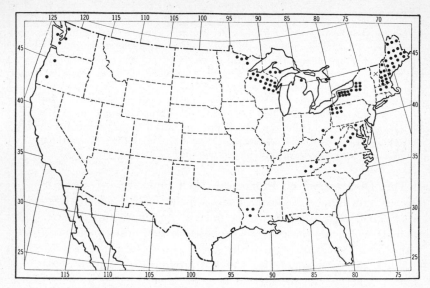

A—The Production of Pulp for Paper from Wood and Other Fibers.

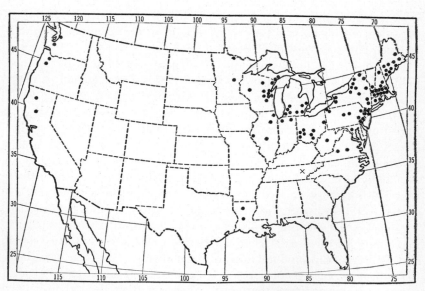

B—Paper Manufacturing in the United States.

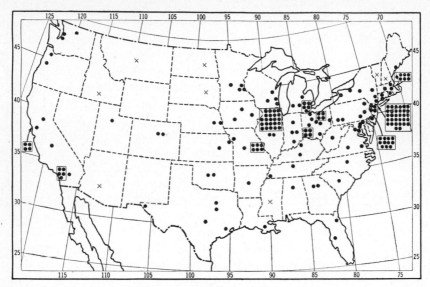

A—Newspaper and Job Printing in the United States.   Each dot indicates one-half
of 1 per cent.

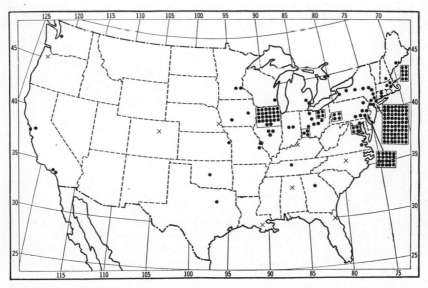

B—The Printing of Periodicals and Books in the United States.   Each dot indicates
one-half of 1 per cent of the total value of production in the United States.

regions where pulp wood is available or to which it can cheaply be brought by water, sites with plenty of pure water and water power like Niagara or the tumbling rivers in the glaciated regions of Canada, northern New England, and northern Wisconsin are preferable.

A comparison of A574 with B574 shows that the great market afforded by the newspapers and other users of paper in the most active manufacturing areas draws the paper industry to a more southerly location than that of the pulp industry. This is partly because wood pulp is shipped south to paper factories, and partly because the best grades of paper are still made of rags which once were the sole raw material. Massachusetts, with its famous factories for high-grade paper in the Connecticut Valley around Holyoke, the "Paper City," and other states like Connecticut, Ohio, Indiana, Illinois, and California, which scarcely appear at all in the pulp map, are important in the paper map. On the other hand, in the southern states of Virginia, North Carolina, Tennessee, and Lousiana the production of paper is relatively less important than that of pulp. Thus a comparison of the pulp and paper maps suggests that from the South as well as the North pulp moves toward the manufacturing belt since that is the area where the market for paper is largest.

2. *Job Printing and Newspapers.*—Coming now to the big users of paper we find that the printing trade is divided into two parts. One is the community industry which includes newspapers and the printing of local jobs like advertisements, programs and notices. The other is the complex industry of making books and magazines. Of course the two industries are much alike and are sometimes combined in the same plants, but they are different in that one supplies local needs while the other serves the whole country. This difference is evident when A575 and B575 are compared. Note that in these maps a dot stands for one half of 1 per cent of the country's production instead of 1 per cent as in most of the maps. In A575, showing newspapers, there are dots or crosses in all states except the four that are least populous. This is natural, since no part of the country is without its local newspapers and local offices where minor printing jobs can be done. Nevertheless, it is also clear that the big cities, the Northeast in general, and the Pacific Coast all have more than their share of dots in proportion to their population. Massachusetts claims 5 per cent of this kind of printing, but only $3\frac{1}{2}$ per cent of the population, New York City 16 per cent with $5\frac{3}{4}$ per cent of the people, Chicago 12 against $2\frac{3}{4}$, and the Pacific Coast 9 against 6. This indicates two main facts. One is that the cities print newspapers for many people outside their limits; the other is that Chicago is particularly noteworthy in this respect. Its metropolitan district has only 4,365,-000 inhabitants compared with 10,900,000 in New York's, and yet Chicago does three-fourths as much job and newspaper printing as New York.

3. *Magazines and Books.*—With books and magazines the story is different (B575). Metropolitan New York prints three times as much as Chicago, and is actually responsible for a third of all the books and magazines in the country. The South and West drop so low that if we were here using a unit of 1 per cent instead of one

half of 1 per cent they would hardly be noticeable.   On the other hand, the metropolitan districts of Boston, New York, Washington, Philadelphia, Pittsburgh, Cleveland, Cincinnati, and Chicago publish three-quarters of all the books and magazines,
and a still larger portion of the books.   Even if printing alone be taken into account,
without regard to authorship, proof reading, and the making of illustrations, the
work requires very high skill.   Printers, on an average, get higher wages than the
workers in any other main branch of manufacturing.   Moreover, authors tend to flock
to New York and other big cities, while the urge to write books, stories, and articles
seems to be especially strong among the educated people from Boston to Chicago.
Again, the cost of shipping books and magazines is small compared with their value,
and the size of the individual shipments of goods is small.   The cost of fuel, as we
saw on page 480, is trivial compared with that of the final product.   Thus, in this

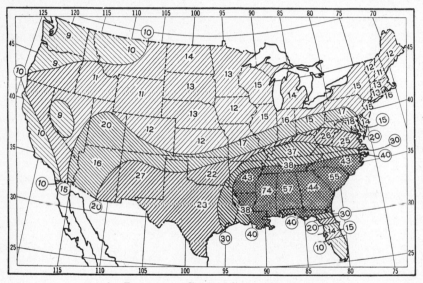

A—Persons per Copy of Curtis Magazines.

industry more than in almost any other, the factor that determines location is the
effect of the environment on human activity.   This acts not merely through health
and energy, but also through the stimulus that comes from great cities, the attraction
which such cities hold out to unusually able people, and the facilities which they offer
for selling and distributing their products.

But how about the final use of the printed pages by the people who buy the books
and magazines?   We cannot answer this exactly for all publications, but we can for
those of the Curtis Publishing Company of Philadelphia, which publishes the *Satur-
day Evening Post, Ladies Home Journal*, and *Country Gentleman*.   A577 shows how
many persons there are for each copy of these very widely read publications.   A
map of the number of other magazines or of books per family would almost certainly
present the same general features.   Those features have now become familiar
through repetition in maps of many kinds ranging from yield of corn per acre, and
egg and milk production, to wages, the consumption of baker's bread, mortality,
and climatic energy.

4. *Chemicals, Petroleum, and Fertilizers.*—Three more maps of progressals are presented in this chapter because they illustrate three main types of distribution. A578 combines a number of chemical industries including druggists' preparations, explosives, paints, varnishes, and what are commonly called chemicals such as acids, salts, and the like.   They show the normal distribution which we find repeated again and again in industries where the location of fuel, heavy raw materials, or some other special factors do not play a large part.   The great majority of progressals show this same type of distribution with abundant production from southern New England to Chicago, almost enough for local use on the Pacific Coast, and little production west of the Missouri River and in the South.

Petroleum products are counted as progressals because their use in automobiles and still more in the form of products of the paraffine type is so largely limited to

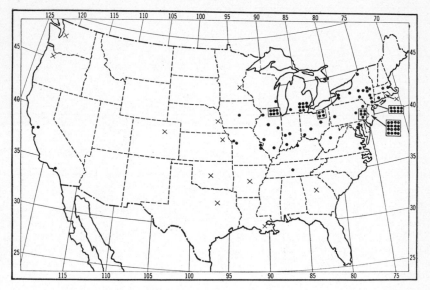

A—Miscellaneous Chemical Industries in the United States.

the most progressive communities (A579).   The great number of dots in California, Texas, Oklahoma, Louisiana, and Wyoming, is obviously a response to a heavy and bulky raw material.   The significant fact, however, is that the drawing power of the activity, wealth, and abundant population of the Northeast causes petroleum refining to be fairly well developed not only in Pennsylvania where oil is still produced, but all the way from Massachusetts to Chicago in regions which have no oil except that which they bring in steamships or pipelines.

Finally in B579 we find a kind of manufacturing whose location depends partly on the presence of cheap, bulky, heavy raw materials such as phosphate rock and the waste products of slaughter houses, and partly on a market due to the quality of the soil, the demands of special crops like cotton and tobacco, and the relative scarcity of other sources of fertilizer from domestic animals.   Such conditions cause the South to be by far the most important part of the country in the manufacture of fertilizers.   Yet they do not prevent the manufacturing belt from New England to

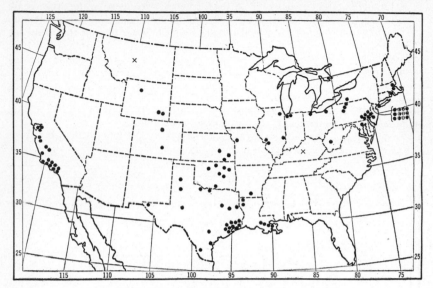

A—Petroleum Refining in the United States.

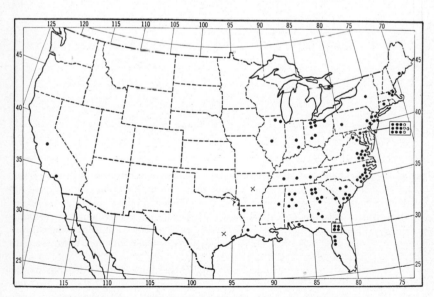

B—Production of Commercial Fertilizers in the United States.

Illinois from producing a quarter of all the fertilizers. This is more than their share in proportion to the land that they cultivate, but intensive and prolonged cultivation causes the market for fertilizers to be relatively much larger than farther west.

EXERCISES

1. Sum up your conclusions as to the relative parts played by iron, other raw materials, fuel, climate, transportation, and markests upon the distribution of manufacturing, giving examples to prove your points.

2. A580 shows the number of persons engaged in the metal-using industries in Europe. Analyze and explain it on the basis of (a) climate, (b) coal, (c) iron,

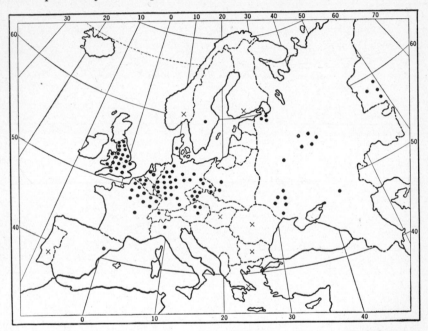

A—Workers in Metal and Machinery Making Industries in Europe. Each dot represents 1 per cent of European total.

(d) water power, (e) density of population, (f) purchasing capacity of markets, and (g) transportation facilities. Bear in mind that the production per worker is far less in eastern than in western Europe. How does this map compare with that of population?

3. Repeat Exercise 5 of the last chapter, changing the wording to fit the present chapter.

4. Prepare an exercise on this chapter to be worked out by some other member of the class. Let the purpose of the exercise be to show by maps and statistics the most fundamental features of the distribution of progressal manufactures.

5. Among all the industries studied in this book, which ones seem to you to be most free to locate themselves without much reference to raw materials,

fuel, and the cost of distributing the final product? Describe and explain the distribution of such industries.

6. Figure B564 shows the distribution of pig-iron production. Summarize the factors which favor the location of the industry in each of the main producing areas as well as in isolated plants. If any of these regions has geographic disadvantages include them in your summary.

7. Suppose that you are asked for advice by a company wishing to go into the business of paper manufacturing. The company plans to have two plants —one to make writing paper, and the other news print. What raw materials will each use? Where will each find its main market? Summarize the geographic relationships of these factors and of others. Pick out several specific localities where you think such plants could be located, and prepare a report showing your reasons.

8. What manufactures of the types discussed in this chapter are found in your home town? Summarize the facts and discuss the factors which influence the nature and extent of these industries. Bring into your discussion not only geographic and economic relationships, but also those that are historic, social, or of some other type.

CHAPTER XXVII

THE PATHS OF COMMERCE

The Nature of Commerce.—Much of the world's food and most of the raw materials and fuels change hands at least once before being used. Such exchanges require a surplus on one side and a demand on the other. One person, family, company, or country must have more of something than it needs, while others must need that thing so much that they are willing to give their surplus of something else in exchange for it. Thus the laws of supply and demand cause trade and commerce to arise. Of course most people sell and buy for money instead of exchanging goods, but that is merely a matter of convenience. Our first object in this chapter is to see why some regions have a surplus and others a demand.

Geographic Conditions That Create a Surplus.—Everything that favors production also favors the creation of a surplus. Level plains with fine, rich soil and easy transportation make it easy to produce an abundance of food, provided the climate is right. Rugged topography may favor the production of metals and lumber, which may be exchanged for a surplus of wheat and pork in a neighboring plain. The people in the plain might raise trees for lumber, and those in the mountains might raise wheat, but neither course would pay. Thus the first principle of profitable trade is that people utilize favorable resources to produce a surplus that does not cost them much, and exchange this for a similar surplus which cannot be produced so cheaply in their own environment. All through this book we have repeatedly seen how climate, soil, relief, natural vegetation, mineral resources, and location in respect to markets cooperate with economic conditions in causing commodities to be produced more abundantly and profitably in one region than in another.

The Optimum Density of Population.—Although these physical conditions are very potent in determining the *kind* of surplus in various regions, other factors are still more important in determining the *amount*. One such factor is the density of population. Here we are confronted once more by the principle of the optimum, for in every geographic environment a certain optimum density of population will create the largest surplus. Suppose, for instance, that the whole of China had

582

only ten million inhabitants evenly scattered over its huge area. Obviously it could not produce the maximum surplus because there would not be enough people to utilize a large part of the resources. Moreover, unless the people were all in one region, the average surplus per person would not be at a maximum, even though everyone used all the land he wanted. With a low density of population the towns would be small and far apart and the roads very poor so that the farmers, and also the lumbermen, miners, and others, if there were any, would have to spend much time and effort merely in getting their goods to market. That of course would diminish the time and energy available for raising crops and thus would cut down the surplus. Even if the farmers hired other people to take their products to market, the high cost of transportation would have to be paid before there would be a real surplus. Now suppose the population increases until all the good land and all the best forests and mineral resources are in use. Will this give a maximum surplus? Yes, if the number of people is right; no, if there are as many people as China now has. In his book, *Chinese Farm Economy*, J. L. Buck shows that the year's work of the average man on farms of different sizes produces crops having the following relative values: on farms with a crop area averaging 2.5 acres, 100; crop area 5.0 acres, 130; and 15.0 acres, 295. In other words, farmers are so numerous that a large part of their work is wasted. A man with 2 acres on which to support his family slaves away to get a maximum yield from the land, but the utmost that he can sell as a surplus may be worth only $5 a year. If the same man had 10 acres, he could cultivate the whole of it. From each acre he might not get quite so much as he now gets from each of his 2 acres, but from the whole he could get enough to let his family live much better than now and still leave a relatively large surplus. The following balance sheet shows how this would work:

	2-Acre Farm	10-Acre Farm
Value of crops per acre	50	40
Total value of crops per farm	100	400
Value of farm products used by family	90	150
Annual surplus per farm to be used in trade	10	250
Annual surplus from 10 acres (five families)	50 (one family)	250

This balance sheet illustrates what happens not only in China, but also in India, Japan, Russia, and large parts of Europe, including even Germany. Because the population is denser than the optimum the agricultural surplus is far less than would otherwise be the case, and the people are correspondingly poorer. Moreover, the number of people whom the agricultural surplus will support in other occupations such as manufacturing is much less than it would be if the farm population had the optimum density. The same principle applies to miners, lumbermen, and other primary producers. A comparison between Java and Siam illustrates the matter. Both countries are admirably adapted to rice culture; each produces about 5,000,000 tons of rice per year, but Java has over 40,000,000 people and Siam only 12,000,000. The average Siamese raises three or four times as much rice as the average Javanese. This is partly because of higher yields per acre in Siam, but mainly because the Javanese population is so dense that the average farmer there has little more than a third as much land as in Siam. Accordingly Java has no surplus rice for export. The farmers eat practically all that they raise, and about 700,000 tons have to be imported each year for the townspeople. Siam on the other hand not only feeds its own townspeople, who are more numerous proportionally than those of Java, but in addition exports about 1,400,000 tons of rice per year. This same principle applies everywhere; the largest surplus and hence the most active trade and commerce arise where the population is neither too sparse nor too dense.

Human Activity and the Volume of Trade.—The activity of trade depends upon the mental ability, energy, and standards of the people quite as much as upon the density of population. In spite of certain disadvantages New Guinea might raise an enormous surplus of rice, sugar, corn, sago, cocoa, tea, coffee, tobacco, and bananas, but its backward people produce little except what they immediately consume. In Java, however, a higher cultural level and the help and supervision of nearly 150,000 Europeans, chiefly Dutch, enable an island a sixth as large as New Guinea to export plantation products worth over half a billion dollars each year, even though food must be imported for the workers. Again, in China the unmined coal is estimated at 1,000 billion tons, of which 427 billion are anthracite, against only 166 billion, or one-sixth as much, in Great Britain. But until Europeans took the lead, the Chinese mined practically no coal even for local consumption. Vast quantities lay in the rocks, but there was no surplus for commerce. Even in 1929 the 440,000,000 people of China mined only 15,000,000 tons of coal, one-sixteenth as much as Great Britain, and less than 1 per cent as much per capita.

On the other hand, Norway has almost no mineral wealth; her cool climate greatly limits the crops; deep soil is found only in a few valleys and on a narrow coastal plain; and the rugged topography permits only 1 acre in 30 to be cultivated. Yet so energetic and capable are the Norwegians that their abundant surplus, mainly based on fish from the warm ocean, water power from the glaciated mountains, and timber from the forests, not only supports an active trade at home, but makes Norwegian exports ten times as valuable as those of Java in proportion to the inhabitants.   Again, Alaska never yielded any surplus worth mentioning while it was in the hands of Eskimos, Indians, and even Russians; but after its purchase by the United States it yielded a salable surplus worth about a billion and a half dollars up to 1930.   So, too, although New England has no coal, few raw materials, and not nearly enough water power, the capacity of its people causes it to produce an enormous surplus of manufactures.

The Conditions that Create a Demand.—The conditions that create a demand are in one sense the opposite of those that create a surplus.   If a region lacks certain natural advantages, it often demands articles which can be produced only with the help of such advantages.   The United States demands a vast quantity of bananas, and gets them from Caribbean America, for the climate there favors banana growing and that of the United States does not.   New England, being too rugged for extensive wheat cultivation, demands wheat from the western plains, while Germany, having little copper, demands it from places like Arizona, Montana, Katanga, and Chile.

In a more important sense a demand and a supply are created by exactly the same conditions.   For example, Denmark and Ceylon are both lacking in coal and iron, but Denmark is so active that it demands ten or perhaps a hundred times as much of these two highly important products as does the larger population of Ceylon.   The factors that count chiefly in creating a demand, just as in creating a supply, are the mental ability, physical energy, and cultural condition of a country.

The Character of Foreign Trade in Three Types of Countries.—Most parts of the world fall into one of three types: (1) Backward countries with poorly developed resources, few and simple products, almost no manufacturing, and a small surplus used to satisfy a demand for a few simple manufactures.   (2) Progressive old countries with resources inadequate to the population, but with a great variety of manufactured products which form a surplus whereby the inhabitants satisfy their demand for raw materials, food, and luxuries.   (3) Progressive new countries with well developed resources, a variety of products, little manufacturing except for home consumption, and a large and varied but unmanufactured surplus which enables the people to satisfy their demand for a great variety of manufactured articles.

Siam is a good example of the first type, Switzerland of the second, and Australia of the third.   The United States perhaps belongs in still a fourth class like No. 3, except that manufacturing is highly developed. Judged merely by its natural resources, Siam with 12 million people ought to excel Switzerland with 4 million both in its supply and its demand for goods to be used in trade. Siam contains 200,000 square miles, Switzerland only 16,000. The climate in Siam is far more favorable for plant growth than in Switzerland, the plains are vastly greater, and excellent deposits of tin and other minerals are available, whereas Switzerland has practically none. If the people of Siam and Switzerland were of exactly equal ability and similar culture, these conditions might cause the foreign trade of Siam to be at least triple that of Switzerland. But Siam does not import a single product to the value of $1 per inhabitant each year and only a limited number to the value of 10 cents or more. Switzerland on the contrary imports 15 times as much per capita as Siam, and 30 or 40 kinds of imports ordinarily have a value of at least $1 per person. This extraordinary difference is due largely to the character and civilization of the people. Remoteness has only a little to do with it, for Argentina and Australia, two of the most distant parts of the world, vie with Switzerland in the variety and amount of their imports.

Marked contrasts appear not only in the amounts but also in the kinds of goods imported into Siam, Switzerland, and Australia. The Siamese imports consist of manufactured goods of a simple nature and few kinds aside from those used in enterprises like mines and railways which are financed in Europe; the Swiss imports include large amounts of food and raw materials and a diversity of complex manufactures; those of Australia, aside from tobacco, tea, timber, and some rubber, include little except a great variety of manufactured goods. These are the normal imports of the three types of countries mentioned above. The differences between these various countries, like many other facts, show that the activity of the people is the chief determinant of the *amount* of trade, but the natural resources, the position, and the stage of development determine the *kind* of trade. The distinction between the amount and the kind is important.

In exports, as in imports, Siam, Australia, and Switzerland afford an important contrast. In spite of great natural resources and a fairly large amount of land per farmer, the Siamese do not work hard enough or use sufficient judgment and skill to produce a large surplus of anything except rice, with some tin and teak. Hence, although their suplus per capita much exceeds that of India and China, its small size limits Siamese foreign trade to about $16 per capita for imports and exports together, even in years of prosperity. In Australia, as in Siam, the exports are entirely different from the imports, as is natural in a new country with abundant resources. The easiest and quickest sources of wealth are found in sheep, cattle, wheat, fruit, and the metals. Therefore, manufacturing of the more complex types has only recently reached the level where Australia supplies its own needs in even a few respects. But Australia has far more varied exports than Siam, as befits its greater activity and higher standards. The great size of Australia has little to do with this, for aside from the sugar-raising Region of Wet Tropical Agriculture, the productive parts of Australia all yield nearly the same products. In Switzerland, on the other hand, the imports and exports are largely the same in name but not in form. For instance, silk and cotton are imported as thread and exported as fine cloth. The Swiss cannot create a surplus from their natural resources; hence they add their skill to raw materials or partly manufactured materials from other countries so that the final products are often many times as valuable as the original materials. The exports of Switzerland, however, are systematically worth less than the imports because the Swiss receive from abroad large sums of money as interest on foreign investments and from the numerous tourists. Part of this money is used to pay for the excess of imports.

Conditions that Promote Active Commerce.—The main conditions that lead to an active exchange of products, both between foreign countries and different parts of the same country, are as follows:

1. *National or Racial Character.*—The vitality of the population causes northwestern Europe, the United States, Canada, New Zealand, Australia, Japan, and the more temperate South American states to be supreme in commerce as well as in other kinds of business. This vitality, as we have seen, although partly due to racial and historic factors, owes much of its intensity to climate.

2. *Diversity of Products.*—This is determined largely by climate and mineral resources, but also by relief and soil. Tropical countries owe most of their trade to the fact that their products differ from those of temperate regions. Costa Rica and Sumatra, for example, would have little foreign trade if people from other climates in the United States and Europe did not come to them for products that are found mainly within the tropics.

3. *Accessibility* is also highly important in determining the amount of trade between two regions. The East Indies might supply us with all that we get from the West Indies, but they actually send little, except rubber, tea, copra, and Manila hemp. It would scarcely pay to carry products 5,000 to 7,000 miles when we need to carry them only 1,000 to 3,000. It should be noted, however, that accessibility rather than mere distance is what counts. It is easier to carry goods 7,000 miles by sea where lines of communication are already established than 100 miles across mountains with no roads.

4. *Language, Customs, and Government.*—Everyone prefers to do business with someone whom he can understand. Hence, while Portugal has only a negligible trade with the rest of South America, a fifth of her exports up to the World War went to her former colony, the Portuguese-speaking country of Brazil. The growing importance of English as the language of commerce has decreased the significance of language as a barrier. An astonishingly small custom may prevent trade even among highly civilized people. For example, American salt pork sells better in England if salted with British salt. American salt leaves an insoluble white residue on the meat. This does no harm and Americans rather like it, but the British object. Hence, in order to maintain a profitable British trade, some packers import British salt which is absorbed completely by the pork.

The *form* of government makes little difference: the *character* is what counts, and that depends largely on the character of the people. A wise government can greatly increase trade by making proper laws as to taxes, shipping, and commercial intercourse. Many people think that Great Britain owed much of her foreign commerce to her policy of free trade, but this has now given place to preferential tariffs whereby goods from the British Empire pay less duty than others. Other people think that a protective tariff has stimulated domestic trade in the United States. Both of these conclusions are disputed, but almost everyone agrees that when backward people are governed and directed by those who are more progressive, trade is usually much stimulated. If India, the Philippines, Java, and the Guianas had never been under foreign governments, their foreign trade would be much smaller than at present.

The eastern United States and Cuba, England and Ceylon, the Netherlands and Java, and Belgium and Belgian Congo are pairs of diverse countries in which the conditions for active trade are especially favorable. This is notably true of the United States and Cuba. In spite of their differences in racial character, government, language, and customs, their proximity to one another and the fact that they have almost the right degree of difference of climate, plus the activity of the United States, cause the per capita trade of the Cubans with the United States to be exceeded only by that which the Dutch are able to carry on with the Germans because they hold the mouth of the Rhine.

The Dutch-German trade illustrates the principle that even though the resources are similar, trade is especially active wherever progressive countries can easily reach one another. The largest trade of the United States is with Canada and England—two countries whose products differ only a little from ours. Such countries often exchange one kind of cloth, machinery, or hardware, for another which differs only a little. Such active, wealthy people can afford to buy goods which differ from their own only in some special qualities which seem desirable.   Thus although the intensity of the trade between any two regions can be partly explained in terms of diversity of products, the activity of the people is at least equally important.

The World's Main Trade Routes.—A590 sums up many of the main facts as to the routes of commerce.   Except between the United States and Canada, and in western and central Europe, where a great many independent countries are crowded into a small space, most of the world's international trade goes by sea.   This is partly because transportation by water is much cheaper than by land.   Copper from Arizona, for example, reaches New York via the Panama Canal rather than by rail.   But international trade goes by water for another reason, namely, because the ocean generally furnishes the easiest routes between the great centers of activity and between these centers and the countries whence food and raw materials are derived.   Thus A590 shows that the greatest trade routes connect the following regions:

Group I. Western Europe with:
   1. The eastern United States.
   2. Eastern Asia via the Mediterranean Sea, India, and the East Indies, with branches to eastern Africa and Australia.
   3. Southeastern South America.
   4. South Africa via the west coast.
   5. The West Indies and Panama.

Group II. The Northeastern United States with:
   6. The western United States via the West Indies and Panama.
   7. The Mediterranean region.
   8. Southeastern South America.
   9. Western South America.

Group III. The Western United States with:
   10. Eastern Asia.
   11. Australia and New Zealand.

The relative importance of these routes is indicated roughly by the heaviness of the lines in A590, but the limits of space on the map cause the most important routes, especially No. 1 and the section where Nos. 2, 3, and 4 are combined, to receive much less than their due weight. Routes by land corresponding to many of the eleven ocean routes named above are impossible, while those which are possible are in most cases slower, more difficult, and more expensive than by sea.

The Part Played by Railroads in World Commerce.—The function of railroads in world commerce is very different from that of ships.

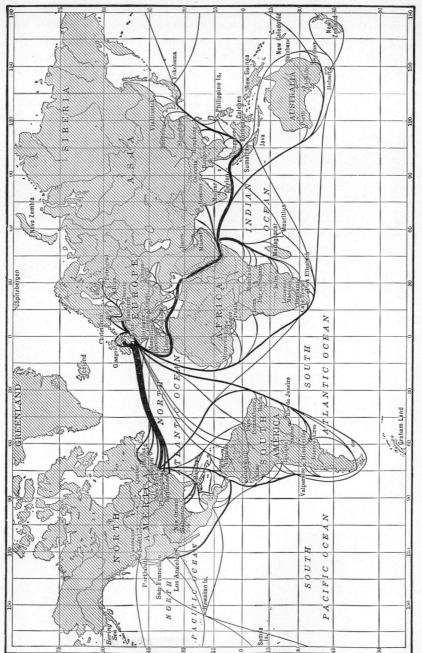

A—The World's Main Routes of Commerce.

Long transcontinental railroads, like the Trans-Siberian line, the line
from Chile to Argentina, and the railroad between west and east Australia, are of minor importance in international or long-distance commerce.   Their chief value lies in local commerce, in the creation of
political unity, and in providing rapid passenger service.   This is true
also of the North American transcontinental lines, although the transcontinental transportation of valuable perishable products, such as

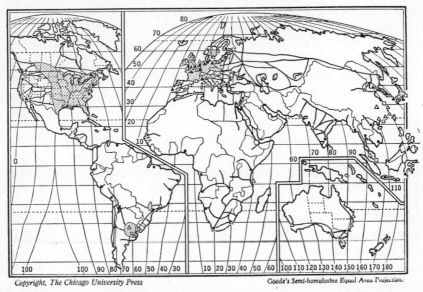

Goode's Semi-homolosine Equal Area Projection.

A—Railroads and Chief Ports of Foreign Commerce. Shaded areas indicate regions
where practically all parts are within 10 miles of a railroad.   Total tonnage of
vessels entering and leaving ports per year is indicated as follows:

■ Over 20,000,000 tons
□ 10–20,000,000
▲ 5–10,000,000
△ 2–5,000,000
• Below 2,000,000

fruit, vegetables, and eggs, is important.   The main task of the railroad
in world commerce is to bring produce from the place of origin to the
export harbors.   The shaded sections of A591 show that in large parts
of Europe and North America, in two small sections of South America,
and in Japan, the density of railroads is so high that few places are farther
than 10 miles from a railroad.   In North America the border line
between such an intensive railroad system and the more open or extensive system depends largely on rainfall on the west and temperature on

the north.   It follows the 20-inch isohyet in the southern United States, but bends westward farther north where lower temperature makes a smaller rainfall sufficient for agriculture.   In Canada it swings far enough west and north to include the dense railroad system of the wheat region of Alberta and Saskatchewan.   In Europe the similar dividing line separates the economically important parts of Norway and Sweden, namely the Oslo region and Svealand, from the northern forests which are too cool for much agriculture.   Across the Baltic the line lies on the eastern border of the regions formerly belonging to the German Empire, but now partly in Poland, and projects eastward in the Danube Basin to include most of the former Austro-Hungarian Empire.   The irregularity of this line is due largely to political considerations, but in general the line lies in the transitional zone where the regular and high crop yields of western Europe give place to the irregular and low yields of eastern Europe.   It is noteworthy that in railroads, as in many other respects, Japan is unlike the rest of Asia.   In South America also the railroads are dense in the two most productive areas.

The selected railroads outside the shaded areas of A591 suggest a tendency which appears much more clearly on maps in an atlas showing the complete railroad system.   This tendency is to radiate from harbors, thus forming an inland fan, tributary to each harbor, or else to run along the coast and connect the different harbors. Africa, South America, and Australia offer excellent examples of both types.   In countries with a more advanced railroad system, for example, Spain, Russia, and India, we see not only railroads centering on harbors, but a political arrangement of railroads so that a great many from all directions join at Madrid in Spain, at Moscow in Russia, and Delhi in India.   The importance of such railroads is mainly local and not international.

The Conditions that Produce Seaports. 1. *The Hinterland.*—In discussing the seaports (A591) where ships meet railroads, we need to consider both the hinterlands and the harbors.   The *hinterland* is the region from which a city receives goods or which it supplies with goods.   If the hinterland produces a large surplus and therefore has a large demand for goods, important seaports will grow up even if the harbors are poor, as appears at Los Angeles.   New York is the world's largest seaport primarily because it serves a large hinterland which is almost unparalleled in natural resources and climate, and in which the density of population has recently been close to the optimum.   Moreover, its hinterland is far larger than that of places like Boston, New London, New Haven, or even Philadelphia and Baltimore because it is connected with the Lake Region and the interior plains by the Hudson and Mohawk Valleys which furnish the easiest of all routes across the Appalachian Highland.

The seaports of the Pacific Coast of both North and South America cannot carry on so much trade as those of the Atlantic Coast because great mountains hem them in. But the degree of activity of the people is even more important than their number in determining the amount of trade at seaports. The average man on the farms in Russia raises less than 70 bushels of grain per year in contrast to 550 in the United States as a whole and 1,350 in Iowa. Obviously the surplus with which to maintain the trade of the seaports must be vastly less in Russia than in the United States. Naturally, then, the world's greatest seaports are found where broad fertile lowlands with resources of minerals as well as agriculture are accessible to the sea and enjoy a climate which is stimulating for both man and crops. A591, with its concentration of seaports in northwestern Europe, the northeastern United States, Japan, and the Plata River region, illustrates the matter. But this map by no means does full justice to the United States, for it omits a vast amount of domestic trade which would be foreign trade if this country were divided into as many small countries as is western Europe.

The quality of the trade of seaports, as distinguished from quantity, depends partly on the resources of the hinterland and partly on its stage of development. In mature, well populated regions of the progressive type like western Europe the activity of the people causes their surplus to consist mainly of manufactured goods, while the density of the population and their industrial character cause the demand to be mainly for food and raw materials. In less mature but progressive regions like Australia almost the reverse is the case, for manufactured goods are imported, while food and raw materials are exported. Between these two extremes there are all sorts of intermediate forms. Thus the northeastern harbors of the United States, although mainly exporting manufactures, also ship grain, fruit, and half-finished iron goods. Even England, which perhaps comes the nearest to being a purely manufacturing country, ships coal in large quantities. Our Northeast is much like England in its kinds of trade, but the South exports mainly cotton and lumber, while the West ships oil, fruit, and copper from the southern half and lumber, grain, and fruit from the north. So the quality of the trade of a harbor depends on the kinds of products in the hinterland.

2. *Harbors.*—Good harbors are a necessity in developing seaports, but they may be artificial, as in the case of Los Angeles and many minor places. Moreover, the mere presence of good natural harbors is not enough to cause the growth of seaports. Some of the world's best harbors, such as Guantanamo Bay in Cuba and Pago Pago in Samoa, have no seaports worth mentioning simply because they have no hinterlands. Nevertheless, wherever nature provides good natural

harbors that are easily accessible to good hinterlands, the greatest cities are bound to grow up beside the best harbors. Although New York is the world's leading seaport primarily because of its marvelous hinterland, it also owes part of its dominance to its marvelous harbor. If the harbor at New York were no better than that at Atlantic City, the greatest city of the United States might have grown up at some neighboring harbor of intermediate quality like New Haven. The point is that the hinterland demands a seaport, not too far away, and the nature of the coast determines in just what locality this seaport shall develop.

Here are the qualities of the ideal harbor. It should be (1) well protected against storms; (2) deep enough for large vessels, with fairly deep water near the shore; (3) wide enough to give space for large ships to turn in; (4) so sinuous in its coastline that there is abundant room for docks and wharves; (5) well provided with land that is well drained and yet level enough to furnish space for the growth of a city; and (6) accessible to the interior by straight and level routes which make it easier to bring goods to it than to other harbors which may perhaps be actually nearer to the place where the goods are produced.

The degree to which these conditions are met depends on the topography of the land and on the degree to which the respective levels of the land and sea have changed in recent geological times. Recently depressed coasts almost invariably have more and better harbors than do emergent coasts. This is evident when the many good harbors from Baltimore northward to Labrador are compared with the relatively poor harbors south of Baltimore. A similar comparison holds good in respect to each of the following pairs of regions: (1) the depressed Pacific Coast of North America from Puget Sound northward versus the uplifted coast from south of San Francisco to Mexico; (2) the depressed coast of western Europe from France to Norway, and the emergent coast of southern Spain and Italy; (3) the depressed coast of Japan and the emergent coast of eastern India; (4) the depressed coast of the southern part of Chile and the emergent Pacific Coast from Valparaiso northward. Except in the eastern United States and the North Sea region these depressed coasts suffer because the ocean covers so large a part of the level land. Rio de Janeiro and San Francisco in areas of local depression are examples of this. Their harbors are superb, but the land rises so steeply from the sea that the cities have to climb steep heights or spread out onto land recovered from the sea. Seattle, Vancouver, Oslo, Yokohama, Fuchow, and Hongkong display the same characteristics.

Much better harbors are found where plains or lowlands of gentle relief have been moderately depressed. Boston, New York, Philadelphia, and Baltimore all lie on coasts of this kind. Similar conditions are found in England with its wide-open drowned river outlets at Liverpool, Hull, Glasgow, and Bristol, as well as London. On the continent of Europe similar drowned harbors in regions of gentle relief have helped to develop seaports at Stockholm, Copenhagen, Hamburg, and Bremen. In Australia the drowned harbor of Sydney is one of the most magnificent in the world.

Emergent coasts and also those due to the recent formation of deltas generally have relatively poor harbors but plenty of space for cities. Long sand bars with *lagoons* behind them are a common feature of such coasts and often provide sufficient protection to determine the site of seaports. Miami in Florida, the Texan port of Galveston with its busy canal to Houston, and San Diego in California are examples of this type in North America. Kingston in Jamaica is also a lagoon harbor, as is Venice in Europe. Dredges are often necessary to keep the outlet deep, and sometimes a canal through the bar has to be dug to make the harbor up-to-date. Amsterdam on the former Zuider Zee has a lagoon harbor on an arm of the sea inside the coastal dunes. The shallowness of the inland waters, and the increasing size and draft of ships, greatly handicapped this port until a canal with the world's most extensive lock was cut through the dunes to connect it directly with the North Sea.

On many emergent coasts *open bays* that need the protection of breakwaters are the best sites available for seaports. Cape Town on Table Bay, Valparaiso in Chile, Genoa, Barcelona, Trieste, and many others in the Mediterranean are examples. In such cases there is often little chance for wharves and docks, and sometimes so little space is available within the protected zone that the open roadstead is still in use. On other coasts that are either emergent or else are being built outward by deposits washed out from the land, *rocky islands* or small *peninsulas* afford almost the only protection for ships. In fact the islands or peninsulas often make better sites for seaports than do the neighboring coasts where silt is rapidly deposited, or where the conditions of health are bad. Zanzibar has thus become one of the main harbors in East Africa. Penang, and Singapore, which is now connected by a bridge with the mainland, are other examples. Hongkong on Victoria Island is still the greatest seaport of southern China. Allied to this type are the seaports located where a small peninsula takes the place of an island in affording protection from storms. The Syrian cities of Sidon and Tyre are classic examples of cities on little rocky peninsulas. A modern representative is Gibraltar. Where neither lagoons, bays, or peninsulas are available, seaports may grow up on rather straight coasts where artificial harbors are needed. In such cases expensive breakwaters and piers are needed to change open roadsteads into harbors in which ships can lie in safety. They are built only where geographical conditions necessitate the making of outlets for trade on coasts without natural harbors. Los Angeles is the most famous example of this sort. Others include Tandjong Priok, the harbor of Batavia, which is built on a flat swampy coast and is entirely artificial, Madras in India, Callao and Montevideo in South America, and Dover, where people cross from England to France. Such emergent or straight coasts abound in low latitudes where the ships anchor in open roadsteads, and the port facilities of a great number of slightly developed coastal settlements are often limited to a jetty, or landing place, for motor boats which ply between ship and shore.

3. *Rivers and Seaports.*—No matter whether a coast is depressed or emergent, crooked or straight, the harbors at the mouths of rivers generally have the advantage over others. The city symbols in A591 show the combined effect of hinterlands, harbors, rivers, and general location in respect to trade routes in causing the seaports of the world to be visited by ships. The symbols do not indicate the size of the cities or the volume of their domestic commerce. They simply show the tonnage of the ships engaged in foreign commerce which enter the ports each year regardless of whether the ships leave any goods or not. Of the five harbors where ships with a tonnage of over 20 million tons enter each year (solid squares in A591), four are located at the mouths of rivers near the North Sea—London, Rotterdam, Antwerp, and Hamburg. The other, New York, the world's most important harbor, is also at the mouth of a river. All five, be it noted, are in the very heart of the regions in

which the climate, relief, and resources provide the finest hinterlands. Among the twelve cities with an entrance tonnage of 10 to 20 million tons (open squares in A591), five, namely, Shanghai, Hongkong, which is the port for the Si River, Marseille, Liverpool, and Buenos Aires are also at the mouths of rivers. This is not true, however, of Tokyo (Yokohama), Kobe, Rio de Janeiro, and Montevideo. The other three among these ports of second size do not count so far as our estimate of the effect of rivers is concerned. Colombo and Singapore owe their very high tonnage to their value as stopping places for steamers on the way from Europe to eastern Asia and Australia, and Cherbourg in France is merely a stopping place where transatlantic liners leave passengers for Paris.

Many river ports are not located directly at the mouths of their rivers. Some, like Montreal and Portland, Oregon, are located as far inland as ocean ships can navigate. Others, like London, are at the lowest point where it is easy to cross the river, and hence at the point where a route parallel to the coast crosses the river route running inland. Such places often have an advantage because the river can be bridged without much difficulty. Again a location away from the mouth of the river may remove the city from the swampy and often unhealthful areas near the outer edges of the deltas, as in the case of New Orleans. In many cases an outer port, like Quebec, is located near the real river outlet and is used for fast passenger traffic, while the main port is farther inland. In some cases also minor branches of the main river are the best places for the development of the harbor, as at Shanghai. If the river itself is of little importance for navigation, so that the traffic goes inland by rail, the seaport may develop on the edge of the delta where it meets the firmer shore as at Alexandria and Marseille.

The recent construction of wharves, docks, and other port facilities at Albany, and the attempt to draw Albany, Troy, and Schenectady into a single great inland port, show how seaports tend to migrate inland as far as possible. But even if this port becomes very important, New York will still have the advantage of a superb harbor and of being located where the great route along the Atlantic Coast crosses the best route inland. In South America, Manáos is the final port on the Amazon for ocean vessels, but Pará on the southern edge of the Amazon Delta is the real harbor. Buenos Aires is located on a small branch of the Plata estuary, but is scarcely a real river harbor. In Africa the river ports aside from Alexandria are very small places like Banana at the mouth of the Congo. In Europe the three great harbors of Hamburg, Rotterdam, and Antwerp are found at the mouths of the Elbe, Rhine, and Scheldt, each harbor being well inland. The Elbe, and especially the Rhine, are excellent rivers for navigation. About 100,000 river steamers pass the Dutch border on the Rhine each year. Rotterdam has an artificial outlet to the river, as the old one was not practical for modern shipping. Canal connections with northern France and the Rhine help to compensate Antwerp for the minor importance of the river on which it is located. Other European seaports at river mouths include Danzig near the mouth of the Vistula, Stettin on the Oder, Bremen on the Weser, Rouen on the Seine with Le Havre as its outer port, Nantes on the Loire, Bordeaux on the Garonne, Marseille which lies on the rocky coast east of the Rhône Delta and is connected by canal through a tunnel with that river, Brăila on the Danube, Odessa near the Dnieper, and Rostov near the Don outlet. Asia, especially the Far East, has numerous examples: Karachi is near the Indus Delta, Calcutta on one of the branches of the Ganges, Rangoon on the Irawadi Delta, Bangkok on the Salween River, Saigon on a side branch of the Mekong, and Canton on the Pearl River. Most impressive of all perhaps is Shanghai on the Whangpoo near the Yangtze outlet, where it is the seaport of a navigable river system of tremendous potential value and has its inner port nearly a thousand miles away at Hankow.

The Distribution of World Trade.—The amount of international trade in the various countries, that is, exports plus imports, is shown in A597 in percentages of the total for the world as a whole. The outstanding position of northwestern and central Europe is evident. Compared with Europe the United States with 15 per cent of the total is by no means so prominent as one would expect. In fact it ranks below Great Britain. Outside the United States and Europe only Canada (4 per cent), Japan (3), India (3), Argentina (2), China (2),

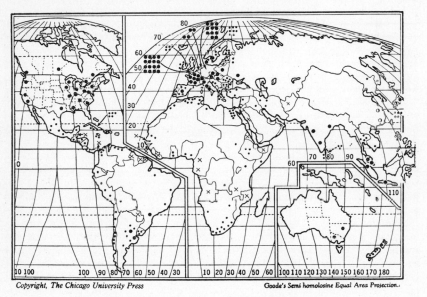

Goode's Semi homolosine Equal Area Projection.:

A—World Map of Total Foreign Trade. Large dots indicate 1 per cent of world total; small dots one-tenth of 1 per cent; crosses minor amount.

Malay States (2), Netherland East Indies (2), Australia (2), and Brazil (1), reach the 1 per cent level, although South Africa, New Zealand, Cuba, Chile, Egypt, and French North Africa come near it. The great accumulation of dots in northwestern and central Europe, however, is more or less misleading, because Europe is divided into so many small countries. If Great Britain, France, the three Scandinavian countries, the two Low Countries, and Switzerland were all united into one country with a population equal to that of the United States, their foreign trade would be reduced just about one-fourth. But these countries are on the whole much alike in climate and production. If the United States with its great diversity of natural regions were divided into eight countries the size of those just named, their combined foreign trade would probably be twice as great as that of the United States at present. Most of the wheat, cotton, fruit, iron ore, coal, and other products that now travel a thousand miles or more within the country would pass from one country to another and be counted as foreign trade. The misapprehension which thus arises because large countries are compared with small ones in A597 could be removed only by making a map of all trade, both foreign and domestic; but no statistics are available for this.

The amount of foreign trade per capita is quite as important as the absolute total. A map of this (A598) presents quite a different aspect

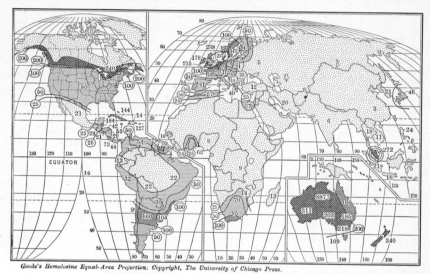

Goode's Homolosine Equal-Area Projection: Copyright, The University of Chicago Press.

A—Total Annual Foreign Trade per Capita, 1927–1929.
Ceylon should be shaded like the United States.

from A597. The density of the population in Europe, Japan, China, and India lowers the rank of those regions, while countries with a low density of population rank much higher. Western Europe as a whole, however, still stands out, but other regions, especially the young countries in temperate climatic regions, like Canada, Australia, New Zealand, South Africa, Chile, Uruguay, and Argentina, become prominent. So do some of the tropical countries, such as those around the Caribbean, the Gold Coast, Ceylon, and the Malay Peninsula. Even here the United States holds a relative position much lower than that of many countries which are commercially far less active. Its foreign trade per capita is less than that of British and Dutch Guiana and only about one-third that of Switzerland and the countries bordering the North Sea. Russia, too, shows a very low figure, only 5, which is far less than that of much more backward and inactive regions like India (6), Persia (20), and Paraguay (30). The low figure for the United States here, just as in total foreign trade, is merely the result of great size and diversity. The United States carries on such an enormous internal trade that its exports amount to only one-tenth of its production. In Europe, on the other hand, the figures for the active countries of the west are very different. Belgium and Denmark export half of all that they produce, Switzerland a third, Great Britain and France a fourth, and Germany a fifth. Only in eastern Europe do we find countries which export so small a share of their production as does the United States. In Russia this is partly because that country is large and highly diverse, although not so much so as the United States. But there, too, as in all of the less active countries of eastern Europe and Asia, the general low level of productivity per man means that only a small part of the production is available for export.

On the other hand, new and progressive countries have a large foreign trade per capita because they not only devote themselves largely to the production of food and raw materials, but work so well and have such large resources in land and minerals that they enjoy a huge surplus. Canada with its exports of wheat, timber, and minerals; Argentina with grain, linseed, meat, hides, and wool; Chile with nitrates and copper; South Africa with gold; Australia with wool and wheat; and New Zealand with wool and butter are typical of active countries in which manufacturing is not yet very advanced. Further development may lower their foreign trade per capita because they will use their own food and raw materials at home to support factories, and will buy their own manufactured goods instead of importing from abroad.

The Wet Tropical Agricultural Regions often show this same tendency toward a large foreign trade per capita because they produce staple plantation products and export them in exchange for food and manufactures. Their trade tends to be kept down, however, by the low buying power of the population. The Netherlands East Indies with its diverse plantation products, the Malay Peninsula with its rubber and tin, Ceylon with its tea, the Philippine Islands with sugar and Manila hemp, the Gold Coast with cacao, Nigeria with palm oil, Brazil with coffee, and the Caribbean region with sugar, tobacco, bananas, and oil represent this group.

Conditions in western Europe lead to high overseas trade per capita in almost the opposite way. The old progressive countries face a large deficit in both food and raw materials, which have to be imported in great quantities. They have, however, a surplus of manufactured goods, as in England, Germany, Belgium, and Switzerland, or else of locally specialized food products like fish in Norway, dairy products in Denmark and Ireland, and both dairy products and garden truck in Holland.

The United States and Japan are intermediate between those two extremes. The United States, once a great food exporter, now imports almost the same amount of food that it exports. Moreover, a great deal of the raw material which it formerly exported is now used at home and exported in the form of manufactures. Cotton, however, is still

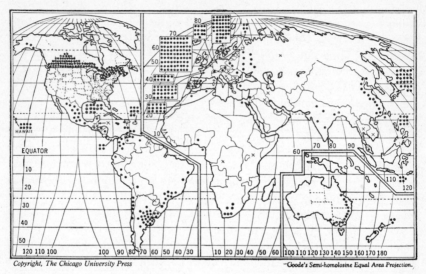

~Goode's Semi-homolosine Equal Area Projection.

A—Exports from the United States in a Busy Year. Each dot indicates a value of $10,000,000. Each cross $1,000,000–$5,000,000.

an exception in this respect, for half of our crop is still exported. Japan still exports one raw material (silk) on a large scale, but imports not only food, especially rice and sugar, but also raw materials, chiefly cotton. Its increasing surplus of manufactures, mainly textiles, swamps the markets of eastern Asia. The large light sections on both A597 and A598 represent the enormous areas which are still of minor significance to world trade. Some of these, especially in China and India, represent great potentialities for the future.

Distribution of American Trade.—A600 and A601 show where the United States sends its exports and gets its imports. The outstanding fact in both maps is the overwhelming preponderance of Canada and the Marine Cyclonic Region of western Europe. The primary cause of this is that in these regions the people are unusually active and productive, but accessibility to the United States also plays a large part. Because of the activity of the people, Japan and the temperate part of South America in Argentina and Chile are conspicuous on both maps, while Australia, New Zealand, and South Africa are fairly conspicuous on the map of exports.   Aside from these cool, active areas the other conspicuous places on both maps are mainly Regions of Wet Tropical Agriculture.   In A602, imports and exports are combined into a single figure showing how the various countries rank in trade per capita with the United States.   There the preeminence of Canada is even more

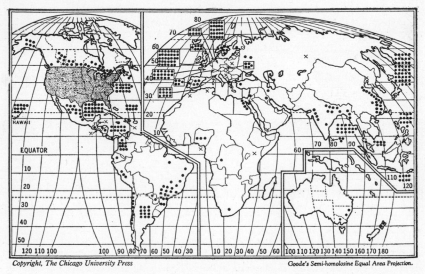

Copyright, The Chicago University Press   *Goode's Semi-homolosine Equal Area Projection.*

A—Origin of the Imports into the United States during a Busy Year.   Each dot indicates $10,000,000.   Each cross indicates $1,000,000-$5,000,000.

marked than in A600 and A601.   Among the cooler parts of the earth, it stands in a class by itself.   In the tropical zone, however, Hawaii with its sugar and pineapples, British Honduras, Puerto Rico, and Cuba with their sugar, and the Malay region with its rubber also stand exceptionally high.   The noteworthy fact in this map is that the trade per capita declines quite regularly in accordance with the acessibility of the various regions to the United States.   Nevertheless, this is altered decidedly by exceptional circumstances like our political control of the Philippines, the competent white population of Hawaii, and the degree to which the climate is favorable for activity in New Zealand.

Another map, A603, shows how the sales of the United States compare with the purchases in various parts of the world.   The lined shading indicates that in the cooler parts of both hemispheres the United States sells considerably more than it buys. In western Europe this excess of sales is made up mainly of cotton, wheat, and other food products; elsewhere of manufactured articles. We are able to sell to Europe far more than we buy only because our bankers keep making loans which the Europeans use to pay us for the goods that we send them. Such a system is obviously very dangerous because the debts of Europe keep piling up with no way to pay them. In the warmer parts of the world the dotted shading shows that the United States as a rule buys more

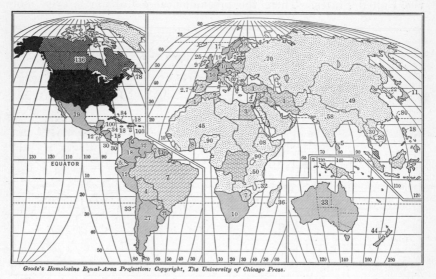

Goode's Homolosine Equal-Area Projection: Copyright, The University of Chicago Press.

A—Total Trade per Capita with the United States.

than it sells. The regions which raise tropical products are generally too poor to buy much. Moreover, they do not have to buy goods in order to balance their trade, for much of the payment for their crops stays in the United States in the form of profits from plantations or interest on loans instead of coming back in the form of goods.

Two other maps complete the picture of the world trade of the United States. A604 shows what percentages of the exports of the various countries come to the United States. This map, to a peculiar degree, brings out the effect of proximity. The heaviest shading, indicating that more than 60 per cent of all the exports of a country go to the United States, is confined to eight Caribbean regions and to the Philippines, where the element of political dominance controls the direction of trade. The political factor is also evident in the small share of the trade of British and French Guiana that comes to us.   Note how isolation reduces the figures for Bolivia, Paraguay, Poland, Hungary, Persia, and other countries.   Similarity between their products and our own also reduces the figures in Argentina, Uruguay, and Australia. On the other hand, the percentages are raised by the local abundance of products that we want, such as silk in Japan, rubber in the Malay Peninsula, and coffee in Brazil.   Turning to B604, we see that because of proximity to the United States all the countries of North America, the Caribbean region, and northwestern South America buy from us at

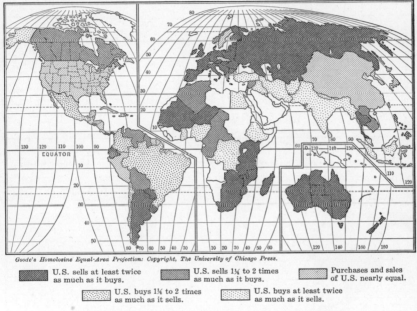

Goode's Homolosine Equal-Area Projection: Copyright, The University of Chicago Press.

U.S. sells at least twice as much as it buys.	U.S. sells 1¼ to 2 times as much as it buys.	Purchases and sales of U.S. nearly equal.
U.S. buys 1¼ to 2 times as much as it sells.	U.S. buys at least twice as much as it sells.	

A—Purchases of the United States Compared with Sales.

least 40 per cent of their imports and generally over 60 per cent.   The political factor is again evident in the heavy shading of the Philippines, and in the light shading of Africa which buys from the countries that rule it.

Trade of the United States with Individual Regions.   1. *Canada.*—The foreign trade of the United States is naturally divided into a number of distinct types according to the climate, resources, distance, accessibility, type of culture, and stage of development of the various countries.   Canada holds a unique position.   Its nearness and accessibility, its high type of culture, which is our own not only in language but in government, habits, and ideals, and the fact that its stage of development is not so advanced as ours all combine to cause its trade with the United States

to exceed that of every other country, including Great Britain. Another factor in
this huge trade is a difference of climate greater than is usually recognized.   In

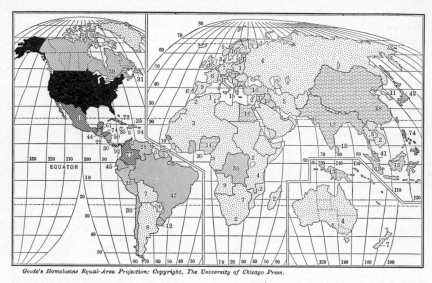

Goode's Homolosine Equal-Area Projection: Copyright, The University of Chicago Press.

A—Percentage of Exports of Foreign Countries Coming to the United States.

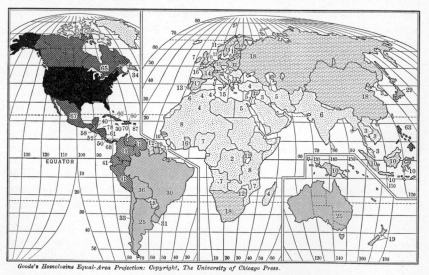

Goode's Homolosine Equal-Area Projection: Copyright, The University of Chicago Press.

B—Percentage of Imports of Foreign Countries Coming from the United States.

Plate I most of Canada lies either in the Cool Continental Interior or the Cool Forest
Region.   Therefore, although we should expect the Canadians to be very active, we
should also expect their types of economic activity to be somewhat different from

ours. Finally, the mineral resources of the two countries are quite different. Thus an uncommonly large number of factors combine to cause active commerce. In contrast with the Canadian conditions, our mineral resources, our stage of development, the climate of our Continental Cyclonic and Warm Temperate Humid Regions lead us to send Canada not only a vast amount of manufactured goods, including machinery, farm implements, automobiles, chemicals, textiles, and a multitude of metal products, but also unmanufactured or only slightly manufactured products in the form of raw cotton; fruit and vegetables; and coal, coke, crude petroleum, and gasoline in enormous quantities. Canada in return sends us considerable food in the form of meat, dairy products, fish, and grain, and even swaps vegetables with us in almost equal quantities. Much more important, however, are the metals. These come mainly from the region north of Lake Superior and include copper, gold, and silver, together with nickel and asbestos, both of which happen to be scarce in the United States. All other Canadian products, however, sink into insignificance in comparison with those derived from the great forests. Lumber, pulp wood, pulp, and the kind of paper called newsprint, which is used for newspapers, form practically half of our imports from Canada. Most of the trade between the United States and Canada crosses the border between Montreal and Detroit. West of the Great Lakes, the land on both sides of the border produces about the same things, and there is little manufacturing. Therefore the farmers on both sides buy farm implements, motor vehicles, gasoline, textiles, and hardware from the same sources in the eastern or southern United States.

2. *Northwestern and Central Europe.*—The relation of the United States to western Europe is much like that of Canada to the United States. That is, although the two regions are much alike in many ways, they belong to different natural regions and are in a different stage of development. The United Kingdom, the Irish Free State, France, Germany, Scandinavia, the Low Countries, Czechoslovakia, Switzerland, Austria, and Hungary form only 2 per cent of the lands of the earth and have only 10 per cent of the inhabitants, but they supply a quarter of all the imports to the United States, and take about two-fifths of all the exports. For the most part they are so densely populated and so advanced in manufacturing that they have little surplus food or raw materials. On the other hand, they have an enormous surplus of manufactured goods. The kinds that they excel in are represented by the substantial cotton, woolen, and linen goods of England; the silks and other fancy textiles of France; the chemicals of Germany; the finely cut precious stones of Belgium and Holland; and the clocks and small hardware of Switzerland. It is interesting, however, to note that northwestern and central Europe do send us a few kinds of food and semi-manufactured products. These are based almost entirely on the fact that the climate favors animal husbandry, fishing, and forests. Thus France, Netherlands, and especially Switzerland send us cheese. Norway and Holland send fish. The moist, mild climate is so good for animals and our capacity to use both leather and wool is so great that almost every one of these countries sends us hides and leather, while England and even France send some wool. This same climate, plus careful forestry practice and our insatiable habit of reading big newspapers and using paper lavishly, allows France, Germany, Norway, and especially Sweden to send us wood pulp or paper; even Czechoslovakia and Austria send a little. This is amusing, for the French, for example, leave unwrapped loaves of bread on doorsteps, but send paper to a country where even men's shirts in stores are often wrapped in cellophane. This simply illustrates the fact that the density of population, the limited natural resources, and the recent wars of western Europe have not allowed the standards of living to rise as they have in the United States.

In return for the manufactures of Europe we send them large amounts of manufactured goods, chiefly in the form of electrical machinery, motor vehicles, sewing machines, industrial machinery, and devices like typewriters and cash registers. Motor vehicles and sewing machines are among our most widely used exports. A far larger part of our exports to western Europe still consists of food and raw materials. In relation to Europe the United States not only is still relatively new, but contains large natural regions not especially adapted to manufacturing but excellent for supplying food, fibers, and minerals. Accordingly most of the 13 countries in northwestern and central Europe receive from us some animal food, especially lard; a certain amount of cereal food, mainly wheat and wheat flour; some feed for animals, which includes cottonseed cake; and a certain amount of fruit and vegetables, partly fresh and partly canned or dried. To the countries near the North Sea we also send some lumber, while most of these 13 countries depend on us for part of their supply of tobacco and copper. Two great products, however, far excel all others as exports from the United States to Europe. The most important of these is cotton, which is the most valuable of all our exports. The other is petroleum products, which stand next to cotton among our exports, unless we group together all kinds of machinery. Cotton and petroleum comprise between 25 and 30 per cent of all our exports to the world as a whole, but form nearly 40 per cent of our exports to western Europe.

3. *Eastern Europe and Northern Asia.*—Although the Soviet Republic, Poland, the Baltic States, Finland, and Rumania cover many times as large an area as northwestern and central Europe and have more people, their total trade with the United States is only about 6 per cent as great (A600–601). Three conditions produce this result. One is their distance from us, or rather their inaccessibility. Not only are they far away in miles, but the sea routes to them are circuitous, their ports do not lie on the way to other important countries, and above all they are much farther from us than from western Europe. Therefore the natural thing is for them to trade with western Europe. Second, eastern Europe does not produce much that we want. Cereals, flax, lumber, hides, wool, and furs are some of their chief articles of trade, but either we have plenty of these ourselves, or can get them much easier somewhere else. Thirdly, these countries are all very poor. Therefore they have only a small surplus and cannot afford to spend much of it in buying goods from west of the Atlantic. The result is that although these countries have nearly 35 times as many people as Sweden, we buy from them only as much as from that country. The only items worth mentioning are some lumber and pulp wood from the Soviet Republic and especially Finland, and some furs, manganese, and sausage casings, mainly from Russia. On the other hand, eastern Europe buys from us nearly three times as much as it sells to us. The reason is that these countries need our motor vehicles, agricultural implements, electrical equipment, and other kinds of machinery. The geographical conditions, however, are such that there is little reason to expect any great growth of trade with eastern Europe and northern Asia.

4. *Southern Europe and Western Asia.*—Here the situation is quite different from that of eastern Europe. Portugal, Spain, Italy, Yugoslavia, Greece, Turkey, Syria, Palestine, and even Bulgaria are more accessible to the United States than is most of eastern Europe, and they are not cut off in the same way by enterprising manufacturing countries. Only Persia is really isolated and it is of negligible importance. All these countries are alike in having a Mediterranean climate. Italy, Spain, and Greece are much the most important, as appears in A600 and A601. Most of these countries have little industrial development, but the Po Valley and the Barcelona

region are marked exceptions. All these Mediterranean regions produce certain products which the United States cannot produce so easily or abundantly. Therefore they sell us four or five times as much and buy from us two or three times as much as does eastern Europe with nearly twice as many people. Italy, Spain, and even Portugal and Yugoslavia on a small scale behave like western Europe in wanting our raw cotton as well as our petroleum. Italy also buys from us a fair amount of wheat, lard, and copper. Greece likewise relies on us for wheat to a surprising degree, sometimes taking as much as or more than it raises. Thus in some respects we play the rôle of the less developed country. On the other hand, they buy our motor cars and machinery far more than we buy theirs. The goods that we get from southern Europe depend mainly on the fact that the Mediterranean Type of climate here reaches its fullest development. So we buy Spanish almonds and peppers; Turkish and Portuguese figs; Italian tomatoes, lemons, walnuts, and other fruits and vegetables; Yugoslavian walnuts; the little Greek raisins known as currants; and attar of roses from Bulgaria. But far in excess of all these we buy pickled olives from Spain and olive oil from both Spain and Italy, while we rely almost entirely upon Spain and Portugal for cork. Thus the Mediterranean peninsulas supply us with certain articles which we should really miss if they could not be imported, whereas the loss of the imports from eastern Europe or western Asia would hardly be noticed.

5. *Japan and China.*—Japan strongly resembles the countries of western Europe in the way in which it takes great amounts of American cotton and considerable quantities of lumber and metals for use in its factories. It also buys automobiles and some kerosene, but not much gasoline because it cannot afford many motor vehicles. Japan is also like western Europe in that it imports our wheat in order to support its industrial population. Thus on the whole Japan treats the United States as a source of raw material and food to aid it in manufacturing. We treat Japan in the same way. We buy only a little food, to be sure, such as crab meat and tea, but we purchase an enormous amount of raw silk. This forms 80 or 85 per cent of our purchases from Japan and more than a third of that country's total exports. One interesting feature of the exchange of our cotton for Japan's silk is that Japan re-exports most of the cotton in manufactured form to China, India, and elsewhere, whereas we use most of the silk at home.

The difference between our foreign trade with China and that with Japan agrees with many other facts in suggesting that perhaps the two ought to be regarded as in separate natural regions, for Japan resembles the Cyclonic Regions in a good many ways, while China suggests the tropics. The two great products which we send to China are tobacco, much of which is in the form of cigarettes, and kerosene, which is very widely used in lighting houses. It seems strange that the next article on the list of exports should be cotton. The reason is that although China raises cotton the demand for food is so pressing that not enough cotton is raised to supply the factories which have recently grown up. Wheat, lumber, machinery, and other iron goods come next among our exports to China, but neither China nor Japan is nearly so good a market for complex manufactured goods as for simpler materials. From China, as from Japan, our chief import is silk, but only about one-twentieth as much. China is so densely populated and therefore so poor and so subject to the ravages of famine that she has a very small foreign commerce per capita. Furs, hides, and wool from the drier and colder north, together with bristles, tea, a variety of textiles, and some beancake almost complete the list of important exports.

6. *Temperate South America.*—All three countries in this part of the world demand

nearly the same goods from the United States, but each supplies a special kind of product in return. Since they are new and sparsely populated, with abundant resources, their buying power is high (A134), but their manufactures are not much developed and they can get abundant food near home. Hence they take our petroleum in all its forms, our lumber in small amounts, textiles, and especially iron, steel, and the machinery and motor vehicles into which they are made. In return we do not want the wheat and corn which are Argentina's chief products. So we take great quantities of linseed and hides, together with wool and the extract of the quebracho tree for tanning. From Chile we take little except copper from the mines in the central mountains, and nitrate and iodine from the northern desert. Since Uruguay has few resources aside from its animals, it naturally sends us wool and hides. Americans sometimes wonder why we have such difficulty in increasing our trade with these active countries of temperate South America. The answer is that their products are almost the same as those of our central and western states. Such products are wanted in western Europe, and therefore it is natural for the trade between Europe and South America to be active.

7. *Australia and New Zealand.*—In proportion to their population, Australia and New Zealand are two of our best customers. Their eight million people actually buy as much from us as do one hundred times as many people in China and India. They do not sell us so much, only one-fifth as much as China and India, but that is twenty times as much per capita. The reason for this active trade is first that these countries are new with plenty of room and no overpopulation such as is the curse not only of southern and eastern Asia but likewise much of Europe. Second, they live in some of the best climates. Third, they have a fine inheritance both biologically and culturally; and fourth, although far away, their activity has caused the establishment of such good steamer service that they are more accessible than much of eastern Europe, Asia, and Africa. Because of their wealth the Australians and New Zealanders have been great buyers of our automobiles, petroleum, and machinery. They also buy considerable wood, especially the Australians, in whose country good timber is scarce. American textiles and clothing, as well as tobacco, also find favor in Australia. In fact there are few parts of the world which are more like the United States and more apt to do things in our way. Since we do not need either the wheat of Australia or the dairy products of New Zealand, both countries send us mainly the skins and hair of their animals. Wool and sheepskins are the most important articles, but rabbit skins along with those of kangaroos and opossums actually are worth more than cattle hides. Sausage casings, made from the intestines of cattle and especially sheep, are another item in the trade of these countries. We raise so many hogs that we have to hunt all over the world to find casings for sausages.

Trade of the United States with Tropical Countries. 1. *Mexico.*—Mexico is tropical and has a small area in the Region of Wet Tropical Agriculture, but it consists mainly of Cool Tropical Highlands, Wet and Dry Low Latitudes, and Deserts. Hence it sells us four kinds of products. From the Wet Tropical Agricultural Regions in the south we get vanilla, a little coffee and fruit, and chicle for chewing gum. The Wet and Dry Low Latitudes send henequen chiefly from Yucatan, rubber from the little desert shrub known as guayule, and cotton from irrigated tracts in the north. Third, from these irrigated tracts and from others in the northern desert along the Rio Grande and Colorado Rivers we get winter vegetables, particularly tomatoes. Last and by far the most important of the imports into the United States from Mexico are silver, lead, copper, and gold from the plateau, and petroleum from the coast of the Gulf of Mexico. Unfortunately the supply of petroleum is steadily diminishing, and Tampico is losing its importance as an oil center.   In return for all this we send Mexico a good deal of food, mainly lard, wheat, and corn, some cloth and wood, and a great deal of machinery, automobiles, and equipment for mines and other industries.

2. *The Caribbean Region.*—This includes the West Indies, Central America, and the South American countries of Colombia, Venezuela, and the Guianas.   Here we find the greatest source of several outstanding products of the Region of Wet Tropical Agriculture.   Our bananas come almost entirely from this region, our sugar in large part, and much of our cocoa and coffee.   Venezuela and especially Colombia furnish us with more than one-third as much coffee as Brazil.   Because of the nearness and accessibility of the Caribbean region and the contrast between its climate and ours, it is one of our most indispensable sources of foreign trade.   That is one reason why we have been so much interested in the Panama Canal, in the political status of Cuba, and in the revolutions and disorders in such places as Nicaragua and Haiti where our marines have stayed for years at various times.   In addition to this the northern coast of South America in Colombia and Venezuela is now an important source of petroleum, while the Colombian plateau furnishes platinum and other metals. In return we supply a great deal of food to Cuba and some to most of these countries. To all we send the usual assortment of manufactures.   As a rule the natives of the Caribbean countries do the manual work on the plantations.   People from the United States and northwestern Europe supply the machines and manufactured goods and do the managing.   (See pages 242, 353.)

3. *Brazil.*—So far as trade with the United States is concerned, Brazil suffers from being several times as far away as the Caribbean region.   No one is going to bring bananas from there when they can be obtained in Jamaica or Costa Rica. But Brazil holds its own in trade with us because its southern plateau is so remarkably good for coffee.   The Colombian highlands are indeed forging ahead, but there the soil is often badly leached, and the climate is so uniform that the coffee berries ripen at all seasons instead of all at once as in Brazil, thus increasing the cost of picking them.   Moreover, coffee is a very easy commodity to ship, so that freight rates from the Caribbean region are not enough lower to overcome the Brazilian advantages of climate and soil.   Aside from coffee Brazil sends little of importance except cocoa and some wild rubber.   She takes from us the usual petroleum products, machinery, iron goods, and automobiles, but not much food because Argentina is a much nearer source of supply.

4. *The Andean Plateau Countries.*—The entire length of the Andean plateau is important to the United States chiefly as a source of metals, while the coast furnishes petroleum and a few minor products.   Omitting Chile and Colombia, which have already been considered and in which the Andean plateau is not the main feature, there remain only Ecuador, Peru, and Bolivia.   The entire trade of the United States with these three is less than with Sweden, and only a little greater than with Switzerland or Denmark.   Peru sends us copper and other metals from the high plateau, while Bolivia sends some tin.   From the eastern side of the mountains Bolivia sends a little wild rubber and some coca for making cocaine and stimulating drinks.   From the dry west coast Peru and Ecuador both send petroleum.   Peru also supplies long-fibered cotton from its oases, while Ecuador exports Panama hats which are so called because they first became familiar to northern nations when sent to Panama.   Since the coast of Ecuador belongs to the Wet Tropical Agricultural Region it formerly shipped considerable cacao to the United States, but a blight has ruined many of the plantations.   All these countries import some of our lard, wheat

flour, and cotton cloth.   Ecuador, having very few roads or mines, takes little else, but both Bolivia and Peru buy mining equipment, and Peru takes some other machinery, automobiles, and lumber.

5. *Southeastern Asia and the East Indies.*—One of the interesting problems of the future is whether in due time the Regions of Wet Tropical Agriculture in India, the Malay Peninsula, Indo-China, and the East Indies will be supplanted by those of tropical America as sources of tropical products for the United States.   As has already been explained (pages 6, 394), this eastern region now holds its own because of its good labor supply, its accessibility, its political stability under European rule, and the fact that some of the most important tropical products are native here. Rubber and quinine, to be sure, were introduced from South America but are now mainly Malaysian.   It is one of the remarkable facts of economic geography that the United States relies largely on this region for its main supply not only of rubber and quinine, but also of jute, Manila hemp, tea, copra, coconut oil, and spices.   Our political domination of the Philippines is one reason for this, but the industrious quality of the people, and our absorption in developing our own country in contrast with the interest of the British and Dutch in developing their colonies, have much to do with it.   So, too, does the fact that the opening of the Suez Canal and the vast possibilities of trade with China and Japan put these Asiatic regions directly on main routes of travel long before the Panama Canal was opened or any much-traveled routes passed through the Caribbean region.   The effect of political control upon commerce is illustrated by the contrast between our trade with the Philippines and the Dutch East Indies.   We buy about 30 per cent more from the Philippines than from the Dutch East Indies, the main items being sugar, coconut oil, copra, and abaca (Manila hemp) from the Philippines, and rubber with some coffee, pepper, and so forth from the Dutch East Indies.   But we sell three times as much to our own colony as to that of the Dutch.   Moreover, in our sales, cotton cloth, wheat, paper, and petroleum products figure much more largely in the Philippines than in the Dutch possessions.   We are not able to sell many manufactured goods to any colonies except our own in competition with Europe.

Changes in American Commerce.—During the last half century, and especially since 1900, there has been a marked change in the character of the exports from the United States.   This is illustrated in A611, where the left hand part shows the percentage of raw materials, food, manufactures, and so forth among the exports of 1876 to 1880, while the right hand half shows the same thing half a century later.   Among our exports, the percentage of crude materials, chiefly cotton, copper, tobacco, and lumber has diminished by more than one-third, while crude foodstuffs such as wheat and meat have fallen to about one-fifth of their former percentage, and manufactured foodstuffs such as flour and canned meat to little more than one-third.   The actual amount of food exported is still as great as ever, and the value is far greater, but the total trade of the country has increased so enormously that the percentages have fallen.   On the other hand, the percentage of semi-manufactured goods like steel plates, prepared lumber, and cotton thread has increased threefold, and that of fully manufactured goods like mill machinery or woolen cloth more than threefold. The lower part of A611 shows that among our imports the change is of an opposite character. The percentage of crude materials has doubled and that of semi-manufactures has nearly doubled, because we now import these materials in vast quantities in order to use them to make finished manufactures in factories. How important they are appears in the fact that raw silk, crude rubber, copper, hides, and paper base stocks hold high rank among our imports. On the other hand, although we now import more foodstuffs than ever, including coffee, sugar, vegetable oils, and fruits, the crude foodstuffs form only two-thirds as large a

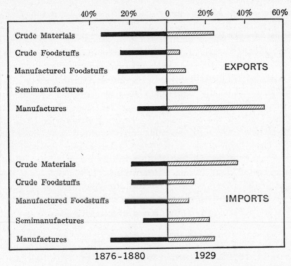

A—Changes of Half a Century in the Quality of the
Foreign Trade of the United States.

percentage as formerly, and the manufactured foodstuffs less than half. The percentage of our imports consisting of finished manufactures has also diminished by one-fourth, for we make an increasing proportion of the goods that we use.

This great change from a country which formerly exported mainly food and raw materials to one that now exports mainly manufactured goods has brought with it a corresponding change in the geographical relationships of our trade. This is illustrated in A612. There it is evident that half a century ago more than 80 per cent of all our exports went to Europe, while about half the imports came from there. In other words, we fed Europe and supplied it with raw materials, and it supplied us with manufactured goods. Today Europe is still our chief source of imports, but relatively it is little more than half as important as formerly. All the other continents have at least doubled their relative importance, but Canada and Asia have forged ahead with special speed. The reason for this is evident in the lower part of A612, showing the change in imports. Since we manufacture so much more than formerly our reliance on Europe for imports of manufactured goods has fallen off very greatly. On the other hand, our demand for sugar and bananas from our neighbors immediately to the south (southern North America) has actually declined so far as percentages of the total trade are concerned, although there has been a large absolute increase. So, too, with

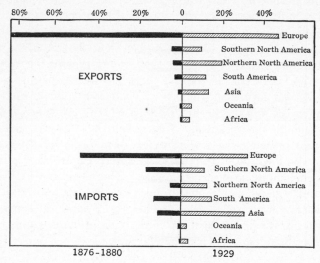

A—Changes of Half a Century in the Relative Importance of the Continents in the Foreign Trade of the United States.

the coffee and other products of South America. Their percentage has increased only a little. On the other hand, the increasing use of newspapers has caused the relative importance of Canada (northern North America) to double, while rubber, silk, vegetable oils, and minor products have caused Asia to be nearly three times as important as formerly.

The Changing Nature of Economic Geography.—These changes in the distribution of commerce illustrate the fact that the science of economic geography is constantly changing. New types of people migrate to a region, or old types die off, and at once there is a change in the nature and degree of man's activities, as happens whenever new regions are settled, or even when a differential birth rate causes one part of the population to increase more rapidly than another. New inventions cause a great demand for products which were previously insignificant, as in the case of rubber, copra, and quinine. A certain region becomes rich, and therefore is able to indulge its taste for luxuries, thus stimulating production and trade in some other part of the world, as happened with silk in the United States and Japan. The soil may become exhausted so that the location of a crop may have to be shifted, as in the case of coffee. Improved machinery or better methods of cooperation may cheapen production in certain regions so much that less-favored regions are driven out of business, as happened when the mowing machine and other agricultural implements made the raising of grain unprofitable in New England in spite of high yields per acre. Steamships, railroads, motor roads, and airways open up new territory, thus stimulating production in one region, but perhaps killing it in another. A new material like rayon may be invented and may displace another like silk with consequences that spread all over the world. Or a new social and economic system may arise, as in Russia, and no one can tell what its ultimate effect may be. There is no end to such changes, and therefore no end to the fluctuations which may arise in the conditions of economic geography. Yet in spite of this changeability the fundamental principles of the influence of climate, relief, soil, natural resources, and location in respect to land and sea are not really altered, although their application may change. Nor does the earth's division into natural regions change materially even though man may shift the boundaries one way or the other. Thus the task of the economic geographer will always be to grasp the underlying principles and then apply them to the changing world in which he lives.

EXERCISES

1. In A597 pick out the five countries that stand highest in total world trade. Explain the relation of this to geographic conditions.

2. In A598 pick out the five countries standing highest in foreign trade per capita, and the five standing lowest. Explain as in Exercise 1.

3. Russia and the United States are often said to be alike. In what ways do the maps and facts of this chapter support or confute such an idea?

4. From the tables of the *Statistical Yearbook of the League of Nations*, or from maps in your atlas, make a list of countries that rank high in both railroad mileage and tonnage of merchant vessels. Reduce your figures to a per capita basis and see whether the countries still rank high. How do you account for the importance of these countries in transportation of both kinds? Why do some stand high in both respects and others in only one?

5. Compare a railroad map with a map of density of population. What areas of dense population are important (*a*) in railroad mileage, (*b*) in merchant marine, (*c*) in both respects? Give reasons in each case.

6. Prepare as long a list as possible of pairs of countries which carry on a fairly active trade by reason, in part at least, of each of the following conditions: (a) differences in climate; (b) high activity on the part of one or both; (c) geographical proximity; (d) similarity of race, language or customs; (e) political relationships; (f) the presence of minerals or other specific resources.

7. Give examples of different types of man-made conditions which tend to hinder trade. Supplement the examples in this book by others.

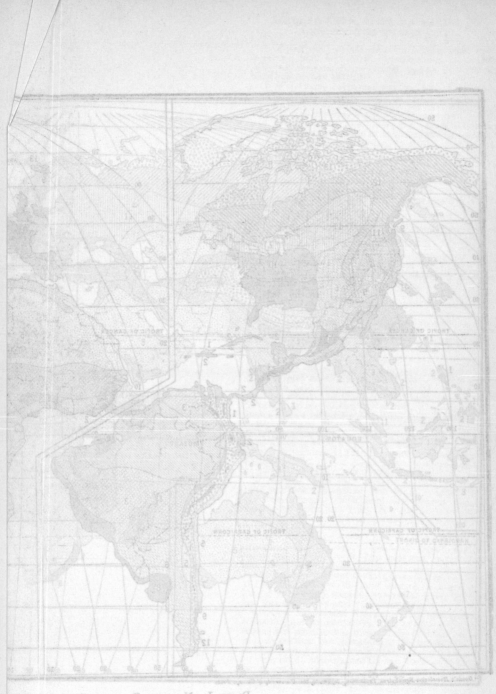

North and South America

B. H.	British Honduras
Br.	British (Guiana)
C. R.	Costa Rica
Dom. Rep.	Dominican Republic
Du.	Dutch (Guiana)
Fr.	French (Guiana)
Gua.	Guatemala
Hon.	Honduras
Nic.	Nicaragua
Pan.	Panama
Par.	Paraguay
Sal.	El Salvador
Uru.	Uruguay

Europe

Aust.	Austria
Bel.	Belgium
Bul.	Bulgaria
Cz. Slav.	Czechoslovakia
Denm.	Denmark
Est.	Estonia
Hun.	Hungary
Lith.	Lithuania
Neth.	Netherlands
Switz.	Switzerland
Yugoslav.	Yugoslavia

Africa

Br. Som.	British Somaliland
Eri.	Eritrea
Fr. S.	French Somaliland
It. S.	Italian Somaliland
Port. Guinea	Portuguese Guinea

INDEX

A

Abaca, 394
Abrasives, 468
Acacia, 245
Accessibility, 331, 587
Acorn, 380
Addison's disease, A125
Adirondacks, 174
Afghanistan, 174
Africa, agriculture, 196; animals, 169, 246, 413; coast, 181; Cool Tropical Highlands, 255; education, 137; labor, 6, 137; Northern, 203; peneplain, 180; rubber, 5 f.; soils, 190, 205; Wet and Dry Low Latitudes, 247
Agriculture, income, 131 ff.; machinery, 99, 566, B568; Milpa type, 14; regions of U. S., A55; and relief, 164 ff.; and temperature, 74 ff.; Warm Temperate Humid Regions, 285; wet tropical, 236, A237
Air, movement, 37
Air traffic, 161 f.
Akron, climate, B24
Alabama, corn, A68, 71; soil, 185
Alaska, 48; climograph, A325; soil, 195; surplus, 585
Albany, port, 596
Albright, A. D., 90
Alcohol, 346
Aldershot, 185
Aleutian, low, 47
Alexandria, weather record, 141
Alfalfa, 336
Algeria, climate, 75; B275; wheat, A76, 222.
Allahabad, climate, A416; deaths, 128
Alligator pear, 144, 367
Alloys and metals, non-ferrous, 572
Allspice, 392
Alluvial deposits, 150; in China, 178
Almonds, 380
Alpaca, 424
Alps, 154 ff., 174
Alsace, 227; potash, 203
Altitude, effect of, 151 f., 168
Amazon Valley, 28, 161, 177; education, 137; life in, 235; rubber, 3 ff., 11 ff.; soil, 196
America, activity of, 312; cyclonic storms, 312; discovery, 511
American Cyclonic Regions, 308; climograph, A310
Amsterdam harbor, 595
Andean Plateau, 152, 253; trade with U. S., 609
Andes Mts., 49, 150; civilization, 254; cross-section, A151; forests, 438; young mountains, 174

Andorra, 174
Angkor, 239
Angola, 249
Animal products, 408, A543; industries, 541
Animal unit, 405
Animals, in Africa, 246; climatic optima, 92 ff.; crops for, 334; and density of population, 405; distribution of, 20, 400 ff., A–B406, B411; uses of, 402 ff.; value, 407
Annam, life in, 235
Annapolis, marks at, 100
Anopheles mosquitoes, 128
Anthracite coal, 472
Anticyclones, 308
Appalachian mountains, 169; and hookworm, 130; motor vehicles, 135; population, 175; peneplain, 180; soil erosion, 164
Apples, 20, 87, 377
Apricots, 373
Arabia, 47; old civilization, 141; plains of, 177
Arabs, diet, 127
Architecture, Marine Cyclonic, 307
Arctic, 328; Ocean, 48
Arequipa, climograph, A259; ruins, 140
Argentina, beef, 417; climate, 120, A283; culture of, 136, 287; droughts, 267; health, 124, 129; plains, 161; railroads, 160; sheep, 422; trade with U. S., 608; wheat, 75, 221
Arizona, climograph, A259; crops, 86; deserts, 261; poultry, 98; Pueblo Indians, 141
Arkansas River, 173
Armenia, mountains, 175
Aroostook County, 86, 204, 349
Arrowroot, 346
Artichoke, 362
Asbestos, 468
Asia, 47, 83; agriculture, 196; climatic energy, 120; deserts, 260; handicaps, 418; horses, 413; labor, 6; manufacturing, 493; monsoons, 48; size, 293; southern villages, 239; Temperate Grasslands, 272; Wet and Dry Low Latitudes, 249
Asparagus, 362
Ass, climatic optimum, 412
Atacama Desert, 202
Atlantic Coast, 182, 184
Atmospheric circulation, A38; pressure, 37
Australia, 49; "Black Fellows," 246; cattle, 417; climatic energy, 120; coast, 182; combines, 76; commercial type, 585; desert flowers, 261; fertilizers, 205; motor vehicles, 134; social conditions in,

615